MATRIX ALGEBRA

MATRIX ALGEBRA

DAVID J. WINTER

University of Michigan, Ann Arbor

Macmillan Publishing Company
New York

Maxwell Macmillan Canada
Toronto

Maxwell Macmillan International
New York Oxford Singapore Sydney

Editor: Robert W. Pirtle
Production Supervisor: Aliza Greenblatt
Production Manager: Phyllis Niklas
Cover Designer: Robert Freese
Illustrations: Folium

This book was set in Times Roman by Polyglot Pte Ltd., and printed and bound by Book Press.

PRINTED IN THE UNITED STATES OF AMERICA

Macmillan Publishing Company
866 Third Avenue, New York, New York 10022

Macmillan Publishing Company is part of the Maxwell Communication Group of Companies.

Maxwell Macmillan Canada, Inc.
1200 Eglinton Avenue East
Suite 200
Don Mills, Ontario M3C 3N1

LIBRARY OF CONGRESS CATALOGING-IN-PUBLICATION DATA

Winter, David J.
Matrix algebra/David J. Winter.
p. cm.
Includes index.
ISBN 0-02-428831-4
1. Matrices. 2. Algebras, Linear. I. Title.
QA188.W57 1992
512.9'434—dc20 91-17414
CIP
r91

Printing: 1 2 3 4 5 6 7 Year: 2 3 4 5 6 7 8

To the memory of I. N. Herstein

PREFACE

Matrix algebra is vitally important as a tool in such subjects as chemistry, economics, engineering, mathematics, physics, and scientific computation. Important problems in these fields can be reduced to problems in matrix algebra, which can be solved accurately on high-speed computers. For this reason, students often get a first course in linear algebra fairly early in their curriculum. A casualty of this is that geometric aspects of linear algebra often get little attention. This is unfortunate, for much of linear algebra owes its existence to the geometric intuitions of its creators, and many of its methods can best be understood in connection with their geometric interpretations.

This book, *Matrix Algebra*, presents computational linear algebra within a geometric context. The general theme is that of matrix manipulation, which keeps things at a concrete and computational level. Geometric phenomena are illustrated by diagrams that complement and simplify the discussion and help the reader gain a deeper, more conceptual grasp of the subject. In this way, the book can be comprehensive as well as accessible.

Although this book can be used as the text for a two-semester course covering all sections, it is intended primarily for use in a one-semester course, wherein Chapters 1 and 2 are covered rapidly and many or all sections marked with asterisks (*) are omitted. This gives the instructor flexibility to add topics appropriate for the particular course, and it makes the book more useful to students for reference purposes later on. Some sample courses are outlined in the Instructor's Manual.

Since a true understanding of linear algebra requires using it from the outset to solve problems, many problems are included to make up a kind of "laboratory," or "proving ground," for developing problem-solving skills. The Instructor's Manual provides solutions to all problems. The Instructor's Manual also provides a detailed Student's Manual, which the instructor can make available to students through any copy center.

The book is divided into three parts:

Part 1 (Chapter 1) is a prologue, or preview in the microcosm of the plane, of what is to come. As such, it should be covered rapidly.

Part 2 (Chapters 2–4) is concerned with vector spaces and linear transformations. To set the stage, Chapter 2 introduces Cartesian n-space. This can be done quickly. Chapter 3 is about linear transformations of Cartesian n-space and should be covered more slowly. The remainder of Part 2, Chapter 4, is concerned with general n-dimensional vector spaces and their linear transformations. In this general setting, bases are discussed and the effect of a change of basis on the matrix of a linear transformation is described. Chapter 4 ends by showing how problems in this general context can be reduced to concrete problems about Cartesian n-space. Specifically, it explains the fundamental principle that problems stated in terms of linear transformations of a vector space of dimension n can be translated by an isomorphism to problems stated in terms of matrices viewed as linear transformations of F^n.

Part 3 (Chapters 5–7) then goes on to develop the linear algebra and geometry of Cartesian n-space, including the theory of quadratic forms.

Appendix A ("Sets, Elements, and Functions"), Appendix B ("Real Numbers"), and Appendix C ("Complex Numbers") are included for students to consult or review as needed.

Each chapter and appendix ends with references to other works that provide background or illustrate some of the richness and diversity of linear algebra.

We take this opportunity to thank the many people who have read the manuscript and made useful comments and contributions. We thank Bill Blair, Dan Britten, and Gene Klotz for their many and varied suggestions, which led to very substantial improvements. We also thank Bob Pirtle, Phyllis Niklas, and Linda Thompson for their excellent editorial help in bringing this book into being. Finally, we thank Molly Thornton and Reese Thornton of Folium for their intricate and creative preparation of the many supporting illustrations.

CONTENTS

* Optional sections; see the Preface.

PART 2: VECTOR SPACES AND LINEAR TRANSFORMATIONS

* Optional sections; see the Preface.

PART 3: THE LINEAR ALGEBRA AND GEOMETRY OF n-SPACE

* Optional sections; see the Preface.

LIST OF SYMBOLS

PART 1
PROLOGUE

CHAPTER

1

THE GEOMETRY AND LINEAR ALGEBRA OF THE CARTESIAN PLANE

The **geometry** of the plane is concerned with points, distance, and angle, as well as with **rigid motions** (congruences), which move lines, circles, etc. without disturbing their shape. Such motions are, simply, *those mappings from the plane to itself that preserve distance and angle.*

When coordinate axes are introduced in the plane, the result is the *Cartesian plane*, where points are denoted by pairs of numbers. Using these numbers, the geometry of the Cartesian plane can be developed quantitatively. The purpose of this chapter is to develop this geometry with the help of vectors. Along the way we preview, in the microcosm of the plane, what is to follow in the remaining chapters.

1.1 THE CARTESIAN PLANE

The **Cartesian plane** is a plane equipped with two **coordinate axes**, the horizontal x_1-axis and the vertical x_2-axis. The x_1-axis is a copy of the real line $\mathbb{R}$ (Appendix B), and the x_2-axis is a copy of the x_1-axis obtained by rotating

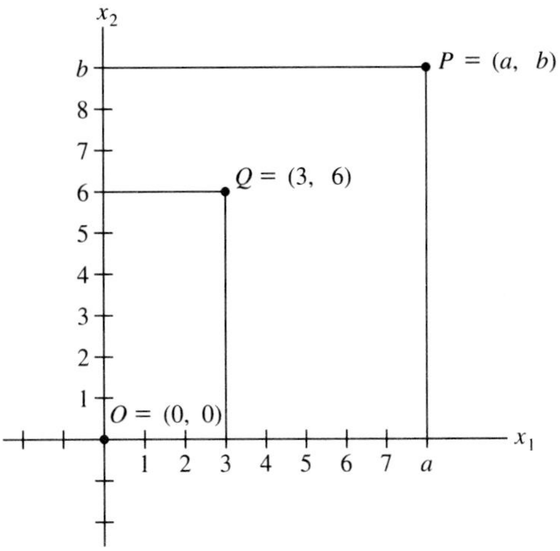

Figure 1.1 The Cartesian plane, the origin $O = (0, 0)$, the point $P = (a, b)$ with x_1-coordinate a and x_2-coordinate b, and the point $Q = (3, 6)$.

it 90° about 0 in the *counterclockwise* direction. The point of intersection of these two axes is called the **origin**, denoted O (Figure 1.1).

If a and b are real numbers, then the ordered pair (a, b) denotes the point P whose x_1-coordinate is a and whose x_2-coordinate is b. You can get to this point by going a units from the origin O along the x_1-axis (go right if a is positive and left if it is not) and then going b units along a line parallel to the x_2-axis (go up if b is positive and down if it is not). The origin O is the point $O = (0, 0)$, whereas the point $(3, 6)$ is plotted 3 units over and 6 units up (Figure 1.1).

Scalars and vectors

Scalars are numbers represented by a, b, c, d, etc., whereas **vectors** are column pairs such as $\mathbf{v} = \begin{bmatrix} a \\ b \end{bmatrix}$, $\mathbf{w} = \begin{bmatrix} c \\ d \end{bmatrix}$, etc. of scalars. We use boldface when denoting vectors, as in $\mathbf{v}$ and $\mathbf{w}$, in order to distinguish them from scalars.

Geometrically, the vector $\mathbf{v} = \begin{bmatrix} a \\ b \end{bmatrix}$ is the directed line segment (arrow) which leads from the origin O to the point $P = (a, b)$ (Figure 1.2.) We refer to O as the **base** and to P as the **tip** of the vector $\mathbf{v}$. In particular, the **zero vector** $\mathbf{0} = \begin{bmatrix} 0 \\ 0 \end{bmatrix}$ is the directed line segment from the origin to itself, and, of course, the origin is both the base and the tip of $\mathbf{0}$.

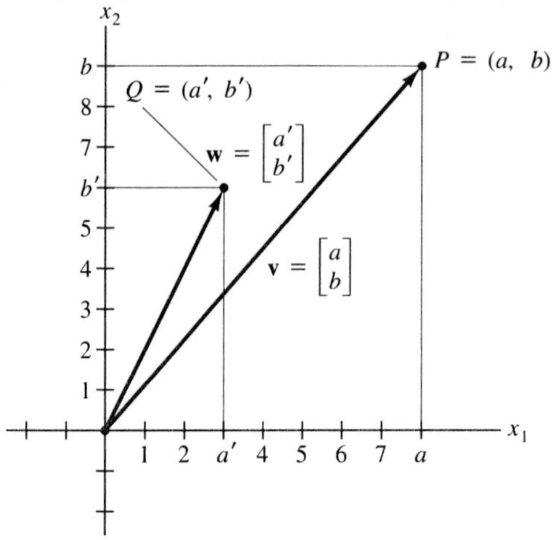

Figure 1.2 The vector $\mathbf{v} = \begin{bmatrix} a \\ b \end{bmatrix}$, which is the directed line segment from the origin O to the point $P = (a, b)$, and the vector $\mathbf{w} = \begin{bmatrix} a' \\ b' \end{bmatrix}$, which is the directed line segment from O to $Q = (a', b')$.

Equality of vectors

Two vectors $\mathbf{v} = \begin{bmatrix} a \\ b \end{bmatrix}$ and $\mathbf{w} = \begin{bmatrix} c \\ d \end{bmatrix}$ are equal if and only if their coordinates are equal; that is, $\mathbf{v} = \mathbf{w}$ if and only if $a = c$ and $b = d$.

EXAMPLE

The vectors $\begin{bmatrix} c \\ 2 \end{bmatrix}$ and $\begin{bmatrix} 3 \\ d+1 \end{bmatrix}$ are known to be equal. From this, it follows that $c = 3$ and $d = 1$.

Cartesian 2-space. Operations on vectors

Whereas $\mathbb{R}$ denotes the set of scalars (real numbers), the set of vectors $\begin{bmatrix} a \\ b \end{bmatrix}$ (a, b real) is denoted by $\mathbb{R}^2$. Each vector $\begin{bmatrix} a \\ b \end{bmatrix}$ in $\mathbb{R}^2$ corresponds to a point (a, b) (its tip) in the Cartesian plane. It is convenient to give $\mathbb{R}^2$ a name to distinguish it from its alter ego, the Cartesian plane. So, we call $\mathbb{R}^2$ **Cartesian 2-space**. Cartesian 2-space $\mathbb{R}^2$ and its n-dimensional counterpart **Cartesian *n*-space**, $\mathbb{R}^n$ ($n = 3, 4, \ldots$), introduced in the next chapter, are the arenas within which we work with vectors throughout the book.

We can combine vectors $\mathbf{v} = \begin{bmatrix} a \\ b \end{bmatrix}$ and $\mathbf{v}' = \begin{bmatrix} a' \\ b' \end{bmatrix}$ and scalars t by vector operations **addition**, **subtraction**, and **scalar multiplication**, as follows:

$$\begin{bmatrix} a \\ b \end{bmatrix} + \begin{bmatrix} a' \\ b' \end{bmatrix} = \begin{bmatrix} a+a' \\ b+b' \end{bmatrix} \quad \text{or} \quad \mathbf{v} + \mathbf{v}' = \begin{bmatrix} a+a' \\ b+b' \end{bmatrix},$$

$$\begin{bmatrix} a \\ b \end{bmatrix} - \begin{bmatrix} a' \\ b' \end{bmatrix} = \begin{bmatrix} a-a' \\ b-b' \end{bmatrix} \quad \text{or} \quad \mathbf{v} - \mathbf{v}' = \begin{bmatrix} a-a' \\ b-b' \end{bmatrix},$$

$$t\begin{bmatrix} a \\ b \end{bmatrix} = \begin{bmatrix} ta \\ tb \end{bmatrix} \quad \text{or} \quad t\mathbf{v} = \begin{bmatrix} ta \\ tb \end{bmatrix}.$$

EXAMPLE

$$\begin{bmatrix} 2 \\ 3 \end{bmatrix} + \begin{bmatrix} 1 \\ -5 \end{bmatrix} = \begin{bmatrix} 3 \\ -2 \end{bmatrix}, \quad \begin{bmatrix} 4 \\ 3 \end{bmatrix} - \begin{bmatrix} 2 \\ 5 \end{bmatrix} = \begin{bmatrix} 2 \\ -2 \end{bmatrix}, \quad 2\begin{bmatrix} 3 \\ -2 \end{bmatrix} = \begin{bmatrix} 6 \\ -4 \end{bmatrix}.$$

The geometric interpretations of these purely algebraic operations on the elements of $\mathbb{R}^2$ are illustrated in Figure 1.3.

Algebraic computation with vectors in $\mathbb{R}^2$ is facilitated by Theorem 1.1.

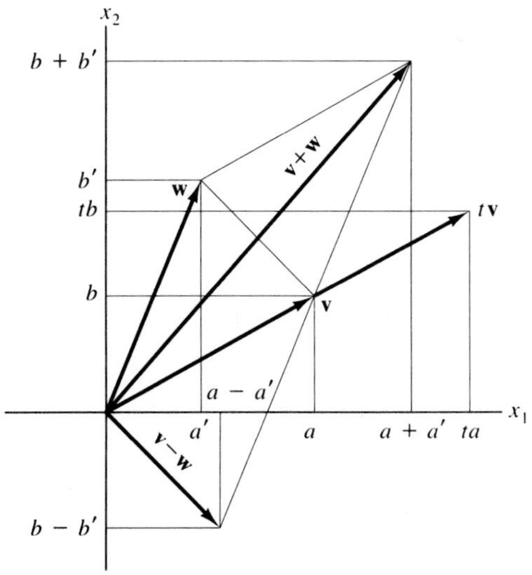

Figure 1.3 The vectors $\mathbf{v} = \begin{bmatrix} a \\ b \end{bmatrix}$, $\mathbf{w} = \begin{bmatrix} a' \\ b' \end{bmatrix}$, $\mathbf{v} + \mathbf{w} = \begin{bmatrix} a+a' \\ b+b' \end{bmatrix}$, $\mathbf{v} - \mathbf{w} = \begin{bmatrix} a-a' \\ b-b' \end{bmatrix}$, and $t\mathbf{v} = \begin{bmatrix} ta \\ tb \end{bmatrix}$.

Theorem 1.1. *Properties of Vector Operations.*

The vector operations of addition and scalar multiplication in the Cartesian plane satisfy the following.

1. $\left(\begin{bmatrix} a \\ b \end{bmatrix} + \begin{bmatrix} a' \\ b' \end{bmatrix}\right) + \begin{bmatrix} a'' \\ b'' \end{bmatrix} = \begin{bmatrix} a \\ b \end{bmatrix} + \left(\begin{bmatrix} a' \\ b' \end{bmatrix} + \begin{bmatrix} a'' \\ b'' \end{bmatrix}\right).$
2. $\begin{bmatrix} a \\ b \end{bmatrix} + \begin{bmatrix} a' \\ b' \end{bmatrix} = \begin{bmatrix} a' \\ b' \end{bmatrix} + \begin{bmatrix} a \\ b \end{bmatrix}$ and $\begin{bmatrix} a \\ b \end{bmatrix} + \mathbf{0} = \begin{bmatrix} a \\ b \end{bmatrix}.$
3. $\begin{bmatrix} a \\ b \end{bmatrix} + \left(-\begin{bmatrix} a \\ b \end{bmatrix}\right) = \mathbf{0},$ where $-\begin{bmatrix} a \\ b \end{bmatrix} = \begin{bmatrix} -a \\ -b \end{bmatrix}.$
4. $(-1)\begin{bmatrix} a \\ b \end{bmatrix} = -\begin{bmatrix} a \\ b \end{bmatrix}.$
5. $t\left(\begin{bmatrix} a \\ b \end{bmatrix} + \begin{bmatrix} a' \\ b' \end{bmatrix}\right) = t\begin{bmatrix} a \\ b \end{bmatrix} + t\begin{bmatrix} a' \\ b' \end{bmatrix}.$
6. $(s+t)\begin{bmatrix} a \\ b \end{bmatrix} = s\begin{bmatrix} a \\ b \end{bmatrix} + t\begin{bmatrix} a \\ b \end{bmatrix}$ and $(st)\begin{bmatrix} a \\ b \end{bmatrix} = s\left(t\begin{bmatrix} a \\ b \end{bmatrix}\right).$

Proof. We simply verify each equation by carrying out the indicated operations:

1. $\left(\begin{bmatrix} a \\ b \end{bmatrix} + \begin{bmatrix} a' \\ b' \end{bmatrix}\right) + \begin{bmatrix} a'' \\ b'' \end{bmatrix} = \begin{bmatrix} a+a' \\ b+b' \end{bmatrix} + \begin{bmatrix} a'' \\ b'' \end{bmatrix} = \begin{bmatrix} a+a'+a'' \\ b+b'+b'' \end{bmatrix};$

   $\begin{bmatrix} a \\ b \end{bmatrix} + \left(\begin{bmatrix} a' \\ b' \end{bmatrix} + \begin{bmatrix} a'' \\ b'' \end{bmatrix}\right) = \begin{bmatrix} a \\ b \end{bmatrix} + \begin{bmatrix} a'+a'' \\ b'+b'' \end{bmatrix} = \begin{bmatrix} a+a'+a'' \\ b+b'+b'' \end{bmatrix}.$
2. $\begin{bmatrix} a \\ b \end{bmatrix} + \begin{bmatrix} a' \\ b' \end{bmatrix} = \begin{bmatrix} a+a' \\ b+b' \end{bmatrix} = \begin{bmatrix} a'+a \\ b'+b \end{bmatrix} = \begin{bmatrix} a' \\ b' \end{bmatrix} + \begin{bmatrix} a \\ b \end{bmatrix}$ and

   $\begin{bmatrix} a \\ b \end{bmatrix} + \mathbf{0} = \begin{bmatrix} a \\ b \end{bmatrix} + \begin{bmatrix} 0 \\ 0 \end{bmatrix} = \begin{bmatrix} a+0 \\ b+0 \end{bmatrix} = \begin{bmatrix} a \\ b \end{bmatrix}.$
3. $\begin{bmatrix} a \\ b \end{bmatrix} + \begin{bmatrix} -a \\ -b \end{bmatrix} = \begin{bmatrix} a-a \\ b-b \end{bmatrix} = \begin{bmatrix} 0 \\ 0 \end{bmatrix} = \mathbf{0}.$
4. $(-1)\begin{bmatrix} a \\ b \end{bmatrix} = \begin{bmatrix} -a \\ -b \end{bmatrix} = -\begin{bmatrix} a \\ b \end{bmatrix}.$
5. $t\left(\begin{bmatrix} a \\ b \end{bmatrix} + \begin{bmatrix} a' \\ b' \end{bmatrix}\right) = t\begin{bmatrix} a+a' \\ b+b' \end{bmatrix} = \begin{bmatrix} ta+ta' \\ tb+tb' \end{bmatrix}$

   $= \begin{bmatrix} ta \\ tb \end{bmatrix} + \begin{bmatrix} ta' \\ tb' \end{bmatrix} = t\begin{bmatrix} a \\ b \end{bmatrix} + t\begin{bmatrix} a' \\ b' \end{bmatrix}.$
6. $(s+t)\begin{bmatrix} a \\ b \end{bmatrix} = \begin{bmatrix} (s+t)a \\ (s+t)b \end{bmatrix} = \begin{bmatrix} sa+ta \\ sb+tb \end{bmatrix} = \begin{bmatrix} sa \\ sb \end{bmatrix} + \begin{bmatrix} ta \\ tb \end{bmatrix} = s\begin{bmatrix} a \\ b \end{bmatrix} + t\begin{bmatrix} a \\ b \end{bmatrix}$

   and $(st)\begin{bmatrix} a \\ b \end{bmatrix} = \begin{bmatrix} sta \\ stb \end{bmatrix} = s\begin{bmatrix} ta \\ tb \end{bmatrix} = s\left(t\begin{bmatrix} a \\ b \end{bmatrix}\right).$ ∎

EXAMPLE

$$\left(\begin{bmatrix}2\\3\end{bmatrix}+\begin{bmatrix}1\\2\end{bmatrix}\right)+\begin{bmatrix}4\\1\end{bmatrix}=\begin{bmatrix}2\\3\end{bmatrix}+\left(\begin{bmatrix}1\\2\end{bmatrix}+\begin{bmatrix}4\\1\end{bmatrix}\right)=\begin{bmatrix}2+1+4\\3+2+1\end{bmatrix} \text{ and}$$

$$(2+3)\begin{bmatrix}4\\3\end{bmatrix}=2\begin{bmatrix}4\\3\end{bmatrix}+3\begin{bmatrix}4\\3\end{bmatrix}=\begin{bmatrix}20\\15\end{bmatrix}.$$

The associative law for sums (Property 1) enables us to drop parentheses.

EXAMPLE

$$\begin{bmatrix}4\\3\end{bmatrix}+\begin{bmatrix}2\\2\end{bmatrix}+\begin{bmatrix}5\\1\end{bmatrix}=\begin{bmatrix}4+2+5\\3+2+1\end{bmatrix}=\begin{bmatrix}11\\6\end{bmatrix}.$$

We *define* $-\begin{bmatrix}a\\b\end{bmatrix}$ to be $\begin{bmatrix}-a\\-b\end{bmatrix}$, which is the same as $\mathbf{0}-\begin{bmatrix}a\\b\end{bmatrix}$ and $(-1)\begin{bmatrix}a\\b\end{bmatrix}$. So, we find that $-\begin{bmatrix}a\\b\end{bmatrix}=\begin{bmatrix}-a\\-b\end{bmatrix}=(-1)\begin{bmatrix}a\\b\end{bmatrix}$. (Explain!)

EXAMPLE

$$-\begin{bmatrix}4\\-3\end{bmatrix}=\begin{bmatrix}-4\\3\end{bmatrix}.$$

Directed line segments

The directed line segment from the origin O to the point $P=(a, b)$ is the vector $\mathbf{v}=\begin{bmatrix}a\\b\end{bmatrix}$, and the directed line segment (arrow) from the point $P=(a, b)$ to the point $Q=(c, d)$ is denoted by $\overrightarrow{\mathbf{v}\,\mathbf{w}}$, where $\mathbf{v}=\begin{bmatrix}a\\b\end{bmatrix}$ and $\mathbf{w}=\begin{bmatrix}c\\d\end{bmatrix}$ (Figure 1.4). In other words, for any two vectors $\mathbf{v}, \mathbf{w}\in\mathbb{R}^2$, $\overrightarrow{\mathbf{v}\,\mathbf{w}}$ is the directed line segment from the tip of $\mathbf{v}$ to the tip of $\mathbf{w}$. Informally, we often drop the word tip and refer to $\overrightarrow{\mathbf{v}\,\mathbf{w}}$ as the directed line segment from $\mathbf{v}$ to $\mathbf{w}$.

Peculiar as it may at first seem, $\mathbf{w}$ and $\overrightarrow{\mathbf{0}\,\mathbf{w}}$ are identical. The reason for this is that both $\mathbf{w}$ and $\overrightarrow{\mathbf{0}\,\mathbf{w}}$ are the directed line segment from $\mathbf{0}$ to the tip of $\mathbf{w}$. Thus, $\mathbf{w}=\overrightarrow{\mathbf{0}\,\mathbf{w}}$. This can be seen from Figure 1.4, where reducing the vector $\mathbf{v}$ to $\mathbf{0}$ reduces $\overrightarrow{\mathbf{v}\,\mathbf{w}}$ to $\overrightarrow{\mathbf{0}\,\mathbf{w}}$, which is $\mathbf{w}$.

Line segments

We sometimes consider the (undirected) line segment joining the points (a, b) and (a', b'), denoted by $\overline{\mathbf{v}\,\mathbf{w}}$, where $\mathbf{v}=\begin{bmatrix}a\\b\end{bmatrix}$ and $\mathbf{w}=\begin{bmatrix}a'\\b'\end{bmatrix}$. The points on this

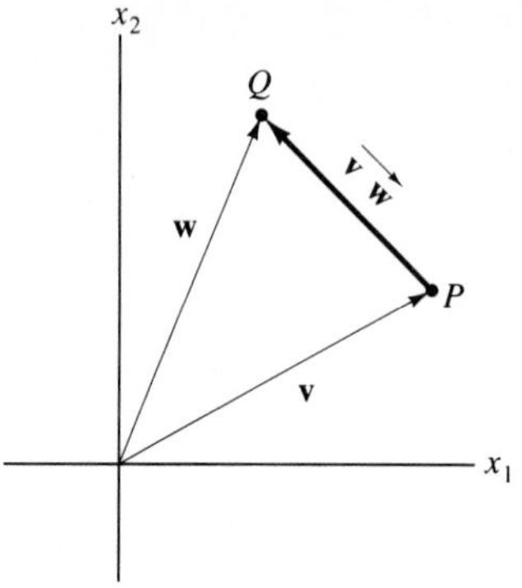

Figure 1.4 The directed line segment (arrow) from the point $P = (a, b)$ to the point $Q = (c, d)$ is denoted by $\overrightarrow{\mathbf{v}\,\mathbf{w}}$, where $\mathbf{v} = \begin{bmatrix} a \\ b \end{bmatrix}$ and $\mathbf{w} = \begin{bmatrix} c \\ d \end{bmatrix}$.

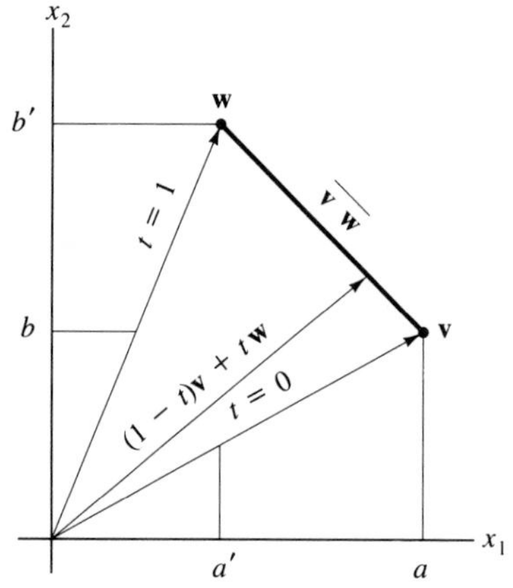

Figure 1.5 The tips of the vectors $(1 - t)\mathbf{v} + t\mathbf{w}$ $(0 \le t \le 1)$ are the points on the line segment $\overline{\mathbf{v}\,\mathbf{w}}$ joining $\mathbf{v} = \begin{bmatrix} a \\ b \end{bmatrix}$ and $\mathbf{w} = \begin{bmatrix} a' \\ b' \end{bmatrix}$.

line segment are the tips of the vectors $(1 - t)\mathbf{v} + t\mathbf{w}$ $(0 \le t \le 1)$, as illustrated in Figure 1.5. Informally, we refer to $\overline{\mathbf{v}\,\mathbf{w}}$ as the line segment joining the vectors **v** and **w**, even though, strictly speaking, it joins the *tips* of **v** and **w**.

EXAMPLE

The tips of the vectors $\frac{1}{4}\begin{bmatrix} 5 \\ 6 \end{bmatrix} + \frac{3}{4}\begin{bmatrix} 9 \\ 7 \end{bmatrix}$ and $\frac{3}{4}\begin{bmatrix} 5 \\ 6 \end{bmatrix} + \frac{1}{4}\begin{bmatrix} 9 \\ 7 \end{bmatrix}$ are on the line segment joining the points (5, 6) and (9, 7).

Translation. Directed line segments parallel to a given vector

For any vector **u**, we can translate the directed line segment $\overrightarrow{\mathbf{v}\,\mathbf{w}}$ by **u** so it becomes the directed line segment $\overrightarrow{\mathbf{u}+\mathbf{v}\;\mathbf{u}+\mathbf{w}}$, as shown in Figure 1.6. The simplest instance of this is translating the vector $\mathbf{v} = \overrightarrow{\mathbf{0}\,\mathbf{v}}$ by **u** to get the directed line segment $\overrightarrow{\mathbf{u}\;\mathbf{u}+\mathbf{v}}$, as shown in Figure 1.7. In contrast to this, we can also translate the directed line segment $\overrightarrow{\mathbf{v}\,\mathbf{w}}$ by $-\mathbf{v}$ to become the directed line segment $\overrightarrow{\mathbf{0}\;\mathbf{w}-\mathbf{v}} = \mathbf{w}-\mathbf{v}$, a vector (Figure 1.8).

Since we can get $\overrightarrow{\mathbf{u}+\mathbf{v}\;\mathbf{u}+\mathbf{w}}$ by translating $\overrightarrow{\mathbf{0}\;\mathbf{u}+\mathbf{w}-(\mathbf{u}+\mathbf{v})} = \mathbf{w} - \mathbf{v}$ by the vector $\mathbf{u} + \mathbf{v}$, we have the following theorem.

Theorem 1.2. *Translations of a Directed Line Segment.*
All the directed line segments obtained from $\overrightarrow{\mathbf{v}\,\mathbf{w}}$ by translation are translations of the vector $\mathbf{w} - \mathbf{v}$.

This discussion leads us to make the following useful definition.

Definition. A directed line segment $\overrightarrow{\mathbf{v}\,\mathbf{w}}$ is **parallel** to a given nonzero vector if $\mathbf{w} - \mathbf{v}$ is a multiple of it.

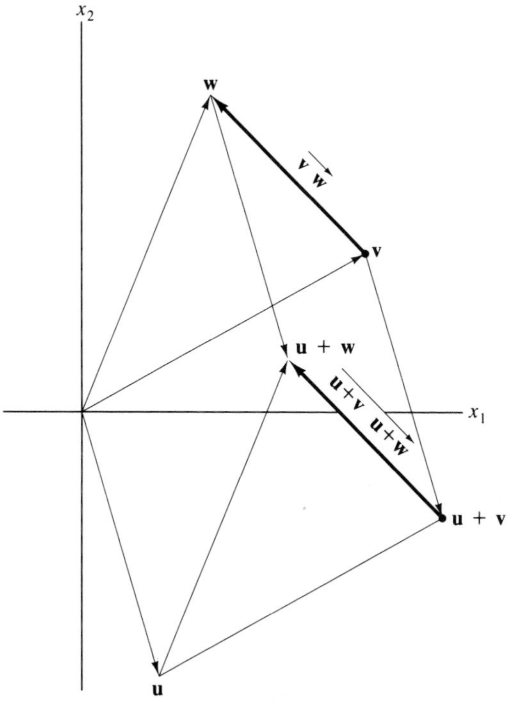

Figure 1.6 Translating $\overrightarrow{\mathbf{v}\,\mathbf{w}}$ by **u** to get $\overrightarrow{\mathbf{u}+\mathbf{v}\;\mathbf{u}+\mathbf{w}}$.

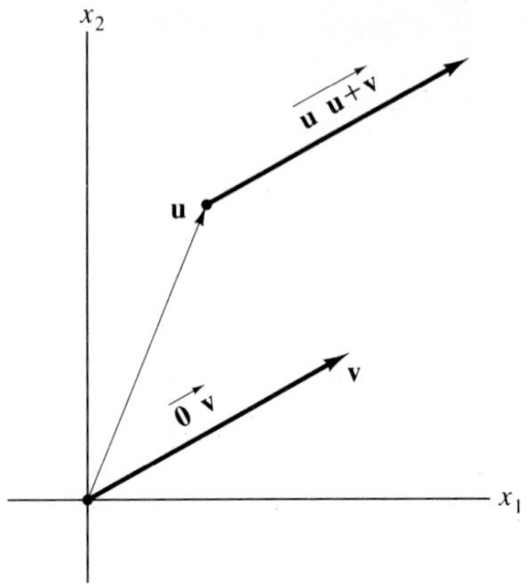

Figure 1.7 Translating $\mathbf{v} = \overrightarrow{\mathbf{0}\,\mathbf{v}}$ by $\mathbf{u}$ to get $\overrightarrow{\mathbf{u}\,\mathbf{u}+\mathbf{v}}$.

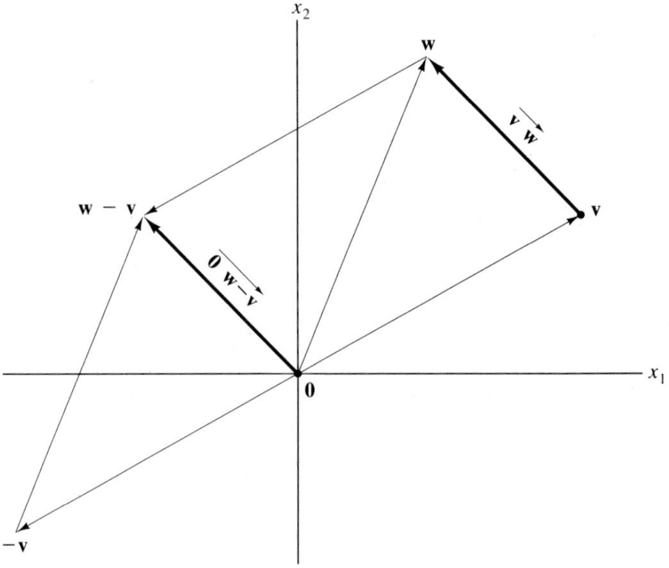

Figure 1.8 Translating $\overrightarrow{\mathbf{v}\,\mathbf{w}}$ by $-\mathbf{v}$ to get $\overrightarrow{\mathbf{0}\,\mathbf{w}-\mathbf{v}} = \mathbf{w} - \mathbf{v}$.

EXAMPLE

If $\mathbf{v} = \begin{bmatrix} 4 \\ 2 \end{bmatrix}$ and $\mathbf{w} = \begin{bmatrix} -4 \\ 3 \end{bmatrix}$, then the directed line segment $\overrightarrow{\mathbf{v}\,\mathbf{w}}$ is parallel to the vector $\begin{bmatrix} -16 \\ 2 \end{bmatrix}$. (Illustrate!) The reason for this is that $\begin{bmatrix} -4 \\ 3 \end{bmatrix} - \begin{bmatrix} 4 \\ 2 \end{bmatrix} = \begin{bmatrix} -8 \\ 1 \end{bmatrix}$ is a multiple of $\begin{bmatrix} -16 \\ 2 \end{bmatrix}$, the scalar being 0.5.

Of course, any two nonzero vectors $a\mathbf{v}$ and $b\mathbf{v}$ which are multiples of the same vector are parallel, by our definition. For instance, the vectors $\begin{bmatrix} -8 \\ 1 \end{bmatrix}$ and $\begin{bmatrix} 16 \\ -2 \end{bmatrix}$ are parallel by this principle.

Translations of a given vector

It is often helpful to translate a given vector to other points, the result being one or more directed line segments, such as those illustrated in Figure 1.9. Any of these directed line segments can be used to represent the original vector. After all, we get the original vector back by translating any of them back to the origin!

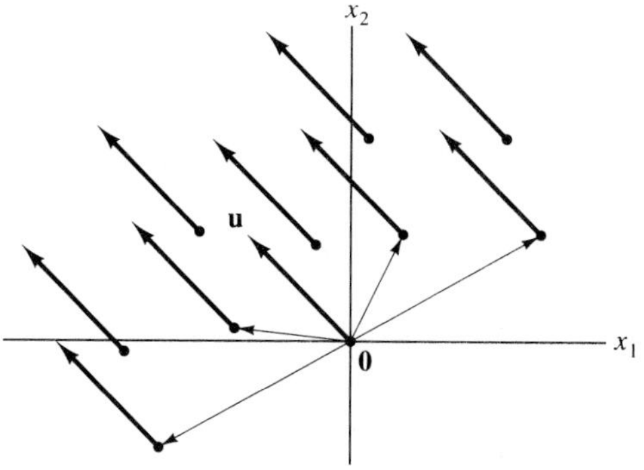

Figure 1.9 Translations of a given vector **u**.

PROBLEMS

NUMERICAL PROBLEMS

1. Draw the following elements of $\mathbb{R}^2$ and plot their tips in the Cartesian plane, approximating π as 3.14 and taking $f = 4$:

$$\begin{bmatrix} 1 \\ -2 \end{bmatrix}, \quad \begin{bmatrix} 2 \\ 9 \end{bmatrix}, \quad \begin{bmatrix} 3 \\ 6 \end{bmatrix}, \quad \begin{bmatrix} \pi \\ -5 \end{bmatrix}, \quad \begin{bmatrix} f \\ 4 \end{bmatrix}.$$

2. Perform the following vector operations.

(a) $\begin{bmatrix} 1 \\ -2 \end{bmatrix} + \begin{bmatrix} 2 \\ 9 \end{bmatrix}$ **(b)** $\begin{bmatrix} 3 \\ 6 \end{bmatrix} - \begin{bmatrix} \pi \\ -5 \end{bmatrix}$ **(c)** $-3\begin{bmatrix} f \\ 4 \end{bmatrix}$

3. Draw the vectors found in Problem 2 in the Cartesian plane.

4. Perform the following vector operations.

(a) $\begin{bmatrix} 2/15 \\ 3c \end{bmatrix} + \begin{bmatrix} 2.1 \\ 3 \end{bmatrix}$ **(b)** $\begin{bmatrix} 3x \\ 4 \end{bmatrix} - \begin{bmatrix} s+q \\ 3 \end{bmatrix}$ **(c)** $-3\begin{bmatrix} a+xz \\ z \end{bmatrix}$

5. Draw the directed line segment from (1, 4) to (3, 2). What vector of $\mathbb{R}^2$ can be translated to this directed line segment?

6. Draw the directed line segment obtained by translating the vector $\begin{bmatrix} 7 \\ 2 \end{bmatrix}$ so that its new base is (2, 3). What is its tip?

7. Draw the directed line segment obtained by translating the vector $\begin{bmatrix} 7 \\ 2 \end{bmatrix}$ so that its new tip is (2, 3). What is its base?

8. Illustrate the following statement by drawing appropriate vectors and other directed line segments:

If the directed line segment $\overrightarrow{\mathbf{v}\,\mathbf{w}}$ is a translation of $\begin{bmatrix} 3 \\ 4 \end{bmatrix}$ and the directed line segment $\overrightarrow{\mathbf{u}\,\mathbf{v}}$ is a translation of $\begin{bmatrix} 7 \\ 2 \end{bmatrix}$, then the directed line segment $\overrightarrow{\mathbf{u}\,\mathbf{w}}$ is a translation of $\begin{bmatrix} 7 \\ 2 \end{bmatrix} + \begin{bmatrix} 3 \\ 4 \end{bmatrix}$.

9. Verify the following for the vector operations of addition and scalar multiplication.

(a) $\left(\begin{bmatrix} 1 \\ 2 \end{bmatrix} + \begin{bmatrix} 2 \\ 2 \end{bmatrix}\right) + \begin{bmatrix} 3 \\ 5 \end{bmatrix} = \begin{bmatrix} 1 \\ 2 \end{bmatrix} + \left(\begin{bmatrix} 2 \\ 2 \end{bmatrix} + \begin{bmatrix} 3 \\ 5 \end{bmatrix}\right)$

(b) $\begin{bmatrix} 1 \\ 2 \end{bmatrix} + \left(-\begin{bmatrix} 1 \\ 2 \end{bmatrix}\right) = \mathbf{0}$, where $-\begin{bmatrix} 1 \\ 2 \end{bmatrix} = \begin{bmatrix} -1 \\ -2 \end{bmatrix}$ and $\mathbf{0} = \begin{bmatrix} 0 \\ 0 \end{bmatrix}$

10. Refer to Problem 9. Do the same for the following.

(a) $(-1)\begin{bmatrix} 1 \\ 2 \end{bmatrix} = -\begin{bmatrix} 1 \\ 2 \end{bmatrix}$

(b) $t\left(\begin{bmatrix} 1 \\ 2 \end{bmatrix} + \begin{bmatrix} 2 \\ 2 \end{bmatrix}\right) = t\begin{bmatrix} 1 \\ 2 \end{bmatrix} + t\begin{bmatrix} 2 \\ 2 \end{bmatrix}$ for all t.

(c) $(st)\begin{bmatrix} 1 \\ 2 \end{bmatrix} = s\left(t\begin{bmatrix} 1 \\ 2 \end{bmatrix}\right)$ for all s, t.

THEORETICAL PROBLEMS

11. Prove that if the vector $\begin{bmatrix} a \\ b \end{bmatrix}$ can be translated to the directed line segment $\overrightarrow{\mathbf{u}\,\mathbf{v}}$ and $\begin{bmatrix} c \\ d \end{bmatrix}$ can be translated to the directed line segment $\overrightarrow{\mathbf{v}\,\mathbf{w}}$, then $\begin{bmatrix} a \\ b \end{bmatrix} + \begin{bmatrix} c \\ d \end{bmatrix}$ can be translated to the directed line segment $\overrightarrow{\mathbf{u}\,\mathbf{w}}$.

12. Explain why, by our definition, any two nonzero vectors $a\mathbf{v}$ and $b\mathbf{v}$ that are multiples of the same vector are parallel.

1.2 LINES AND LINEAR EQUATIONS

Lines in the Cartesian plane

A **linear function** on the Cartesian plane is a function of the form $y = ax_1 + bx_2$, whereby a value for y is determined for each point (x_1, x_2) in the Cartesian plane.

EXAMPLE

$y = 3x_1 - 2x_2$ is a linear function. For $(x_1, x_2) = (1, 3)$, the corresponding value of y is $3 \cdot 1 - 2 \cdot 3 = -3$.

If $p \in \mathbb{R}$, the linear function $y = ax_1 + bx_2$ gives us a corresponding **linear equation** $ax_1 + bx_2 = p$. For example, if $a = 3$, $b = -2$, and $p = -3$, we get the linear equation $3x_1 - 2x_2 = -3$.

A **line** in the Cartesian plane is just the set of points (x_1, x_2) in $\mathbb{R}^2$ satisfying a linear equation $ax_1 + bx_2 = p$, where not both of a and b are 0. Here, we say that a point (c_1, c_2) **satisfies** the equation $ax_1 + bx_2 = p$ if $ac_1 + bc_2 = p$. In the Cartesian plane, this line is the **graph** (*set of points*) of the equation.

EXAMPLES

1. $3x_1 - 2x_2 = -3$ is an equation of a line passing through the points (1, 3) and (3, 6).
2. $3x_1 - 2x_2 = 0$ is an equation of a line passing through the points (0, 0) and (2, 3).

The equation $ax_1 + bx_2 = p$ of a line breaks the Cartesian plane into three parts: the line $\{(x_1, x_2) \mid ax_1 + bx_2 = p\}$ itself and the two **half-spaces** $\{(x_1, x_2) \mid ax_1 + bx_2 > p\}$, $\{(x_1, x_2) \mid ax_1 + bx_2 < p\}$ (Figure 1.10).

Points and lines in the Cartesian 2-space $\mathbb{R}^2$. Vector notation

The subject of linear algebra is developed in terms of vectors, the elements of Cartesian 2-space $\mathbb{R}^2$. So, by considering counterparts in Cartesian 2-space of the points, lines, etc. in the Cartesian plane, we can use vector notation and vector operations in conjunction with points, lines, etc.

The counterpart in $\mathbb{R}^2$ of the point (a, b) in the Cartesian plane is the vector $\begin{bmatrix} a \\ b \end{bmatrix}$ whose tip is (a, b). For this reason, *we often refer to the vector* $\begin{bmatrix} a \\ b \end{bmatrix}$ *as a point in* $\mathbb{R}^2$. Similarly, we refer to the set of vectors $\begin{bmatrix} x_1 \\ x_2 \end{bmatrix}$

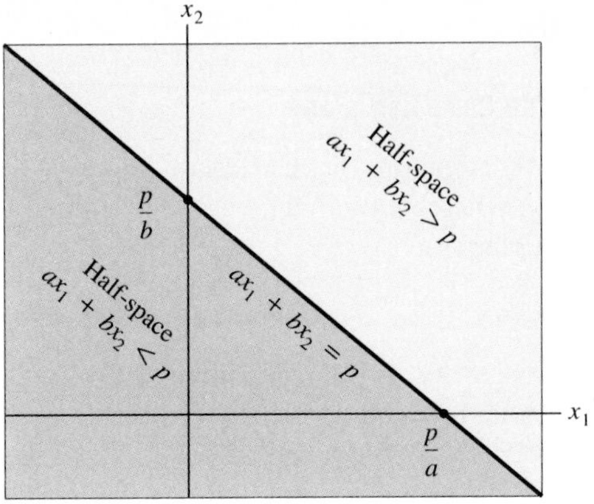

Figure 1.10 The line $ax_1 + bx_2 = p$ and the two half-spaces $ax_1 + bx_2 < p$ and $ax_1 + bx_2 > p$. This illustrates the case when a, b, p are all positive.

in $\mathbb{R}^2$ satisfying the linear equation $ax_1 + bx_2 = p$, where not both of a and b are 0, as a **line** in $\mathbb{R}^2$.

This having been said, we can interpret the linear function $y = ax_1 + bx_2$ as a function $f(\mathbf{x}) = ax_1 + bx_2$ of the vector $\mathbf{x} = \begin{bmatrix} x_1 \\ x_2 \end{bmatrix} \in \mathbb{R}^2$. This function is called a **linear function** on Cartesian 2-space. When not both of a and b are 0, the linear equation $ax_1 + bx_2 = p$ determines a line in $\mathbb{R}^2$, namely, the line consisting of those vectors $\begin{bmatrix} x_1 \\ x_2 \end{bmatrix}$ for which $ax_1 + bx_2 = p$.

EXAMPLES

1. $f(\mathbf{x}) = 3x_1 - 2x_2$ is a linear function which maps the vector $\begin{bmatrix} 1 \\ 3 \end{bmatrix}$ to $3 \cdot 1 - 2 \cdot 3 = -3$ and the vector $\begin{bmatrix} 2 \\ 3 \end{bmatrix}$ to $3 \cdot 2 - 2 \cdot 3 = 0$.

2. $3x_1 - 2x_2 = -3$ is the equation of a line in Cartesian 2-space passing through $\begin{bmatrix} 1 \\ 3 \end{bmatrix}$ and $\begin{bmatrix} 3 \\ 6 \end{bmatrix}$ in $\mathbb{R}^2$.

3. The line in Cartesian 2-space whose equation is $3x_1 - 2x_2 = -3$, which passes through the points $\begin{bmatrix} 1 \\ 3 \end{bmatrix}$ and $\begin{bmatrix} 3 \\ 6 \end{bmatrix}$, can also be described as the set of vectors $\begin{bmatrix} 1 \\ 3 \end{bmatrix} + t \begin{bmatrix} 3-1 \\ 6-3 \end{bmatrix}$, with t in $\mathbb{R}$. (This *parametric* description is discussed in detail later in this section.)

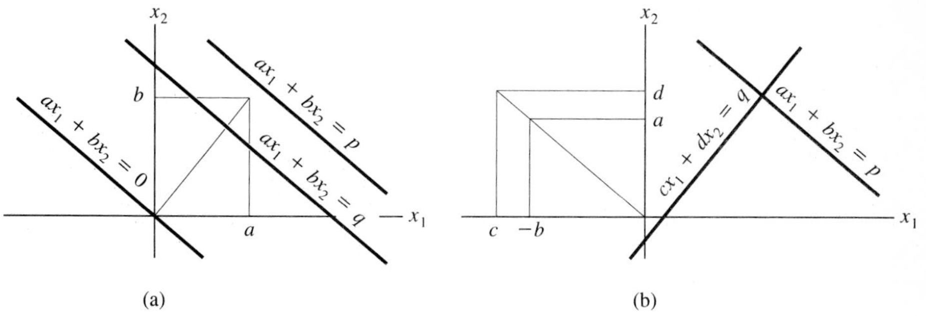

Figure 1.11 (a) Parallel lines $ax_1 + bx_2 = p$, $ax_1 + bx_2 = q$, and $ax_1 + bx_2 = 0$. (b) Intersecting lines $ax_1 + bx_2 = p$ and $cx_1 + dx_2 = q$.

Parallel and intersecting lines

Two lines are **parallel** if either they are equal or they do not **intersect**—that is, if they are equal or have no point in common (Figure 1.11). So, the lines corresponding to the equations $ax_1 + bx_2 = p$ and $tax_1 + tbx_2 = q$ are parallel for any $t \neq 0$ and any for any q. (Explain!)

We will see from Cramer's rule, discussed later in this section, that the lines corresponding to the equations $ax_1 + bx_2 = p$ and $cx_1 + dx_2 = q$ are parallel only when the *determinant* $\begin{vmatrix} a & b \\ c & d \end{vmatrix} = ad - bc$ is zero.

EXAMPLES

1. The lines $2x_1 + 3x_2 = 7$ and $4x_1 + 6x_2 = 0$ are parallel.
2. The lines $2x_1 + 3x_2 = 1$ and $3x_1 + 5x_2 = 2$ intersect.

Systems of linear equations

The set of solutions $\begin{bmatrix} x_1 \\ x_2 \end{bmatrix}$ of a single linear equation $ax_1 + bx_2 = p$ is a line if one of a, b is nonzero, the empty set if $a = b = 0$ and p is nonzero, and the entire plane $\mathbb{R}^2$ if $a = b = c = 0$. (Explain!) Since the set of **simultaneous** solutions $\begin{bmatrix} x_1 \\ x_2 \end{bmatrix}$ of a **system of linear equations**

$$\begin{aligned} a_1x_1 + b_1x_2 &= p_1 \\ a_2x_1 + b_2x_2 &= p_2 \\ &\vdots \\ a_mx_1 + b_mx_2 &= p_m \end{aligned}$$

is the intersection of these three kinds of sets, we get a nice description for the set of simultaneous solutions.

Theorem 1.3. *Set of Simultaneous Solutions to Equations in Two Unknowns.* The set of simultaneous solutions to any number of equations in two unknowns is the plane, a line, a point, or the empty set.

The intersection of two or more sets, each of which is the entire plane, a line, or the empty set, can be expressed as the intersection of three of them (two if the intersection is nonempty). (Explain!) So, we have the following.

Theorem 1.4. *Determination of the Set of Simultaneous Solutions.* The set of simultaneous solutions of a system of linear equations in two unknowns is the set of simultaneous solutions of some subsystem consisting of at most three of them.

The determinant and Cramer's rule

When the **determinant** $\begin{vmatrix} a & b \\ b & d \end{vmatrix} = ad - bc$ of a system

$$\begin{aligned} ax_1 + bx_2 &= p \\ cx_1 + dx_2 &= q \end{aligned}$$

of two linear equations is 0, the system is of the form

$$\begin{aligned} ax_1 + bx_2 &= p \\ tax_1 + tbx_2 &= q \end{aligned}$$

or

$$\begin{aligned} tcx_1 + tdx_2 &= p \\ cx_1 + dx_2 &= q. \end{aligned}$$

So, the solution set is empty, the whole plane, or a line. Otherwise, it consists of the unique intersection point $\begin{bmatrix} x_1 \\ x_2 \end{bmatrix}$ of two lines, found as follows. To get x_1, multiply the first equation by d and the second by b, getting

$$\begin{aligned} adx_1 + bdx_2 &= pd, \\ cbx_1 + dbx_2 &= qb. \end{aligned}$$

Subtracting the second from the first to eliminate the variable x_2 gives $(ad - bc)x_1 = pd - bq$. Since the lines are not parallel, the determinant $ad - bc$ is not zero, so we can solve for x_1, getting $x_1 = (pd - bq)/(ad - bc)$.

By a similar strategy for x_2, we get $x_2 = (aq - pc)/(ad - bc)$. Using determinant notation gives Cramer's rule.

Theorem 1.5. *Cramer's Rule.*

If $\begin{vmatrix} a & b \\ c & d \end{vmatrix} \neq 0$, then $\begin{bmatrix} x_1 \\ x_2 \end{bmatrix}$ where

$$x_1 = \frac{\begin{vmatrix} p & b \\ q & d \end{vmatrix}}{\begin{vmatrix} a & b \\ c & d \end{vmatrix}}, \qquad x_2 = \frac{\begin{vmatrix} a & p \\ c & q \end{vmatrix}}{\begin{vmatrix} a & b \\ c & d \end{vmatrix}}$$

is a solution of

$$ax_1 + bx_2 = p,$$
$$cx_1 + dx_2 = q.$$

EXAMPLE

The lines $2x_1 + 3x_2 = 1$, $3x_1 + 5x_2 = 2$ intersect at $x_1 = -1$, $x_2 = 1$, as shown in Figure 1.12.

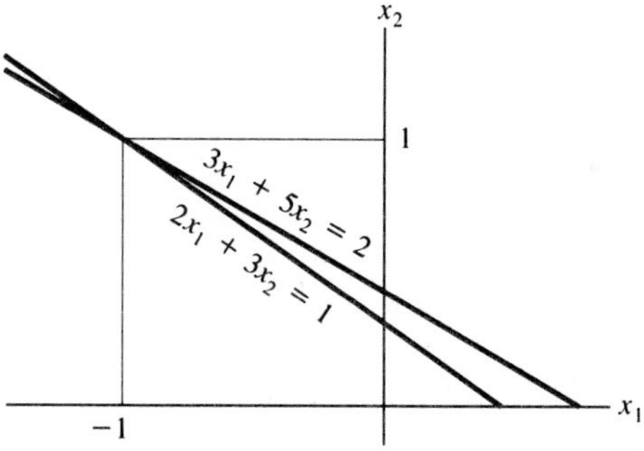

Figure 1.12 The lines $2x_1 + 3x_2 = 1$, $3x_1 + 5x_2 = 2$ intersect at $\begin{bmatrix} x_1 \\ x_2 \end{bmatrix}$ where

$$x_1 = \frac{\begin{vmatrix} 1 & 3 \\ 2 & 5 \end{vmatrix}}{\begin{vmatrix} 2 & 3 \\ 3 & 5 \end{vmatrix}} = -1, \qquad x_2 = \frac{\begin{vmatrix} 2 & 1 \\ 3 & 2 \end{vmatrix}}{\begin{vmatrix} 2 & 3 \\ 3 & 5 \end{vmatrix}} = 1.$$

Lines parallel to a vector

We close this section by constructing the lines through a point parallel and perpendicular to a given vector $\begin{bmatrix} a \\ b \end{bmatrix}$ in terms of linear and parametric equations.

A line $ex_1 + fx_2 = g$ is said to be *parallel* to the vector $\begin{bmatrix} a \\ b \end{bmatrix}$ if it is parallel to the line passing through 0 and the point $\begin{bmatrix} a \\ b \end{bmatrix}$. (Here we are using vector notation for points.) So, $ex_1 + fx_2 = g$ is parallel to the vector $\begin{bmatrix} a \\ b \end{bmatrix}$ if and only if $ea + fb = 0$.

The line $-bx_1 + ax_2 = ad - bc$ passes through $\begin{bmatrix} c \\ d \end{bmatrix}$, and it is parallel to the line $-bx_1 + ax_2 = 0$ through 0 and $\begin{bmatrix} a \\ b \end{bmatrix}$. (Explain!) Thus, it is the line through $\begin{bmatrix} c \\ d \end{bmatrix}$ parallel to $\begin{bmatrix} a \\ b \end{bmatrix}$. See Figure 1.13. Since the equation $-bx_1 + ax_2 = ad - bc$ can be rewritten as $\dfrac{x_2 - d}{x_1 - c} = \dfrac{b}{a}$ if a is not zero, we have the following theorem.

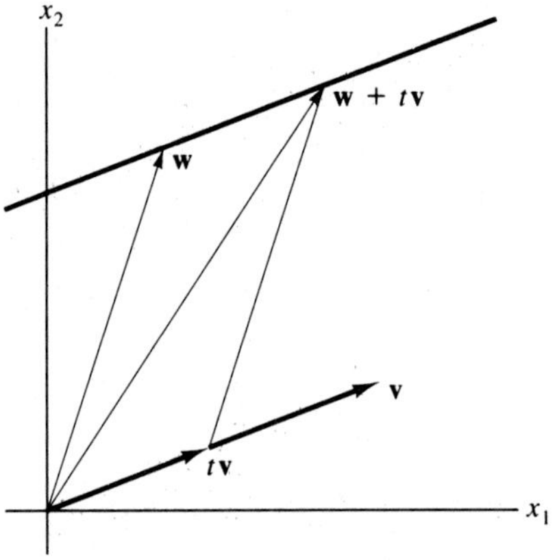

Figure 1.13 The line parallel to the vector $\mathbf{v} = \begin{bmatrix} a \\ b \end{bmatrix}$ through the point $\mathbf{w} = \begin{bmatrix} c \\ d \end{bmatrix}$ consists of the vectors $\mathbf{w} + t\mathbf{v} = \begin{bmatrix} c \\ d \end{bmatrix} + t\begin{bmatrix} a \\ b \end{bmatrix}$.

Theorem 1.6. *The Line Parallel to the Vector* $\begin{bmatrix} a \\ b \end{bmatrix}$ *through the Point* $\begin{bmatrix} c \\ d \end{bmatrix}$.

The line $-bx_1 + ax_2 = ad - bc$ is the line parallel to $\begin{bmatrix} a \\ b \end{bmatrix}$ through $\begin{bmatrix} c \\ d \end{bmatrix}$. For $a \neq 0$, it is

$$\frac{x_2 - d}{x_1 - c} = \frac{b}{a}.$$

EXAMPLES

1. The line parallel to the vector $\begin{bmatrix} 7 \\ 2 \end{bmatrix}$ through the point $\begin{bmatrix} 3 \\ 5 \end{bmatrix}$ is

$$\frac{x_2 - 5}{x_1 - 3} = \frac{2}{7}.$$

2. The line passing through two different points $\begin{bmatrix} a \\ b \end{bmatrix}$ and $\begin{bmatrix} c \\ d \end{bmatrix}$ is the same as the line parallel to the vector $\begin{bmatrix} a-c \\ b-d \end{bmatrix}$ through the point $\begin{bmatrix} c \\ d \end{bmatrix}$. (Check!) In fact, it is $\dfrac{x_2 - d}{x_1 - c} = \dfrac{b - d}{a - c}$ if $a \neq c$.

3. The line passing through the points $\begin{bmatrix} 3 \\ 2 \end{bmatrix}$ and $\begin{bmatrix} 7 \\ 8 \end{bmatrix}$ is $\dfrac{x_2 - 8}{x_1 - 7} = \dfrac{2 - 8}{3 - 7}$.

Parametric representation of a line

For any nonzero vector $\begin{bmatrix} a \\ b \end{bmatrix}$ and any point $\begin{bmatrix} c \\ d \end{bmatrix}$, the set of vectors $\begin{bmatrix} x_1 \\ x_2 \end{bmatrix} = t\begin{bmatrix} a \\ b \end{bmatrix} + \begin{bmatrix} c \\ d \end{bmatrix}$, where t ranges throughout $\mathbb{R}$, is just the line parallel to $\begin{bmatrix} a \\ b \end{bmatrix}$ passing through the point $\begin{bmatrix} c \\ d \end{bmatrix}$. (Explain!) We refer to

$$\begin{bmatrix} x_1 \\ x_2 \end{bmatrix} = t\begin{bmatrix} a \\ b \end{bmatrix} + \begin{bmatrix} c \\ d \end{bmatrix}$$

as a **parametric equation** and to t as the **parameter**.

EXAMPLES

1. The parametric equation for the line through the point $\begin{bmatrix} 2 \\ 4 \end{bmatrix}$ parallel to the vector $\begin{bmatrix} 1 \\ 3 \end{bmatrix}$ is

$$\begin{bmatrix} x_1 \\ x_2 \end{bmatrix} = t\begin{bmatrix} 1 \\ 3 \end{bmatrix} + \begin{bmatrix} 2 \\ 4 \end{bmatrix}.$$

Letting $t = 0$, we see that $\begin{bmatrix} x_1 \\ x_2 \end{bmatrix} = \begin{bmatrix} 2 \\ 4 \end{bmatrix}$, so that this line does pass through the tip of $\mathbf{v} = \begin{bmatrix} 2 \\ 4 \end{bmatrix}$. Letting $t = 1$, we see that it also passes through the tip of $\mathbf{w} = \begin{bmatrix}1\\3\end{bmatrix} + \begin{bmatrix}2\\4\end{bmatrix}$. So, $\overrightarrow{\mathbf{v}\mathbf{w}}$ is indeed parallel to the vector $\mathbf{w} - \mathbf{v} = \begin{bmatrix}1\\3\end{bmatrix}$.

2. The line passing through two different points $\begin{bmatrix}a\\b\end{bmatrix}$ and $\begin{bmatrix}c\\d\end{bmatrix}$ is the same as the line parallel to $\begin{bmatrix}a-c\\b-d\end{bmatrix}$ through $\begin{bmatrix}c\\d\end{bmatrix}$. So, the parametric equation for this line is $\begin{bmatrix}x_1\\x_2\end{bmatrix} = t\begin{bmatrix}a-c\\b-d\end{bmatrix} + \begin{bmatrix}c\\d\end{bmatrix}$, which can also be written as the **weighted average** $\begin{bmatrix}x_1\\x_2\end{bmatrix} = t\begin{bmatrix}a\\b\end{bmatrix} + (1-t)\begin{bmatrix}c\\d\end{bmatrix}$ of the vectors $\begin{bmatrix}a\\b\end{bmatrix}$ and $\begin{bmatrix}c\\d\end{bmatrix}$. (Check!) See Figure 1.14.

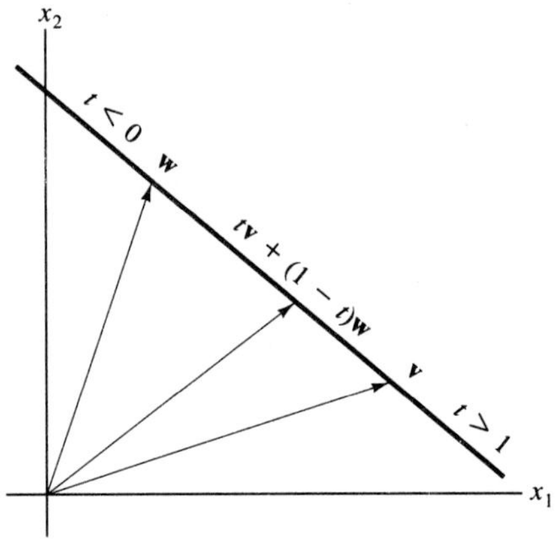

Figure 1.14 The line $t\mathbf{v} + (1-t)\mathbf{w}$ through $\mathbf{v} = \begin{bmatrix}a\\b\end{bmatrix}$ and $\mathbf{w} = \begin{bmatrix}c\\d\end{bmatrix}$.

Lines perpendicular to a vector

The line through **0** perpendicular to the line through **0** and the tip of the vector $\begin{bmatrix}a\\b\end{bmatrix}$ is $ax_1 + bx_2 = 0$, which passes through **0** and the tip of $\begin{bmatrix}-b\\a\end{bmatrix}$ (Figure 1.15). So, we say that a line is **perpendicular** (or **normal**) to the vector $\begin{bmatrix}a\\b\end{bmatrix}$ if it is parallel to the line $ax_1 + bx_2 = 0$. Therefore, the lines perpen-

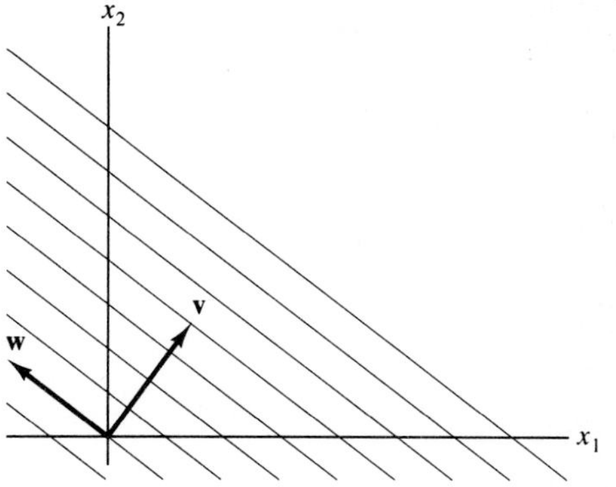

Figure 1.15 The lines normal to $\mathbf{v} = \begin{bmatrix} a \\ b \end{bmatrix}$ are the lines parallel to $\mathbf{w} = \begin{bmatrix} -b \\ a \end{bmatrix}$.

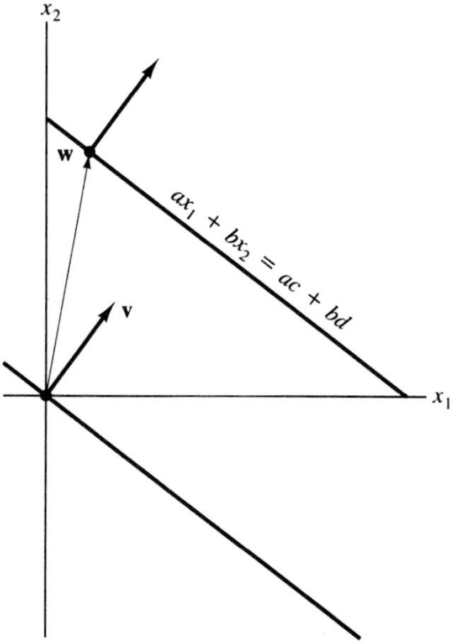

Figure 1.16 The line perpendicular to the vector $\mathbf{v} = \begin{bmatrix} a \\ b \end{bmatrix}$ through the point $\mathbf{w} = \begin{bmatrix} c \\ d \end{bmatrix}$.

dicular to the vector $\begin{bmatrix} a \\ b \end{bmatrix}$ are the lines $ax_1 + bx_2 = g$ for any g. Exactly one of these passes through the tip of $\begin{bmatrix} c \\ d \end{bmatrix}$, namely, the line with $g = ac + bd$ (Figure 1.16). This proves the following theorem.

Theorem 1.7. *The Perpendicular to the Vector* $\begin{bmatrix} a \\ b \end{bmatrix}$ *through the Point* $\begin{bmatrix} c \\ d \end{bmatrix}$.

The line $ax_1 + bx_2 = ac + bd$ is the one and only line perpendicular to $\begin{bmatrix} a \\ b \end{bmatrix}$ through the point $\begin{bmatrix} c \\ d \end{bmatrix}$.

Since the line $ax_1 + bx_2 = g$ is normal to the vector $\begin{bmatrix} a \\ b \end{bmatrix}$, we refer to the vector $\begin{bmatrix} a \\ b \end{bmatrix}$ as a *normal* to the line $ax_1 + bx_2 = g$.

For any nonzero vector $\begin{bmatrix} a \\ b \end{bmatrix}$ and any point $\begin{bmatrix} c \\ d \end{bmatrix}$, $\begin{bmatrix} x_1 \\ x_2 \end{bmatrix} = t\begin{bmatrix} -b \\ a \end{bmatrix} + \begin{bmatrix} c \\ d \end{bmatrix}$ $(t \in \mathbb{R})$ is the parametric equation for the line perpendicular to the vector $\begin{bmatrix} a \\ b \end{bmatrix}$ through the point $\begin{bmatrix} c \\ d \end{bmatrix}$ (Figure 1.15).

EXAMPLE

The parametric equation for the line through the point $\begin{bmatrix} 2 \\ 4 \end{bmatrix}$ perpendicular to the vector $\begin{bmatrix} 1 \\ 3 \end{bmatrix}$ is $\begin{bmatrix} x_1 \\ x_2 \end{bmatrix} = t\begin{bmatrix} -3 \\ 2 \end{bmatrix} + \begin{bmatrix} 2 \\ 4 \end{bmatrix}$. It can also be represented by $1x_1 + 3x_2 = 14$. Letting $t = 0$, we see that this line does pass through the tip of the vector $\mathbf{v} = \begin{bmatrix} 2 \\ 4 \end{bmatrix}$. Letting $t = 1$, we see that it also passes through the tip of $\mathbf{w} = \begin{bmatrix} -3 \\ 2 \end{bmatrix} + \begin{bmatrix} 2 \\ 4 \end{bmatrix}$. So, in this case, the directed line segment $\overrightarrow{\mathbf{v}\,\mathbf{w}}$ is parallel to the vector $\mathbf{w} - \mathbf{v} = \begin{bmatrix} -3 \\ 2 \end{bmatrix}$.

PROBLEMS

NUMERICAL PROBLEMS

1. Describe the set of simultaneous solutions to the following systems of linear equations as a plane, line, point, or empty set.

(a) $2x_1 + 3x_2 = 4$
$5x_1 + 6x_2 = 7$
$3x_1 + 3x_2 = 3$
$4x_1 + 6x_2 = 8$

(b) $2x_1 + 3x_2 = 4$
$5x_1 + 6x_2 = 7$
$7x_1 + 9x_2 = 10$

(c) $2x_1 - 3x_2 = 5$
$4x_1 - 6x_2 = 10$
$3x_1 + 3x_2 = 6$

2. Find a system with as few equations as possible (three, two, or one) having the same solution set in cases (a), (b), and (c) of Problem 1.

3. Draw the lines $2x_1 - 5x_2 = 0$, $2x_1 + 5x_2 = 7$, and $2x_1 - 5x_2 = -8$ in the Cartesian plane.

4. Describe the half-spaces determined by the lines in Problem 3.

5. Show that the locus points of the equation $\begin{vmatrix} x_1 & x_2 \\ 4 & 2 \end{vmatrix} = 2$ is a line, find two points on it, and draw the line.

6. Show that the locus points of the equation $\begin{vmatrix} x_1 & x_2 \\ -1-3x_1 & 2-3x_2 \end{vmatrix} = 3$ is a line, find two points on it, and draw the line.

7. Find the point of intersection of the lines in the preceding two problems.

8. Show that if $\begin{bmatrix} a \\ b \end{bmatrix}$ is a point on the line $\begin{vmatrix} x_1 & x_2 \\ 4 & 2 \end{vmatrix} = 0$ and $\begin{bmatrix} c \\ d \end{bmatrix}$ is a point on the line $\begin{vmatrix} x_1 & x_2 \\ -1-3x_1 & 2-3x_2 \end{vmatrix} = 0$, then $ac + bd = 0$.

(*Note:* In the next section, we see that the vectors $\begin{bmatrix} a \\ b \end{bmatrix}$ and $\begin{bmatrix} c \\ d \end{bmatrix}$ are perpendicular to each other if and only if $ac + bd = 0$.)

9. Find the point of intersection of the lines $2x_1 + 5x_2 = 3$ and $3x_1 + 8x_2 = 7$.

10. Give the linear equation for the line through the point $\begin{bmatrix} 2 \\ 4 \end{bmatrix}$ which

   (a) Is parallel to the vector $\begin{bmatrix} 3 \\ 4 \end{bmatrix}$;

   (b) Is perpendicular to the vector $\begin{bmatrix} 3 \\ 4 \end{bmatrix}$;

   (c) Is parallel to the vector $\begin{bmatrix} -4 \\ 3 \end{bmatrix}$;

   (d) Is perpendicular to the vector $\begin{bmatrix} -4 \\ 3 \end{bmatrix}$;

   (e) Passes through the point $\begin{bmatrix} 5 \\ 2 \end{bmatrix}$.

11. Give the parametric equation for the line through the point $\begin{bmatrix} 2 \\ 4 \end{bmatrix}$ which

   (a) Is parallel to the vector $\begin{bmatrix} 1 \\ 5 \end{bmatrix}$;

   (b) Is perpendicular to the vector $\begin{bmatrix} 2 \\ 5 \end{bmatrix}$;

   (c) Is parallel to the vector $\begin{bmatrix} -2 \\ 5 \end{bmatrix}$;

   (d) Is perpendicular to the vector $\begin{bmatrix} -1 \\ 5 \end{bmatrix}$;

   (e) Passes through $\begin{bmatrix} 5 \\ 2 \end{bmatrix}$.

THEORETICAL PROBLEMS

12. Use Cramer's rule to find a formula for the point of intersection of the lines $\frac{x_2 - b}{x_1 - a} = r$ and $\frac{x_2 - d}{x_1 - c} = s$.

13. Show that the line passing through the tips of two vectors $\mathbf{v}$ and $\mathbf{w}$ contains the line segment $\overline{\mathbf{v}\,\mathbf{w}}$ consisting of the tips of the vectors $t\mathbf{v} + (1 - t)\mathbf{w}$ $(0 \le t \le 1)$.

14. Verify that the equation of the line passing through $\begin{bmatrix} c \\ d \end{bmatrix}$ parallel to the vector $\begin{bmatrix} a \\ b \end{bmatrix}$ is $\frac{x_2 - d}{x_1 - c} = \frac{b}{a}$ when $a \neq 0$.

15. Verify that the equation of the line passing through two different points $\begin{bmatrix} a \\ b \end{bmatrix}$ and $\begin{bmatrix} c \\ d \end{bmatrix}$ is $\frac{x_2 - d}{x_1 - c} = \frac{b - d}{a - c}$ if $a \neq c$.

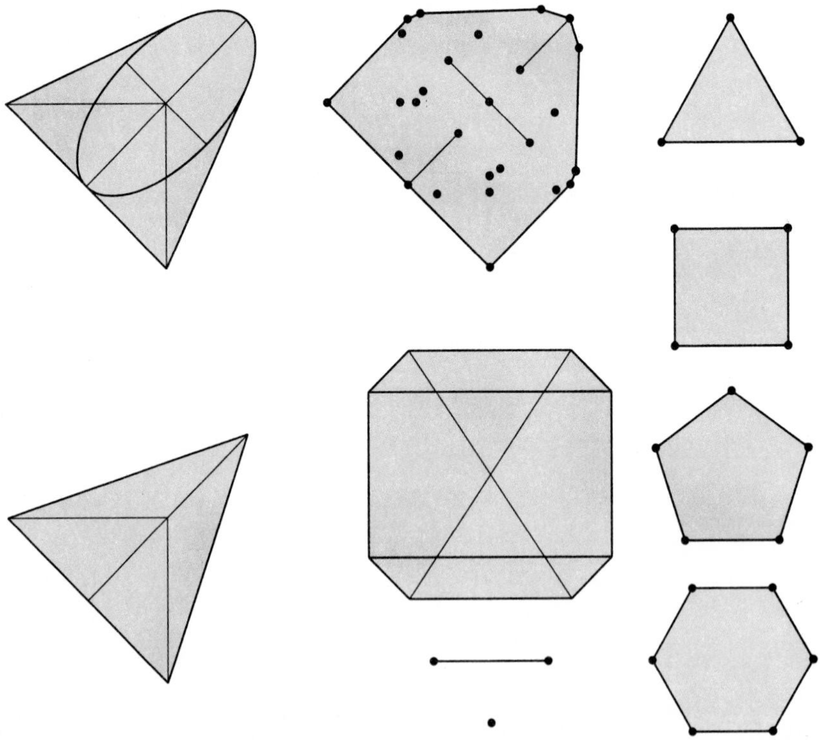

Figure 1.17 Convex hulls of several sets in the plane.

Hard

16. A set C of points of the Cartesian plane is **convex** if whenever the tips of vectors $\mathbf{v}$ and $\mathbf{w}$ are in C, the tips of the vectors $t\mathbf{v} + (1 - t)\mathbf{w}$ $(0 \le t \le 1)$ are in C. Show that

(a) The line $ax_1 + bx_2 = p$ is convex;

(b) The half-space $ax_1 + bx_2 > p$ is convex;

(c) The half-space $ax_1 + bx_2 < p$ is convex.

17. Show that:

(a) The intersection of any two convex sets is convex;

(b) The intersection of any number of convex sets is convex.

Use this to show that the set $\hat{S}$ of all vectors contained in every convex set containing S is convex for any set S. (The set $\hat{S}$ is called the **convex hull** of S. See Figure 1.17.)

18. Describe all possibilities for convex hulls of sets of at most four elements.

1.3 LINEAR TRANSFORMATIONS OF THE PLANE

At the very heart of linear algebra lies the *set, or algebra, of linear transformations.*

Definition. *Linear Transformation.*

A **linear transformation** of $\mathbb{R}^2$ is a mapping R from $\mathbb{R}^2$ to itself of the form $R\begin{bmatrix} x_1 \\ x_2 \end{bmatrix} = \begin{bmatrix} ax_1 + bx_2 \\ cx_1 + dx_2 \end{bmatrix}$.

EXAMPLE

$R\begin{bmatrix} x_1 \\ x_2 \end{bmatrix} = \begin{bmatrix} 1x_1 + 2x_2 \\ 6x_1 + 5x_2 \end{bmatrix}$ is a linear transformation that maps $\begin{bmatrix} 3 \\ 4 \end{bmatrix}$ to $\begin{bmatrix} 1 \cdot 3 + 2 \cdot 4 \\ 6 \cdot 3 + 5 \cdot 4 \end{bmatrix}$.

The vectors $\mathbf{e}_1 = \begin{bmatrix} 1 \\ 0 \end{bmatrix}$ and $\mathbf{e}_2 = \begin{bmatrix} 0 \\ 1 \end{bmatrix}$ are the **standard unit vectors**. They are mapped by $R\begin{bmatrix} x_1 \\ x_2 \end{bmatrix} = \begin{bmatrix} ax_1 + bx_2 \\ cx_1 + dx_2 \end{bmatrix}$ to $\begin{bmatrix} a \\ c \end{bmatrix}$ and $\begin{bmatrix} b \\ d \end{bmatrix}$, since $R\begin{bmatrix} 1 \\ 0 \end{bmatrix} = \begin{bmatrix} a1 + b0 \\ c1 + d0 \end{bmatrix} = \begin{bmatrix} a \\ c \end{bmatrix}$ and $R\begin{bmatrix} 0 \\ 1 \end{bmatrix} = \begin{bmatrix} a0 + b1 \\ c0 + d1 \end{bmatrix} = \begin{bmatrix} b \\ d \end{bmatrix}$. See Figure 1.18. There is only one linear transformation that does this. (Prove!)

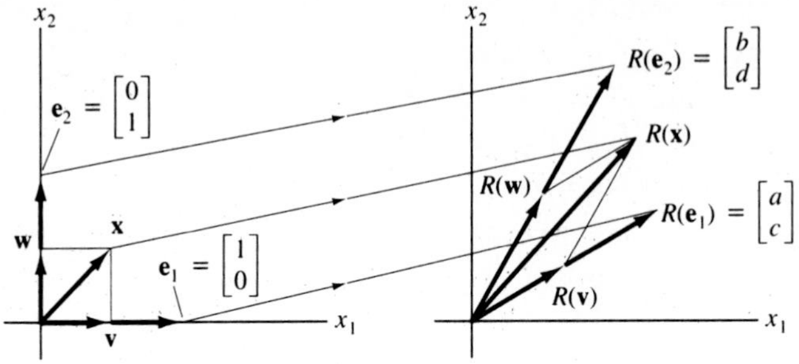

Figure 1.18 The linear transformation R sending $\mathbf{e}_1 = \begin{bmatrix} 1 \\ 0 \end{bmatrix}$ and $\mathbf{e}_2 = \begin{bmatrix} 0 \\ 1 \end{bmatrix}$ to $\begin{bmatrix} a \\ c \end{bmatrix}$ and $\begin{bmatrix} b \\ d \end{bmatrix}$.

EXAMPLE

$$R\begin{bmatrix} x_1 \\ x_2 \end{bmatrix} = \begin{bmatrix} 1x_1 + 2x_2 \\ 6x_1 + 5x_2 \end{bmatrix} \text{ maps } \begin{bmatrix} 1 \\ 0 \end{bmatrix} \text{ to } \begin{bmatrix} 1 \\ 6 \end{bmatrix} \text{ and } \begin{bmatrix} 0 \\ 1 \end{bmatrix} \text{ to } \begin{bmatrix} 2 \\ 5 \end{bmatrix}.$$

Theorem 1.8. *Specifying a Linear Transformation by Giving Two Vectors.* For any two vectors $\begin{bmatrix} a \\ c \end{bmatrix}$ and $\begin{bmatrix} b \\ d \end{bmatrix}$, there is one and only one linear transformation R which maps $\begin{bmatrix} 1 \\ 0 \end{bmatrix}$ to $\begin{bmatrix} a \\ c \end{bmatrix}$ and $\begin{bmatrix} 0 \\ 1 \end{bmatrix}$ to $\begin{bmatrix} b \\ d \end{bmatrix}$.

The linearity property of a linear transformation

Every linear transformation R of $\mathbb{R}^2$ has the following **linearity property**:

$$R(a\mathbf{v} + b\mathbf{w}) = aR(\mathbf{v}) + bR(\mathbf{w}) \qquad (a, b \in \mathbb{R}; \mathbf{v}, \mathbf{w} \in \mathbb{R}^2).$$

It follows that *any linear transformation R maps lines to lines or points* (see Problems 9 and 10) and that

$$R(\mathbf{v} + \mathbf{w}) = R(\mathbf{v}) + R(\mathbf{w})$$
$$R(a\mathbf{v}) = aR(\mathbf{v})$$

for all a, $\mathbf{v}$, $\mathbf{w}$.

We defer the proof of the linearity property until later, where we treat more general linear transformations. For now, the following examples should suffice to illustrate how and why it works.

EXAMPLES

$R\begin{bmatrix} x_1 \\ x_2 \end{bmatrix} = \begin{bmatrix} 3x_1 + 2x_2 \\ 2x_1 + 4x_2 \end{bmatrix}$ maps $\begin{bmatrix} 1 \\ 0 \end{bmatrix}$ to $\begin{bmatrix} 3 \\ 2 \end{bmatrix}$ and $\begin{bmatrix} 0 \\ 1 \end{bmatrix}$ to $\begin{bmatrix} 2 \\ 4 \end{bmatrix}$. So:

1. R maps $3\begin{bmatrix} 1 \\ 0 \end{bmatrix} + 5\begin{bmatrix} 0 \\ 1 \end{bmatrix} = \begin{bmatrix} 3 \\ 5 \end{bmatrix}$ to $3\begin{bmatrix} 3 \\ 2 \end{bmatrix} + 5\begin{bmatrix} 2 \\ 4 \end{bmatrix}$. (Verify!)

2. R maps $\begin{bmatrix} a \\ b \end{bmatrix}$ to $a\begin{bmatrix} 3 \\ 2 \end{bmatrix} + b\begin{bmatrix} 2 \\ 4 \end{bmatrix}$. (Verify!)

3. Since R maps $\begin{bmatrix} 1 \\ 1 \end{bmatrix}$ to $\begin{bmatrix} 5 \\ 6 \end{bmatrix}$ and $\begin{bmatrix} 1 \\ -1 \end{bmatrix}$ to $\begin{bmatrix} 1 \\ -2 \end{bmatrix}$, R maps $2\begin{bmatrix} 1 \\ 1 \end{bmatrix} - 3\begin{bmatrix} 1 \\ -1 \end{bmatrix}$ to $2\begin{bmatrix} 5 \\ 6 \end{bmatrix} - 3\begin{bmatrix} 1 \\ -2 \end{bmatrix}$. (Verify!)

4. $R\left(\begin{bmatrix} 2 \\ 3 \end{bmatrix} + \begin{bmatrix} 1 \\ 0 \end{bmatrix}\right) = R\begin{bmatrix} 2 \\ 3 \end{bmatrix} + R\begin{bmatrix} 1 \\ 0 \end{bmatrix}$. (Verify!)

5. $R\left(5\begin{bmatrix} 2 \\ 3 \end{bmatrix}\right) = 5R\begin{bmatrix} 2 \\ 3 \end{bmatrix}$. (Verify!)

The determinant of a linear transformation

The square with edge vectors $\begin{bmatrix} 1 \\ 0 \end{bmatrix}$ and $\begin{bmatrix} 0 \\ 1 \end{bmatrix}$ is called the **unit square**, denoted by I. It has area equal to 1. The linear transformation $R\begin{bmatrix} x_1 \\ x_2 \end{bmatrix} = \begin{bmatrix} ax_1 + bx_2 \\ cx_1 + dx_2 \end{bmatrix}$ maps the area of this square to the area of the **parallelogram with edge vectors** $\begin{bmatrix} a \\ c \end{bmatrix}$ and $\begin{bmatrix} b \\ d \end{bmatrix}$, which we label R. (See Figure 1.19.)

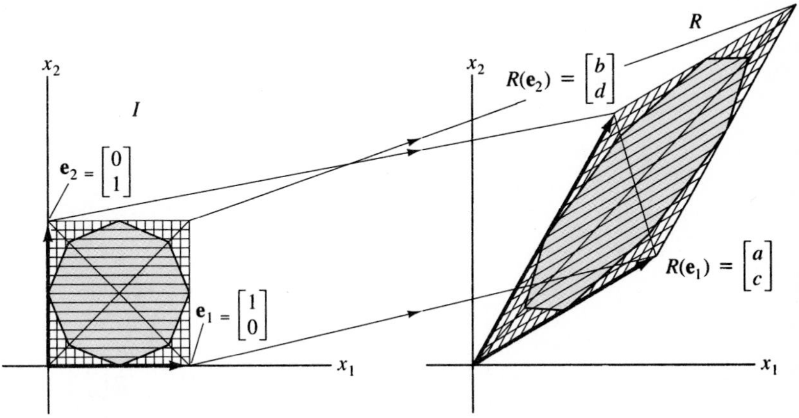

Figure 1.19 The image of the unit square I and contents under R.

It follows that an important measure associated with R is the area of the parallelogram with edge vectors $\begin{bmatrix} a \\ c \end{bmatrix}$ and $\begin{bmatrix} b \\ d \end{bmatrix}$. This area is $\begin{vmatrix} a & b \\ c & d \end{vmatrix} = ad - bc$, as we show in Section 1.6.

Definition. *The Determinant of a Linear Transformation.*

The **determinant** of a linear transformation $R\left(\begin{bmatrix} x_1 \\ x_2 \end{bmatrix}\right) = \begin{bmatrix} ax_1 + bx_2 \\ cx_1 + dx_2 \end{bmatrix}$ is the determinant $\begin{vmatrix} a & b \\ c & d \end{vmatrix} = ad - bc$.

EXAMPLE

The determinant of $R\begin{bmatrix} x_1 \\ x_2 \end{bmatrix} = \begin{bmatrix} 1x_1 + 2x_2 \\ 6x_1 + 5x_2 \end{bmatrix}$ is $1 \cdot 5 - 2 \cdot 6 = -7$.

Some special linear transformations

We now look at some special linear transformations and the images of vectors under them.

1. For $R\begin{bmatrix} x_1 \\ x_2 \end{bmatrix} = \begin{bmatrix} 0x_1 + 0x_2 \\ 0x_1 + 0x_2 \end{bmatrix}$, every vector is mapped to $\mathbf{0}$. The determinant is 0. This R is called **zero**, denoted by 0.

2. For $R\begin{bmatrix} x_1 \\ x_2 \end{bmatrix} = \begin{bmatrix} 1x_1 + 0x_2 \\ 0x_1 + 1x_2 \end{bmatrix}$, we get $R\begin{bmatrix} e \\ f \end{bmatrix} = \begin{bmatrix} e \\ f \end{bmatrix}$ for all e, f. The determinant is 1. This R is called the **identity**, denoted by I.

3. For $R\begin{bmatrix} x_1 \\ x_2 \end{bmatrix} = \begin{bmatrix} ax_1 + 0x_2 \\ 0x_1 + ax_2 \end{bmatrix}$, we get $R\begin{bmatrix} e \\ f \end{bmatrix} = a\begin{bmatrix} e \\ f \end{bmatrix}$ for all e, f. The determinant of R is a^2. This R is **scalar multiplication** by a (Figure 1.20(a)).

4. For $R\begin{bmatrix} x_1 \\ x_2 \end{bmatrix} = \begin{bmatrix} ax_1 + 0x_2 \\ 0x_1 + dx_2 \end{bmatrix}$, we get $R\begin{bmatrix} 1 \\ 0 \end{bmatrix} = a\begin{bmatrix} 1 \\ 0 \end{bmatrix}$, $R\begin{bmatrix} 0 \\ 1 \end{bmatrix} = d\begin{bmatrix} 0 \\ 1 \end{bmatrix}$. The determinant of R is ad. This R is a **diagonal** linear transformation (Figure 1.20(b)).

5. For $R\begin{bmatrix} x_1 \\ x_2 \end{bmatrix} = \begin{bmatrix} 1x_1 + bx_2 \\ 0x_1 + 1x_2 \end{bmatrix}$, we get $R\begin{bmatrix} 1 \\ 0 \end{bmatrix} = \begin{bmatrix} 1 \\ 0 \end{bmatrix}$, $R\begin{bmatrix} 0 \\ 1 \end{bmatrix} = \begin{bmatrix} b \\ 1 \end{bmatrix}$. The determinant of R is 1. This is a **shear** linear transformation (Figure 1.20(c)).

6. For $R\begin{bmatrix} x_1 \\ x_2 \end{bmatrix} = \begin{bmatrix} 0x_1 + 1x_2 \\ 1x_1 + 0x_2 \end{bmatrix}$, we get

$$R\begin{bmatrix} 1 \\ 0 \end{bmatrix} = \begin{bmatrix} 0 \\ 1 \end{bmatrix}, \quad R\begin{bmatrix} 0 \\ 1 \end{bmatrix} = \begin{bmatrix} 1 \\ 0 \end{bmatrix}, \quad R\begin{bmatrix} 1 \\ 1 \end{bmatrix} = \begin{bmatrix} 1 \\ 1 \end{bmatrix}.$$

   The determinant of R is -1. This linear transformation R is a **reflection** across the line $x_1 = x_2$ (Figure 1.21(a)).

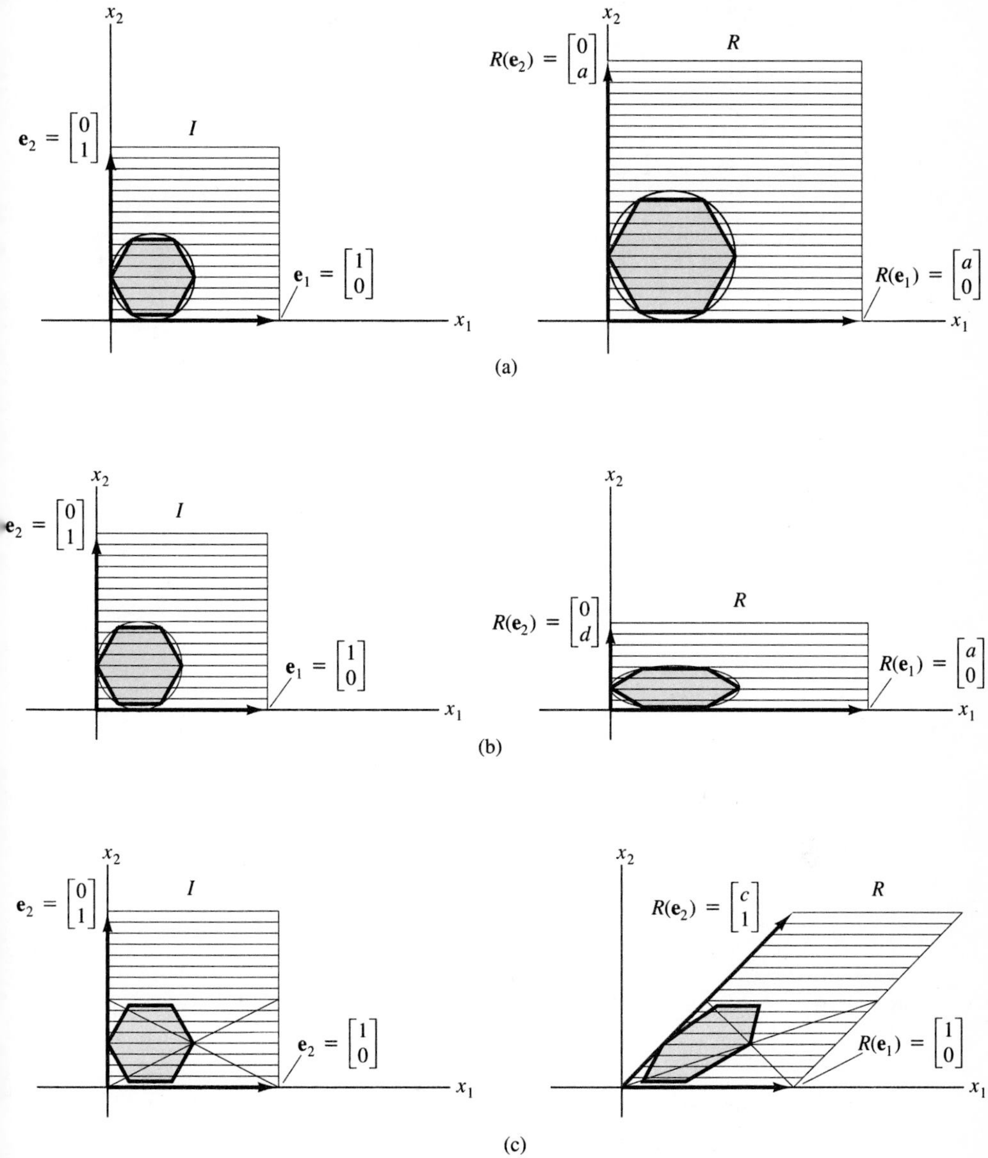

Figure 1.20 Image of I under (a) scalar, (b) diagonal, and (c) shear linear transformations.

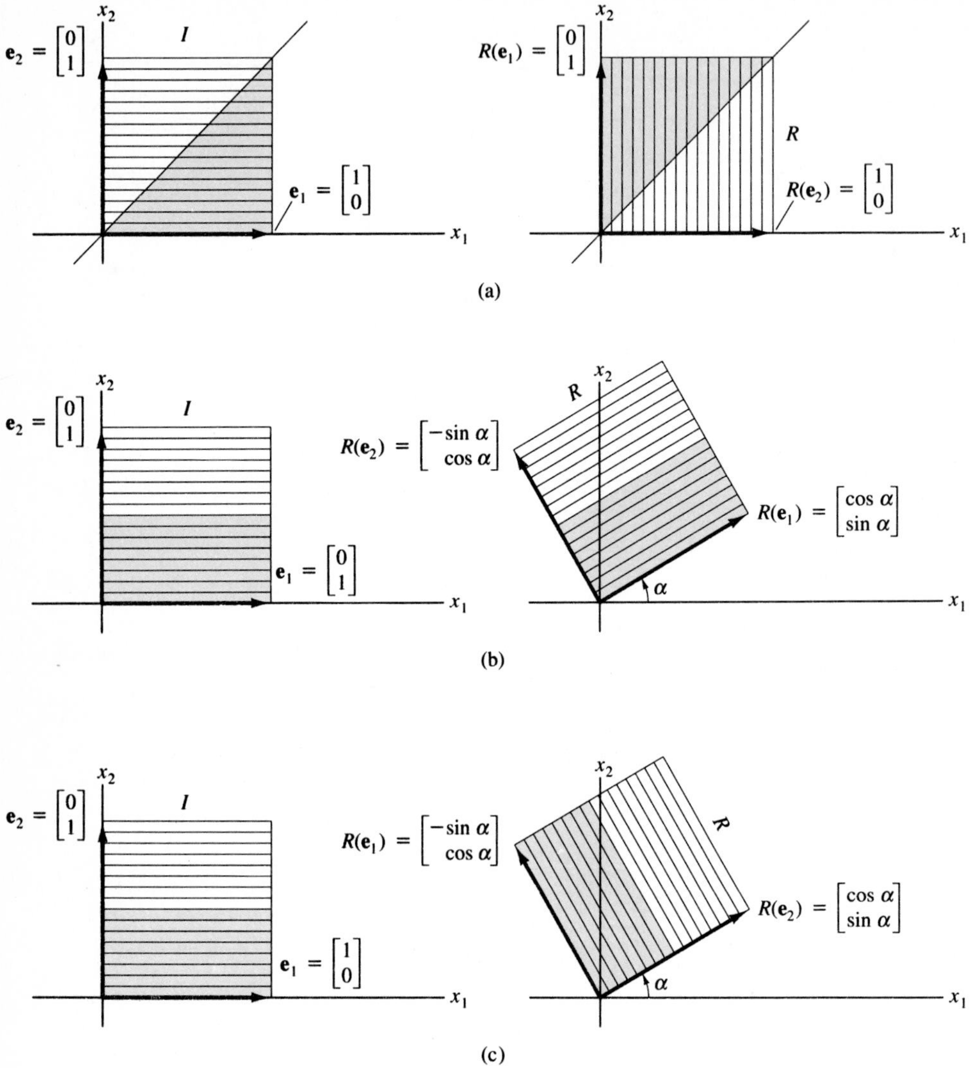

Figure 1.21 (a) Reflection R across the line $x_1 = x_2$; (b) rotation R by α; (c) reflection R across the line $x_1 = x_2$ followed by the rotation by α.

7. For $R_\alpha\begin{bmatrix}x_1\\x_2\end{bmatrix}=\begin{bmatrix}(\cos\alpha)x_1-(\sin\alpha)x_2\\(\sin\alpha)x_1+(\cos\alpha)x_2\end{bmatrix}$, we get

$$R_\alpha\begin{bmatrix}1\\0\end{bmatrix}=\begin{bmatrix}\cos\alpha\\ \sin\alpha\end{bmatrix},\quad R_\alpha\begin{bmatrix}0\\1\end{bmatrix}=\begin{bmatrix}-\sin\alpha\\ \cos\alpha\end{bmatrix}.$$

The determinant of R is 1. This transformation is **rotation by α** (Figure 1.21(b)).

8. For $R\begin{bmatrix}x_1\\x_2\end{bmatrix}=\begin{bmatrix}-(\sin\alpha)x_1+(\cos\alpha)x_2\\(\cos\alpha)x_1+(\sin\alpha)x_2\end{bmatrix}$, we get

$$R\begin{bmatrix}1\\0\end{bmatrix}=\begin{bmatrix}-\sin\alpha\\ \cos\alpha\end{bmatrix},\quad R\begin{bmatrix}0\\1\end{bmatrix}=\begin{bmatrix}\cos\alpha\\ \sin\alpha\end{bmatrix}.$$

The determinant of R_α is -1. This transformation is *reflection across the line $x_1 = x_2$ followed by rotation* by α (Figure 1.21(c)).

PROBLEMS

NUMERICAL PROBLEMS

1. Find a linear transformation R such that $R\begin{bmatrix}1\\0\end{bmatrix}=\mathbf{v}$, $R\begin{bmatrix}0\\1\end{bmatrix}=\mathbf{w}$ for

(a) $\mathbf{v}=\begin{bmatrix}3\\2\end{bmatrix}$, $\mathbf{w}=\begin{bmatrix}-2\\3\end{bmatrix}$; **(b)** $\mathbf{v}=\begin{bmatrix}1\\\pi\end{bmatrix}$, $\mathbf{w}=\begin{bmatrix}1\\2\end{bmatrix}$;

(c) $\mathbf{v}=\begin{bmatrix}0\\3\end{bmatrix}$, $\mathbf{w}=\begin{bmatrix}3\\0\end{bmatrix}$.

2. In the following cases, if a linear transformation R maps $\begin{bmatrix}1\\0\end{bmatrix}$ to $\mathbf{v}$ and $\begin{bmatrix}0\\1\end{bmatrix}$ to $\mathbf{w}$, where does it map $\mathbf{x}$?

(a) $\mathbf{v}=\begin{bmatrix}1\\4\end{bmatrix}$, $\mathbf{w}=\begin{bmatrix}2\\4\end{bmatrix}$, $\mathbf{x}=\begin{bmatrix}-3\\4\end{bmatrix}$

(b) $\mathbf{v}=\begin{bmatrix}5\\3\end{bmatrix}$, $\mathbf{w}=\begin{bmatrix}5\\6\end{bmatrix}$, $\mathbf{x}=\begin{bmatrix}3\\3\end{bmatrix}$

(c) $\mathbf{v}=\begin{bmatrix}0\\3\end{bmatrix}$, $\mathbf{w}=\begin{bmatrix}1\\5\end{bmatrix}$, $\mathbf{x}=\begin{bmatrix}11\\3\end{bmatrix}$

3. Find the determinants of the linear transformations in Problem 2.

4. Find the determinant of

(a) The diagonal linear transformation $R\begin{bmatrix}x_1\\x_2\end{bmatrix}=\begin{bmatrix}4x_1\\-5x_2\end{bmatrix}$;

(b) A shear linear transformation;

(c) The reflection through the line $x_1 = x_2$;

(d) Rotation by α;

(e) Rotation by α followed by a shear;

(f) The diagonal linear transformation of (a) followed by reflection through the line $x_1 = x_2$.

5. A linear transformation R maps $\mathbf{e}_1$ to $\begin{bmatrix} 3 \\ 4 \end{bmatrix}$ and $\mathbf{e}_2$ to $\begin{bmatrix} 3 \\ d \end{bmatrix}$. If the determinant of R is 400, what is d?

6. Find the image of $\begin{bmatrix} 2 \\ 3 \end{bmatrix}$ and compare it with $2\mathbf{v} + 3\mathbf{w}$ for each of the linear transformations in Problem 1.

7. Compute the image of $\begin{bmatrix} 1 \\ -1 \end{bmatrix}$ and $\begin{bmatrix} 1 \\ 1 \end{bmatrix}$ under the rotation by $\pi/3$.

8. For each of the following pairs of vectors, find a rotation R that maps the first to the second or show that there is none.

(a) $\begin{bmatrix} 1 \\ -1 \end{bmatrix}, \begin{bmatrix} -1 \\ 1 \end{bmatrix}$ **(b)** $\begin{bmatrix} 1 \\ 1 \end{bmatrix}, \begin{bmatrix} -1 \\ 1 \end{bmatrix}$ **(c)** $\begin{bmatrix} 3 \\ -4 \end{bmatrix}, \begin{bmatrix} -5 \\ 0 \end{bmatrix}$

(d) $\begin{bmatrix} 5 \\ -3 \end{bmatrix}, \begin{bmatrix} -6 \\ 2 \end{bmatrix}$ **(e)** $\begin{bmatrix} 2 \\ -1 \end{bmatrix}, \begin{bmatrix} 2 \\ 2 \end{bmatrix}$

THEORETICAL PROBLEMS

9. If R is a linear transformation of $\mathbb{R}^2$, show that R maps the line $\mathbf{x} = t\mathbf{v} + \mathbf{w}$ through $\mathbf{v}$ parallel to $\mathbf{w}$ onto the line $\mathbf{x} = tR(\mathbf{v}) + R(\mathbf{w})$ or onto the point $R(\mathbf{w})$.

10. Describe a linear transformation R which maps $\begin{bmatrix} 1 \\ 0 \end{bmatrix}$ to $\begin{bmatrix} 2 \\ 0 \end{bmatrix}$ and maps each point on the line $t\begin{bmatrix} 0 \\ 1 \end{bmatrix} + \begin{bmatrix} 2 \\ 3 \end{bmatrix}$ to the point $\begin{bmatrix} 4 \\ 0 \end{bmatrix}$.

1.4 ALGEBRAIC OPERATIONS ON LINEAR TRANSFORMATIONS

Addition, subtraction, and multiplication

The linear transformations of the plane can be combined algebraically, making it possible to build algebraic expressions for a vector or transformation. Usually, most of the battle is building the right such expression, before any actual computations are performed. Specifically, we can add, subtract, scalar multiply, and multiply linear transformations. See Figure 1.22.

Definition. *Sums, Differences, and Products of Linear Transformations.* For two linear transformations R and S of $\mathbb{R}^2$, the sum $R + S$, difference $R - S$, scalar product rR (r real), and product RS are the functions defined

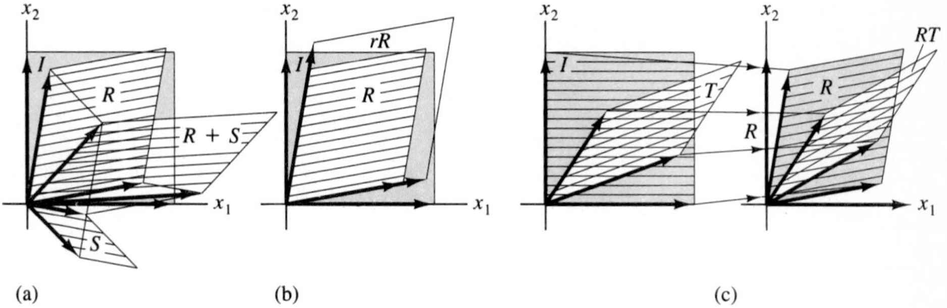

Figure 1.22 Images of I under (a) R, S, $R + S$ and (b) R, rR. (c) Image of I under RT is the composite of the image of I under T and the image of T under R.

for $\mathbf{x} = \begin{bmatrix} x_1 \\ x_2 \end{bmatrix} \in \mathbb{R}^2$ by

1. $(R + S)(\mathbf{x}) = R(\mathbf{x}) + S(\mathbf{x})$;
2. $(R - S)(\mathbf{x}) = R(\mathbf{x}) - S(\mathbf{x})$;
3. $(rR)(\mathbf{x}) = rR(\mathbf{x})$;
4. $(RS)(\mathbf{x}) = R(S(\mathbf{x}))$.

EXAMPLE

For $R\begin{bmatrix} x_1 \\ x_2 \end{bmatrix} = \begin{bmatrix} 1x_1 + 1x_2 \\ 2x_1 + 1x_2 \end{bmatrix}$ and $S\begin{bmatrix} x_1 \\ x_2 \end{bmatrix} = \begin{bmatrix} 1x_1 + 0x_2 \\ 1x_1 + 2x_2 \end{bmatrix}$, we have

$$(R + S)\begin{bmatrix} x_1 \\ x_2 \end{bmatrix} = \begin{bmatrix} 2x_1 + 1x_2 \\ 3x_1 + 3x_2 \end{bmatrix}, \qquad (R - S)\begin{bmatrix} x_1 \\ x_2 \end{bmatrix} = \begin{bmatrix} 0x_1 + 1x_2 \\ 1x_1 - 1x_2 \end{bmatrix},$$

$$(5R)\begin{bmatrix} x_1 \\ x_2 \end{bmatrix} = \begin{bmatrix} 5x_1 + 5x_2 \\ 10x_1 + 5x_2 \end{bmatrix}, \qquad (RS)\begin{bmatrix} x_1 \\ x_2 \end{bmatrix} = R\begin{bmatrix} 1x_1 + 0x_2 \\ 1x_1 + 2x_2 \end{bmatrix} = \begin{bmatrix} 2x_1 + 2x_2 \\ 3x_1 + 2x_2 \end{bmatrix}.$$

(Verify!)

Theorem 1.9. *Operations on Linear Transformations in Terms of Entries.* Let linear transformations R and S be given by

$$R\begin{bmatrix} x_1 \\ x_2 \end{bmatrix} = \begin{bmatrix} ax_1 + bx_2 \\ cx_1 + dx_2 \end{bmatrix}, S\begin{bmatrix} x_1 \\ x_2 \end{bmatrix} = \begin{bmatrix} ex_1 + fx_2 \\ gx_1 + hx_2 \end{bmatrix}.$$

Then:

1. $(R + S)\begin{bmatrix} x_1 \\ x_2 \end{bmatrix} = \begin{bmatrix} (a+e)x_1 + (b+f)x_2 \\ (c+g)x_1 + (d+h)x_2 \end{bmatrix}$

2. $(R - S)\begin{bmatrix} x_1 \\ x_2 \end{bmatrix} = \begin{bmatrix} (a-e)x_1 + (b-f)x_2 \\ (c-g)x_1 + (d-h)x_2 \end{bmatrix}$

3. $(rR)\begin{bmatrix} x_1 \\ x_2 \end{bmatrix} = \begin{bmatrix} rax_1 + rbx_2 \\ rcx_1 + rdx_2 \end{bmatrix}$

4. $(RS)\begin{bmatrix} x_1 \\ x_2 \end{bmatrix} = \begin{bmatrix} (ae+bg)x_1 + (af+bh)x_2 \\ (ce+dg)x_1 + (cf+dh)x_2 \end{bmatrix}$

Proof. We prove (1) and (4), leaving (2) and (3) as exercises for the reader. For (1), simply observe that

$$(R + S)\begin{bmatrix} x_1 \\ x_2 \end{bmatrix} = R\begin{bmatrix} x_1 \\ x_2 \end{bmatrix} + S\begin{bmatrix} x_1 \\ x_2 \end{bmatrix} = \begin{bmatrix} ax_1 + bx_2 \\ cx_1 + dx_2 \end{bmatrix} + \begin{bmatrix} ex_1 + fx_2 \\ gx_1 + hx_2 \end{bmatrix}$$
$$= \begin{bmatrix} (a+e)x_1 + (b+f)x_2 \\ (c+g)x_1 + (d+h)x_2 \end{bmatrix}.$$

For (4), unwind the equation $(RS)(\mathbf{x}) = R(S(\mathbf{x}))$ for the product (composite) RS of R and S:

$$(RS)\begin{bmatrix} x_1 \\ x_2 \end{bmatrix} = R\left(S\begin{bmatrix} x_1 \\ x_2 \end{bmatrix}\right) = R\begin{bmatrix} ex_1 + fx_2 \\ gx_1 + hx_2 \end{bmatrix} = \begin{bmatrix} a(ex_1 + fx_2) + b(gx_1 + hx_2) \\ c(ex_1 + fx_2) + d(gx_1 + hx_2) \end{bmatrix};$$

that is,

$$(RS)\begin{bmatrix} x_1 \\ x_2 \end{bmatrix} = \begin{bmatrix} (ae+bg)x_1 + (af+bh)x_2 \\ (ce+dg)x_1 + (cf+dh)x_2 \end{bmatrix}. \qquad \blacksquare$$

The algebra of linear transformations of $\mathbb{R}^2$

The basic properties of linear transformations and their operations are collected in the following theorem, where 0 and I denote the zero and identity linear transformations. Such systems are called **algebras**. So, the set of all linear transformations of $\mathbb{R}^2$ is called the **algebra of linear transformations** of $\mathbb{R}^2$.

Theorem 1.10. *Algebraic Properties of Linear Transformations.*
Linear transformations R, S, and T and real numbers a and b satisfy the following properties.

1. $(R + S) + T = R + (S + T)$.
2. $R + 0 = 0 + R = R$.
3. $R + S = T$ has a unique solution S for any R and T, namely, $S = T - R$.
4. $IR = RI = R$ and $0R = R0 = 0$.
5. $(RS)T = R(ST)$.

6. $(R + S)T = RT + ST$ and $R(S + T) = RS + RT$.
7. $(a + b)R = aR + bR$.
8. $R + S = S + R$.
9. $a(RS) = (aR)S = R(aS)$.
10. $IR = R$ and $0R = 0$ (where the first 0 is real and the second is the 0 linear transformation).

Proof. The fifth property follows from the associative law for functions, and the others are easy to prove by calculating each side of the equation and verifying equality. For example, to prove $R + S = S + R$, use the following straightforward computations:

$$(R + S)(\mathbf{x}) = R(\mathbf{x}) + S(\mathbf{x}) = S(\mathbf{x}) + R(\mathbf{x});$$

$$(S + R)(\mathbf{x}) = S(\mathbf{x}) + R(\mathbf{x}) = R(\mathbf{x}) + S(\mathbf{x}) = S(\mathbf{x}) + R(\mathbf{x}). \qquad \blacksquare$$

EXAMPLES

Let $R\begin{bmatrix} x_1 \\ x_2 \end{bmatrix} = \begin{bmatrix} 1x_1 + 0x_2 \\ 0x_1 + 2x_2 \end{bmatrix}$, $S\begin{bmatrix} x_1 \\ x_2 \end{bmatrix} = \begin{bmatrix} 0x_1 + 1x_2 \\ 0x_1 + 1x_2 \end{bmatrix}$, and $T\begin{bmatrix} x_1 \\ x_2 \end{bmatrix} = \begin{bmatrix} 2x_1 + 3x_2 \\ 0x_1 + 1x_2 \end{bmatrix}$.

1. RS and SR are not equal, since $RS\begin{bmatrix} 0 \\ 1 \end{bmatrix} = \begin{bmatrix} 1 \\ 2 \end{bmatrix}$ and $SR\begin{bmatrix} 0 \\ 1 \end{bmatrix} = \begin{bmatrix} 2 \\ 2 \end{bmatrix}$. (Verify!)

2. Whereas there is a linear transformation U such that $UR = I$, namely $T\begin{bmatrix} x_1 \\ x_2 \end{bmatrix} = \begin{bmatrix} 1x_1 + 0x_2 \\ 0x_1 + (1/2)x_2 \end{bmatrix}$ (prove), there is no linear transformation U such that $US = I$. (Prove!)

3. $(R + S)T\begin{bmatrix} x_1 \\ x_2 \end{bmatrix} = (R + S)\begin{bmatrix} 2x_1 + 3x_2 \\ 0x_1 + 1x_2 \end{bmatrix} = \begin{bmatrix} 2x_1 + 4x_2 \\ 0x_1 + 3x_2 \end{bmatrix} = (RS + ST)\begin{bmatrix} x_1 \\ x_2 \end{bmatrix}$. (Verify!)

Before moving on, some additional comments are in order.

1. The linear transformation $S = 0 - R$ is the unique solution to $R + S = 0$ (Property 3). Since $R + (-1)R = 0$ as well (prove), we have $0 - R = (-1)R$. Denoting them both by $-R$, we have $0 - R = (-1)R = -R$.
2. The distributive law for subtraction, $(R - S)T = RT - ST$, can be proved using (6). (Do so!)
3. The scalar linear transformations can now be represented as aI. (Explain!)

Invertible linear transformations

Armed with the simple but powerful concept of invertible functions and fortified as we are by Cramer's rule, we can easily determine when a linear transformation is invertible.

Theorem 1.11. *Determinant Criteria for Invertibility.*
The determinant of a linear transformation R of $\mathbb{R}^2$ is nonzero if and only if R is invertible as a function from $\mathbb{R}^2$ to itself, in which case R^{-1} is also a linear transformation.

Proof. If the determinant of R is 0, then the image of R is a line or the one-point set $\{0\}$ (prove), so that the image of R cannot be $\mathbb{R}^2$ and R cannot be invertible.

Suppose, on the other hand, that the determinant $ad - bc$ of $R\begin{bmatrix} x_1 \\ x_2 \end{bmatrix} = \begin{bmatrix} ax_1 + bx_2 \\ cx_1 + dx_2 \end{bmatrix}$ is nonzero. To show that R is invertible, we use Cramer's rule. Since the determinant $ad - bc$ is nonzero, the system of linear equations

$$ax_1 + bx_2 = y_1$$
$$cx_1 + dx_2 = y_2$$

that expresses $R\begin{bmatrix} x_1 \\ x_2 \end{bmatrix} = \begin{bmatrix} y_1 \\ y_2 \end{bmatrix}$ has one and only one solution, $\begin{bmatrix} x_1 \\ x_2 \end{bmatrix} \in \mathbb{R}^2$ for any given $\begin{bmatrix} y_1 \\ y_2 \end{bmatrix} \in \mathbb{R}^2$. So, the function R is invertible, with inverse function $S = R^{-1}$ defined by the rule that $S\begin{bmatrix} y_1 \\ y_2 \end{bmatrix} = \begin{bmatrix} x_1 \\ x_2 \end{bmatrix}$ if and only if $R\begin{bmatrix} x_1 \\ x_2 \end{bmatrix} = \begin{bmatrix} y_1 \\ y_2 \end{bmatrix}$. To show that this function S is a linear transformation, we simply use Cramer's rule to solve for the x's and see how they depend on the y's. We get

$$x_1 = \frac{dy_1 - by_2}{ad - bc} = \left(\frac{d}{ad-bc}\right)y_1 - \left(\frac{b}{ad-bc}\right)y_2,$$

$$x_2 = \frac{ay_2 - cy_1}{ad - bc} = -\left(\frac{c}{ad-bc}\right)y_1 + \left(\frac{a}{ad-bc}\right)y_2,$$

so that

$$S\begin{bmatrix} y_1 \\ y_2 \end{bmatrix} = \begin{bmatrix} ey_1 + fy_2 \\ gy_1 + hy_2 \end{bmatrix}$$

where $e = d/(ad - bc)$, $f = -b/(ad - bc)$, $g = -c/(ad - bc)$, and $h = a/(ad - bc)$. So, S is a linear transformation. ■

The proof of Theorem 1.11 gives us a formula for the inverse of R when it exists (see Figures 1.23 and 1.24).

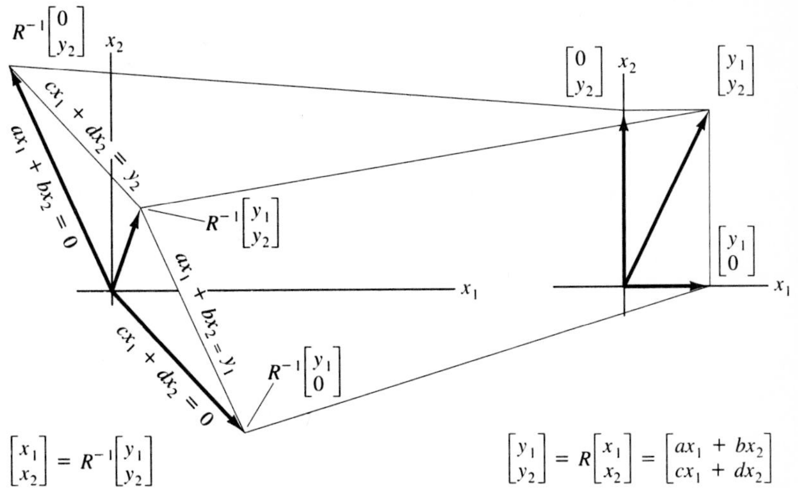

Figure 1.23 To invert $\begin{bmatrix}ax_1+bx_2\\cx_1+dx_2\end{bmatrix} = \begin{bmatrix}y_1\\y_2\end{bmatrix}$, solve $\begin{matrix}ax_1 + bx_2 = y_1\\cx_1 + dx_2 = y_2\end{matrix}$ for x_1, x_2.

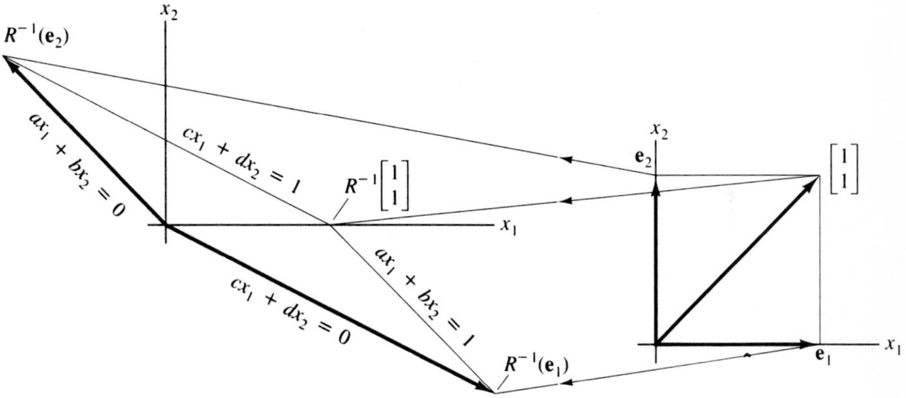

Figure 1.24 The preimages $R^{-1}(\mathbf{e}_1)$ and $R^{-1}(\mathbf{e}_2)$ of $\mathbf{e}_1 = \begin{bmatrix}1\\0\end{bmatrix}$ and $\mathbf{e}_2 = \begin{bmatrix}0\\1\end{bmatrix}$ under $R\begin{bmatrix}x_1\\x_2\end{bmatrix} = \begin{bmatrix}ax_1+bx_2\\cx_1+dx_2\end{bmatrix}$.

Corollary. The inverse of a linear transformation $R\begin{bmatrix}x_1\\x_2\end{bmatrix} = \begin{bmatrix}ax_1+bx_2\\cx_1+dx_2\end{bmatrix}$ with nonzero determinant is

$$S\begin{bmatrix}y_1\\y_2\end{bmatrix} = \frac{1}{ad-bc}\begin{bmatrix}dy_1-by_2\\-cy_1+ay_2\end{bmatrix}.$$

EXAMPLE

The inverse of $R\begin{bmatrix}x_1\\x_2\end{bmatrix}=\begin{bmatrix}1x_1+2x_2\\0x_1+3x_2\end{bmatrix}$ is $S\begin{bmatrix}x_1\\x_2\end{bmatrix}=\begin{bmatrix}1x_1-(2/3)x_2\\0x_1+(1/3)x_2\end{bmatrix}$.

Since the determinant of an invertible linear transformation is nonzero, representing a nonzero area, we get a clear picture of the transformation and its inverse by looking at the images under them of the unit square I (Figure 1.25).

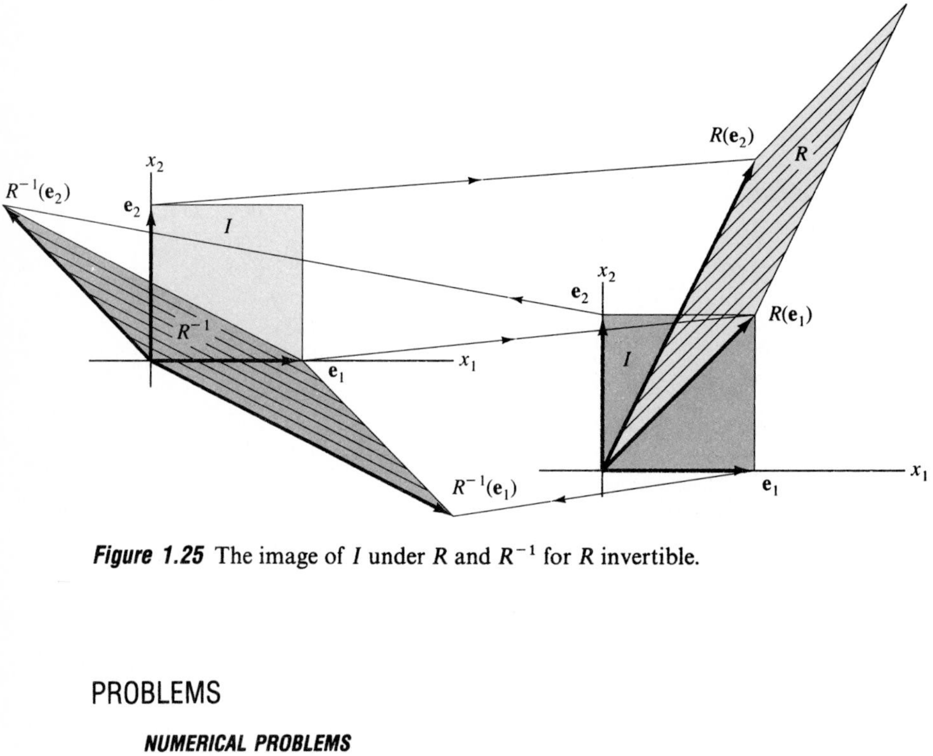

Figure 1.25 The image of I under R and R^{-1} for R invertible.

PROBLEMS

NUMERICAL PROBLEMS

Problems 1–8 refer to the linear transformations

$$R\begin{bmatrix}x_1\\x_2\end{bmatrix}=\begin{bmatrix}1x_1+2x_2\\0x_1+1x_2\end{bmatrix},\quad S\begin{bmatrix}x_1\\x_2\end{bmatrix}=\begin{bmatrix}1x_1+3x_2\\0x_1+1x_2\end{bmatrix},\quad T\begin{bmatrix}x_1\\x_2\end{bmatrix}=\begin{bmatrix}1x_1+0x_2\\1x_1+2x_2\end{bmatrix}.$$

1. Compute the following linear transformations.

(a) $R(3S+2T)$ **(b)** $S(R-T)$ **(c)** RS

(d) ST **(e)** $\pi R-3S^2$

2. Find all values r such that the linear transformation $rR+S$ is not invertible.

3. Compute $(rR + S)^{-1}$ and solve $(rR + S)(\mathbf{x}) = \begin{bmatrix} 1 \\ 4 \end{bmatrix}$ for $\mathbf{x}$ if $r = 2$.

4. Find all values r such that the linear transformation $rR + T$ is not invertible.

5. Find the inverses of R, S, and T. Use them to solve the following equations for $\mathbf{x}$.

(a) $R(\mathbf{x}) = \begin{bmatrix} 2 \\ 3 \end{bmatrix}$ (b) $RS(\mathbf{x}) = \begin{bmatrix} 5 \\ 3 \end{bmatrix}$ (c) $ST(\mathbf{x}) = \begin{bmatrix} 2 \\ 5 \end{bmatrix}$

6. Find R^3.

Hard

7. Find an explicit formula for R^n for all positive integers n.

8. Find an explicit formula for T^n for all positive integers n.

THEORETICAL PROBLEMS

9. Prove parts 2 and 3 of Theorem 1.1.

10. Prove parts 1, 6, and 7 of Theorem 1.10.

11. Show that $-R$ is the unique solution to $R + S = 0$.

12. Show that $(R - S)\,T = RT - ST$.

13. Show that if R is a nonzero linear transformation with determinant 0, then the image of $\mathbb{R}^2$ under R is a line through $\mathbf{0}$.

14. Show that aI ($a \in \mathbb{R}$) is the typical scalar linear transformation.

15. If R is a linear transformation and $RS = SR$ for all linear transformations S, show that R is a scalar $R = aI$ for some a.

16. Show that if R and S are invertible linear transformations of $\mathbb{R}^2$, then so is RS, and its inverse is $S^{-1}R^{-1}$.

17. Show that if R and RS are invertible linear transformations, then S is invertible.

18. Show that a linear transformation R of $\mathbb{R}^2$ is invertible if it is either 1-1 or onto.

19. Show that if R and S are linear transformations and RS is invertible, then R and S are invertible.

Hard

20. Show that if a set C is convex in $\mathbb{R}^2$, so is its image $R(C)$ and its *inverse image* $\{\mathbf{v} \in \mathbb{R}^2 \mid R(\mathbf{v}) \in C\}$ for any linear transformation R.

21. Show that the image $R(\hat{S})$ of the convex hull of S is the convex hull of $R(S)$ for any set S and linear transformation R. (See Problem 17 of Section 1.2.)

22. For $S(\mathbf{x}) = \begin{bmatrix} 2x_1 + x_2 \\ 2x_2 \end{bmatrix}$, find a linear transformation R such that $R^2 = S$.

1.5 THE ALGEBRA OF 2 × 2 MATRICES

A linear transformation can be represented by the array, or **matrix**, of coefficients needed to define it. Of course, operations on linear transformations then transfer to operations on the matrices representing them.

Ideas expressed in terms of linear transformations tend to be geometric in nature, whereas those expressed in terms of matrices tend to be more algebraic or computational. Since the geometric, algebraic, and computational aspects are all important, the correspondence between linear transformations and their properties on the one hand and matrices and their properties on the other plays a very significant role in linear algebra. This section is devoted to this correspondence.

Matrices

If you glance back through the section on linear transformations, with but a few exceptions you see changes in the coefficients but not in the variables. So, we represent the linear transformation $R\begin{bmatrix} x_1 \\ x_2 \end{bmatrix} = \begin{bmatrix} ax_1 + bx_2 \\ cx_1 + dx_2 \end{bmatrix}$ by its **matrix of coefficients** $\begin{bmatrix} a & b \\ c & d \end{bmatrix}$ and its effect on $\begin{bmatrix} x_1 \\ x_2 \end{bmatrix}$ by the equation $\begin{bmatrix} a & b \\ c & d \end{bmatrix}\begin{bmatrix} x_1 \\ x_2 \end{bmatrix} = \begin{bmatrix} ax_1 + bx_2 \\ cx_1 + dx_2 \end{bmatrix}$.

Definition. *Matrix.*

A 2×2 **matrix** is an array $A = \begin{bmatrix} a & b \\ c & d \end{bmatrix}$ of real numbers a, b, c, d. The numbers a, b, c, d are called the **entries** of A.

In order that different linear transformations correspond to different matrices and conversely, we say that two matrices $A = \begin{bmatrix} a & b \\ c & d \end{bmatrix}$ and $B = \begin{bmatrix} e & f \\ g & h \end{bmatrix}$ as **equal** if and only if the corresponding entries of A and B are equal—that is, $a = e$, $b = f$, $c = g$, and $d = h$.

The matrix of a linear transformation

Representing a transformation by a matrix amounts to showing how to use a matrix to perform the transformation, which is done in the following definition.

Definition. *Product of a Matrix and a Vector.*

The **product** of the matrix $A = \begin{bmatrix} a & b \\ c & d \end{bmatrix}$ and vector $\mathbf{x} = \begin{bmatrix} x_1 \\ x_2 \end{bmatrix}$ is $A\mathbf{x} = \begin{bmatrix} ax_1 + bx_2 \\ cx_1 + dx_2 \end{bmatrix}$, and we write $\begin{bmatrix} a & b \\ c & d \end{bmatrix} \begin{bmatrix} x_1 \\ x_2 \end{bmatrix} = \begin{bmatrix} ax_1 + bx_2 \\ cx_1 + dx_2 \end{bmatrix}$.

We constantly use the matrix representation of a linear transformation, so we give it a name.

Definition. *The Matrix of Coefficients of a Linear Transformation.*

For any linear transformation $R\begin{bmatrix} x_1 \\ x_2 \end{bmatrix} = \begin{bmatrix} ax_1 + bx_2 \\ cx_1 + dx_2 \end{bmatrix}$, its **matrix of coefficients** (or *matrix*) is the matrix $m(R) = \begin{bmatrix} a & b \\ c & d \end{bmatrix}$.

EXAMPLE

The matrix of $R\begin{bmatrix} x_1 \\ x_2 \end{bmatrix} = \begin{bmatrix} 1x_1 + 2x_2 \\ 4x_1 - 5x_2 \end{bmatrix}$ is $\begin{bmatrix} 1 & 2 \\ 4 & -5 \end{bmatrix}$, and $R\begin{bmatrix} x_1 \\ x_2 \end{bmatrix} = \begin{bmatrix} 1 & 2 \\ 4 & -5 \end{bmatrix} \begin{bmatrix} x_1 \\ x_2 \end{bmatrix}$.

So, the matrix $m(R)$ of R is the matrix such that $R(\mathbf{x}) = m(R)\mathbf{x}$ for all vectors $\mathbf{x}$. And, since the columns of a matrix A are the vectors $A\begin{bmatrix} 1 \\ 0 \end{bmatrix}$, $A\begin{bmatrix} 0 \\ 1 \end{bmatrix}$, the matrix $m(R)$ of a linear transformation R is the matrix $m(R)$ whose columns are $R\begin{bmatrix} 1 \\ 0 \end{bmatrix}$, $R\begin{bmatrix} 0 \\ 1 \end{bmatrix}$.

It follows that the matrix $m(R)$ of R completely determines R. So, the function $m(R)$ is a 1-1 function from the set of linear transformations to the set of matrices. On the other hand, for any matrix A the linear transformation $R(\mathbf{x}) = A\mathbf{x}$ has matrix $m(R) = A$. This establishes the following.

Theorem 1.12. *Correspondence Between Linear Transformations and Matrices.*

$m(R)$ is an invertible function from the set of linear transformations R to the set of 2×2 matrices A.

The determinant of a matrix

Attributes of linear transformations correspond to attributes of their matrices.

Definition. *Determinant of a Matrix.*

The **determinant** of the matrix $A = \begin{bmatrix} a & b \\ c & d \end{bmatrix}$ is the determinant $\begin{vmatrix} a & b \\ c & d \end{vmatrix} = ad - bc$ of the linear transformation $R(\mathbf{x}) = A\mathbf{x}$.

By this definition, the determinants of R and $m(R)$ are the same.

EXAMPLE

The determinant of $\begin{bmatrix} 1 & 2 \\ 4 & -5 \end{bmatrix}$ is $\begin{vmatrix} 1 & 2 \\ 4 & -5 \end{vmatrix} = 1 \cdot (-5) - 2 \cdot 4 = -13$, which is the determinant of the linear transformation $R(\mathbf{x}) = \begin{bmatrix} 1 & 2 \\ 4 & -5 \end{bmatrix} \begin{bmatrix} x_1 \\ x_2 \end{bmatrix} = \begin{bmatrix} 1x_1 + 2x_2 \\ 4x_1 - 5x_2 \end{bmatrix}$, whose matrix $m(R)$ is $\begin{bmatrix} 1 & 2 \\ 4 & -5 \end{bmatrix}$.

Some special matrices

All linear transformations have corresponding matrices, so the special linear transformations of Section 1.4 have counterparts for matrices.

1. The matrix $\begin{bmatrix} 0 & 0 \\ 0 & 0 \end{bmatrix}$ is called the **zero matrix** and is denoted by 0. Its determinant is 0. The corresponding linear transformation is $\begin{bmatrix} 0 & 0 \\ 0 & 0 \end{bmatrix} \begin{bmatrix} x_1 \\ x_2 \end{bmatrix} = 0$, the zero linear transformation.

2. The matrix $\begin{bmatrix} 1 & 0 \\ 0 & 1 \end{bmatrix}$ is called the **identity matrix** and is denoted by I. Its determinant is 1. The corresponding linear transformation is $\begin{bmatrix} 1 & 0 \\ 0 & 1 \end{bmatrix} \begin{bmatrix} x_1 \\ x_2 \end{bmatrix} = \begin{bmatrix} x_1 \\ x_2 \end{bmatrix}$, the identity linear transformation.

3. The matrix $\begin{bmatrix} a & 0 \\ 0 & a \end{bmatrix}$ is **scalar multiplication by *a***. Its determinant is a^2. The corresponding linear transformation is $\begin{bmatrix} a & 0 \\ 0 & a \end{bmatrix} \begin{bmatrix} x_1 \\ x_2 \end{bmatrix} = a \begin{bmatrix} x_1 \\ x_2 \end{bmatrix}$, scalar multiplication by a.

4. The matrix $\begin{bmatrix} a & 0 \\ 0 & d \end{bmatrix}$ is the **diagonal matrix** with diagonal entries a and d. Its determinant is ad. The corresponding linear transformation is $\begin{bmatrix} a & 0 \\ 0 & d \end{bmatrix} \begin{bmatrix} x_1 \\ x_2 \end{bmatrix} = \begin{bmatrix} ax_1 \\ dx_2 \end{bmatrix}$.

5. The matrix $\begin{bmatrix} 1 & b \\ 0 & 1 \end{bmatrix}$ is an **upper triangular matrix** with 1s on the diagonal. Its determinant is 1. The corresponding linear transformation is the shear $\begin{bmatrix} 1 & b \\ 0 & 1 \end{bmatrix} \begin{bmatrix} x_1 \\ x_2 \end{bmatrix} = \begin{bmatrix} x_1 + bx_2 \\ x_2 \end{bmatrix}$.

6. The matrix $\begin{bmatrix} 0 & 1 \\ 1 & 0 \end{bmatrix}$ is the **transposition** of columns 1 and 2. Its determinant is -1. The corresponding linear transformation is the reflection $\begin{bmatrix} 0 & 1 \\ 1 & 0 \end{bmatrix}\begin{bmatrix} x_1 \\ x_2 \end{bmatrix} = \begin{bmatrix} x_2 \\ x_1 \end{bmatrix}$ across the line $x_1 = x_2$.

7. The matrix $\begin{bmatrix} \cos\alpha & -\sin\alpha \\ \sin\alpha & \cos\alpha \end{bmatrix}$ is **rotation** by α. Its determinant is 1. The corresponding matrix is the rotation $\begin{bmatrix} \cos\alpha & -\sin\alpha \\ \sin\alpha & \cos\alpha \end{bmatrix}\begin{bmatrix} x_1 \\ x_2 \end{bmatrix} = \begin{bmatrix} x_1\cos\alpha - x_2\sin\alpha \\ x_1\sin\alpha + x_2\cos\alpha \end{bmatrix}$.

8. The matrix $\begin{bmatrix} -\sin\alpha & \cos\alpha \\ \cos\alpha & \sin\alpha \end{bmatrix}$ is the product of rotation by α and transposition of columns 1 and 2.

Algebraic operations

Since matrix correspondence $m(R) = A$ is a 1-1 onto mapping between linear transformations $R(\mathbf{x}) = A\mathbf{x}$ and matrices A, operations on linear transformations induce operations on matrices. For example, the sum $R + S$ between the linear transformations $R\begin{bmatrix} x_1 \\ x_2 \end{bmatrix} = \begin{bmatrix} ax_1 + bx_2 \\ cx_1 + dx_2 \end{bmatrix}$ and $S\begin{bmatrix} x_1 \\ x_2 \end{bmatrix} = \begin{bmatrix} ex_1 + fx_2 \\ gx_1 + hx_2 \end{bmatrix}$ is given by $(R + S)\begin{bmatrix} x_1 \\ x_2 \end{bmatrix} = \begin{bmatrix} (a+e)x_1 + (b+f)x_2 \\ (c+g)x_1 + (d+h)x_2 \end{bmatrix}$. So, we *define* the corresponding operation

$$\begin{bmatrix} a & b \\ c & d \end{bmatrix} + \begin{bmatrix} e & f \\ g & h \end{bmatrix} = \begin{bmatrix} a+e & b+f \\ c+g & d+h \end{bmatrix}$$

for matrices. It is then not surprising that

$$m(R + S) = \begin{bmatrix} a+e & b+f \\ c+g & d+h \end{bmatrix} = \begin{bmatrix} a & b \\ c & d \end{bmatrix} + \begin{bmatrix} e & f \\ g & h \end{bmatrix} = m(R) + m(S),$$

that is, $m(R + S) = m(R) + m(S)$. Following this strategy for the other operations as well, we define

$$\begin{bmatrix} a & b \\ c & d \end{bmatrix} - \begin{bmatrix} e & f \\ g & h \end{bmatrix} = \begin{bmatrix} a-e & b-f \\ c-g & d-h \end{bmatrix};$$

$$r\begin{bmatrix} a & b \\ c & d \end{bmatrix} = \begin{bmatrix} ra & rb \\ rc & rd \end{bmatrix};$$

$$\begin{bmatrix} a & b \\ c & d \end{bmatrix}\begin{bmatrix} e & f \\ g & h \end{bmatrix} = \begin{bmatrix} ae+bg & af+bh \\ ce+dg & cf+dh \end{bmatrix}.$$

Counterparts of the equation $m(R + S) = m(R) + m(S)$ that we obtained for addition can be derived for subtraction and scalar multiplication just as easily.

Theorem 1.13. *Properties of the Matrix Correspondence.*
$m(R+S) = m(R) + m(S)$, $m(R-S) = m(R) - m(S)$, $m(rR) = rm(R)$, and $m(RS) = m(R)m(S)$ for any linear transformations R and S and any real number r.

EXAMPLE

For $R\begin{bmatrix} x_1 \\ x_2 \end{bmatrix} = \begin{bmatrix} 1x_1 + 2x_2 \\ 4x_1 - 5x_2 \end{bmatrix}$ and $S\begin{bmatrix} x_1 \\ x_2 \end{bmatrix} = \begin{bmatrix} 2x_1 + 3x_2 \\ 4x_1 - 3x_2 \end{bmatrix}$, we can get the matrices of $R + S$, $R - S$, $5R$, and RS by performing the corresponding operations on the matrices of R and S. These give

$$\begin{bmatrix} 3 & 5 \\ 8 & -8 \end{bmatrix}, \quad \begin{bmatrix} -1 & -1 \\ 0 & -2 \end{bmatrix}, \quad \begin{bmatrix} 5 & 10 \\ 20 & -25 \end{bmatrix}, \quad \begin{bmatrix} 10 & -3 \\ -12 & 27 \end{bmatrix}.$$

By the matrix correspondence, the algebraic properties of linear transformations transfer to the properties of matrices listed in the following theorem. In the theorem, 0 and I denote the zero and identity matrices.

Theorem 1.14. *Algebraic Properties of Matrices.*
Matrices A, B, and C and real numbers a and b satisfy the following properties.

1. $(A + B) + C = A + (B + C)$.
2. $A + 0 = 0 + A = A$.
3. $A + B = C$ has a unique solution B for any A and C, namely, $B = C - A$.
4. $IA = AI = A$ and $0A = A0 = 0$.
5. $(AB)C = A(BC)$.
6. $(A + B)C = AC + BC$ and $A(B + C) = AB + AC$.
7. $(a + b)A = aA + bA$.
8. $A + B = B + A$.
9. $a(AB) = (aA)B = A(aB)$.
10. $1A = A$ and $0A = 0$ (where the first 0 is real and the second is the 0 matrix).

Proof. This follows easily from Theorem 1.10 and the above properties of $m(R)$. For example, to prove (8) that $A + B = B + A$, use (8) of Theorem 1.10 that $R + S = S + R$, where $R\begin{bmatrix} x_1 \\ x_2 \end{bmatrix} = A\begin{bmatrix} x_1 \\ x_2 \end{bmatrix}$ and $S\begin{bmatrix} x_1 \\ x_2 \end{bmatrix} = B\begin{bmatrix} x_1 \\ x_2 \end{bmatrix}$:

$$A + B = m(R) + m(S) = m(R + S) = m(S + R) = m(S) + m(R) = B + A$$

■

EXAMPLE

$$\left(\begin{bmatrix} 3 & 5 \\ 8 & -8 \end{bmatrix} + \begin{bmatrix} -1 & -1 \\ 0 & -2 \end{bmatrix}\right)\begin{bmatrix} 1 & 1 \\ 0 & -2 \end{bmatrix} = \begin{bmatrix} 2 & 4 \\ 8 & -10 \end{bmatrix}\begin{bmatrix} 1 & 1 \\ 0 & -2 \end{bmatrix} = \begin{bmatrix} 2 & -6 \\ 8 & 28 \end{bmatrix}$$

and

$$\begin{bmatrix} 3 & 5 \\ 8 & -8 \end{bmatrix}\begin{bmatrix} 1 & 1 \\ 0 & -2 \end{bmatrix} + \begin{bmatrix} -1 & -1 \\ 0 & -2 \end{bmatrix}\begin{bmatrix} 1 & 1 \\ 0 & -2 \end{bmatrix} = \begin{bmatrix} 3 & -7 \\ 8 & 24 \end{bmatrix} + \begin{bmatrix} -1 & 1 \\ 0 & 4 \end{bmatrix} = \begin{bmatrix} 2 & -6 \\ 8 & 28 \end{bmatrix}.$$

Theorem 1.15. *Properties of Matrix-Vector Operations.*
For any two matrices A and B, any vector $\mathbf{x}$, and any real number r, we have

1. $A(\mathbf{x} + \mathbf{x}') = A\mathbf{x} + A\mathbf{x}'$ and $A(\mathbf{x} - \mathbf{x}') = A\mathbf{x} - A\mathbf{x}'$;
2. $A(r\mathbf{x}) = r(A\mathbf{x})$;
3. $A(B\mathbf{x}) = (AB)\mathbf{x}$.

Proof. Let $R(\mathbf{x}) = A\mathbf{x}$ and $S(\mathbf{x}) = B\mathbf{x}$. Then $A(\mathbf{x} + \mathbf{x}') = R(\mathbf{x} + \mathbf{x}') = R(\mathbf{x}) + R(\mathbf{x}') = A\mathbf{x} + A\mathbf{x}'$. Similarly, $A(\mathbf{x} - \mathbf{x}') = A\mathbf{x} - A\mathbf{x}'$ and $A(r\mathbf{x}) = r(A\mathbf{x})$. Finally, $A(B\mathbf{x}) = R(S(\mathbf{x})) = (RS)(\mathbf{x}) = m(RS)\mathbf{x} = (m(R)m(S))\mathbf{x} = (AB)\mathbf{x}$. ∎

EXAMPLE

$$\begin{bmatrix} 3 & 1 \\ 2 & -1 \end{bmatrix}\left(\begin{bmatrix} 1 \\ 0 \end{bmatrix} + \begin{bmatrix} 0 \\ 2 \end{bmatrix}\right) = \begin{bmatrix} 5 \\ 0 \end{bmatrix} \text{ and } \begin{bmatrix} 3 & 1 \\ 2 & -1 \end{bmatrix}\begin{bmatrix} 1 \\ 0 \end{bmatrix} + \begin{bmatrix} 3 & 1 \\ 2 & -1 \end{bmatrix}\begin{bmatrix} 0 \\ 2 \end{bmatrix} = \begin{bmatrix} 3 \\ 2 \end{bmatrix} + \begin{bmatrix} 2 \\ -2 \end{bmatrix}.$$

As for linear transformations, a few additional comments are in order before we move on.

1. The matrix $B = 0 - A$ is the unique solution to $A + B = 0$ (Property 3). Since $A + (-1)A = 0$ as well, we have $0 - A = (-1)A$. Denoting them both by $-A$, we have $0 - A = (-1)A = -A$. Moreover, we also have $m(-R) = -m(R)$.
2. The distributive laws over addition imply corresponding distributive laws over subtraction. For example, $(A - B)C = AC - BC$ can be proved using (1).
3. The scalar matrices can now be represented as aI. (Explain!)

Transpose of a matrix. Symmetric matrices

We pause now to mention an operation for matrices that does not come from an operation already defined for linear transformations.

Definition. *Transpose of a Matrix and Symmetric Matrices.*
If $A = \begin{bmatrix} a & b \\ c & d \end{bmatrix}$, then $A^T = \begin{bmatrix} a & c \\ b & d \end{bmatrix}$ is called the **transpose** of A. If $A = A^T$, we say that A is **symmetric**.

For a linear transformation $R(\mathbf{x}) = A\mathbf{x}$, we define its *transpose* to be the linear transformation $R^T(\mathbf{x}) = A^T\mathbf{x}$. If $R = R^T$, then we say that R is *symmetric*. Of course, we have

1. $m(R^T) = m(R)^T$;
2. R is symmetric if and only if $m(R)$ is symmetric.

EXAMPLE

The transpose of $\begin{bmatrix} 1 & 2 \\ 3 & 4 \end{bmatrix}$ is $\begin{bmatrix} 1 & 3 \\ 2 & 4 \end{bmatrix}$ and the transpose of $R\begin{bmatrix} x_1 \\ x_2 \end{bmatrix} = \begin{bmatrix} 1x_1 + 2x_2 \\ 3x_1 + 4x_2 \end{bmatrix}$ is $S\begin{bmatrix} x_1 \\ x_2 \end{bmatrix} = \begin{bmatrix} 1x_1 + 3x_2 \\ 2x_1 + 4x_2 \end{bmatrix}$. The matrix $\begin{bmatrix} 1 & 2 \\ 2 & 4 \end{bmatrix}$ is symmetric.

The transpose operation and the symmetric matrices are extremely important, so we list their basic properties in preparation for what is to come.

1. $(A + B)^T = A^T + B^T$, $(A - B)^T = A^T - B^T$, and $(rA)^T = rA^T$.
2. $(AB)^T = B^TA^T$.
3. If A and B are symmetric, then so are $A + B$, $A - B$, and rA;
4. If A and B are symmetric and $AB = BA$, then AB is symmetric. Of course, using the mapping $m(R)$ and property $m(R^T) = m(R)^T$, we can derive the corresponding basic properties for linear transformations.

Invertible matrices

In order to carry over the concept of an invertible linear transformation to matrices, we introduce the following definition.

Definition. *Invertible Matrices.*
The matrix A is **invertible** if the linear transformation $R(\mathbf{x}) = A\mathbf{x}$ is invertible. If A is invertible, its **inverse** is the matrix $A^{-1} = m(R^{-1})$ of the inverse of the linear transformation $R(\mathbf{x}) = A\mathbf{x}$.

From Theorem 1.11 and its corollary, we get Theorem 1.16.

Theorem 1.16. *Determinant Criteria for Invertibility of a Matrix.*
The matrix $A = \begin{bmatrix} a & b \\ c & d \end{bmatrix}$ is invertible if and only if its determinant $ad - bc$ is nonzero. If it is invertible, its inverse is given by $A^{-1} = \dfrac{1}{ad - bc}\begin{bmatrix} d & -b \\ -c & a \end{bmatrix}$.

By definition, the linear transformation R is invertible if and only if there exists a function S such that $SR = I = RS$; and when R is invertible, any such S is $S = R^{-1}$. By Theorem 1.16, we know that the inverse of an invertible linear transformation is a linear transformation. This leads to the following.

Theorem 1.17. *Algebraic Criteria for Invertibility of a Matrix.*
The matrix A is invertible if and only if there is a matrix B such that $AB = BA = I$; and when A is invertible, any such B is $B = A^{-1}$.

Proof. Let $R(\mathbf{x})$ be the linear transformation $R(\mathbf{x}) = A\mathbf{x}$. If A is invertible, then so is R, so that there exists a linear transformation S such that $RS = SR = I$. Letting $B = m(S)$, we have $I = m(RS) = m(R)m(S) = AB$ and, similarly, $I = m(SR) = BA$. But then $AB = BA = I$.

Conversely, suppose that $AB = BA = I$ and let $S(\mathbf{x})$ be the linear transformation $B\mathbf{x}$. Then $I = m(R)m(S) = m(RS)$ and $I = m(S)m(R) = m(SR)$, from which we learn that $RS = SR = I$. It follows that R is invertible and, therefore, that A is invertible.

When A is invertible, R is invertible and $RS = SR = I$ if and only if $S = R^{-1}$. Using m in the same manner as before, it follows that $AB = BA = I$ if and only if $B = A^{-1}$. ■

PROBLEMS

NUMERICAL PROBLEMS

Problems 1–7 *refer to the matrices* $A = \begin{bmatrix} 1 & 2 \\ 0 & 1 \end{bmatrix}$, $B = \begin{bmatrix} 1 & 3 \\ 0 & 1 \end{bmatrix}$, and $C = \begin{bmatrix} 1 & 0 \\ 1 & 2 \end{bmatrix}$.

1. Compute the following matrices.
   (a) $A(3B + 2C)$ **(b)** $A(B - C)$ **(c)** AB
   (d) BC **(e)** $(BC)^T$ **(f)** $(B^T - C^T)A^T$

2. Find all values r such that the matrix $rA + B$ is not invertible.

3. Compute $(rA + B)^{-1}$ and solve $(rA + B)\mathbf{x} = \begin{bmatrix} 1 \\ 4 \end{bmatrix}$ for $\mathbf{x}$ if $r = 2$.

4. Find all values r such that the matrix $rA + C$ is not invertible.

5. Find the inverses of A, B, and C. Use them to solve the followi equations for $\mathbf{x}$.

(a) $A\mathbf{x} = \begin{bmatrix} 2 \\ 3 \end{bmatrix}$ (b) $AB\mathbf{x} = \begin{bmatrix} 5 \\ 3 \end{bmatrix}$ (c) $BC\mathbf{x} = \begin{bmatrix} 2 \\ 5 \end{bmatrix}$

6. Find R^3.

7. Express the following in terms of A, B, C, and compute.

(a) $3\begin{bmatrix} 1 & 2 \\ 0 & 1 \end{bmatrix} - 5\begin{bmatrix} 1 & 3 \\ 0 & 1 \end{bmatrix} - \begin{bmatrix} 1 & 0 \\ 1 & 2 \end{bmatrix}$

(b) $4\left(\begin{bmatrix} 1 & 2 \\ 0 & 1 \end{bmatrix}\left(3\begin{bmatrix} 1 & 3 \\ 0 & 1 \end{bmatrix} + 7\begin{bmatrix} 1 & 0 \\ 1 & 2 \end{bmatrix}\right)\right)$

(c) $\left(\begin{bmatrix} 1 & 2 \\ 0 & 1 \end{bmatrix}\begin{bmatrix} 1 & 3 \\ 0 & 1 \end{bmatrix}\right)\begin{bmatrix} 1 & 0 \\ 1 & 2 \end{bmatrix}$ and $\begin{bmatrix} 1 & 2 \\ 0 & 1 \end{bmatrix}\left(\begin{bmatrix} 1 & 3 \\ 0 & 1 \end{bmatrix}\begin{bmatrix} 1 & 0 \\ 1 & 2 \end{bmatrix}\right)$

(d) $\begin{bmatrix} 1 & 2 \\ 0 & 1 \end{bmatrix}^{-5}$ (e) $\left(\begin{bmatrix} 1 & 3 \\ 1 & 1 \end{bmatrix} - \begin{bmatrix} 1 & 2 \\ 1 & 1 \end{bmatrix}\right)^6$

Hard

8. Find a formula for A^n for all positive integers n.

9. Find a formula for C^n for all positive integers n.

THEORETICAL PROBLEMS

In Problems 10–14, A, B, *and* C *denote* 2×2 *matrices.*

10. Show that $A + (-1)A = 0$.

11. Show that $m(-A) = -m(A)$.

12. Verify that $(A - B)C = AC - BC$, using only the properties of Theorem 1.14.

13. If A is a matrix and $AB = BA$ for all linear transformations B, show that A is a scalar $A = aI$ for some a.

14. Show that if A and B are invertible matrices, then AB is invertible and its inverse is $B^{-1}A^{-1}$.

Hard

15. For $B = \begin{bmatrix} 2 & 1 \\ 0 & 2 \end{bmatrix}$, find a matrix A such that $A^2 = B$.

1.6 GEOMETRY IN THE PLANE

The geometry of the Cartesian plane is based on definitions for distance and angle that are given by explicit formulas. Surprisingly, we can use the same formulas for distance and angle in Cartesian n-dimensional space for any positive integer n. So, the geometry of the Cartesian plane is just the special case when $n = 2$. We develop it here as a prelude to the next chapter, "Cartesian n-Space."

The dot product

The great success of Descartes' method of introducing coordinates to represent points can be attributed to the simple formulas for length and angle given in terms of coordinates. The dot product is a main ingredient in these formulas.

Definition. *The Dot Product of Two Vectors.*

The **dot product** of vectors $\mathbf{v} = \begin{bmatrix} a \\ b \end{bmatrix}$ and $\mathbf{w} = \begin{bmatrix} c \\ d \end{bmatrix}$ is $\mathbf{v} \cdot \mathbf{w} = ac + bd$. It is sometimes written as $\mathbf{v} \cdot \mathbf{w} = \mathbf{v}^T\mathbf{w} = [a \quad b] \begin{bmatrix} c \\ d \end{bmatrix}$.

EXAMPLES

1. The dot product of $\begin{bmatrix} 4 \\ 6 \end{bmatrix}$ and $\begin{bmatrix} -3 \\ 5 \end{bmatrix}$ is $-12 + 30 = 18$.
2. For $\mathbf{v} = \begin{bmatrix} a \\ b \end{bmatrix}$, the dot product $\mathbf{v} \cdot \mathbf{v}$ is $a^2 + b^2$. Note that $\mathbf{v} \cdot \mathbf{v}$ is 0 if $\mathbf{v}$ is 0 and positive if $\mathbf{v}$ is nonzero.
3. The dot product of $\begin{bmatrix} a \\ b \end{bmatrix}$ and $\begin{bmatrix} -b \\ a \end{bmatrix}$ is 0. (Draw $\mathbf{v}$ and $\mathbf{w}$!)

Since dot products are used for many things, we give their key properties.

Theorem 1.18. *Properties of the Dot Product.*
The dot product $\mathbf{v} \cdot \mathbf{w}$ of vectors in $\mathbb{R}^2$ satisfies the following.

1. $\mathbf{v} \cdot \mathbf{v}$ is 0 if $\mathbf{v}$ is $\mathbf{0}$ and positive otherwise.
2. $\mathbf{v} \cdot \mathbf{w} = \mathbf{w} \cdot \mathbf{v}$.
3. $\mathbf{u} \cdot (\mathbf{v} + \mathbf{w}) = \mathbf{u} \cdot \mathbf{v} + \mathbf{u} \cdot \mathbf{w}$ and $(\mathbf{u} + \mathbf{v}) \cdot \mathbf{w} = \mathbf{v} \cdot \mathbf{w} + \mathbf{v} \cdot \mathbf{w}$.
4. $(r\mathbf{v}) \cdot \mathbf{w} = r(\mathbf{v} \cdot \mathbf{w}) = \mathbf{v} \cdot (r\mathbf{w})$ for real numbers r.

Proof. Let $\mathbf{u} = \begin{bmatrix} a \\ b \end{bmatrix}$, $\mathbf{v} = \begin{bmatrix} c \\ d \end{bmatrix}$, and $\mathbf{w} = \begin{bmatrix} e \\ f \end{bmatrix}$. Then,

1. $\mathbf{v} \cdot \mathbf{v} = c^2 + d^2$ is 0 if c and d are 0 and is positive otherwise.
2. $\mathbf{v} \cdot \mathbf{w} = ce + df$ and $\mathbf{w} \cdot \mathbf{v} = ec + fd$, so they are equal.
3. $\mathbf{u} \cdot (\mathbf{v} + \mathbf{w}) = \begin{bmatrix} a \\ b \end{bmatrix} \cdot \begin{bmatrix} c+e \\ d+f \end{bmatrix} = a(c + e) + b(d + f)$ and $\mathbf{u} \cdot \mathbf{v} + \mathbf{u} \cdot \mathbf{w} =$ $\begin{bmatrix} a \\ b \end{bmatrix} \cdot \begin{bmatrix} c \\ d \end{bmatrix} + \begin{bmatrix} a \\ b \end{bmatrix} \cdot \begin{bmatrix} e \\ f \end{bmatrix} = ac + bd + ae + bf$, so they are equal. The other equation goes the same way.

4. $(r\mathbf{v}) \cdot \mathbf{w} = \begin{bmatrix} rc \\ rd \end{bmatrix} \cdot \begin{bmatrix} e \\ f \end{bmatrix} = rce + rdf$ and $r(\mathbf{v} \cdot \mathbf{w}) = r(ce + df)$, so they are equal. The other equation again goes the same way. ■

Length and distance

The length of a vector $\mathbf{v} = \begin{bmatrix} a \\ b \end{bmatrix}$ should, in view of the Pythagorean theorem of Euclidean geometry, be the square root of the sum of squares of the legs of any triangle having $\mathbf{v}$ as its hypothesis (Figure 1.26).

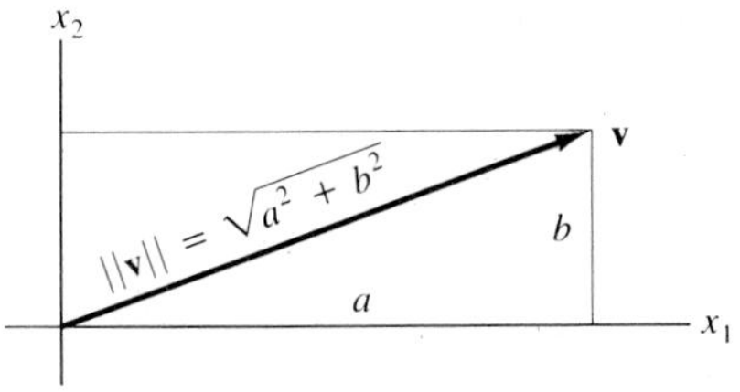

Figure 1.26 The length $\|\mathbf{v}\|$ of $\mathbf{v} = \begin{bmatrix} a \\ b \end{bmatrix}$ is the square root of $a^2 + b^2$.

Since $\mathbf{v} \cdot \mathbf{v} = a^2 + b^2$, we can give an explicit definition of length of $\mathbf{v}$ as $\sqrt{\mathbf{v} \cdot \mathbf{v}}$. The length of the directed line segment $\overrightarrow{\mathbf{v}\,\mathbf{w}}$ is then defined as the length of $\mathbf{w} - \mathbf{v}$, which is also the *distance* from the tip of $\mathbf{v}$ to the tip of $\mathbf{w}$. (Later on, armed with this definition, we prove the Pythagorean theorem in this context.)

Definition. *Length of a Vector and Distance between Two Points.*

The **length** of $\mathbf{v}$ is $\|\mathbf{v}\| = \sqrt{\mathbf{v} \cdot \mathbf{v}}$, and the **distance** from a point $\mathbf{v}$ to a point $\mathbf{w}$ in $\mathbb{R}^2$ is $d(\mathbf{v}, \mathbf{w}) = \|\mathbf{w} - \mathbf{v}\|$.

The distance from $\mathbf{v}$ to $\mathbf{w}$ is simply the length of the vector $\mathbf{w} - \mathbf{v}$ that represents the directed segment $\overrightarrow{\mathbf{v}\,\mathbf{w}}$. For this reason, we define the *length* of $\overrightarrow{\mathbf{v}\,\mathbf{w}}$ to be $\|\mathbf{w} - \mathbf{v}\| = \|\mathbf{v} - \mathbf{w}\|$ (Figure 1.27).

Since $\|\mathbf{w} - \mathbf{v}\| = \|(\mathbf{u} + \mathbf{w}) - (\mathbf{u} + \mathbf{v})\|$, we have the following theorem.

Theorem 1.19. *Invariance of Length under Translations.*

All directed line segments obtained from $\overrightarrow{\mathbf{v}\,\mathbf{w}}$ by translation have the same length.

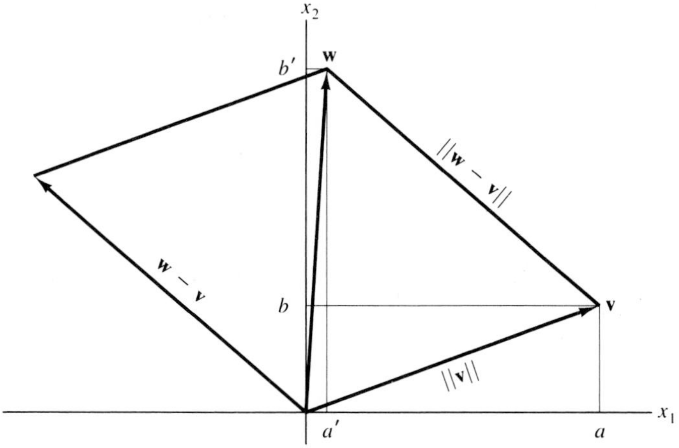

Figure 1.27 The length $||\mathbf{v}||$ of $\mathbf{v}$ and distance $||\mathbf{w} - \mathbf{v}||$ from $\mathbf{v} = \begin{bmatrix} a \\ b \end{bmatrix}$ to $\mathbf{w} = \begin{bmatrix} a' \\ b' \end{bmatrix}$.

EXAMPLES

1. The length of $\begin{bmatrix} 2 \\ 4 \end{bmatrix}$ is $\sqrt{2^2 + 4^2} = \sqrt{20}$.

2. The distance from $\mathbf{v} = \begin{bmatrix} 1 \\ 3 \end{bmatrix}$ to $\mathbf{w} = \begin{bmatrix} 3 \\ 2 \end{bmatrix}$ is the length of $\begin{bmatrix} 1 \\ 3 \end{bmatrix} - \begin{bmatrix} 3 \\ 2 \end{bmatrix} = \begin{bmatrix} -2 \\ 1 \end{bmatrix}$, which is $\sqrt{4 + 1} = \sqrt{5}$. So, the lengths of the directed segments $\overrightarrow{\mathbf{v}\,\mathbf{w}}$ and $\overrightarrow{\mathbf{u}+\mathbf{v}\ \mathbf{u}+\mathbf{w}}$ for any $\mathbf{u}$ are $\sqrt{5}$.

3. The distance from $\begin{bmatrix} a \\ 0 \end{bmatrix}$ to $\begin{bmatrix} b \\ 0 \end{bmatrix}$ along the horizontal axis is $\sqrt{(a - b)^2}$, which is the absolute value $|a - b|$ of the real number $a - b$.

Note that $||a\mathbf{v}|| = |a|\,||\mathbf{v}||$ for real numbers a and vectors $\mathbf{v}$ in the Cartesian plane, which gives the following theorem.

Theorem 1.20. *Length of a Scalar Times a Vector.*
The length of the product of a scalar a and vector $\mathbf{v}$ is the product of the absolute value of a and the length of $\mathbf{v}$.

Replacing a given nonzero vector $\mathbf{v}$ by $\frac{1}{||\mathbf{v}||}\mathbf{v} = \frac{\mathbf{v}}{||\mathbf{v}||}$, the resulting vector has length 1, since $\left\|\frac{\mathbf{v}}{||\mathbf{v}||}\right\| = \left\|\frac{1}{||\mathbf{v}||}\mathbf{v}\right\| = \frac{1}{||\mathbf{v}||}||\mathbf{v}|| = 1$. Vectors of length 1, called

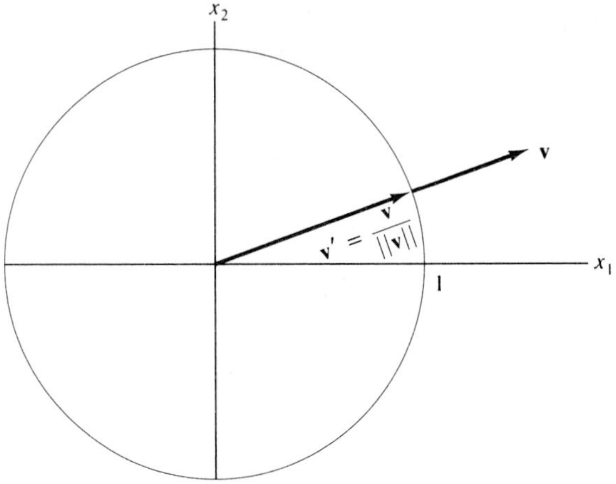

Figure 1.28 The direction $\mathbf{v}' = \dfrac{\mathbf{v}}{\|\mathbf{v}\|}$ of $\mathbf{v}$.

unit vectors, simply designate a direction. So, $\dfrac{\mathbf{v}}{\|\mathbf{v}\|}$ is the *direction* of $\mathbf{v}$, or the *unit vector* corresponding to $\mathbf{v}$ (Figure 1.28).

EXAMPLE

For $\mathbf{v} = \begin{bmatrix} 3 \\ 4 \end{bmatrix}$, $\dfrac{\mathbf{v}}{\|\mathbf{v}\|} = \frac{1}{5}\begin{bmatrix} 3 \\ 4 \end{bmatrix}$ has length 1. (Verify!)

Perpendicularity. The Pythagorean theorem

For a nonzero vector $\mathbf{v} = \begin{bmatrix} a \\ b \end{bmatrix}$, a vector $\mathbf{w}$ satisfies $\mathbf{v} \cdot \mathbf{w} = 0$ if and only if $\mathbf{w}$ is a multiple of $\begin{bmatrix} -b \\ a \end{bmatrix}$. (Prove!) Since $\begin{bmatrix} a \\ b \end{bmatrix}$ and $\begin{bmatrix} -b \\ a \end{bmatrix}$ are at right angles to each other, this leads us to *define* perpendicularity as follows (see Figure 1.29).

Definition. *Perpendicular Vectors.*
Vectors $\mathbf{v}$ and $\mathbf{w}$ are **perpendicular** if $\mathbf{v} \cdot \mathbf{w} = 0$.

EXAMPLES

1. The vectors $\begin{bmatrix} 1 \\ 0 \end{bmatrix}$ and $\begin{bmatrix} 0 \\ 1 \end{bmatrix}$ are perpendicular.
2. $\begin{bmatrix} a \\ b \end{bmatrix}$ and $\begin{bmatrix} -b \\ a \end{bmatrix}$ are perpendicular for all a, b.

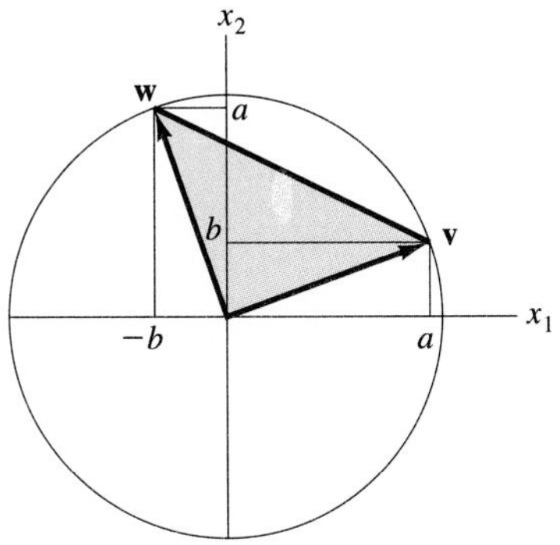

Figure 1.29 The right triangle with legs $\mathbf{v} = \begin{bmatrix} a \\ b \end{bmatrix}$ and $\mathbf{w} = \begin{bmatrix} -b \\ a \end{bmatrix}$.

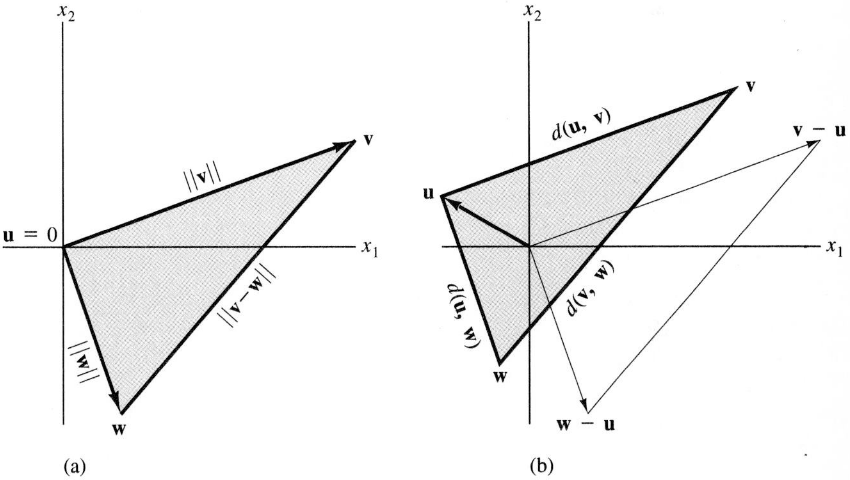

Figure 1.30 The Pythagorean theorem: $d(\mathbf{u}, \mathbf{v})^2 + d(\mathbf{u}, \mathbf{w})^2 = d(\mathbf{v}, \mathbf{w})^2$ for right triangles (a) $\mathbf{u} = 0, \mathbf{v}, \mathbf{w}$ and (b) $\mathbf{u}, \mathbf{v}, \mathbf{w}$.

Having thus defined perpendicularity, we can use algebra to prove the Pythagorean theorem (Figure 1.30).

Theorem 1.21. *The Pythagorean Theorem.*
Let vectors $\mathbf{v}$ and $\mathbf{w}$ in the Cartesian plane be perpendicular. Then $\|\mathbf{v}\|^2 + \|\mathbf{w}\|^2 = \|\mathbf{v} \pm \mathbf{w}\|^2$.

Proof.
$$\|\mathbf{v} \pm \mathbf{w}\|^2 = (\mathbf{v} \pm \mathbf{w}) \cdot (\mathbf{v} \pm \mathbf{w}) = \mathbf{v} \cdot \mathbf{v} \pm \mathbf{v} \cdot \mathbf{w} + \mathbf{w} \cdot \mathbf{w} \pm \mathbf{w} \cdot \mathbf{v}$$
$$= \mathbf{v} \cdot \mathbf{v} + \mathbf{w} \cdot \mathbf{w} = \|\mathbf{v}\|^2 + \|\mathbf{w}\|^2,$$

since $\mathbf{v}$ and $\mathbf{w}$ are perpendicular. ■

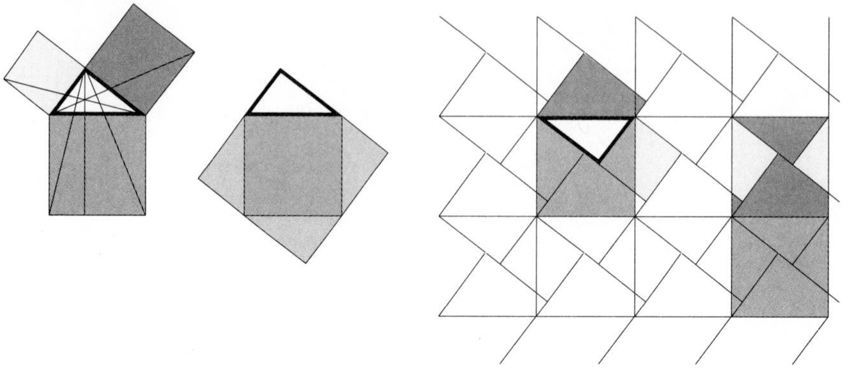

Figure 1.31 Three geometric proofs of the Pythagorean theorem: (a) by comparing triangles; (b) by using the binomial theorem; and (c) by partitioning the plane.

When $\mathbf{v}$ and $\mathbf{w}$ are nonzero perpendicular vectors, the equation $\|\mathbf{v}\|^2 + \|\mathbf{w}\|^2 = \|\mathbf{v} - \mathbf{w}\|^2$ is the classical Pythagorean theorem for the triangle with vertices at $\mathbf{0}$, $\mathbf{v}$, and $\mathbf{w}$. And, for a *right triangle* $\mathbf{u}$, $\mathbf{v}$, $\mathbf{w}$ (one where $\mathbf{v} - \mathbf{u}$ and $\mathbf{w} - \mathbf{u}$ are perpendicular), it is $d(\mathbf{u}, \mathbf{v})^2 + d(\mathbf{u}, \mathbf{w})^2 = d(\mathbf{v}, \mathbf{w})^2$. The proof, however, does not resemble the classical geometric proofs (Figure 1.31).

EXAMPLES

1. For $\mathbf{v} = \begin{bmatrix} 1 \\ 3 \end{bmatrix}$, $\mathbf{w} = \begin{bmatrix} -6 \\ 2 \end{bmatrix}$, $\|\mathbf{v}\|^2 + \|\mathbf{w}\|^2 = 1 + 9 + 26 + 4 = 50$ and $\|\mathbf{v} + \mathbf{w}\|^2 = 25 + 25 = 50$, so $\|\mathbf{v}\|^2 + \|\mathbf{w}\|^2 = \|\mathbf{v} + \mathbf{w}\|^2$.
2. For $\mathbf{u} = \begin{bmatrix} 2 \\ 4 \end{bmatrix}$, $\mathbf{v} = \begin{bmatrix} 3 \\ 7 \end{bmatrix}$, $\mathbf{w} = \begin{bmatrix} -4 \\ 6 \end{bmatrix}$, $d(\mathbf{u}, \mathbf{v})^2 + d(\mathbf{u}, \mathbf{w})^2 = \|\mathbf{v} - \mathbf{u}\|^2 + \|\mathbf{w} - \mathbf{u}\|^2 = 10 + 40 = 50$ and $d(\mathbf{v}, \mathbf{w})^2 = \|\mathbf{w} - \mathbf{v}\|^2 = 49 + 1 = 50$, so $d(\mathbf{u}, \mathbf{v})^2 + d(\mathbf{u}, \mathbf{w})^2 = d(\mathbf{v}, \mathbf{w})^2$.

Decomposing a vector into perpendicular components. Projections

Given a nonzero vector $\mathbf{w}$, any vector $\mathbf{v} \in \mathbb{R}^2$ can be expressed as a sum of two perpendicular vectors, one of which is a multiple of $\mathbf{w}$. We now illustrate this, define the perpendicular vectors, and derive the decomposition.

EXAMPLE

If $\mathbf{w} = \begin{bmatrix} 2 \\ 3 \end{bmatrix}$, $\begin{bmatrix} -2 \\ 10 \end{bmatrix}$ can be written as $\begin{bmatrix} -2 \\ 10 \end{bmatrix} = 2\begin{bmatrix} 2 \\ 3 \end{bmatrix} + \begin{bmatrix} -6 \\ 4 \end{bmatrix}$.

Definition. *Projection of a Vector* $\mathbf{v}$ *onto the Line through* $\mathbf{w}$.

For $\mathbf{v}, \mathbf{w} \in \mathbb{R}^2$, we let $\mathbf{v}_{\mathbf{w}} = \dfrac{\mathbf{v} \cdot \mathbf{w}}{\mathbf{w} \cdot \mathbf{w}} \mathbf{w}$ and $\mathbf{v}_{\mathbf{w}}^{\perp} = \mathbf{v} - \dfrac{\mathbf{v} \cdot \mathbf{w}}{\mathbf{w} \cdot \mathbf{w}} \mathbf{w}$. We call $\mathbf{v}_{\mathbf{w}}$ *the projection of* $\mathbf{v}$ *on* $\mathbf{w}$ and refer to $\mathbf{v}_{\mathbf{w}}$ and $\mathbf{v}_{\mathbf{w}}^{\perp}$ as *the components of* $\mathbf{v}$ *parallel and perpendicular to* $\mathbf{w}$.

Theorem 1.22. *Decomposition* $\mathbf{v} = \mathbf{v}_{\mathbf{w}} + \mathbf{v}_{\mathbf{w}}^{\perp}$.
Given any nonzero $\mathbf{w} \in \mathbb{R}$, we can decompose $\mathbf{v}$ as sum $\mathbf{v} = \mathbf{v}_{\mathbf{w}} + \mathbf{v}_{\mathbf{w}}^{\perp}$ of a vector $\mathbf{v}_{\mathbf{w}}$ parallel to $\mathbf{w}$ and a vector $\mathbf{v}_{\mathbf{w}}^{\perp}$ perpendicular to $\mathbf{w}$ in one and only one way (Figure 1.32).

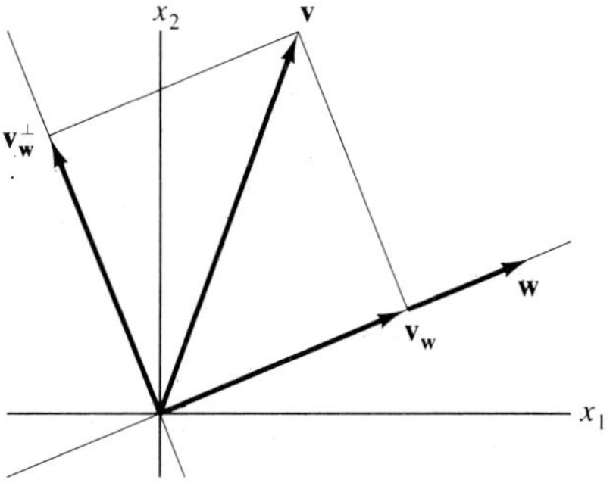

Figure 1.32 Decomposing $\mathbf{v}$ as a sum $\mathbf{v} = \mathbf{v}_{\mathbf{w}} + \mathbf{v}_{\mathbf{w}}^{\perp}$ of perpendicular vectors, given $\mathbf{w}$.

Proof. $\mathbf{v} = \mathbf{v}_{\mathbf{w}} + \mathbf{v}_{\mathbf{w}}^{\perp}$ by definition and $\mathbf{v}_{\mathbf{w}}$ is a multiple of $\mathbf{w}$, whereas $\mathbf{v}_{\mathbf{w}}^{\perp}$ and $\mathbf{w}$ are perpendicular, since

$$\mathbf{v}_{\mathbf{w}}^{\perp} \cdot \mathbf{w} = \left(\mathbf{v} - \frac{\mathbf{v} \cdot \mathbf{w}}{\mathbf{w} \cdot \mathbf{w}} \mathbf{w}\right) \cdot \mathbf{w}$$

$$= \mathbf{v} \cdot \mathbf{w} - \left(\frac{\mathbf{v} \cdot \mathbf{w}}{\mathbf{w} \cdot \mathbf{w}} \mathbf{w}\right) \cdot \mathbf{w} = \mathbf{v} \cdot \mathbf{w} - \left(\frac{\mathbf{v} \cdot \mathbf{w}}{\mathbf{w} \cdot \mathbf{w}}\right) \mathbf{w} \cdot \mathbf{w} = \mathbf{v} \cdot \mathbf{w} - \mathbf{v} \cdot \mathbf{w} = 0.$$

Conversely, if $\mathbf{v} = a\mathbf{w} + \mathbf{w}'$, where $\mathbf{w}'$ is perpendicular to $\mathbf{w}$, then we have $\mathbf{v} \cdot \mathbf{w} = (a\mathbf{w}) \cdot \mathbf{w} + \mathbf{w}' \cdot \mathbf{w} = a(\mathbf{w} \cdot \mathbf{w}) + 0$ and $a = \dfrac{\mathbf{v} \cdot \mathbf{w}}{\mathbf{w} \cdot \mathbf{w}} \mathbf{w}$, so that $a\mathbf{w} = \mathbf{v}_{\mathbf{w}}$ and $\mathbf{w}' = \mathbf{v} - \mathbf{v}_{\mathbf{w}} = \mathbf{v}_{\mathbf{w}}^{\perp}$. ■

EXAMPLE

If $\mathbf{w} = \begin{bmatrix} 2 \\ 3 \end{bmatrix}$ and $\mathbf{v} = \begin{bmatrix} -2 \\ 10 \end{bmatrix}$, $\mathbf{v}_{\mathbf{w}} = \dfrac{2 \cdot (-2) + 3 \cdot 10}{2 \cdot 2 \quad + 3 \cdot 3} \begin{bmatrix} 2 \\ 3 \end{bmatrix} = 2 \begin{bmatrix} 2 \\ 3 \end{bmatrix}$, giving the same decomposition $\begin{bmatrix} -2 \\ 10 \end{bmatrix} = 2 \begin{bmatrix} 2 \\ 3 \end{bmatrix} + \begin{bmatrix} -6 \\ 4 \end{bmatrix}$ as in the preceding example.

Some important equalities and inequalities of length

Putting our theorem on the components of $\mathbf{v}$ parallel and perpendicular to $\mathbf{w}$ together with the Pythagorean theorem, we have the following corollary.

Corollary. Suppose that $\mathbf{v}, \mathbf{w} \in \mathbb{R}^2$ and $\mathbf{w}$ is nonzero. Then

$$\|\mathbf{v}\|^2 = \|\mathbf{v}_{\mathbf{w}}\|^2 + \|\mathbf{v}_{\mathbf{w}}^{\perp}\|^2.$$

From this follows a simple but very useful inequality for projections.

Theorem 1.23. *Length of the Projection of a Vector* $\mathbf{v}$ *on* $\mathbf{w}$.
The length of the projection $\mathbf{v}_{\mathbf{w}}$ of a vector $\mathbf{v}$ on a nonzero vector $\mathbf{w}$ is less than or equal to the length of $\mathbf{v}$. (Strictly less if $\mathbf{v}$ is not a multiple of $\mathbf{w}$.)

This, in turn, leads to the following inequality, needed to discuss angles.

Theorem 1.24. *Schwarz Inequality.*
$|\mathbf{v} \cdot \mathbf{w}| \leq \|\mathbf{v}\|\|\mathbf{w}\|$ for any $\mathbf{v}$, $\mathbf{w}$ in the Cartesian plane, with equality only if $\mathbf{v}$ and $\mathbf{w}$ are on the same line through 0.

Proof. Rewriting the inequality $\|\mathbf{v}_{\mathbf{w}}\| \leq \|\mathbf{v}\|$ as $\left\|\dfrac{\mathbf{v} \cdot \mathbf{w}}{\mathbf{w} \cdot \mathbf{w}}\mathbf{w}\right\| \leq \|\mathbf{v}\|$, we get

$$\|\mathbf{v}\|\|\mathbf{w}\| \geq \left\|\frac{\mathbf{v} \cdot \mathbf{w}}{\mathbf{w} \cdot \mathbf{w}}\mathbf{w}\right\|\|\mathbf{w}\| = \left|\frac{\mathbf{v} \cdot \mathbf{w}}{\mathbf{w} \cdot \mathbf{w}}\right|\|\mathbf{w}\|^2 = \frac{|\mathbf{v} \cdot \mathbf{w}|}{\mathbf{w} \cdot \mathbf{w}}\|\mathbf{w}\|^2 = |\mathbf{v} \cdot \mathbf{w}|.$$

We have equality only if $\mathbf{v}$ is a multiple of $\mathbf{w}$, since otherwise $\|\mathbf{v}_{\mathbf{w}}\| < \|\mathbf{v}\|$. ■

From the Schwarz inequality follows an inequality of length.

Theorem 1.25. *The Triangle Inequality.*
For any $\mathbf{u}, \mathbf{v}, \mathbf{w} \in \mathbb{R}^2$,

1. $\|\mathbf{u} \pm \mathbf{v}\| \leq \|\mathbf{u}\| + \|\mathbf{v}\|$, with equality only if $\mathbf{0}$ is on the line through $\mathbf{u}$ and $\mathbf{v}$.
2. $d(\mathbf{u}, \mathbf{v}) \leq d(\mathbf{u}, \mathbf{w}) + d(\mathbf{w}, \mathbf{v})$, with equality only if $\mathbf{w}$ is on the line through $\mathbf{u}$ and $\mathbf{v}$.

Proof. For (1), we simply compute the squared length (using the Schwarz inequality at one point in the computations) noting that the equality can occur only if 0 is on the line through $\mathbf{u}$ and $\mathbf{v}$:

$$\begin{aligned}\|\mathbf{u} \pm \mathbf{v}\|^2 &= (\mathbf{u} \pm \mathbf{v}) \cdot (\mathbf{u} \pm \mathbf{v}) \\ &= \mathbf{u} \cdot \mathbf{u} \pm 2(\mathbf{u} \cdot \mathbf{v}) + \mathbf{v} \cdot \mathbf{v} \\ &\leq \|\mathbf{u}\|^2 + 2\|\mathbf{u}\|\|\mathbf{v}\| + \|\mathbf{v}\|^2 = (\|\mathbf{u}\| + \|\mathbf{v}\|)^2.\end{aligned}$$

The condition for equality is that $\pm\mathbf{u}\cdot\mathbf{v} = \|\mathbf{u}\|\|\mathbf{v}\|$. This condition implies that $\mathbf{u}$ and $\mathbf{v}$ are on the same line through 0, by Theorem 1.24.

For (2), it suffices to note that $\|(\mathbf{u}-\mathbf{w})-(\mathbf{v}-\mathbf{w})\| \le \|\mathbf{u}-\mathbf{w}\| + \|\mathbf{v}-\mathbf{w}\|$, with equality only if 0 is on the line through $\mathbf{u}-\mathbf{w}$ and $\mathbf{v}-\mathbf{w}$. (Explain!) ■

For the triangle with vertices $\mathbf{0}$, $\mathbf{u}$, and $\mathbf{v}$, the triangle inequality says that the sum of the lengths of the sides $\mathbf{u}$ and $\mathbf{v}$ is greater than the length $\|\mathbf{u}-\mathbf{v}\|$ of the remaining side (Figure 1.33).

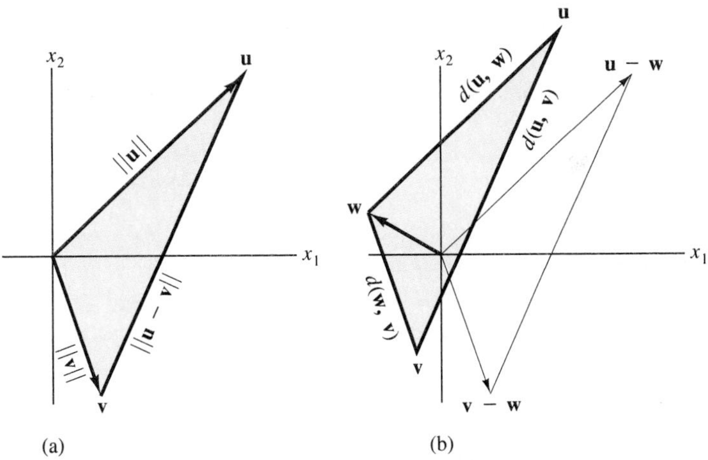

Figure 1.33 The triangle inequalities (a) $\|\mathbf{u}-\mathbf{v}\| \le \|\mathbf{u}\| + \|\mathbf{v}\|$ and (b) $d(\mathbf{u},\mathbf{v}) \le d(\mathbf{u},\mathbf{w}) + d(\mathbf{w},\mathbf{v})$.

EXAMPLES

Let $\mathbf{u} = \begin{bmatrix} -2 \\ 10 \end{bmatrix}$, $\mathbf{v} = \begin{bmatrix} 2 \\ 3 \end{bmatrix}$. Then $\mathbf{u}_\mathbf{v} = \begin{bmatrix} 4 \\ 6 \end{bmatrix}$ and

1. $\|\mathbf{u}\|^2 = 104$, $\|\mathbf{u}_\mathbf{v}\|^2 = 16 + 36 = 52$ and $\|\mathbf{u}_\mathbf{v}\| \le \|\mathbf{u}\|$;
2. $\|\mathbf{u}\|^2\|\mathbf{v}\|^2 = 104 \cdot 13$ and $|\mathbf{u}\cdot\mathbf{v}|^2 = 26^2 \le \|\mathbf{u}\|^2\|\mathbf{v}\|^2$;
3. $\|\mathbf{u}+\mathbf{v}\|^2 = 13^2$ and $\|\mathbf{u}\|^2 = 104$, $\|\mathbf{v}\|^2 = 13$, so $\|\mathbf{u}+\mathbf{v}\| = 13 \le \|\mathbf{u}\| + \|\mathbf{v}\|$. (Verify!)

Angles between vectors

We all have used the concept of angle in many ways. Now is the time to define it explicitly. Since we have already introduced rotations, it makes sense to say that the angle between nonzero vectors $\mathbf{v}$ and $\mathbf{w}$ is the angle through which one must be rotated for it to become parallel to the other. This definition can be generalized to angle between directed line segments (Figure 1.34).

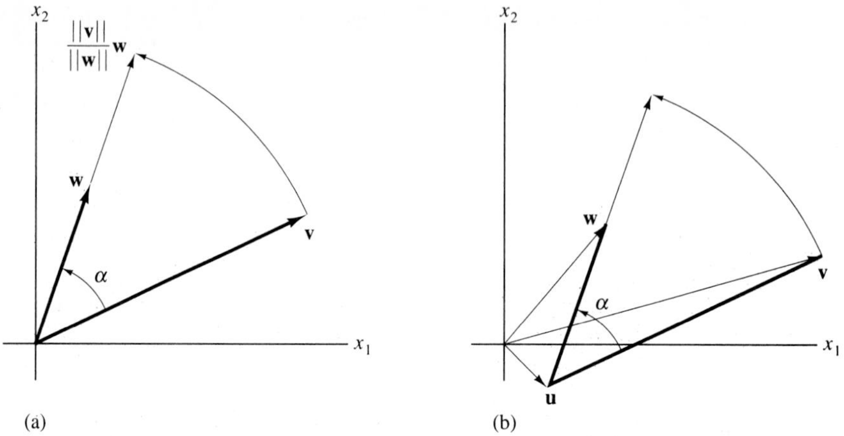

Figure 1.34 Angle between (a) vectors **v**, **w** and (b) segments $\overrightarrow{\mathbf{uv}}$, $\overrightarrow{\mathbf{uw}}$.

Definition. *Angle between Vectors and Directed Line Segments.*
The **angle between two nonzero vectors** $\mathbf{v}$ and $\mathbf{w}$ is the angle α between 0 and π through which one vector must be rotated to get a positive multiple of the other. The **angle between directed segments** $\overrightarrow{\mathbf{u}\,\mathbf{v}}$ and $\overrightarrow{\mathbf{u}\,\mathbf{w}}$ is the angle between $\mathbf{v} - \mathbf{u}$ and $\mathbf{w} - \mathbf{u}$.

By interchanging $\mathbf{v}$ and $\mathbf{w}$ if necessary, we can assume that $\mathbf{v}$ gets rotated to a positive multiple of $\mathbf{w}$. In this case, we say that $\mathbf{v}$ *precedes* $\mathbf{w}$. Rotation through the angle α is the linear transformation $R_\alpha(\mathbf{x}) = \begin{bmatrix} \cos\alpha & -\sin\alpha \\ \sin\alpha & \cos\alpha \end{bmatrix}\mathbf{x}$. Since R_α preserves length (see Problem 19), this multiple of $\mathbf{w}$ has length $\|\mathbf{v}\|$ and must be $\dfrac{\|\mathbf{v}\|}{\|\mathbf{w}\|}\mathbf{w}$. So, our definition can be restated as

The angle between two nonzero vectors $\mathbf{v}$ *and* $\mathbf{w}$, *where* $\mathbf{v}$ *precedes* $\mathbf{w}$, *is the angle* α *between* 0 *and* π *such that* $R_\alpha(\mathbf{v}) = \dfrac{\|\mathbf{v}\|}{\|\mathbf{w}\|}\mathbf{w}$.

To compute α, let $\mathbf{v} = \begin{bmatrix} a \\ b \end{bmatrix}$, $\mathbf{w} = \begin{bmatrix} c \\ d \end{bmatrix}$. Then the condition $R_\alpha(\mathbf{v}) = \dfrac{\|\mathbf{v}\|}{\|\mathbf{w}\|}\mathbf{w}$ is $\begin{bmatrix} \cos\alpha & -\sin\alpha \\ \sin\alpha & \cos\alpha \end{bmatrix}\begin{bmatrix} a \\ b \end{bmatrix} = \dfrac{\|\mathbf{v}\|}{\|\mathbf{w}\|}\begin{bmatrix} c \\ d \end{bmatrix}$; that is,

$$a\cos\alpha - b\sin\alpha = \frac{\|\mathbf{v}\|}{\|\mathbf{w}\|}c,$$

$$b\cos\alpha + a\sin\alpha = \frac{\|\mathbf{v}\|}{\|\mathbf{w}\|}d.$$

Solving for cos α and sin α by Cramer's rule, we get

$$\cos\alpha = \frac{\|\mathbf{v}\|}{\|\mathbf{w}\|}\frac{\begin{vmatrix} c & -b \\ d & a\end{vmatrix}}{\begin{vmatrix} a & -b \\ b & a\end{vmatrix}}, \qquad \sin\alpha = \frac{\|\mathbf{v}\|}{\|\mathbf{w}\|}\frac{\begin{vmatrix} a & c \\ b & d\end{vmatrix}}{\begin{vmatrix} a & -b \\ b & a\end{vmatrix}}.$$

Since $\begin{vmatrix} a & -b \\ b & a\end{vmatrix} = a^2 + b^2 = \|\mathbf{v}\|^2$ and $\begin{vmatrix} c & -b \\ d & a\end{vmatrix} = ac + bd = \mathbf{v}\cdot\mathbf{w}$, we get $\cos\alpha = \dfrac{\mathbf{v}\cdot\mathbf{w}}{\|\mathbf{v}\|\,\|\mathbf{w}\|}$, $\sin\alpha = \dfrac{|\mathbf{v},\mathbf{w}|}{\|\mathbf{v}\|\,\|\mathbf{w}\|}$. This determines the following theorem.

Theorem 1.26. *Angle between* **v** *and* **w**.

The sine and cosine of the angle between **v** and **w** are $\cos\alpha = \dfrac{\mathbf{v}\cdot\mathbf{w}}{\|\mathbf{v}\|\,\|\mathbf{w}\|}$, $\sin\alpha = \dfrac{|\mathbf{v},\mathbf{w}|}{\|\mathbf{v}\|\,\|\mathbf{w}\|}$, where $|\mathbf{v},\mathbf{w}|$ denotes $\begin{vmatrix} a & c \\ b & d\end{vmatrix}$.

EXAMPLES

1. The cosine and sine of the angle between $\mathbf{v} = \begin{bmatrix} 2 \\ 1\end{bmatrix}$ and $\mathbf{w} = \begin{bmatrix} 3 \\ 4\end{bmatrix}$ are

$$\cos\alpha \frac{6+4}{\sqrt{4+1}\sqrt{9+16}} = \frac{10}{5\sqrt{5}} = \frac{2}{\sqrt{5}} \text{ and } \sin\alpha = \frac{8-3}{5\sqrt{5}} = \frac{1}{\sqrt{5}}.$$

2. For $\mathbf{u} = \begin{bmatrix} 1 \\ 3\end{bmatrix}$, $\mathbf{v} = \begin{bmatrix} 3 \\ 4\end{bmatrix}$, and $\mathbf{w} = \begin{bmatrix} 4 \\ 7\end{bmatrix}$, the cosine and sine of the angle between $\overrightarrow{\mathbf{u}\,\mathbf{v}}$ and $\overrightarrow{\mathbf{u}\,\mathbf{w}}$ are the same as in (1). (Explain!)

Let's pause to observe the following.

1. The angle between any nonzero vectors **v** and **w** is the angle α between 0 and π such that $\cos\alpha = \dfrac{\mathbf{v}\cdot\mathbf{w}}{\|\mathbf{v}\|\,\|\mathbf{w}\|}$. Since $\mathbf{v}\cdot\mathbf{w} = \mathbf{w}\cdot\mathbf{v}$, we no longer have to worry about whether **v** precedes **w**.
2. *This angle always exists,* since we are assured that $-1 \le \dfrac{\mathbf{v}\cdot\mathbf{w}}{\|\mathbf{v}\|\,\|\mathbf{w}\|} \le 1$ by the Cauchy-Schwarz inequality.
3. The angle between perpendicular vectors **v** and **w** is $\pi/2$.
4. The angle between **v** and **w** does not change if we multiply **v** and **w** by positive numbers.
5. For vectors **v** and **w** of length 1, the cosine of the angle α between **v** and **w** is the dot product $\mathbf{v}\cdot\mathbf{w}$. Since $\mathbf{v}\cdot\mathbf{w} = |\mathbf{v},\mathbf{w}^{\perp}|$ (explain), we can also express $\cos\alpha = \sin\beta$ and $\sin\alpha = \cos\beta$ for complementary angles α and β (Figure 1.35).

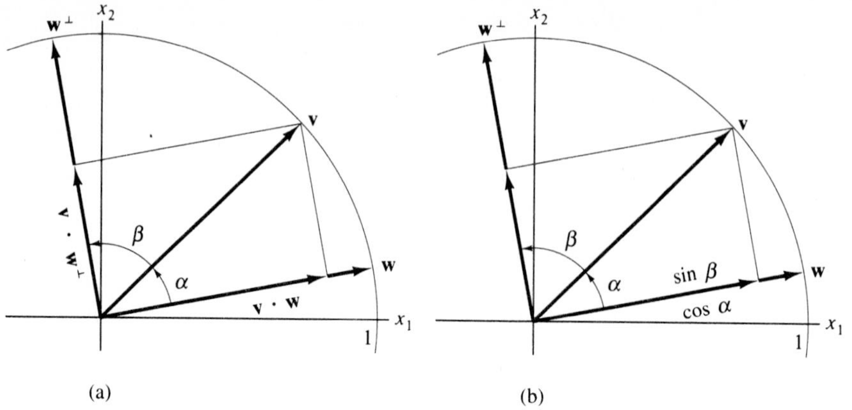

Figure 1.35 (a) Dot products of unit vectors as lengths of projections; (b) sines and cosines as lengths of projections.

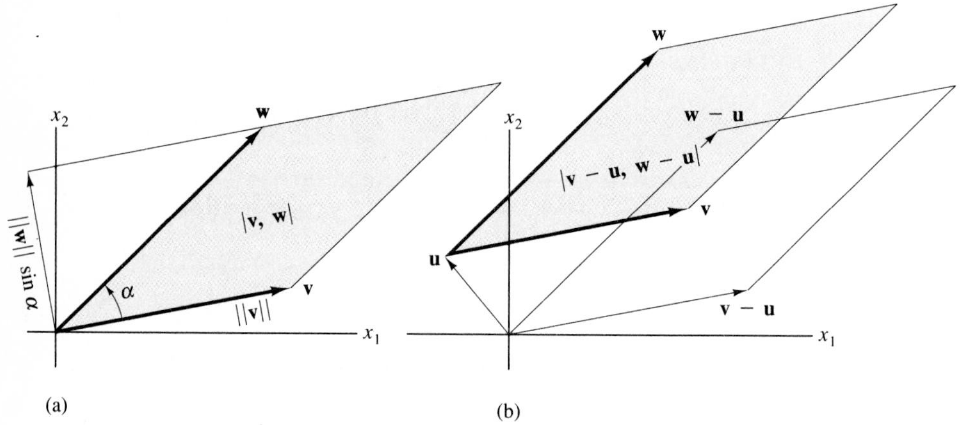

Figure 1.36 The area of the parallelogram (a) with edge vectors **v** and **w** and (b) with edge segments $\overrightarrow{\mathbf{u}\,\mathbf{v}}, \overrightarrow{\mathbf{u}\,\mathbf{w}}$.

Area

The formula $|\mathbf{v}, \mathbf{w}| = \|\mathbf{v}\|\|\mathbf{w}\| \sin \alpha$ and its interpretation in the plane as area (Figure 1.36) leads us to the following definition.

Definition. *Area of a Parallelogram with Given Edge Vectors.*
The **area of the parallelogram** with edge vectors **v** and **w** is the absolute value of the determinant $|\mathbf{v}, \mathbf{w}|$.

The area of the parallelogram with edge segments $\overrightarrow{\mathbf{u}\,\mathbf{v}}, \overrightarrow{\mathbf{u}\,\mathbf{w}}$ is defined as the area of the parallelogram with edge vectors $\mathbf{v} - \mathbf{u}, \mathbf{w} - \mathbf{u}$.

EXAMPLE

For $\mathbf{u} = \begin{bmatrix} 1 \\ 3 \end{bmatrix}$, $\mathbf{v} = \begin{bmatrix} 3 \\ 4 \end{bmatrix}$, and $\mathbf{w} = \begin{bmatrix} 4 \\ 7 \end{bmatrix}$, the area of the parallelogram with edge segments $\overrightarrow{\mathbf{u}\,\mathbf{v}}$ and $\overrightarrow{\mathbf{u}\,\mathbf{w}}$ is the same as the area of the parallelogram with edge vectors $\begin{bmatrix} 2 \\ 1 \end{bmatrix}$ and $\begin{bmatrix} 3 \\ 4 \end{bmatrix}$, which is $\begin{vmatrix} 2 & 3 \\ 1 & 4 \end{vmatrix} = 8 - 3 = 5$.

For vectors $\mathbf{v}$ and $\mathbf{w}$ of length 1, the sine of the angle α between $\mathbf{v}$ and $\mathbf{w}$ is the area $|\mathbf{v}, \mathbf{w}|$. Because $\sin \alpha = \cos \beta$ for complementary angles α and β, we can interpret cosines as areas as well (Figure 1.37).

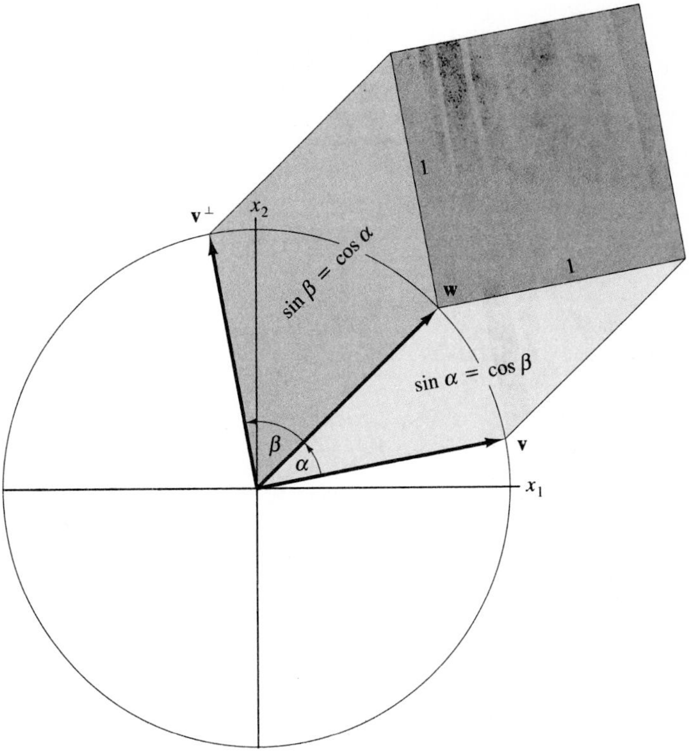

Figure 1.37 Sines and cosines as areas.

The normal to a line. Perpendicular lines

Having defined two vectors to be perpendicular if their dot product is zero, the discussion of normals and perpendicular lines (Section 1.2) reduces to observing that the set of vectors $\begin{bmatrix} x_1 \\ x_2 \end{bmatrix}$ for which $\begin{bmatrix} x_1 \\ x_2 \end{bmatrix} - \begin{bmatrix} u_1 \\ u_2 \end{bmatrix}$ is perpendicular to $\begin{bmatrix} a \\ b \end{bmatrix}$ is the line $a(x_1 - u_1) + b(x_2 - u_1) = 0$. To verify this amounts to observing that $\left(\begin{bmatrix} x_1 \\ x_2 \end{bmatrix} - \begin{bmatrix} u_1 \\ u_2 \end{bmatrix}\right) \cdot \begin{bmatrix} a \\ b \end{bmatrix} = a(x_1 - u_1) + b(x_2 - u_1)$. This determines the following theorem.

Theorem 1.27. *Lines Perpendicular to a Given Vector.*
The line through $\begin{bmatrix} u_1 \\ u_2 \end{bmatrix}$ perpendicular to $\begin{bmatrix} a \\ b \end{bmatrix}$ is $a(x_1 - u_1) + b(x_2 - u_1) = 0$.

Its normals are $t\begin{bmatrix} a \\ b \end{bmatrix}$ $(t \neq 0)$.

EXAMPLE

The line through 0 with normal $\begin{bmatrix} 2 \\ 3 \end{bmatrix}$ is $2x_1 + 3x_2 = 0$. The line through $\begin{bmatrix} 1 \\ 1 \end{bmatrix}$ with normal $\begin{bmatrix} 2 \\ 3 \end{bmatrix}$ is $2(x_1 - 1) + 3(x_2 - 1) = 0$, or $2x_1 + 3x_2 = 5$ (Figure 1.38).

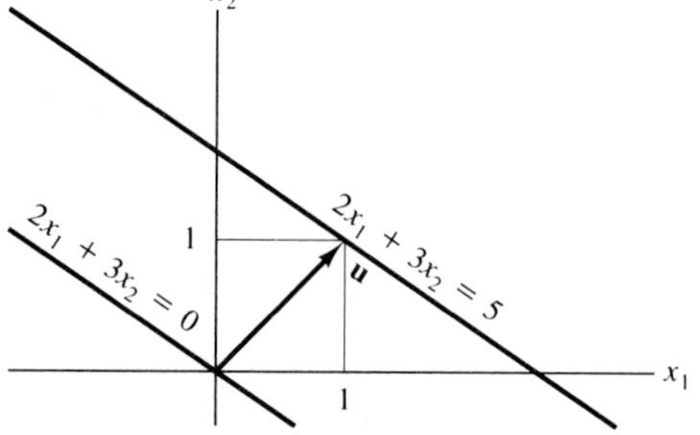

Figure 1.38 The line $2x_1 + 3x_2 = 0$ through 0 and its translation $2x_1 + 3x_2 = 5$ by $\mathbf{u} = \begin{bmatrix} 1 \\ 1 \end{bmatrix}$.

Accordingly, we say that $ax_1 + bx_2 = p$ and $cx_1 + dx_2 = q$ are *perpendicular* if their normals $\begin{bmatrix} a \\ b \end{bmatrix}$ and $\begin{bmatrix} c \\ d \end{bmatrix}$ are perpendicular—that is, if $ac + bd = 0$. For example, this happens when $c = -b$ and $d = a$ (Figure 1.39).

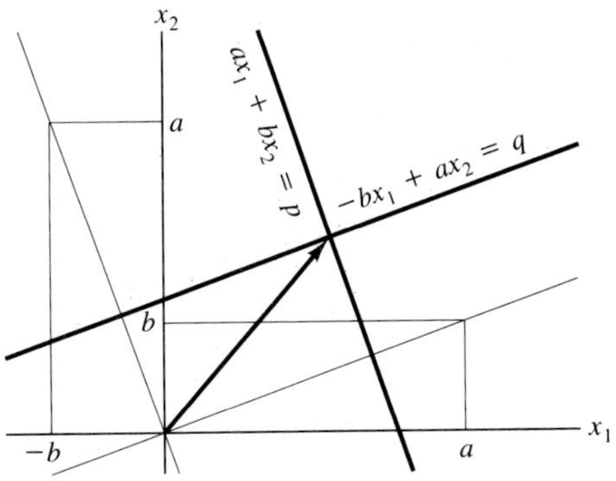

Figure 1.39 The perpendicular lines $ax_1 + bx_2 = p$ and $-bx_1 + ax_2 = q$.

PROBLEMS

NUMERICAL PROBLEMS

1. Compute the dot product of $\mathbf{v}$ and $\mathbf{w}$ in the following cases.

(a) $\mathbf{v} = \begin{bmatrix} 3 \\ -2 \end{bmatrix}, \mathbf{w} = \begin{bmatrix} 2 \\ 3 \end{bmatrix}$ **(b)** $\mathbf{v} = \begin{bmatrix} 2 \\ -2 \end{bmatrix}, \mathbf{w} = \begin{bmatrix} 3 \\ 4 \end{bmatrix}$

(c) $\mathbf{v} = \begin{bmatrix} 3 \\ 2 \end{bmatrix}, \mathbf{w} = \begin{bmatrix} 1 \\ 9 \end{bmatrix}$ **(d)** $\mathbf{v} = 3\begin{bmatrix} 3 \\ 2 \end{bmatrix} + 4\begin{bmatrix} 2 \\ 1 \end{bmatrix}, \mathbf{w} = \begin{bmatrix} 1 \\ 3 \end{bmatrix}$

(e) $\mathbf{v} = 3\begin{bmatrix} 3 \\ 2 \end{bmatrix} + 4\begin{bmatrix} 2 \\ 1 \end{bmatrix}, \mathbf{w} = 2\begin{bmatrix} 1 \\ 2 \end{bmatrix} + 3\begin{bmatrix} 1 \\ 1 \end{bmatrix}$

(f) $\mathbf{v} = 3\begin{bmatrix} 3 \\ 2 \end{bmatrix} - 4\begin{bmatrix} 2 \\ 1 \end{bmatrix}, \mathbf{w} = 3\begin{bmatrix} 3 \\ 2 \end{bmatrix} + 4\begin{bmatrix} 2 \\ 1 \end{bmatrix}$

2. In Problem 1, what pairs of vectors $\mathbf{v}$ and $\mathbf{w}$ are perpendicular?

3. Compute the lengths of $\mathbf{v} = \begin{bmatrix} 1 \\ 2 \end{bmatrix}$, $\mathbf{w} = \begin{bmatrix} 2 \\ 9 \end{bmatrix}$, $\mathbf{v} + \mathbf{w} = \begin{bmatrix} 1 \\ 2 \end{bmatrix} + \begin{bmatrix} 2 \\ 9 \end{bmatrix}$, and $(-3)\begin{bmatrix} 1 \\ 2 \end{bmatrix}$. Then verify the triangle inequality $\|\mathbf{v} + \mathbf{w}\| \leq \|\mathbf{v}\| + \|\mathbf{w}\|$ and the equality $|t\mathbf{w}| = |t|\|\mathbf{w}\|$ for these vectors $\mathbf{v}$ and $\mathbf{w}$ when $t = -3$.

4. Compute the length of the directed segment from $\mathbf{v}$ to $\mathbf{w}$ where

(a) $\mathbf{v} = \begin{bmatrix} 2 \\ -2 \end{bmatrix}, \mathbf{w} = \begin{bmatrix} 3 \\ 9 \end{bmatrix}$;

(b) $\mathbf{v} = \begin{bmatrix} 3 \\ -2 \end{bmatrix}, \mathbf{w} = \begin{bmatrix} 2 \\ 5 \end{bmatrix}$;

(c) $\mathbf{v} = \begin{bmatrix} 4 \\ -4 \end{bmatrix}, \mathbf{w} = \begin{bmatrix} 4 \\ 4 \end{bmatrix}$.

5. Compute the unit vectors corresponding to

(a) $\mathbf{v} = \begin{bmatrix} 2 \\ 4 \end{bmatrix}$; (b) $\mathbf{v} = \begin{bmatrix} 4 \\ 5 \end{bmatrix}$; (c) $\mathbf{v} = \begin{bmatrix} 3 \\ 4 \end{bmatrix}$;

6. Verify the Pythagorean theorem for the right triangle **u**, **v**, **w**, where

(a) $\mathbf{u} = \begin{bmatrix} 0 \\ 0 \end{bmatrix}$, $\mathbf{v} = \begin{bmatrix} 1 \\ -2 \end{bmatrix}$, $\mathbf{w} = \begin{bmatrix} 2 \\ 1 \end{bmatrix}$;

(b) $\mathbf{u} = \begin{bmatrix} 1 \\ 0 \end{bmatrix}$, $\mathbf{v} = \begin{bmatrix} 2 \\ 3 \end{bmatrix}$, $\mathbf{w} = \begin{bmatrix} -2 \\ 1 \end{bmatrix}$;

(c) $\mathbf{u} = \begin{bmatrix} 2 \\ -2 \end{bmatrix}$, $\mathbf{v} = \begin{bmatrix} 4 \\ 1 \end{bmatrix}$, $\mathbf{w} = \begin{bmatrix} -1 \\ 0 \end{bmatrix}$.

7. Decompose **v** as $\mathbf{v} = \mathbf{v}_{\mathbf{w}} + \mathbf{v}_{\mathbf{w}}^{\perp}$, where

(a) $\mathbf{v} = \begin{bmatrix} 2 \\ -1 \end{bmatrix}$, $\mathbf{w} = \begin{bmatrix} 1 \\ 1 \end{bmatrix}$; (b) $\mathbf{v} = \begin{bmatrix} 2 \\ -2 \end{bmatrix}$, $\mathbf{w} = \begin{bmatrix} 2 \\ 1 \end{bmatrix}$;

(c) $\mathbf{v} = \begin{bmatrix} 1 \\ -1 \end{bmatrix}$, $\mathbf{w} = \begin{bmatrix} 1 \\ 1 \end{bmatrix}$.

8. Verify the Schwarz inequality for **v** and **w** in the following cases.

(a) $\mathbf{v} = \begin{bmatrix} 3 \\ -2 \end{bmatrix}$, $\mathbf{w} = \begin{bmatrix} 2 \\ 3 \end{bmatrix}$ (b) $\mathbf{v} = \begin{bmatrix} 2 \\ -2 \end{bmatrix}$, $\mathbf{w} = \begin{bmatrix} 3 \\ 4 \end{bmatrix}$

(c) $\mathbf{v} = \begin{bmatrix} 3 \\ 2 \end{bmatrix}$, $\mathbf{w} = \begin{bmatrix} 1 \\ 9 \end{bmatrix}$

9. Compute the cosine of the angle between **v** and **w** in the following cases.

(a) $\mathbf{v} = \begin{bmatrix} 3 \\ -2 \end{bmatrix}$, $\mathbf{w} = \begin{bmatrix} 2 \\ 3 \end{bmatrix}$ (b) $\mathbf{v} = \begin{bmatrix} 2 \\ -2 \end{bmatrix}$, $\mathbf{w} = \begin{bmatrix} 3 \\ 4 \end{bmatrix}$

(c) $\mathbf{v} = \begin{bmatrix} 3 \\ 2 \end{bmatrix}$, $\mathbf{w} = \begin{bmatrix} 1 \\ 9 \end{bmatrix}$

10. Find the equations of the lines through $\begin{bmatrix} 3 \\ 4 \end{bmatrix}$ perpendicular to

(a) $2x_1 + 5x_2 = 3$; (b) $5x_1 + 2x_2 = 8$;

(c) $3(x_1 - 5) + 61(x_2 + 12)$.

11. Find the equations for all lines perpendicular to each of the lines in Problem 10.

12. Verify the triangle inequality for the triangle **u**, **v**, **w**, where

(a) $\mathbf{u} = \begin{bmatrix} 0 \\ 1 \end{bmatrix}$, $\mathbf{v} = \begin{bmatrix} 1 \\ -2 \end{bmatrix}$, $\mathbf{w} = \begin{bmatrix} 2 \\ 1 \end{bmatrix}$;

(b) $\mathbf{u} = \begin{bmatrix} 1 \\ 1 \end{bmatrix}$, $\mathbf{v} = \begin{bmatrix} 2 \\ 3 \end{bmatrix}$, $\mathbf{w} = \begin{bmatrix} -2 \\ 1 \end{bmatrix}$.

13. Compute the cosine of the angle between $\overrightarrow{\mathbf{u}\,\mathbf{w}}$ and $\overrightarrow{\mathbf{w}\,\mathbf{v}}$ for the vectors **u**, **v**, **w** in Problem 12.

THEORETICAL PROBLEMS

14. Show that if α is the angle between $\begin{bmatrix}1\\0\end{bmatrix}$ and a vector $\begin{bmatrix}c\\d\end{bmatrix}$ of length 1, then $\begin{bmatrix}c\\|d|\end{bmatrix} = \begin{bmatrix}\cos\alpha\\|\sin\alpha|\end{bmatrix}$.

15. Show that if α is the angle between $\begin{bmatrix}1\\0\end{bmatrix}$ and $\begin{bmatrix}c\\d\end{bmatrix}$, then α is also the angle between $\begin{bmatrix}1\\0\end{bmatrix}$ and $\begin{bmatrix}c\\-d\end{bmatrix}$.

Hard

16. Through a given point $\begin{bmatrix}r\\s\end{bmatrix}$ and parallel to a given line $ax_1 + bx_2 = p$, there is one and only one line.

17. Through two *distinct* (different) points $\begin{bmatrix}r\\s\end{bmatrix}$ and $\begin{bmatrix}r'\\s'\end{bmatrix}$, there passes one and only one line.

18. Through a given point $\begin{bmatrix}r\\s\end{bmatrix}$ and perpendicular to a given line $ax_1 + bx_2 = p$, there is one and only one line.

19. Prove that $\mathbf{x}$ and $R_\alpha(\mathbf{x})$ are of the same length for all $\mathbf{x}$, α.

20. Show that $\mathbf{v} \cdot \mathbf{w}$ can be expressed in terms of the lengths of the vectors $\mathbf{v} + \mathbf{w}$ and $\mathbf{v} - \mathbf{w}$ alone by computing an explicit formula.

21. Show that a matrix A is a *rotation matrix* $\begin{bmatrix}\cos\alpha & -\sin\alpha\\ \sin\alpha & \cos\alpha\end{bmatrix}$ for some α if and only if $A = \begin{bmatrix}r & -s\\ s & r\end{bmatrix}$ for some vector $\begin{bmatrix}r\\s\end{bmatrix}$ of length 1.

Very Hard

22. Show that:

(a) The inverse of a rotation matrix $\begin{bmatrix}r & -s\\ s & r\end{bmatrix}$ is $\begin{bmatrix}r & s\\ -s & r\end{bmatrix}$;

(b) For any two vectors $\mathbf{v} = \begin{bmatrix}a\\b\end{bmatrix}$, $\mathbf{w} = \begin{bmatrix}c\\d\end{bmatrix}$ of length 1,

$$\begin{bmatrix}\mathbf{v}\cdot\mathbf{w} & -|\mathbf{v}, \mathbf{w}|\\ |\mathbf{v}, \mathbf{w}| & \mathbf{v}\cdot\mathbf{w}\end{bmatrix}\begin{bmatrix}a & -b\\ b & a\end{bmatrix} = \begin{bmatrix}c & -d\\ d & c\end{bmatrix}.$$

(c) Use (b) to give another proof of Theorem 1.26.

23. For vectors $\mathbf{v} = \begin{bmatrix}a\\b\end{bmatrix}$ and $\mathbf{w} = \begin{bmatrix}c\\d\end{bmatrix}$ of length 1, define

$$\mathbf{v}\#\mathbf{w} = \begin{bmatrix}\mathbf{v}\cdot\mathbf{w}\\ |\mathbf{v}, \mathbf{w}|\end{bmatrix}, \quad \mathbf{v}^* = \begin{bmatrix}a\\-b\end{bmatrix}, \quad \mathbf{1} = \begin{bmatrix}1\\0\end{bmatrix}, \quad \mathbf{i} = \begin{bmatrix}0\\1\end{bmatrix}.$$

Then define $\mathbf{vw} = (\mathbf{v}^*)\#\mathbf{w}$. Show that

(a) $\mathbf{vw}$ is the first column of the rotation $\begin{bmatrix} a & -b \\ b & a \end{bmatrix}\begin{bmatrix} c & -d \\ d & c \end{bmatrix}$;
(b) $\mathbf{1v} = \mathbf{v}$ ($\mathbf{v}$ of length 1);
(c) $\mathbf{vw} = \mathbf{wv}$ ($\mathbf{v}$, $\mathbf{w}$ of length 1);
(d) $\mathbf{vv}^* = \mathbf{1}$ ($\mathbf{v}$ of length 1);
(e) $(\mathbf{uv})\mathbf{w} = \mathbf{u}(\mathbf{vw})$ ($\mathbf{u}$, $\mathbf{v}$, $\mathbf{w}$ of length 1);
(f) $\mathbf{ii} = -\mathbf{1}$.

The set of vectors of length 1 with this product is the **circle group**.

24. For any vectors $\mathbf{v} = \begin{bmatrix} a \\ b \end{bmatrix}$ and $\mathbf{w} = \begin{bmatrix} c \\ d \end{bmatrix}$, define $\mathbf{vw} = \begin{bmatrix} \mathbf{v}^* \cdot \mathbf{w} \\ |\mathbf{v}^*, \mathbf{w}| \end{bmatrix}$, where $\mathbf{v}^* = \begin{bmatrix} a \\ -b \end{bmatrix}$. Using the results of Problem 23, show for all vectors $\mathbf{u}$, $\mathbf{v}$, $\mathbf{w}$ that

(a) $(s\mathbf{v})\mathbf{w} = \mathbf{v}(s\mathbf{w}) = s(\mathbf{vw})$ for any real number s;
(b) $\mathbf{1v} = \mathbf{v}$;
(c) $\mathbf{vw} = \mathbf{wv}$;
(d) $\mathbf{vv}^* = (a^2 + b^2)\mathbf{1}$;
(e) $(\mathbf{uv})\mathbf{w} = \mathbf{u}(\mathbf{vw})$;
(f) $\mathbf{ii} = -\mathbf{1}$.

The product $\mathbf{uv}$ is called **formal complex multiplication.**

25. Complete the geometric proofs of the Pythagorean theorem represented in Figure 1.31.

26. Verify the statements depicted in Figure 1.40.

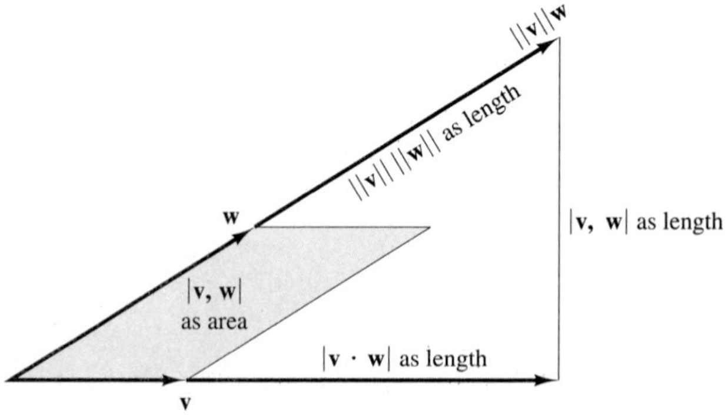

Figure 1.40 Areas and lengths associated with vectors **v** and **w**.

1.7 RIGID MOTIONS IN THE PLANE

Definition of rigid motion

A **rigid motion** of $\mathbb{R}^2$ is a mapping f from $\mathbb{R}^2$ to itself which *preserves distance*; that is,

$$d(f(\mathbf{x}), f(\mathbf{x}')) = d(\mathbf{x}, \mathbf{x}') \text{ for all } \mathbf{x}, \mathbf{x}' \in \mathbb{R}^2.$$

This section is devoted to describing rigid motions in terms of the translations, rotations, and reflections we've been experimenting with.

Orthogonal linear transformations and orthogonal matrices

Let's begin with a few simple observations:

1. If f is a rigid motion, then $g(\mathbf{x}) = f(\mathbf{x}) - f(\mathbf{0})$ is a rigid motion such that $g(\mathbf{0}) = \mathbf{0}$. (See Theorem 1.19.)
2. Any rigid motion f such that $f(\mathbf{0}) = \mathbf{0}$ also preserves length, since $\|f(\mathbf{x}')\| = \|f(\mathbf{x}') - f(\mathbf{0})\| = \|\mathbf{x}' - \mathbf{0}\| = \|\mathbf{x}'\|$ for all $\mathbf{x}' \in \mathbb{R}^2$.
3. Let $f(\mathbf{x})$ be a rigid motion mapping $\mathbf{0}$ to $\mathbf{0}$, and suppose that $\mathbf{v} \cdot \mathbf{w} = 0$. Then $\mathbf{0}$, $\mathbf{v}$, $\mathbf{w}$ are the vertices of a right triangle, and we have $\|\mathbf{v}\|^2 + \|\mathbf{w}\|^2 = \|\mathbf{w} - \mathbf{v}\|^2$ (Pythagorean theorem). Since f preserves length and distance, it follows that $\|f(\mathbf{v})\|^2 + \|f(\mathbf{w})\|^2 = \|f(\mathbf{w}) - f(\mathbf{v})\|^2$. Expanding the latter equation in terms of dot products, we get $f(\mathbf{v}) \cdot f(\mathbf{w}) = 0$. (Explain!) So, $\mathbf{0}$, $f(\mathbf{v})$, and $f(\mathbf{w})$ are the vertices of a right triangle (Figure 1.41(a)). This verifies that f preserves right angles. In particular, f maps the vectors $\begin{bmatrix} 1 \\ 0 \end{bmatrix}$ and $\begin{bmatrix} 0 \\ 1 \end{bmatrix}$ to perpendicular vectors $\begin{bmatrix} a \\ c \end{bmatrix}$ and $\begin{bmatrix} b \\ d \end{bmatrix}$ of length 1.

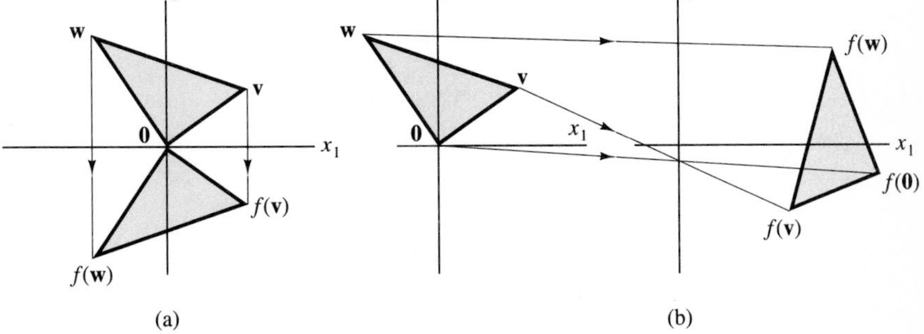

Figure 1.41 If $f(\mathbf{x})$ is a rigid motion, then f maps vertices of a right triangle to vertices of a right triangle. (a) $f(\mathbf{0}) = \mathbf{0}$; (b) $f(\mathbf{0}) \neq \mathbf{0}$.

4. If $f(\mathbf{x})$ is a linear transformation of $\mathbb{R}^2$ that preserves length, then f is a rigid motion, since $\|f(\mathbf{x}') - f(\mathbf{x})\| = \|f(\mathbf{x}' - \mathbf{x})\| = \|\mathbf{x}' - \mathbf{x}\|$ for all $\mathbf{x}$, $\mathbf{x}' \in \mathbb{R}^2$. Such linear transformations are called *orthogonal.*

Definition. *Orthogonal Linear Transformations.*
A linear transformation $f(\mathbf{x})$ of $\mathbb{R}^2$ which preserves length is called an **orthogonal linear transformation.**

Such linear transformations deserve this name, as we show in (5) and (6).

5. If $f(\mathbf{x})$ is an orthogonal linear transformation, then it is a rigid motion mapping $\mathbf{0}$ to $\mathbf{0}$, by (4). So, by (3), f maps the vectors $\begin{bmatrix} 1 \\ 0 \end{bmatrix}$ and $\begin{bmatrix} 0 \\ 1 \end{bmatrix}$ to perpendicular vectors $\begin{bmatrix} a \\ c \end{bmatrix}$ and $\begin{bmatrix} b \\ d \end{bmatrix}$ of length 1. Then $f(\mathbf{x}) = \begin{bmatrix} a & b \\ c & d \end{bmatrix}\mathbf{x}$.

6. Conversely, if the columns of $A = \begin{bmatrix} a & b \\ c & d \end{bmatrix}$ are perpendicular of length 1, then $f(\mathbf{x}) = A\mathbf{x}$ is an orthogonal linear transformation since it preserves squared length:

$$f\left(\begin{bmatrix} x_1 \\ x_2 \end{bmatrix}\right) \cdot f\left(\begin{bmatrix} x_1 \\ x_2 \end{bmatrix}\right) = \left(\begin{bmatrix} a & b \\ c & d \end{bmatrix}\begin{bmatrix} x_1 \\ x_2 \end{bmatrix}\right) \cdot \left(\begin{bmatrix} a & b \\ c & d \end{bmatrix}\begin{bmatrix} x_1 \\ x_2 \end{bmatrix}\right)$$

$$= \begin{bmatrix} x_1 \\ x_2 \end{bmatrix}^T \begin{bmatrix} a & b \\ c & d \end{bmatrix}^T \begin{bmatrix} a & b \\ c & d \end{bmatrix}\begin{bmatrix} x_1 \\ x_2 \end{bmatrix}$$

$$= \begin{bmatrix} x_1 \\ x_2 \end{bmatrix}^T \begin{bmatrix} 1 & 0 \\ 0 & 1 \end{bmatrix}\begin{bmatrix} x_1 \\ x_2 \end{bmatrix} = \begin{bmatrix} x_1 \\ x_2 \end{bmatrix} \cdot \begin{bmatrix} x_1 \\ x_2 \end{bmatrix}$$

It is now clear that $f(\mathbf{x}) = A\mathbf{x}$ is an orthogonal linear transformation if and only if the columns of A are perpendicular and of length 1. We now define *orthogonal matrices* accordingly.

Definition. *Orthogonal Matrix.*
The matrix $\begin{bmatrix} a & b \\ c & d \end{bmatrix}$ is an **orthogonal matrix** if its columns are perpendicular and of length 1.

We thus have the following criteria.

Theorem 1.28. *Criteria for Orthogonal Matrices and Linear Transformations.*
Let $A = \begin{bmatrix} a & b \\ c & d \end{bmatrix}$.

1. The linear transformation $f(\mathbf{x}) = A\mathbf{x}$ is orthogonal if and only if the matrix A is orthogonal.
2. A is orthogonal if and only if $A^TA = I$ if and only if $AA^T = I$.
3. If A is orthogonal, then A is invertible with inverse A^T.

Proof. We've already proved (1). For (2) and (3), note that A is orthogonal if and only if $A^TA = I$. From this, it follows that $AA^T = I$, and conversely. (Explain!) So, A is orthogonal if and only if A is invertible with inverse A^T. ■

Given these criteria, it is easy to construct orthogonal matrices and their inverses.

EXAMPLE

To construct all orthogonal matrices whose first columns are parallel to $\begin{bmatrix} 3 \\ 4 \end{bmatrix}$, observe that the second column must be a multiple of $\begin{bmatrix} -4 \\ 3 \end{bmatrix}$. To make the column lengths 1, divide each column by its length 5, getting $\frac{1}{5}\begin{bmatrix} 3 & -4 \\ 4 & 3 \end{bmatrix}$, $\frac{1}{5}\begin{bmatrix} 3 & 4 \\ 4 & -3 \end{bmatrix}$, $\frac{1}{5}\begin{bmatrix} -3 & -4 \\ -4 & 3 \end{bmatrix}$, and $\frac{1}{5}\begin{bmatrix} -3 & 4 \\ -4 & -3 \end{bmatrix}$. Their inverses are just their transposes.

Orthogonal transformations preserve length and dot products and map $\begin{bmatrix} 1 \\ 0 \end{bmatrix}, \begin{bmatrix} 0 \\ 1 \end{bmatrix}$ to perpendicular vectors, so it is not surprising that they also preserve angles.

Theorem 1.29. *Preservation of Dot Products and Angles by Orthogonal Transformations.*

Let $\begin{bmatrix} a & b \\ c & d \end{bmatrix}$ be an orthogonal matrix, let $\mathbf{v}$, $\mathbf{w}$ be two vectors, and let $\mathbf{v}' = \begin{bmatrix} a & b \\ c & d \end{bmatrix}\mathbf{v}$, $\mathbf{w}' = \begin{bmatrix} a & b \\ c & d \end{bmatrix}\mathbf{w}$. Then $\mathbf{v} \cdot \mathbf{w} = \mathbf{v}' \cdot \mathbf{w}'$, and the angle between $\mathbf{v}$ and $\mathbf{w}$ equals the angle between $\mathbf{v}'$ and $\mathbf{w}'$.

Proof. $\mathbf{v}' \cdot \mathbf{w}' = \mathbf{v} \cdot \mathbf{w}$ by (3), so $\cos \alpha' = \dfrac{\mathbf{v}' \cdot \mathbf{w}'}{\|\mathbf{v}'\|\|\mathbf{w}'\|} = \dfrac{\mathbf{v} \cdot \mathbf{w}}{\|\mathbf{v}\|\|\mathbf{w}\|} = \cos \alpha.$ ■

Rigid motions are translates of orthogonal transformations

We need a *distance criteria* for when a point $\mathbf{w}$ is on the segment $\{\mathbf{u} + t(\mathbf{v} - \mathbf{u}) \mid 0 \le t \le 1\}$ joining $\mathbf{u}$ and $\mathbf{v}$ (Figure 1.42).

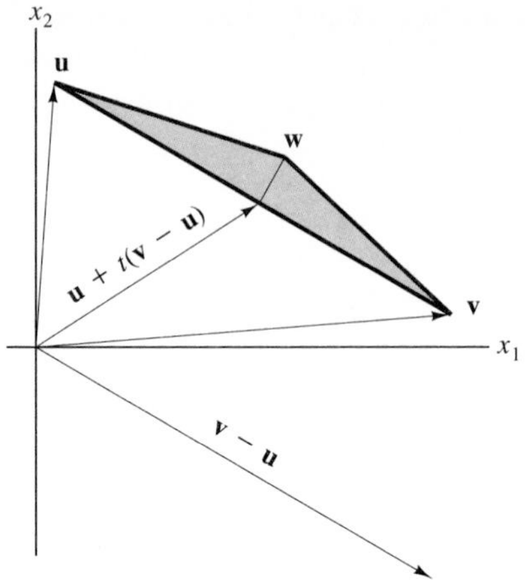

Figure 1.42 The conditions $d(\mathbf{u}, \mathbf{w}) + d(\mathbf{w}, \mathbf{v}) = d(\mathbf{u}, \mathbf{v})$ and $\mathbf{w} = \mathbf{u} + t(\mathbf{v} - \mathbf{u})$, $0 \le t \le 1$. The vector $\mathbf{w}$ is on the line segment joining $\mathbf{u}$, $\mathbf{v}$ when the triangle collapses.

Theorem 1.30. *Distance Criteria for Points on a Segment.*
Let $\mathbf{u}$, $\mathbf{v}$, and $\mathbf{w}$ be vectors in the plane such that $d(\mathbf{u}, \mathbf{w}) + d(\mathbf{w}, \mathbf{v}) = d(\mathbf{u}, \mathbf{v})$. Then $\mathbf{w} = \mathbf{u} + t(\mathbf{v} - \mathbf{u})$ for some $0 \le t \le 1$.

Proof. This follows from Theorem 1.25. The details are left as an exercise for the reader. ■

Corollary. Let g be a rigid motion of V which fixes $\mathbf{0}$ and the points $\mathbf{u}$ and $\mathbf{v}$. Then

1. g fixes all points on the segment $\{\mathbf{u} + t(\mathbf{v} - \mathbf{u}) \mid 0 \le t \le 1\}$ joining $\mathbf{u}$ and $\mathbf{v}$;
2. g fixes all multiples of $\mathbf{u}$ and $\mathbf{v}$.

Proof. We first prove (1). Let $\mathbf{w} = \mathbf{u} + t(\mathbf{v} - \mathbf{u})$ for some $0 \le t \le 1$, and let $\mathbf{w}' = g(\mathbf{w})$. Then $d(\mathbf{u}, \mathbf{w}) + d(\mathbf{w}, \mathbf{v}) = d(\mathbf{u}, \mathbf{v})$ and $d(\mathbf{u}, \mathbf{w}') + d(\mathbf{w}', \mathbf{v}) = d(\mathbf{u}, \mathbf{v})$. (Explain!) It follows that $\mathbf{w}' = \mathbf{u} + t'(\mathbf{v} - \mathbf{u})$ for some $0 \le t' \le 1$, by the preceding theorem, and $t = t'$ since $d(\mathbf{u}, \mathbf{w}) = d(\mathbf{u}, \mathbf{w}')$. (Explain!) But then $\mathbf{w} = \mathbf{w}' = g(\mathbf{w})$.

For (2), we show that $g(t\mathbf{v}) = t\mathbf{v}$ for all t. If t is negative, then we have $\|\mathbf{v} - t\mathbf{v}\| = \|\mathbf{v}\| + \|t\mathbf{v}\|$. Since g preserves length and distance and fixes $\mathbf{v}$, it follows that $\|\mathbf{v} - g(t\mathbf{v})\| = \|\mathbf{v}\| + \|g(t\mathbf{v})\|$. By Theorem 1.25, this implies that $\mathbf{0}$, $\mathbf{v}$, and $g(t\mathbf{v})$ lie on the same line and $g(t\mathbf{v}) = s\mathbf{v}$ for some negative s. Since $g(t\mathbf{v})$ has the same length as $t\mathbf{v}$, $s = t$ and $g(t\mathbf{v}) = t\mathbf{v}$. In particular, $g(-\mathbf{v}) = -\mathbf{v}$. For t negative, it follows that $g(t(-\mathbf{v})) = t(-\mathbf{v})$. But then

$g(r\mathbf{v}) = r\mathbf{v}$ for the positive number $r = -t$. Similarly, $g(t\mathbf{u}) = t\mathbf{u}$ and $g(r\mathbf{u}) = r\mathbf{u}$ for t negative and r positive. ■

We now find that any rigid motion $f(\mathbf{x})$ is an orthogonal linear transformation followed by translation by $f(\mathbf{0})$ (Figure 1.43).

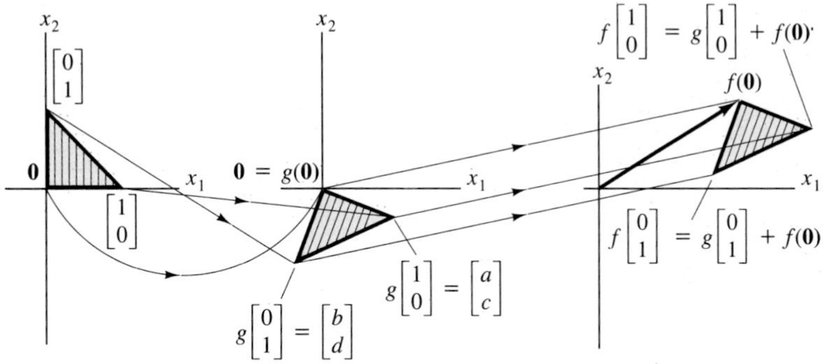

Figure 1.43 The rigid motion $f(\mathbf{x}) = g(\mathbf{x}) + f(\mathbf{0})$.

Theorem 1.31. *Criteria for a Rigid Motion.*
Any rigid motion f of the Cartesian plane is $f(\mathbf{x}) = g(\mathbf{x}) + f(\mathbf{0})$ for some orthogonal linear transformation $g(\mathbf{x})$. Conversely, $f(\mathbf{x}) = g(\mathbf{x}) + \mathbf{v}$ is a rigid motion for any orthogonal linear transformation $g(\mathbf{x})$ and vector $\mathbf{v}$.

Proof. We've proved one direction. For the other, suppose that $f(\mathbf{x})$ is a rigid motion and let $g(\mathbf{x}) = f(\mathbf{x}) - f(\mathbf{0})$. It then suffices to show that $g(\mathbf{x})$ is an orthogonal linear transformation. By (4), g maps $\begin{bmatrix}1\\0\end{bmatrix}, \begin{bmatrix}0\\1\end{bmatrix}$ to perpendicular vectors $\begin{bmatrix}a\\c\end{bmatrix}, \begin{bmatrix}b\\d\end{bmatrix}$ of length 1. The linear transformation $h(\mathbf{x}) = \begin{bmatrix}a & c\\b & d\end{bmatrix}\mathbf{x}$ is then orthogonal. The composite hg is a rigid motion mapping $\mathbf{0}$ to $\mathbf{0}$, $\begin{bmatrix}1\\0\end{bmatrix}$ to $hg\begin{bmatrix}1\\0\end{bmatrix} = h\begin{bmatrix}a\\c\end{bmatrix} = \begin{bmatrix}1\\0\end{bmatrix}$, and $\begin{bmatrix}0\\1\end{bmatrix}$ to $hg\begin{bmatrix}0\\1\end{bmatrix} = h\begin{bmatrix}b\\d\end{bmatrix} = \begin{bmatrix}0\\1\end{bmatrix}$. By the preceding corollary, hg fixes the vectors $\begin{bmatrix}r\\0\end{bmatrix}, \begin{bmatrix}0\\s\end{bmatrix}$ and, therefore, all points on the segment $\left\{\begin{bmatrix}r\\0\end{bmatrix} + t\left(\begin{bmatrix}r\\0\end{bmatrix} - \begin{bmatrix}0\\s\end{bmatrix}\right) \middle| 0 \le t \le 1\right\}$ joining $\mathbf{u}$ and $\mathbf{v}$. Since r and s are arbitrary, hg fixes every vector in the plane. It follows that $g = h^{-1}$ and, since h is orthogonal, so is g. ■

To find a function $f(\mathbf{x}) = \begin{bmatrix} a & b \\ c & d \end{bmatrix}\mathbf{x} + \mathbf{t}$ mapping points $\mathbf{u}$, $\mathbf{v}$, and $\mathbf{w}$ to $\mathbf{u}'$, $\mathbf{v}'$, and $\mathbf{w}'$ amounts to solving the matrix equation

$$\begin{bmatrix} a & b \\ c & d \end{bmatrix}(\mathbf{v} - \mathbf{u}, \mathbf{w} - \mathbf{u}) = (\mathbf{v}' - \mathbf{u}', \mathbf{w}' - \mathbf{u}')$$

for a, b, c, d and then letting $\mathbf{t} = \mathbf{u}' - \begin{bmatrix} a & b \\ c & d \end{bmatrix}\mathbf{u}$. Then $f(\mathbf{x})$ maps $\mathbf{u}, \mathbf{v}, \mathbf{w}$ to $\mathbf{u}', \mathbf{v}', \mathbf{w}'$:

$$f(\mathbf{u}) = \begin{bmatrix} a & b \\ c & d \end{bmatrix}\mathbf{u} + \mathbf{u}' - \begin{bmatrix} a & b \\ c & d \end{bmatrix}\mathbf{u} = \mathbf{u}',$$

$$f(\mathbf{v}) = \begin{bmatrix} a & b \\ c & d \end{bmatrix}\mathbf{v} + \mathbf{u}' - \begin{bmatrix} a & b \\ c & d \end{bmatrix}\mathbf{u} = \begin{bmatrix} a & b \\ c & d \end{bmatrix}(\mathbf{v} - \mathbf{u}) + \mathbf{u}' = \mathbf{v}' - \mathbf{u}' + \mathbf{u}' = \mathbf{v}';$$

$$f(\mathbf{w}) = \begin{bmatrix} a & b \\ c & d \end{bmatrix}\mathbf{w} + \mathbf{u}' - \begin{bmatrix} a & b \\ c & d \end{bmatrix}\mathbf{u} = \begin{bmatrix} a & b \\ c & d \end{bmatrix}(\mathbf{w} - \mathbf{u}) + \mathbf{u}' = \mathbf{w}' - \mathbf{u}' + \mathbf{u}' = \mathbf{w}'.$$

If these represent corresponding points of two congruent triangles, $g(\mathbf{x})$ will be orthogonal and $f(\mathbf{x})$ will be a rigid motion.

EXAMPLE

To find a function $f(\mathbf{x}) = \begin{bmatrix} a & b \\ c & d \end{bmatrix}\mathbf{x} + \mathbf{t}$ mapping points $\begin{bmatrix} 0 \\ 0 \end{bmatrix}, \begin{bmatrix} 3 \\ 0 \end{bmatrix}, \begin{bmatrix} 3 \\ 4 \end{bmatrix}$ to $\begin{bmatrix} 5 \\ 7 \end{bmatrix}, \begin{bmatrix} 2 \\ 7 \end{bmatrix}, \begin{bmatrix} 2 \\ 3 \end{bmatrix}$, solve the matrix equation

$$\begin{bmatrix} a & b \\ c & d \end{bmatrix}\begin{bmatrix} 3 & 3 \\ 0 & 4 \end{bmatrix} = \begin{bmatrix} -3 & -3 \\ 0 & -4 \end{bmatrix},$$

getting $\begin{bmatrix} a & b \\ c & d \end{bmatrix} = \begin{bmatrix} -1 & 0 \\ 0 & -1 \end{bmatrix}$, which is orthogonal. Then $\mathbf{t} = \begin{bmatrix} 5 \\ 7 \end{bmatrix}$ and $f(\mathbf{x}) = -\mathbf{x} + \begin{bmatrix} 5 \\ 7 \end{bmatrix}$, a rigid motion.

Rotations and reflections

By Theorem 1.31, any rigid motion is a translation followed by an orthogonal linear transformation. We now complete the study of rigid motions by studying orthogonal linear transformations, which turn out to be rotations or reflections. (See Figures 1.44(a) and (b), p. 74.)

The rotation matrix $R_\alpha = \begin{bmatrix} \cos\alpha & -\sin\alpha \\ \sin\alpha & \cos\alpha \end{bmatrix}$ and corresponding rotation transformation $R_\alpha\mathbf{x}$ played the leading role in the discussion of angle. Now, it is the vehicle for introducing reflection matrices. Since $R_\alpha \begin{bmatrix} -1 & 0 \\ 0 & 1 \end{bmatrix}$ is the matrix $S_\alpha = \begin{bmatrix} -\cos\alpha & -\sin\alpha \\ -\sin\alpha & \cos\alpha \end{bmatrix}$, the composite of the rotation $R_\alpha \mathbf{x}$ and the reflection $\begin{bmatrix} -1 & 0 \\ 0 & 1 \end{bmatrix}\mathbf{x}$ about the x_2-axis is the linear transformation $S_\alpha \mathbf{x} = \begin{bmatrix} -\cos\alpha & -\sin\alpha \\ -\sin\alpha & \cos\alpha \end{bmatrix}\mathbf{x}$. This is the *reflection* across the line $x_1 \cos(\alpha/2) + x_2 \sin(\alpha/2) = 0$, illustrated in Figure 1.44(b). Both R_α and S_α are orthogonal matrices. Conversely, we have Theorem 1.32.

Theorem 1.32. *Orthogonal Matrices Are Rotations or Reflections.* An orthogonal matrix $\begin{bmatrix} a & b \\ c & d \end{bmatrix}$ is either a rotation $R_\alpha = \begin{bmatrix} \cos\alpha & -\sin\alpha \\ \sin\alpha & \cos\alpha \end{bmatrix}$ or a reflection $S_\alpha = \begin{bmatrix} -\cos\alpha & -\sin\alpha \\ -\sin\alpha & \cos\alpha \end{bmatrix}$.

Proof. The columns of $\begin{bmatrix} a & b \\ c & d \end{bmatrix}$ are perpendicular and of length 1, so $\begin{bmatrix} b \\ d \end{bmatrix} = \begin{bmatrix} -\sin\alpha \\ \cos\alpha \end{bmatrix}$ for some angle α. Since $\begin{bmatrix} a \\ c \end{bmatrix}$ is perpendicular to $\begin{bmatrix} -\sin\alpha \\ \cos\alpha \end{bmatrix}$ and of length 1, it is one of $\begin{bmatrix} \cos\alpha \\ \sin\alpha \end{bmatrix}$ and $\begin{bmatrix} -\cos\alpha \\ -\sin\alpha \end{bmatrix}$. (Prove!) ■

The reflection $S_\alpha \mathbf{x} = \begin{bmatrix} -\cos\alpha & -\sin\alpha \\ -\sin\alpha & \cos\alpha \end{bmatrix}\mathbf{x}$ across the line $x_1 \cos(\alpha/2) + x_2 \sin(\alpha/2) = 0$ is also denoted by $r_\mathbf{w}(\mathbf{x})$, where $\mathbf{w} = \begin{bmatrix} w_1 \\ w_2 \end{bmatrix} = \begin{bmatrix} \cos(\alpha/2) \\ \sin(\alpha/2) \end{bmatrix}$. So, for $\mathbf{w} = \begin{bmatrix} \cos\alpha \\ \sin\alpha \end{bmatrix}$, $r_\mathbf{w}(\mathbf{x})$ denotes the reflection

$$S_{2\alpha}\mathbf{x} = \begin{bmatrix} -\cos 2\alpha & -\sin 2\alpha \\ -\sin 2\alpha & \cos 2\alpha \end{bmatrix}\mathbf{x}$$

across the line $x_1 \cos\alpha + x_2 \sin\alpha = 0$ normal to $\mathbf{w}$.

Definition. *The Reflection $r_\mathbf{w}$ across the Line through* **0** *Normal* to **w**. $r_{\left[\begin{smallmatrix} \cos\alpha \\ \sin\alpha \end{smallmatrix}\right]}(\mathbf{x}) = \begin{bmatrix} -\cos 2\alpha & -\sin 2\alpha \\ -\sin 2\alpha & \cos 2\alpha \end{bmatrix}\mathbf{x}$ is called *the reflection across the line through* **0** *normal to* $\begin{bmatrix} \cos\alpha \\ \sin\alpha \end{bmatrix}$.

Fortunately, we can avoid using coordinates by using the following formula, which is used extensively in n-dimensional numerical linear algebra. (See Section 7.7.)

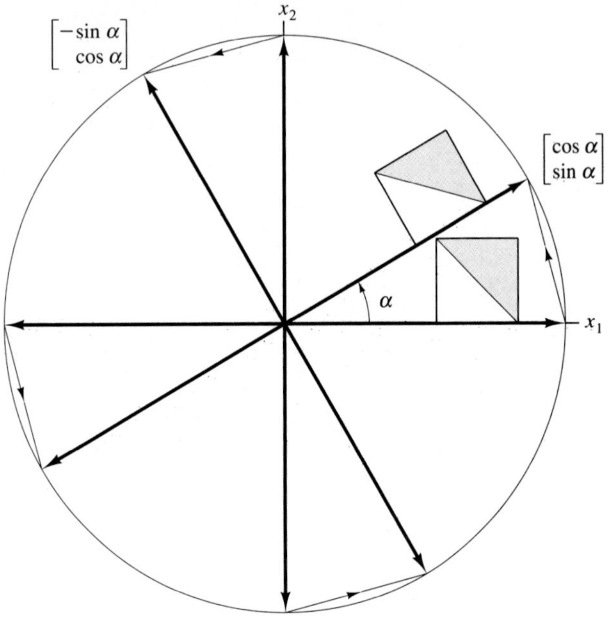

(a)

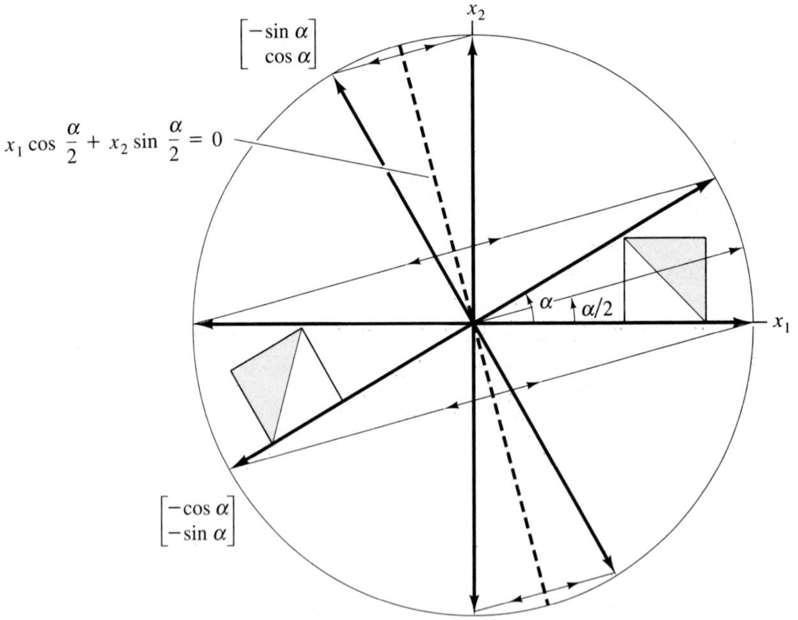

(b)

Figure 1.44 (a) Rotation R_α by α. (b) Reflection S_α across $x_1 \cos(\alpha/2) + x_2 \sin(\alpha/2) = 0$.

Theorem 1.33. *Householder Formula for the Reflection* $r_{\mathbf{w}}$.

$r_{\mathbf{w}}(\mathbf{v}) = \mathbf{v} - 2\dfrac{\mathbf{v}\cdot\mathbf{w}}{\mathbf{w}\cdot\mathbf{w}}\mathbf{w}$ of $\mathbb{R}^2$.

Proof. Letting $s_{\mathbf{w}}(\mathbf{v}) = \mathbf{v} - 2\dfrac{\mathbf{v}\cdot\mathbf{w}}{\mathbf{w}\cdot\mathbf{w}}\mathbf{w}$ of $\mathbb{R}^2$, simply verify the equality $r_{\mathbf{w}}(\mathbf{v}) = s_{\mathbf{w}}(\mathbf{v})$ for all possible $\mathbf{v}$.

1. $s_{\mathbf{w}}(a\mathbf{w}) = -a\mathbf{w}$, since $a\mathbf{w} - 2\dfrac{a\mathbf{w}\cdot a\mathbf{w}}{a\mathbf{w}\cdot a\mathbf{w}}a\mathbf{w} = -a\mathbf{w}$.
2. If $\mathbf{v}$ is perpendicular to $\mathbf{w}$, then $s_{\mathbf{w}}(\mathbf{v}) = \mathbf{v}$, since $\mathbf{v} - 2\dfrac{\mathbf{v}\cdot\mathbf{w}}{\mathbf{w}\cdot\mathbf{w}}\mathbf{w} = \mathbf{v} - \mathbf{0}$.
3. If $\mathbf{v} = \mathbf{v}_{\mathbf{w}} + \mathbf{v}_{\mathbf{w}}^{\perp}$, where $\mathbf{v}_{\mathbf{w}} = a\mathbf{w}$ and $\mathbf{v}_{\mathbf{w}}^{\perp}$ is perpendicular to $\mathbf{w}$, then $s_{\mathbf{w}}(\mathbf{v}_{\mathbf{w}} + \mathbf{v}_{\mathbf{w}}^{\perp}) = s_{\mathbf{w}}(\mathbf{v}_{\mathbf{w}}) + s_{\mathbf{w}}(\mathbf{v}_{\mathbf{w}}^{\perp}) = -\mathbf{v}_{\mathbf{w}} + \mathbf{v}_{\mathbf{w}}^{\perp}$.

But $r_{\mathbf{w}}(\mathbf{w}) = -\mathbf{w}$ and $r_{\mathbf{w}}(\mathbf{v}) = \mathbf{v}$ if $\mathbf{v}$ is perpendicular to $\mathbf{w}$, since

$$\begin{bmatrix} -\cos 2\alpha & -\sin 2\alpha \\ -\sin 2\alpha & \cos 2\alpha \end{bmatrix}\begin{bmatrix} \cos\alpha \\ \sin\alpha \end{bmatrix} = -\begin{bmatrix} \cos\alpha \\ \sin\alpha \end{bmatrix}$$

$$\begin{bmatrix} -\cos 2\alpha & -\sin 2\alpha \\ -\sin 2\alpha & \cos 2\alpha \end{bmatrix}\begin{bmatrix} -\sin\alpha \\ \cos\alpha \end{bmatrix} = \mathbf{0},$$

by the double-angle formulas. (Verify!) So,

$$r_{\mathbf{w}}(\mathbf{v}_{\mathbf{w}} + \mathbf{v}_{\mathbf{w}}^{\perp}) = r_{\mathbf{w}}(\mathbf{v}_{\mathbf{w}}) + r_{\mathbf{w}}(\mathbf{v}_{\mathbf{w}}^{\perp}) = -\mathbf{v}_{\mathbf{w}} + \mathbf{v}_{\mathbf{w}}^{\perp}$$

and $r_{\mathbf{w}}$ has the same image as does $s_{\mathbf{w}}$ for all vectors. ∎

The formula $r_{\mathbf{w}}(\mathbf{v}) = \mathbf{v} - 2\dfrac{\mathbf{v}\cdot\mathbf{w}}{\mathbf{w}\cdot\mathbf{w}}\mathbf{w}$ can be used even if $\mathbf{w}$ is not of length 1. If $\mathbf{w}$ is nonzero, then $r_{c\mathbf{w}}(\mathbf{v}) = \mathbf{v} - 2\dfrac{\mathbf{v}\cdot c\mathbf{w}}{c\mathbf{w}\cdot c\mathbf{w}}c\mathbf{w} = r_{\mathbf{w}}(\mathbf{v})$ for all nonzero c.

A variation of the Householder formula is $r_{\mathbf{w}}(\mathbf{v}) = \mathbf{v} - 2\dfrac{\mathbf{w}\mathbf{w}^T}{\mathbf{w}\cdot\mathbf{w}}\mathbf{v}$, that is, $r_{\mathbf{w}}(\mathbf{v}) = \left[I - 2\dfrac{\mathbf{w}\mathbf{w}^T}{\mathbf{w}\cdot\mathbf{w}}\right]\mathbf{v}$. (Verify!) So, we refer to the matrix $H_{\mathbf{w}} = I - 2\dfrac{\mathbf{w}\mathbf{w}^T}{\mathbf{w}\cdot\mathbf{w}}$ as the **Householder matrix** and to the linear transformation $r_{\mathbf{w}}(\mathbf{v}) = H_{\mathbf{w}}\mathbf{v} = \mathbf{v} - 2\dfrac{\mathbf{w}\mathbf{w}^T}{\mathbf{w}\cdot\mathbf{w}}\mathbf{v}$ as the **Householder reflection** corresponding to $\mathbf{w}$.

EXAMPLES

1. $r_{\left[\begin{smallmatrix}1\\3\end{smallmatrix}\right]}\begin{bmatrix}5\\4\end{bmatrix} = \begin{bmatrix}5\\4\end{bmatrix} - 2\dfrac{1\cdot 5 + 3\cdot 4}{1\cdot 1 + 3\cdot 3}\begin{bmatrix}1\\3\end{bmatrix} = \begin{bmatrix}5\\4\end{bmatrix} - 2\dfrac{17}{10}\begin{bmatrix}1\\3\end{bmatrix}$.

2. For $\mathbf{w} = \begin{bmatrix} a \\ b \end{bmatrix}$, $H_{\mathbf{w}} = I - \dfrac{2}{a^2 + b^2}\begin{bmatrix} a^2 & ab \\ ab & b^2 \end{bmatrix}$ and

$$r_{\mathbf{w}}(\mathbf{v}) = \left(I - \frac{2}{a^2 + b^2}\begin{bmatrix} a^2 & ab \\ ab & b^2 \end{bmatrix}\right)\mathbf{v}$$

since $\begin{bmatrix} a \\ b \end{bmatrix}\begin{bmatrix} a & b \end{bmatrix} = \begin{bmatrix} a^2 & ab \\ ab & b^2 \end{bmatrix}$.

3. The matrix of $r_{\left[\begin{smallmatrix} a \\ b \end{smallmatrix}\right]}$ is $H_{\left[\begin{smallmatrix} a \\ b \end{smallmatrix}\right]} = \dfrac{1}{a^2 + b^2}\begin{bmatrix} -a^2+b^2 & -2ab \\ -2ab & a^2-b^2 \end{bmatrix}$, by (2).

Theorem 1.34. *Properties of the Rotations $R_\alpha x$ and Reflections $r_{\mathbf{w}}(\mathbf{x})$.* The matrices $R_\alpha\mathbf{x}$ and $r_{\mathbf{w}}(\mathbf{x})$ satisfy the following.

1. $R_0\mathbf{x}$ is the identity mapping.
2. $R_\alpha R_\beta\mathbf{x} = R_{\alpha+\beta}\mathbf{x}$ for any angles α, β.
3. $R_\alpha\mathbf{x}$ is invertible and $R_\alpha^{-1}\mathbf{x} = R_{-\alpha}\mathbf{x}$ for any angle α.
4. $r_{\mathbf{w}}^2 = I$ (the identity mapping).

Proof. (2) follows from the double-angle formulas for sines and cosines (explain); and (1) and (3) follow from (2). We leave (4) to the reader. (See Figure 1.45.) ■

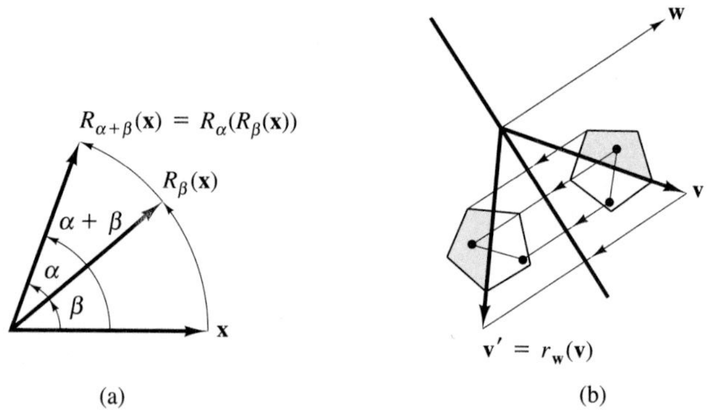

Figure 1.45 (a) The rotations R_α and the property $R_{\alpha+\beta} = R_\alpha R_\beta$. (b) The reflection $\mathbf{v}' = r_{\mathbf{w}}(\mathbf{v})$ across the line through $\mathbf{0}$ normal to $\mathbf{w}$.

PROBLEMS

NUMERICAL PROBLEMS

1. In each of the following cases, find a matrix A and vector $\begin{bmatrix} r \\ s \end{bmatrix}$ such that $f(\mathbf{x}) = A\mathbf{x} + \begin{bmatrix} r \\ s \end{bmatrix}$ is a linear transformation mapping the first geometric figure to the second, or show that no such A exists.

(a) Triangle **0**, $\begin{bmatrix}3\\0\end{bmatrix}, \begin{bmatrix}0\\4\end{bmatrix}$ to triangle $\begin{bmatrix}2\\1\end{bmatrix}, \begin{bmatrix}2\\4\end{bmatrix}, \begin{bmatrix}6\\1\end{bmatrix}$

(b) Triangle **0**, $\begin{bmatrix}1\\0\end{bmatrix}, \begin{bmatrix}1\\1\end{bmatrix}$ to triangle $\begin{bmatrix}6\\2\end{bmatrix}, \begin{bmatrix}7\\5\end{bmatrix}, \begin{bmatrix}9\\9\end{bmatrix}$

(c) Triangle **0**, $\begin{bmatrix}1\\2\end{bmatrix}, \begin{bmatrix}3\\4\end{bmatrix}$ to degenerate triangle $\begin{bmatrix}1\\2\end{bmatrix}, \begin{bmatrix}3\\4\end{bmatrix}, \begin{bmatrix}5\\6\end{bmatrix}$

(d) Degenerate triangle $\begin{bmatrix}1\\2\end{bmatrix}, \begin{bmatrix}3\\4\end{bmatrix}, \begin{bmatrix}5\\6\end{bmatrix}$ to degenerate triangle $\begin{bmatrix}-1\\-1\end{bmatrix}$, $\begin{bmatrix}3\\3\end{bmatrix}, \begin{bmatrix}7\\7\end{bmatrix}$

(e) Directed line segment $\overrightarrow{\mathbf{v}\,\mathbf{w}}$ to $\overrightarrow{\mathbf{v}'\,\mathbf{w}'}$, where $\mathbf{v} = \begin{bmatrix}5\\5\end{bmatrix}$, $\mathbf{w} = \begin{bmatrix}2\\9\end{bmatrix}$, $\mathbf{v}' = \begin{bmatrix}2\\1\end{bmatrix}$, and $\mathbf{w}' = \begin{bmatrix}6\\4\end{bmatrix}$

(f) Directed line segment $\overrightarrow{\mathbf{v}\,\mathbf{w}}$ to $\overrightarrow{\mathbf{v}'\,\mathbf{w}'}$, where $\mathbf{v} = \begin{bmatrix}5\\5\end{bmatrix}$, $\mathbf{w} = \begin{bmatrix}2\\9\end{bmatrix}$, $\mathbf{v}' = \begin{bmatrix}2\\1\end{bmatrix}$, and $\mathbf{w}' = \begin{bmatrix}4\\9\end{bmatrix}$

2. (a) In which of the preceding cases is there only one possible function f?
(b) In which cases are there infinitely many f?

3. In which of the cases in Problem 1 can f be a rigid motion?

4. In which cases of Problem 1 is it possible to take an A that is not orthogonal?

5. Find an orthogonal matrix A of determinant d whose first column is $\mathbf{v}$ in each of the following cases.

(a) $\mathbf{v} = \begin{bmatrix}1/2\\\sqrt{3/4}\end{bmatrix}$, $d = 1$ (b) $\mathbf{v} = \begin{bmatrix}-1/3\\\sqrt{8/9}\end{bmatrix}$, $d = 1$

(c) $\mathbf{v} = \begin{bmatrix}-\sin\alpha\\\cos\alpha\end{bmatrix}$, $d = -1$

6. Find a matrix A such that $f(\mathbf{x}) = A\mathbf{x}$ is reflection across
(a) the line $3x_1 + 2x_2 = 0$; (b) the line $-x_1 + 3x_2 = 0$.

Hard

7. Find a matrix A and vector $\mathbf{v}$ such that $f(\mathbf{x}) = A\mathbf{x} + \mathbf{v}$ is reflection across
(a) the line $3x_1 + 2x_2 = 5$; (b) the line $-x_1 + 3x_2 = 7$.

8. Find a matrix A and vector $\mathbf{v}$ such that $f(\mathbf{x}) = A\mathbf{x} + \mathbf{v}$ is rotation by α about the point $\mathbf{u}$ for

(a) $\mathbf{u} = \begin{bmatrix}1\\-2\end{bmatrix}$; (b) $\mathbf{u} = \begin{bmatrix}1\\3\end{bmatrix}$.

THEORETICAL PROBLEMS

9. If f is a rigid motion, show that $g(\mathbf{x}) = f(\mathbf{x}) - f(\mathbf{0})$ is a rigid motion such that $g(\mathbf{0}) = \mathbf{0}$.

10. Show that every orthogonal matrix is one of the following two for some α:

$$\begin{bmatrix} \cos\alpha & -\sin\alpha \\ \sin\alpha & \cos\alpha \end{bmatrix}, \quad \begin{bmatrix} -\cos\alpha & \sin\alpha \\ \sin\alpha & \cos\alpha \end{bmatrix}$$

11. Verify the following properties of translations $T_{\mathbf{u}}(\mathbf{v}) = \mathbf{u} + \mathbf{v}$.

(a) T_0 is the identity mapping.

(b) $T_{\mathbf{u}}T_{\mathbf{u}'} = T_{\mathbf{u}+\mathbf{u}'}$ for all $\mathbf{u}, \mathbf{u}'$.

(c) $T_{\mathbf{u}}$ is an invertible function from $\mathbb{R}^2$ to itself with inverse $T_{-\mathbf{u}}$.

12. Verify the following properties of rotations.

(a) R_0 is the identity.

(b) The composite $R_\alpha R_\beta$ of any two rotations R_α, R_β is $R_{\alpha+\beta}$.

(c) The inverse R_α^{-1} of any rotation R_α is $R_{-\alpha}$.

13. Verify the variation $r_{\mathbf{w}}(\mathbf{v}) = \mathbf{v} - 2\dfrac{\mathbf{w}\mathbf{w}^T}{\mathbf{w}\cdot\mathbf{w}}\mathbf{v}$ of the Householder formula.

14. When $\mathbf{w} = \begin{bmatrix} a \\ b \end{bmatrix}$ is nonzero, show:

(a) $r_{\mathbf{w}}$ maps $\begin{bmatrix} 1 \\ 0 \end{bmatrix}, \begin{bmatrix} 0 \\ 1 \end{bmatrix}$ to the vectors

$$\frac{1}{a^2+b^2}\begin{bmatrix} -a^2+b^2 \\ -2ab \end{bmatrix}, \frac{1}{a^2+b^2}\begin{bmatrix} -2ab \\ a^2-b^2 \end{bmatrix};$$

(b) The matrix of $r_{\left[\begin{smallmatrix} a \\ b \end{smallmatrix}\right]}$ is $\dfrac{1}{a^2+b^2}\begin{bmatrix} -a^2+b^2 & -2ab \\ -2ab & a^2-b^2 \end{bmatrix}$.

15. Verify the equality $(-a^2+b^2)^2 + (-2ab)^2 = (a^2+b^2)^2$ illustrated in Figure 1.46.

16. Defining the right triangle $(a_0, b_0, c_0) = (3, 4, 5)$ and the next right triangle $(a_{i+1}, b_{i+1}, c_{i+1}) = (-a_i^2 + b_i^2, 2a_ib_i, c_i^2)$ for all natural numbers i, describe (a_1, b_1, c_1) and (a_2, b_2, c_2). See Problem 15.

17. Express $H_{\left[\begin{smallmatrix} 0 \\ 1 \end{smallmatrix}\right]}\begin{bmatrix} -\sin\alpha & \cos\alpha \\ \cos\alpha & \sin\alpha \end{bmatrix}$ as a rotation R_β by finding β.

18. Show that any rigid motion f is either $T_{\mathbf{u}}R_\alpha$ or $T_{\mathbf{u}}r_{\left[\begin{smallmatrix} 1 \\ 0 \end{smallmatrix}\right]}R_\alpha$ for some α, $\mathbf{u}$.

19. Express $\begin{bmatrix} -\cos\alpha & \sin\alpha \\ \sin\alpha & \cos\alpha \end{bmatrix}\mathbf{v}$ as $r_{\mathbf{w}}(\mathbf{v})$ for some $\mathbf{w}$.

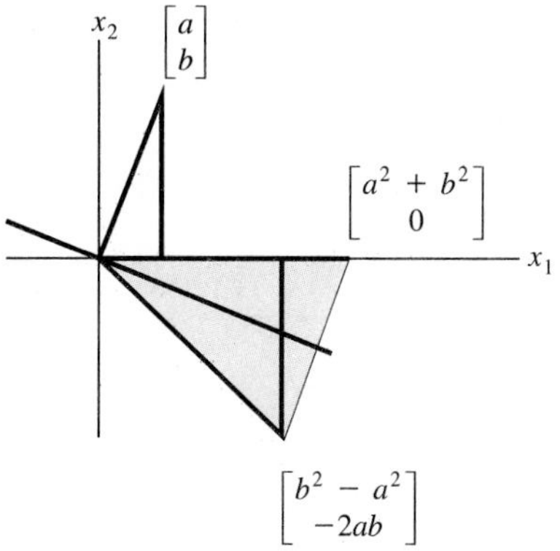

Figure 1.46 Generation of right triangle $b^2 - a^2$, $-2ab$, c^2 by right triangle a, b, c. Reflection of $\mathbf{v} = \begin{bmatrix} a^2+b^2 \\ 0 \end{bmatrix}$ to $\mathbf{u} = \begin{bmatrix} b^2-a^2 \\ -2ab \end{bmatrix}$ across the line $ax + by = 0$ normal to $\begin{bmatrix} a \\ b \end{bmatrix}$.

Hard

20. For nonnegative a and b, show that the point $\begin{bmatrix} a \\ b \end{bmatrix}$ is the only point in $\mathbb{R}^2$ whose distance from $\begin{bmatrix} a+b \\ 0 \end{bmatrix}$ is $\sqrt{2}b$ and whose distance from $\begin{bmatrix} 0 \\ a+b \end{bmatrix}$ is $\sqrt{2}a$.
$\left(\textbf{\textit{Hint:}}\text{ If } \sqrt{2}b = \left\| \begin{bmatrix} a+b \\ 0 \end{bmatrix} - \begin{bmatrix} a+s \\ b+t \end{bmatrix} \right\| \text{ and } \sqrt{2}a = \left\| \begin{bmatrix} 0 \\ a+b \end{bmatrix} - \begin{bmatrix} a+s \\ b+t \end{bmatrix} \right\|, \text{ then simplification leads to } s(a+b) = t(a+b) \text{ and } s^2 - 2bs + 2bt + t^2 = 0.\right)$

21. Show that a rigid motion f of the Cartesian plane fixing two different points fixes all points on the line containing them.

22. Show that a rigid motion f of the Cartesian plane fixing each of three noncollinear points fixes all points.

23. Express the composite fg of two rigid motions $f(\mathbf{x}) = A\mathbf{x} + \begin{bmatrix} r \\ s \end{bmatrix}$ and $g(\mathbf{x}) = B\mathbf{x} + \begin{bmatrix} t \\ u \end{bmatrix}$ in the form $(fg)(\mathbf{x}) = C\mathbf{x} + \begin{bmatrix} p \\ q \end{bmatrix}$.

24. Find all rigid motions preserving the corners of the square in Figure 1.47(a).

25. Find all rigid motions preserving the corners of the square in Figure 1.47(b).

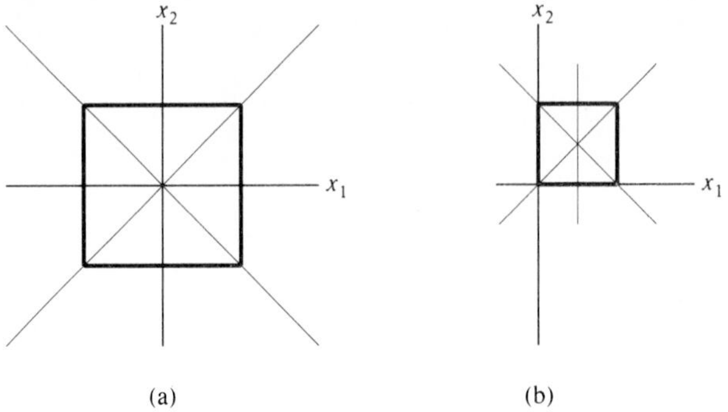

Figure 1.47 (a) The rigid motions of the unit square preserve a point. In case (b), they do also.

1.8 QUADRATIC FUNCTIONS

Conics

A **quadratic function** is a function of the form

$$f(x_1, x_2) = ax_1^2 + cx_1x_2 + dx_2^2 + rx_1 + sx_2 + t$$

(where $a, c, d, r, s, t \in \mathbb{R}$, a or c or $d \neq 0$). The set of solutions to the corresponding **quadratic equation** $ax_1^2 + cx_1x_2 + dx_2^2 + rx_1 + sx_2 + t = 0$ is called a **conic**. Conics were studied by Apollonius of Perga (around 200 B.C.) and, in the Cartesian plane, by Pierre de Fermat (1601–1665). They are so named since each can be represented as a *section* of a cone or degenerate cone (line, cylinder, plane) (Figure 1.48).

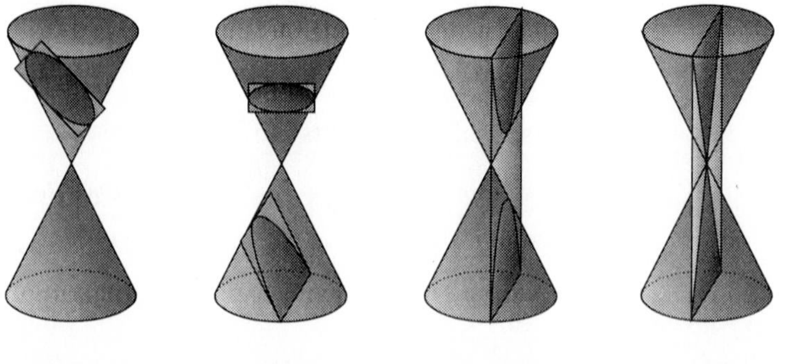

(a) Ellipse (b) Circle Parabola (c) Hyperbola (d) Intersecting lines

Figure 1.48 Some conic sections.

Change of axes

The **change of axes** (or *coordinates*) $\mathbf{x} = U\mathbf{x}'$ determined by an orthogonal matrix U corresponds to the rigid motion $\mathbf{x}' = U^T\mathbf{x}$. Here, U^T is the inverse of U, since U is orthogonal (Figure 1.49). Similarly, the change of axes $\mathbf{x}' = \mathbf{x}'' - \mathbf{u}$ corresponds to the rigid motion $\mathbf{x}'' = \mathbf{x}' + \mathbf{u}$ (Figure 1.50). These can be combined into Figure 1.51. So, the composite change of axes $\mathbf{x} = U(\mathbf{x}'' - \mathbf{u})$ corresponds to the rigid motion $\mathbf{x}'' = hg(\mathbf{x}) = U^T\mathbf{x} + \mathbf{u}$.

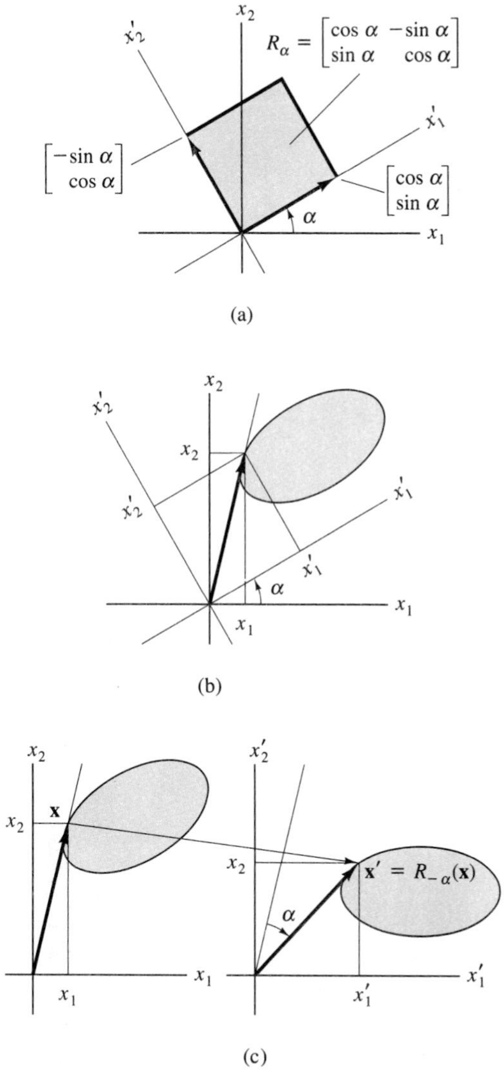

Figure 1.49 Consider $U = R_\alpha$. Then (a) and (b) $\mathbf{x} = U\mathbf{x}'$ is a change of axes; and (c) $\mathbf{x}' = U^T\mathbf{x}$ is a rigid motion.

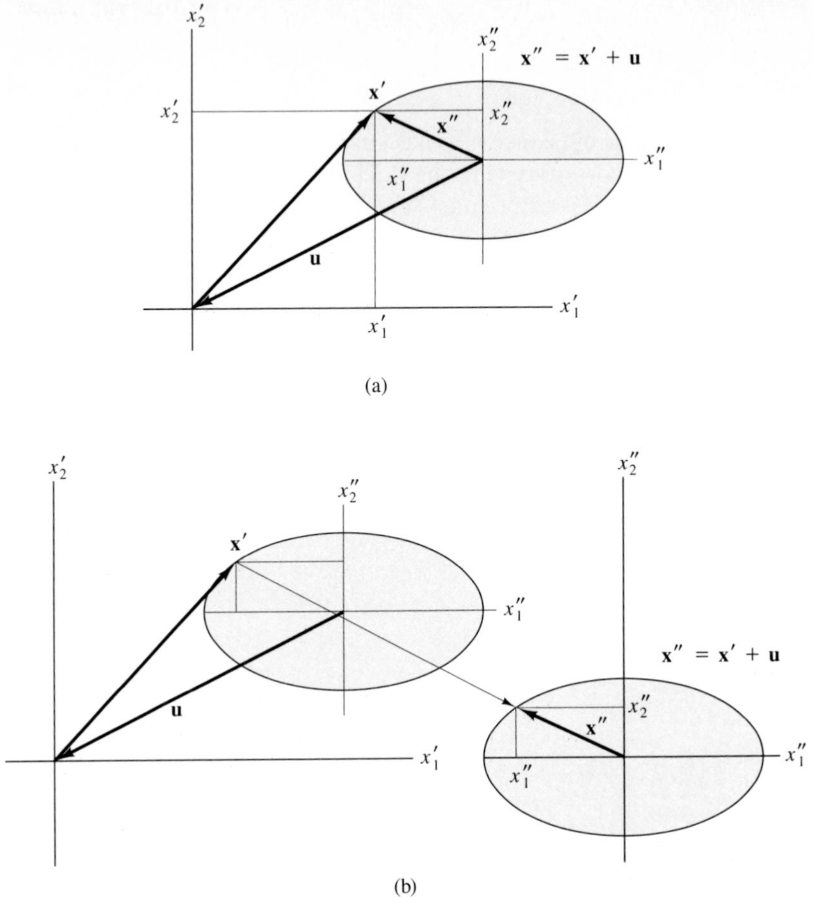

Figure 1.50 (a) $\mathbf{x}' = \mathbf{x}'' - \mathbf{u}$ as a change of axes and (b) $\mathbf{x}'' = \mathbf{x}' + \mathbf{u}$ as a rigid motion.

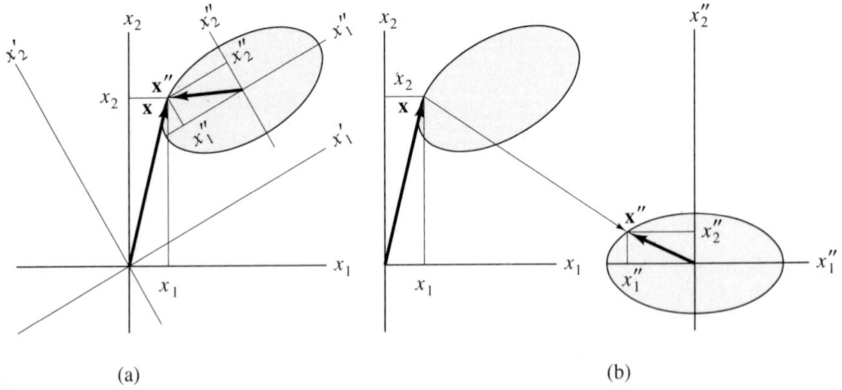

Figure 1.51 (a) $\mathbf{x} = U(\mathbf{x}'' - \mathbf{u})$ as a change of axes and (b) $\mathbf{x}'' = U^T\mathbf{x} + \mathbf{u}$ as a rigid motion.

EXAMPLES

1. Under the change of axes

$$\begin{bmatrix} x_1 \\ x_2 \end{bmatrix} = \begin{bmatrix} 0 & 1 \\ 1 & 0 \end{bmatrix} \left(\begin{bmatrix} x_1'' \\ x_2'' \end{bmatrix} - \begin{bmatrix} 1 \\ 1 \end{bmatrix} \right) = \begin{bmatrix} x_2'' - 1 \\ x_1'' - 1 \end{bmatrix},$$

the equation $2x_1 + 3x_2 - 5 = 0$ becomes $2(x_2'' + 1) + 3(x_1'' + 1) - 5 = 0$, or $2x_1'' + 3x_2'' = 0$. (Verify!)

2. The rigid motion $\begin{bmatrix} x_1'' \\ x_2'' \end{bmatrix} = \begin{bmatrix} 0 & 1 \\ 1 & 0 \end{bmatrix} \begin{bmatrix} x_1 \\ x_2 \end{bmatrix} + \begin{bmatrix} 1 \\ 1 \end{bmatrix}$ maps the points on the line $2x_1 + 3x_2 - 5 = 0$ to the points on the line $2x_2'' + 3x_1'' = 0$, since $x_1'' = x_2 + 1$ and $x_2'' = x_1 + 1$.

In terms of change of axes, the general conic can be described as the empty set, a point, a line, a pair of lines, a plane (see Problem 1) or one of the following (see Theorem 1.38).

Definition. *Ellipse, Hyperbola, or Parabola.*
An **ellipse, hyperbola**, or **parabola** is any conic which can be brought to one of the following by a change of axes $\mathbf{x} = U(\mathbf{x}'' - \mathbf{u})$, where U is an orthogonal matrix.

$$a(x_1'')^2 + d(x_2'')^2 = t \qquad (a, d, t > 0) \qquad \text{(ellipse)}$$

$$\pm a(x_1'')^2 \mp d(x_2'')^2 = t \qquad (a, d, t > 0) \qquad \text{(hyperbolas)}$$

$$a(x_1'')^2 + sx_2'' = t \qquad (a, d \text{ nonzero}) \qquad \text{(parabola)}$$

See Figure 1.52.

Quadratic functions are of great importance in the mathematical sciences. One reason for this is that *the sum of the constant first- and second-degree terms of the Taylor series of a function of x_1, x_2 with continuous third partial derivatives is a quadratic function closely approximating the function.* We will see quadratic functions in other contexts as well.

The quadratic function $f = ax_1^2 + cx_1x_2 + dx_2^2 + rx_1 + sx_2 + t$ can be written in vector form as $f = \mathbf{x}^T A\mathbf{x} + \mathbf{w}^T\mathbf{x} + t$, where $b = c/2$, $A = \begin{bmatrix} a & b \\ b & d \end{bmatrix}$, and $\mathbf{w} = \begin{bmatrix} r \\ s \end{bmatrix}$. (Verify!) We call $\mathbf{x}^T A\mathbf{x}$ the **quadratic form**, $\mathbf{w}^T\mathbf{x}$ the **linear form** (or *part*), and t the **constant term** of f. The matrix $A = \begin{bmatrix} a & b \\ b & d \end{bmatrix}$ is the **matrix of the quadratic function** f. It is symmetric in the following sense.

Definition. *Symmetric Matrices.*
A matrix A is **symmetric** if $A = A^T$.

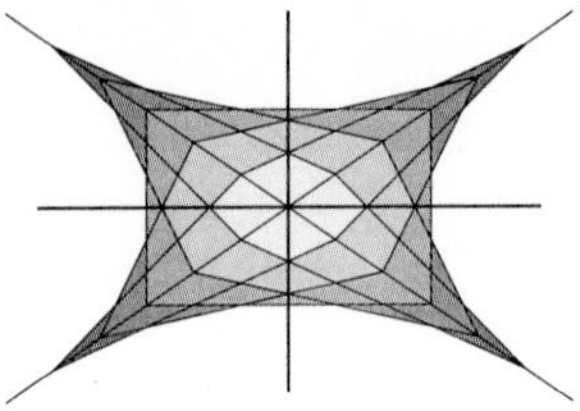

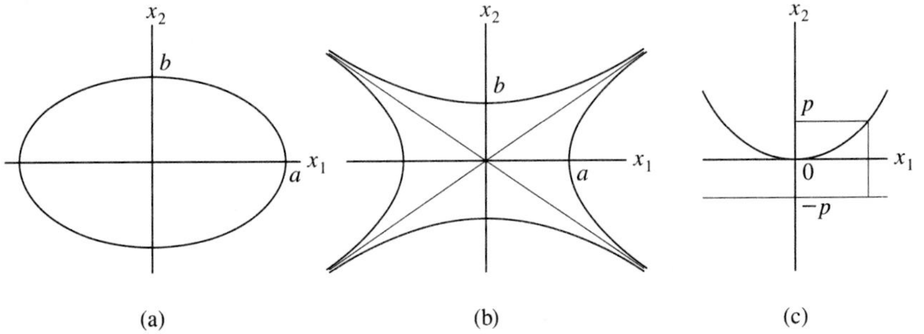

Figure 1.52 The (a) ellipse $\frac{x_1^2}{a^2} + \frac{x_2^2}{b^2} = 1$, (b) hyperbolas $\pm\frac{x_1^2}{a^2} \mp \frac{x_2^2}{b^2} = 1$, and (c) parabola $x_2 = 2ax_1^2$.

If the determinant of the matrix $\begin{bmatrix} a & b \\ b & d \end{bmatrix}$ of a quadratic function is nonzero, we say that f and the equation $f = 0$ is **nondegenerate**. Otherwise, we say that they are degenerate.

EXAMPLE

The ellipse $a(x_1'')^2 + d(x_2'')^2 = t$ $(a, d, t > 0)$ and the hyperbolas

$$\pm a(x_1'')^2 \mp d(x_2'')^2 = t \ (a, d, t > 0)$$

are nondegenerate (explain), whereas the parabola $a(x_1'')^2 + sx_2'' = t$ is degenerate, since its matrix is $\begin{bmatrix} a & 0 \\ 0 & 0 \end{bmatrix}$.

Quadratic functions without mixed terms

When A is a diagonal matrix $\begin{bmatrix} a & 0 \\ 0 & d \end{bmatrix}$, the quadratic form $\mathbf{x}^T A\mathbf{x}$ of $f = \mathbf{x}^T A\mathbf{x} + \mathbf{w}^T\mathbf{x} + t$ is $ax_1^2 + dx_2^2$, which has no mixed term x_1x_2, and $f = ax_1^2 + dx_2^2 + \mathbf{w}^T\mathbf{x} + t$. Case by case, the possibilities are then as follows.

1. If both a and d are zero, then $f = rx_1 + sx_2 + t$ is not a quadratic function.
2. If one of a or d is nonzero, say $a \neq 0$, we *complete the square*, letting $x_1 = x'_1 - \frac{r}{2a}$. This leads further to $f = a(x'_1)^2 + dx_2^2 + sx_2 + t'$ for some constant t'. (Prove!)
3. If d is zero, then the set of solutions of the corresponding quadratic equation $a(x'_1)^2 + sx_2 + t'$ is a parabola if s is nonzero and a vertical line or pair of vertical lines if s is zero. (Prove!)
4. If, on the other hand, d is also nonzero, letting $x_2 = x'_2 - \frac{s}{2d}$ then leads still further to $f = a(x'_1)^2 + d(x'_2)^2 + t''$ for some constant t''. The equation $f = 0$ is then $a(x'_1)^2 + d(x'_2)^2 + t'' = 0$ with a and d nonzero, which is an ellipse, hyperbola, point, two intersecting lines, or empty set. (Verify!)

EXAMPLE

The equation $2x_1^2 + 4x_1 + 3x_2^2 + 12x_2 + 10 = 0$ is brought to $2(x'_1)^2 + 3(x'_2)^2 - 4 = 0$ by the change of axes $\begin{bmatrix} x_1 \\ x_2 \end{bmatrix} = \begin{bmatrix} x'_1 \\ x'_2 \end{bmatrix} - \begin{bmatrix} 1 \\ 2 \end{bmatrix}$, since it can be written as $2(x_1 + 1)^2 + 3(x_2 + 1)^2 - 4 = 0$. (Verify!) So, it is the equation of an ellipse.

From this, we find in all cases that the solution set is an ellipse, hyperbola, parabola (degenerate hyperbola), point (degenerate ellipse), line or pair of lines (degenerate hyperbola), empty set, or the whole plane.

To treat quadratic functions with cross terms, we need the next powerful theorem.

Theorem 1.35. *Spectral Theorem for Symmetric Matrices.*
Let A be symmetric. Then there are real numbers a', d' and nonzero orthogonal vectors $\mathbf{v}$, $\mathbf{w}$ such that $A\mathbf{v} = a'\mathbf{v}$ and $A\mathbf{w} = d'\mathbf{w}$.

Proof. Let $A = \begin{bmatrix} a & b \\ b & d \end{bmatrix}$. If $b = 0$, we take $\mathbf{v} = \begin{bmatrix} 1 \\ 0 \end{bmatrix}$, $\mathbf{w} = \begin{bmatrix} 0 \\ 1 \end{bmatrix}$. So, we may suppose that b is nonzero. If $A\mathbf{v} = c\mathbf{v}$, where $\mathbf{v}$ is nonzero, then $\begin{bmatrix} a-c & b \\ b & d-c \end{bmatrix}\mathbf{v} = 0$. (Prove!) But then the determinant $\begin{vmatrix} a-c & b \\ b & d-c \end{vmatrix} = (a - c)(d - c) - b^2 = c^2 - (a + d)c + (ad - b^2)$ is 0. By the quadratic formula, the possibilities a', d' for c are

$$a' = \frac{a + d + \sqrt{(a + d)^2 - 4(ad - b^2)}}{2}, \qquad d' = \frac{a + d - \sqrt{(a + d)^2 - 4(ad - b^2)}}{2}.$$

These simplify to

$$a' = \frac{a + d + \sqrt{(a-d)^2 + 4b^2}}{2}, \qquad d' = \frac{a + d - \sqrt{(a-d)^2 + 4b^2}}{2},$$

which, fortunately, are real! Since $(a - c)(d - c) - b^2 = 0$ for $c = a'$ or d', we have $(a - a')(d - a') - b^2 = 0$, $(a - d')(d - d') - b^2 = 0$. So, we can find nonzero solutions $\mathbf{v}$ and $\mathbf{w}$ to $\begin{bmatrix} a-a' & b \\ b & d-a' \end{bmatrix}\mathbf{v} = \mathbf{0}$, $\begin{bmatrix} a-d' & b \\ b & d-d' \end{bmatrix}\mathbf{w} = \mathbf{0}$. In fact, we can use $\mathbf{v} = \begin{bmatrix} d-a' \\ -b \end{bmatrix}$, $\mathbf{w} = \begin{bmatrix} d-d' \\ -b \end{bmatrix}$, since $(a - a')(d - a') - b^2 = 0$ and $(a - d')(d - d') - b^2 = 0$. Note that $\mathbf{v}$ and $\mathbf{w}$ are nonzero since b is.

It only remains to verify that $\mathbf{v} \cdot \mathbf{w} = 0$:

$$\mathbf{v} \cdot \mathbf{w} = \begin{bmatrix} d-a' \\ -b \end{bmatrix} \cdot \begin{bmatrix} d-d' \\ -b \end{bmatrix} = (d - a')(d - d') + b^2$$

$$= \left(\frac{2d - a - d - \sqrt{(a-d)^2 + 4b^2}}{2}\right)\left(\frac{2d - a - d + \sqrt{(a-d)^2 + 4b^2}}{2}\right) + b^2$$

$$= \frac{(d-a) - (a-d)^2 - 4b^2}{4} + b^2 = -b^2 + b^2 = 0. \qquad \blacksquare$$

The numbers a' and d' play a very important role in the theory of matrices. They are the characteristic roots of A in the sense of the following.

Definition. *Characteristic Roots and Vectors.*
A **characteristic vector** for a matrix A or linear transformation $A\mathbf{x}$ is a nonzero vector $\mathbf{v}$ such that $A\mathbf{v} = c\mathbf{v}$ for some c. A **characteristic root** for A is any value c such that $A\mathbf{v} = c\mathbf{v}$ for some nonzero vector $\mathbf{v}$.

From the proof of the spectral theorem, we get the tool needed to find the characteristic roots of A.

Corollary. A symmetric matrix A has two real characteristic roots a' and d', which are the roots of the quadratic polynomial $|A - cI| = c^2 - (a + d)c + (ad - b^2)$ in the unknown c.

For this reason, the polynomial $|A - cI| = c^2 - (a + d)c + ad - b^2$ is called the **characteristic polynomial** of A. The set of roots of the characteristic polynomial of A is called the **spectrum** of A.

To use the spectral theorem to get a', d', $\mathbf{v}$, and $\mathbf{w}$ for a given symmetric matrix A, we follow the method given in its proof.

EXAMPLE

Let $A = \begin{bmatrix} 2 & 3 \\ 3 & 2 \end{bmatrix}$. Then $\begin{vmatrix} 2-c & 3 \\ 3 & 2-c \end{vmatrix} = (2-c)(2-c) - 3^2 = c^2 - 4c - 5$, whose roots are $a' = 5$, $d' = -1$. But then $\mathbf{v} = \begin{bmatrix} 2-5 \\ -3 \end{bmatrix} = -3\begin{bmatrix} 1 \\ 1 \end{bmatrix}$ and $\mathbf{w} = \begin{bmatrix} 2+1 \\ -3 \end{bmatrix} = -3\begin{bmatrix} -1 \\ 1 \end{bmatrix}$.

Replacing the perpendicular vectors $\mathbf{v}$ and $\mathbf{w}$ in the spectral theorem by nonzero scalar multiples of themselves does not disturb the equalities $A\mathbf{v} = a'\mathbf{v}$ and $A\mathbf{w} = d'\mathbf{w}$. (Verify!) So, we can take them to have length 1, in which case the matrix $B = [\mathbf{v} \quad \mathbf{w}]$ whose columns are $\mathbf{v}$ and $\mathbf{w}$ is an orthogonal matrix. Moreover, we have

$$AB = A[\mathbf{v} \quad \mathbf{w}] = [A\mathbf{v} \quad A\mathbf{w}] = [a'\mathbf{v} \quad d'\mathbf{w}] = [\mathbf{v} \quad \mathbf{w}]\begin{bmatrix} a' & 0 \\ 0 & d' \end{bmatrix} \text{ (Verify)},$$

so that $AB = B\begin{bmatrix} a' & 0 \\ 0 & d' \end{bmatrix}$. Since B is orthogonal, multiplying by $B^T = B^{-1}$ leads to $B^TAB = \begin{bmatrix} a' & 0 \\ 0 & d' \end{bmatrix}$, which proves the following variation of the spectral theorem.

Theorem 1.36. *Spectral Theorem Revisited.*
If A is a symmetric matrix, then there are real numbers a', d' and an orthogonal matrix B such that $B^TAB = \begin{bmatrix} a' & 0 \\ 0 & d' \end{bmatrix}$.

EXAMPLE

In the earlier example, where $A = \begin{bmatrix} 2 & 3 \\ 3 & 2 \end{bmatrix}$, we got $a' = 5$, $d' = -1$, $\mathbf{v} = \begin{bmatrix} 2-5 \\ -3 \end{bmatrix}$, and $\mathbf{w} = \begin{bmatrix} 2+1 \\ -3 \end{bmatrix}$. Multiplying each by a suitable scalar, we can take $\mathbf{v} = \frac{1}{\sqrt{2}}\begin{bmatrix} 1 \\ 1 \end{bmatrix}$ and $\mathbf{w} = \frac{1}{\sqrt{2}}\begin{bmatrix} -1 \\ 1 \end{bmatrix}$ instead. Letting $B = [\mathbf{v} \quad \mathbf{w}] = \frac{1}{\sqrt{2}}\begin{bmatrix} 1 & -1 \\ 1 & 1 \end{bmatrix}$, we have $B^TAB = \begin{bmatrix} 5 & 0 \\ 0 & -1 \end{bmatrix}$. If we want to check against the possibility of a computational error, it suffices to check whether $AB = B\begin{bmatrix} 5 & 0 \\ 0 & -1 \end{bmatrix}$, which is so:

$$\begin{bmatrix} 2 & 3 \\ 3 & 2 \end{bmatrix}\frac{1}{\sqrt{2}}\begin{bmatrix} 1 & -1 \\ 1 & 1 \end{bmatrix} = \frac{1}{\sqrt{2}}\begin{bmatrix} 1 & -1 \\ 1 & 1 \end{bmatrix}\begin{bmatrix} 5 & 0 \\ 0 & -1 \end{bmatrix}.$$

The general quadratic function

We've seen that the most general quadratic function can be written in the vector form $f(\mathbf{x}) = \mathbf{x}^T\begin{bmatrix} a & b \\ b & d \end{bmatrix}\mathbf{x} + \mathbf{w}^T\mathbf{x} + t$. Applying the spectral theorem to $\begin{bmatrix} a & b \\ b & d \end{bmatrix}$, we get real numbers a', d' and an orthogonal matrix B such that $B^TAB = \begin{bmatrix} a' & 0 \\ 0 & d' \end{bmatrix}$. The orthogonal transformation $\mathbf{x} = B\mathbf{x}'$ then leads to the equations

$$\mathbf{x}^T A\mathbf{x} = \mathbf{x}'^T B^T AB\mathbf{x}' = \mathbf{x}'^T\begin{bmatrix} a' & 0 \\ 0 & d' \end{bmatrix}\mathbf{x}' = a'(x_1')^2 + d'(x_2')^2$$

$$\mathbf{w}^T\mathbf{x} = \mathbf{w}^T B\mathbf{x}' = \mathbf{w}'^T\mathbf{x}'$$

for $\mathbf{w}' = B^T\mathbf{w}$. (Verify!) So, we have

$$\mathbf{x}^T A\mathbf{x} + \mathbf{w}^T\mathbf{x} + t = a'(x_1')^2 + d'(x_2')^2 + \mathbf{w}'^T\mathbf{x}' + t.$$

This gives us the

Theorem 1.37. *Normal Form of a Quadratic Function.*

Given a quadratic function $f(\mathbf{x}) = \mathbf{x}^T\begin{bmatrix} a & b \\ b & d \end{bmatrix}\mathbf{x} + \mathbf{w}^T\mathbf{x} + t$ of $\mathbf{x}$, there is an orthogonal linear transformation $\mathbf{x} = B\mathbf{x}'$ such that

$$f(\mathbf{x}) = \mathbf{x}'^T\begin{bmatrix} a' & 0 \\ 0 & d' \end{bmatrix}\mathbf{x}' + \mathbf{w}'^T\mathbf{x}' + t.$$

In our theorem, we call $\mathbf{x} = B\mathbf{x}'$ the **orthogonal linear transformation to the principal axes** of the quadratic form f. The *principal axes* themselves are just the columns $\mathbf{v} = B\begin{bmatrix} 1 \\ 0 \end{bmatrix}$ and $\mathbf{w} = B\begin{bmatrix} 0 \\ 1 \end{bmatrix}$ of B, which were found to solve $A\mathbf{v} = a'\mathbf{v}$ and $A\mathbf{w} = d'\mathbf{w}$.

Upon applying Theorem 1.37, we get $f = a'(x_1')^2 + d'(x_2')^2 + \mathbf{w}'^T\mathbf{x}' + t$. Now, f can be simplified further if either or both of a' and d' are nonzero. These simplifications come from a translation, so we have the following.

Corollary. Given a quadratic function $f = \mathbf{x}^T\begin{bmatrix} a & b \\ b & d \end{bmatrix}\mathbf{x} + \mathbf{w}^T\mathbf{x} + t$ of $\mathbf{x}$, there is a change of axes $\mathbf{x} = U(\mathbf{x}'' - \mathbf{u})$ which brings the equation $f = 0$ to one of the following normal forms:

$$\frac{(x_1'')^2}{(a')^2} + \frac{d'(x_2'')^2}{(b')^2} = t'' \qquad \text{(ellipse)}$$

$$\frac{(x_1'')^2}{(a')^2} - \frac{d'(x_2'')^2}{(b')^2} = t'' \qquad \text{(hyperbola)}$$

$$\frac{(x_1'')^2}{(a')^2} = 2px_1'' \qquad \text{(parabola)}$$

This corollary, in turn, gives us a classification of quadratic equations into different types.

Theorem 1.38. *Classification of Quadratic Equations.*
The set of solutions of a quadratic equation

$$f(x_1, x_2) = ax_1^2 + cx_1x_2 + dx_2^2 + rx_1 + sx_2 + t$$

is an ellipse, hyperbola, parabola, point, line or pair of lines, empty set.

This theorem leads to the following corollary. The proof is left as an exercise for the reader.

Corollary. If a quadratic function f is nondegenerate, then $f = 0$ is an ellipse (or point) or a hyperbola.

EXAMPLE

$f(x) = 2x_1x_2 + 3x_1 + 4$ is nondegenerate, so $f = 0$ is either an ellipse or a hyperbola. (Which of these types is it?)

PROBLEMS

NUMERICAL PROBLEMS

1. Find a quadratic equation with solution set S when
- **(a)** S is the empty set;
- **(b)** S is the set consisting of the point $\begin{bmatrix} 1 \\ 5 \end{bmatrix}$;
- **(c)** S is the union of two lines, $3x_1 + 4x_2 = 5$ and $5x_1 + 4x_2 = 3$;
- **(d)** S is the line $3x_1 + 4x_2 = 5$.

2. Express each of the following quadratic functions f in the vector form $f(x) = \mathbf{x}^T A \mathbf{x} + \mathbf{w}^T \mathbf{x} + t$, where A is a symmetric matrix.
- **(a)** $x_1^2 + 4x_1x_2 + x_2^2 + x_1 + x_2 + 1$
- **(b)** $2x_1^2 + 4x_1x_2 + 4x_2^2 + 5x_1 + 6x_2 + 7$
- **(c)** $2x_1x_2 + x_2^2 + x_1 + 4$
- **(d)** $2x_1x_2 + 3x_1 + 5$

3. For each of the following symmetric matrices A, find its spectrum and find two nonzero orthogonal characteristic vectors.

(a) $\begin{bmatrix} 2 & 0 \\ 0 & 5 \end{bmatrix}$ **(b)** $\begin{bmatrix} 0 & 4 \\ 4 & 0 \end{bmatrix}$ **(c)** $\begin{bmatrix} 5 & 1 \\ 1 & 5 \end{bmatrix}$

(d) $\begin{bmatrix} 1 & 1 \\ 1 & 1 \end{bmatrix}$ **(e)** $\begin{bmatrix} 14 & -2 \\ -2 & 11 \end{bmatrix}$

4. For each of the quadratic functions f in Problem 2, find the spectrum of A and describe the graph of $f = 0$.

Hard

5. For each of the matrices A in Problem 3, find an orthogonal matrix B such that $B^T AB$ is diagonal.

6. Use the orthogonal transformation to the principal axes to express the quadratic function $f(\mathbf{x}) = \mathbf{x}^T \begin{bmatrix} 14 & -2 \\ -2 & 11 \end{bmatrix} \mathbf{x}$ in normal form.

7. Describe the entries of the ninth power of the matrix $\begin{bmatrix} 14 & -2 \\ -2 & 11 \end{bmatrix}$.

THEORETICAL PROBLEMS

8. Show that the general equation of the circle is $ax_1^2 + ax_2^2 + rx_1 + sx_2 + t = 0$, where $a \neq 0$.

Hard

9. Prove the corollary to Theorem 1.38.

10. If a symmetric matrix A does not have two different characteristic roots, show that it is a *scalar matrix* $\begin{bmatrix} a & 0 \\ 0 & a \end{bmatrix}$ for some a.

11. Show that the sum of the diagonal elements of a symmetric matrix equals the sum of its two characteristic roots.

Very Hard

12. If a symmetric matrix A has two different characteristic roots, show that any matrix C such that $AC = CA$ is symmetric.

13. If two matrices A and B commute, that is, $AB = BA$, then either neither of them is symmetric, one of them is a scalar matrix, or both of them are symmetric.

SUGGESTED READING

Carl B. Boyer, *A History of Mathematics*, Princeton University Press, Princeton, N.J., 1985. [This excellent history of mathematics traces the development of mathematics from its primitive origins to the twentieth century. Mathematics is discussed within the appropriate historical contexts.]

I. N. Bronshtein and K. A. Semendyayev, *Handbook of Mathematics*, Van Nostrand Reinhold Co., New York, 1985. [A definitive, easy-to-read handbook. Mathematics is organized into interrelated disciplines and subdisciplines, making it easy to find material relating to a particular subject.]

Donald J. Lewis and Wilfred Kaplan, *Calculus and Linear Algebra*, Volumes 1 and 2, John Wiley, New York, 1970. [An excellent treatment of calculus and linear algebra. By integrating these two subjects into one, each gains insights into the other. Chapters 9–14 cover vector spaces, matrices, and determinants, linear Euclidean geometry, calculus of several variables, and ordinary differential equations.]

PART 2

VECTOR SPACES AND LINEAR TRANSFORMATIONS

CHAPTER

2

CARTESIAN n-SPACE

2.1 INTRODUCTION: SCALARS

Chapter 1 gives a preview, in the microcosm of the plane, of Cartesian n-space over the field $\mathbb{R}$ of real numbers for $n = 2$. This chapter introduces Cartesian n-space over the field F of real or complex numbers. Everything we do over F applies whether we take F to be the field $\mathbb{R}$ of real numbers or the field $\mathbb{C}$ of complex numbers.

We refer to F as the **field of scalars** and to its elements as **scalars**. So, if F is the field $\mathbb{R}$, then we say that the field of scalars is the field $\mathbb{R}$ of real numbers and that the scalars are real. The scalars are the "atomic building blocks" used throughout the book to construct polynomials and other functions, vectors, matrices, linear transformations, dot and inner products, quadratic functions, and the like.

2.2 CARTESIAN n-SPACE

Cartesian n-space F^n $(n \geq 1)$ is the set of *ordered n-tuples*

$$\mathbf{a} = \begin{bmatrix} a_1 \\ \vdots \\ a_n \end{bmatrix}$$

of scalars $a_1, \ldots, a_n \in F$, where

$$\begin{bmatrix} a_1 \\ \vdots \\ a_n \end{bmatrix} = \begin{bmatrix} b_1 \\ \vdots \\ b_n \end{bmatrix}$$

if and only if $a_r = b_r$ for $1 \leq r \leq n$. The element

$$\begin{bmatrix} 0 \\ \vdots \\ 0 \end{bmatrix}$$

is denoted simply by $\mathbf{0}$. For example, the 3-tuple

$$\mathbf{v} = \begin{bmatrix} 1 \\ 2 \\ -2 \end{bmatrix}$$

is an element of $\mathbb{R}^3$ and the ordered pair $\mathbf{w} = \begin{bmatrix} 1-4i \\ 2+i \end{bmatrix}$ is an element of $\mathbb{C}^2$.

As with Cartesian 2-space $\mathbb{R}^2$ in Chapter 1, the elements of F^n are referred to as *vectors* and as *points.*

Real Cartesian 3-space

Linear algebra is a many-faceted subject, since it can be introduced and expressed algebraically, interpreted geometrically, and applied numerically using high-speed computers. The subject thrives on its intrinsic geometric nature. Often, a two- or three-dimensional figure can point the way to solving a problem or applying a theorem. So, it is worthwhile to pause from time to time for geometric interpretation.

When $n = 3$, a point or vector

$$\mathbf{v} = \begin{bmatrix} a \\ b \\ c \end{bmatrix}$$

of $\mathbb{R}^3$ can be represented geometrically in a **system of three coordinates**, the x_1-axis, x_2-axis, and x_3-axis. The first two are just the axes of the Cartesian plane. The x_3-axis is the copy of the x_1-axis perpendicular to the x_1 and x_2 axes depicted in Figure 2.1. As in the plane, the point or vector

$$\mathbf{v} = \begin{bmatrix} a \\ b \\ c \end{bmatrix}$$

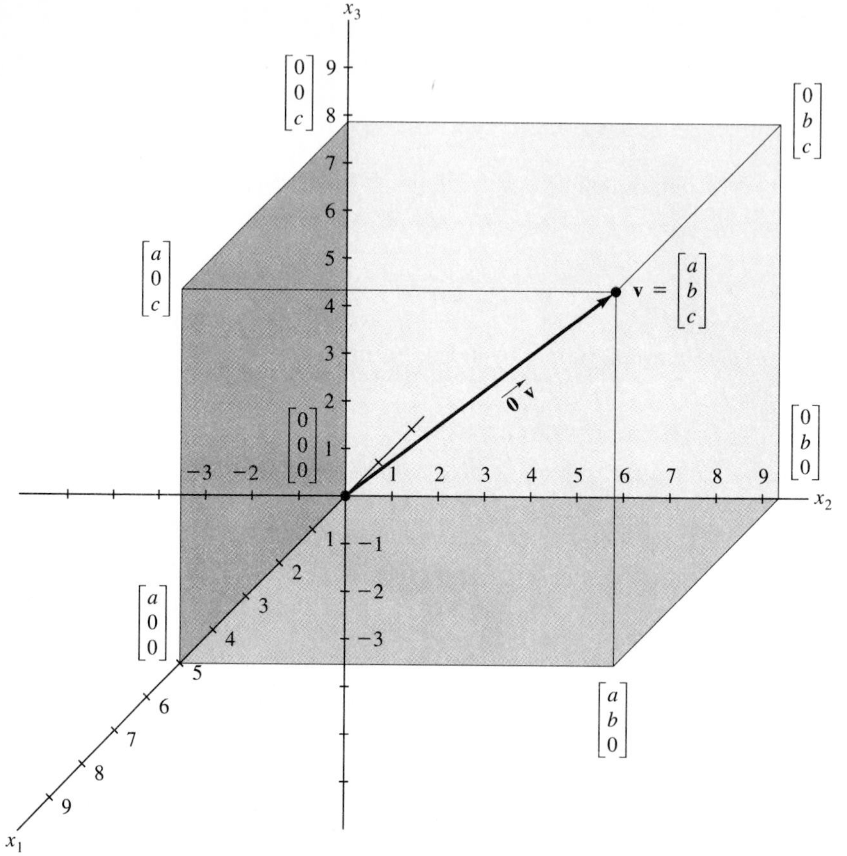

Figure 2.1 The element $\mathbf{v} \in \mathbb{R}^3$ as point $\mathbf{v} = \begin{bmatrix} a \\ b \\ c \end{bmatrix}$ and as directed segment $\mathbf{v} = \overrightarrow{\mathbf{0}\,\mathbf{v}}$.

is also represented by the **directed segment** (*arrow*) $\overrightarrow{\mathbf{0}\,\mathbf{v}}$ which leads from $\mathbf{0}$ to $\mathbf{v}$. So, we equate $\mathbf{v}$ with

$$\begin{bmatrix} a \\ b \\ c \end{bmatrix} = \overrightarrow{\mathbf{0}\,\mathbf{v}}.$$

PROBLEMS

NUMERICAL PROBLEMS

1. For what values of a, if any, are the vectors $\mathbf{v}$ and $\mathbf{w}$ equal in each of the following cases?

(a) $\mathbf{v} = \begin{bmatrix} 1+a \\ 2 \\ 3 \end{bmatrix}, \mathbf{w} = \begin{bmatrix} 2 \\ 3-a \\ 3 \end{bmatrix}$ (b) $\mathbf{v} = \begin{bmatrix} 1-a^2 \\ 1+a^2 \\ 3 \end{bmatrix}, \mathbf{w} = \begin{bmatrix} 0 \\ 2 \\ 3 \end{bmatrix}$

(c) $\mathbf{v} = \begin{bmatrix} 2a \\ 3a \\ 3a \end{bmatrix}, \mathbf{w} = \begin{bmatrix} 3 \\ 4 \\ 5 \end{bmatrix}$

2. For what values of a, if any, are the vectors $\mathbf{v}$ and $\mathbf{w}$ equal in each of the following cases?

(a) $\mathbf{v} = \begin{bmatrix} 6+2a \\ 5 \\ 3 \end{bmatrix}, \mathbf{w} = \begin{bmatrix} 2 \\ 3-a \\ 3 \end{bmatrix}$ (b) $\mathbf{v} = \begin{bmatrix} 3-a^3 \\ 2+a^4 \\ 3 \end{bmatrix}, \mathbf{w} = \begin{bmatrix} 2 \\ 2 \\ 3 \end{bmatrix}$

3. Plot the vectors in Problem 2, as in Figure 2.1, for $a = 1$ and for $a = 2$.

VECTOR OPERATIONS IN n-SPACE

The points

$$\mathbf{a} = \begin{bmatrix} a_1 \\ \vdots \\ a_n \end{bmatrix}$$

of F^n are also called *vectors*. If the entries $a_1, \ldots, a_n$ of $\mathbf{a}$ come from $\mathbb{R}^n$, $\mathbf{a}$ is called a **real vector**. And if they come from $\mathbb{C}^n$, $\mathbf{a}$ is called a **complex vector**. Just as in the plane, we can combine vectors

$$\mathbf{a} = \begin{bmatrix} a_1 \\ \vdots \\ a_n \end{bmatrix} \quad \text{and} \quad \mathbf{b} = \begin{bmatrix} b_1 \\ \vdots \\ b_n \end{bmatrix}$$

and scalars t by certain vector operations.

Definition. *Addition, Subtraction, and Scalar Multiplication of Vectors.*

$$\begin{bmatrix} a_1 \\ \vdots \\ a_n \end{bmatrix} + \begin{bmatrix} b_1 \\ \vdots \\ b_n \end{bmatrix} = \begin{bmatrix} a_1+b_1 \\ \vdots \\ a_n+b_n \end{bmatrix}, \quad \begin{bmatrix} a_1 \\ \vdots \\ a_n \end{bmatrix} - \begin{bmatrix} b_1 \\ \vdots \\ b_n \end{bmatrix} = \begin{bmatrix} a_1-b_1 \\ \vdots \\ a_n-b_n \end{bmatrix}, \quad t\begin{bmatrix} a_1 \\ \vdots \\ a_n \end{bmatrix} = \begin{bmatrix} ta_1 \\ \vdots \\ ta_n \end{bmatrix}.$$

For $\mathbb{R}^3$, these purely algebraic operations on vectors are interpreted geometrically, as shown in Figure 2.2. When t is a nonzero scalar and $\mathbf{a} \in F^n$, we sometimes write $\frac{1}{t}\mathbf{a}$ as $\frac{\mathbf{a}}{t}$ or $\mathbf{a}/t$.

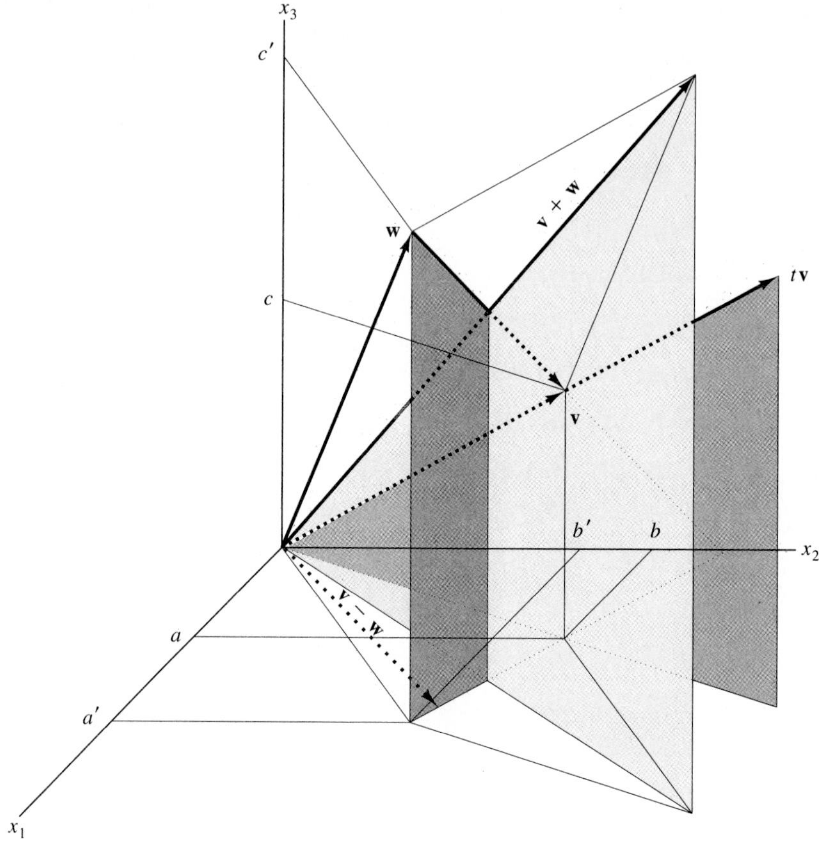

Figure 2.2 The vectors

$$\mathbf{v} = \begin{bmatrix} a \\ b \\ c \end{bmatrix}, \quad \mathbf{w} = \begin{bmatrix} a' \\ b' \\ c' \end{bmatrix}, \quad \mathbf{v} + \mathbf{w} = \begin{bmatrix} a \\ b \\ c \end{bmatrix} + \begin{bmatrix} a' \\ b' \\ c' \end{bmatrix}, \quad \mathbf{v} - \mathbf{w} = \begin{bmatrix} a \\ b \\ c \end{bmatrix} - \begin{bmatrix} a' \\ b' \\ c' \end{bmatrix}, \quad t\mathbf{v} = \begin{bmatrix} ta \\ tb \\ tc \end{bmatrix}.$$

EXAMPLE

$$\begin{bmatrix} 3 \\ 1 \\ 2 \end{bmatrix} + \begin{bmatrix} 2 \\ -3 \\ 1 \end{bmatrix} = \begin{bmatrix} 5 \\ -2 \\ 3 \end{bmatrix}, \quad \begin{bmatrix} 3 \\ 1 \\ 2 \end{bmatrix} - \begin{bmatrix} 2 \\ -3 \\ 1 \end{bmatrix} = \begin{bmatrix} 1 \\ 4 \\ 1 \end{bmatrix}, \quad 4\begin{bmatrix} 3 \\ i \\ 2 \end{bmatrix} = \begin{bmatrix} 12 \\ 4i \\ 8 \end{bmatrix},$$

$$\frac{1}{4}\begin{bmatrix} 3 \\ i \\ 2 \end{bmatrix} = \begin{bmatrix} 3/4 \\ i/4 \\ 2/4 \end{bmatrix}.$$

The dot product, which played a key role in the geometry of the plane, is just as useful here.

Definition. *The Dot Product.*
The **dot product** of

$$\mathbf{a} = \begin{bmatrix} a_1 \\ \vdots \\ a_n \end{bmatrix} \quad \text{and} \quad \mathbf{b} = \begin{bmatrix} b_1 \\ \vdots \\ b_n \end{bmatrix}$$

is $\mathbf{a} \cdot \mathbf{b} = a_1 b_1 + \cdots + a_n b_n$. If $\mathbf{a} \cdot \mathbf{b} = 0$, $\mathbf{a}$ and $\mathbf{b}$ are *perpendicular* (Figure 2.3).

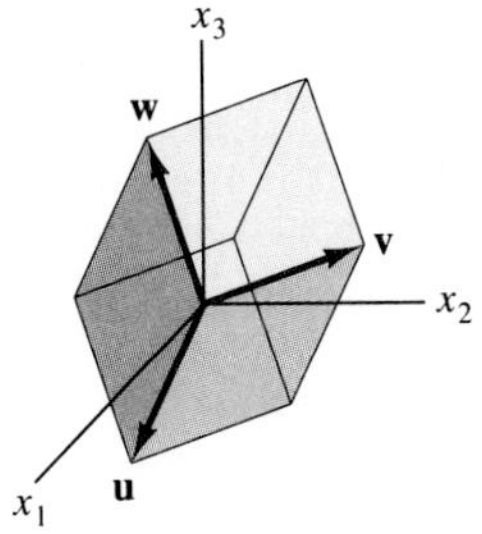

Figure 2.3 Perpendicular vectors **u**, **v**, and **w**. Each is perpendicular to the other two.

Operations on complex vectors

When $F = \mathbb{C}$, a complex vector

$$\mathbf{z} = \begin{bmatrix} z_1 \\ \vdots \\ z_n \end{bmatrix} = \begin{bmatrix} a_1 + b_1 i \\ \vdots \\ a_n + b_n i \end{bmatrix}$$

can be written as the sum

$$\mathbf{z} = \begin{bmatrix} a_1 \\ \vdots \\ a_n \end{bmatrix} + i \begin{bmatrix} b_1 \\ \vdots \\ b_n \end{bmatrix}$$

of its **real part**

$$\mathbf{a} = \begin{bmatrix} a_1 \\ \vdots \\ a_n \end{bmatrix}$$

and **pure imaginary part**

$$i\mathbf{b} = i\begin{bmatrix} b_1 \\ \vdots \\ b_n \end{bmatrix},$$

the vectors **a** and **b** being real. The **conjugate**

$$\bar{\mathbf{z}} = \begin{bmatrix} \bar{z}_1 \\ \vdots \\ \bar{z}_n \end{bmatrix} = \begin{bmatrix} a_1 - b_1 i \\ \vdots \quad \vdots \\ a_n - b_n i \end{bmatrix}$$

of **z** can then be written as $\bar{\mathbf{z}} = \mathbf{a} - i\mathbf{b}$. Note that

1. A complex vector **z** is real if and only if $\mathbf{z} = \bar{\mathbf{z}}$;
2. The real part of **z** is $(\mathbf{z} + \bar{\mathbf{z}})/2$;
3. The pure imaginary part of **z** is $(\mathbf{z} - \bar{\mathbf{z}})/2$. (Prove!)

EXAMPLE

If

$$\mathbf{w} = \begin{bmatrix} 3+2i \\ 1-3i \\ 2+2i \end{bmatrix},$$

then

$$\mathbf{w} = \begin{bmatrix} 3 \\ 1 \\ 2 \end{bmatrix} + i\begin{bmatrix} 2 \\ -3 \\ 2 \end{bmatrix} \quad \text{and} \quad \bar{\mathbf{w}} = \begin{bmatrix} 3-2i \\ 1+3i \\ 2-2i \end{bmatrix} = \begin{bmatrix} 3 \\ 1 \\ 2 \end{bmatrix} - i\begin{bmatrix} 2 \\ -3 \\ 2 \end{bmatrix}.$$

A variation of the dot product that plays an important role in the geometry of $\mathbb{C}^n$ is the *inner product.*

Definition. *The Inner Product.*

The **inner product** of $\mathbf{a} = \begin{bmatrix} a_1 \\ \vdots \\ a_n \end{bmatrix}$ and $\mathbf{b} = \begin{bmatrix} b_1 \\ \vdots \\ b_n \end{bmatrix}$ is $\langle \mathbf{a}, \mathbf{b} \rangle = a_1\overline{b_1} + \cdots + a_n\overline{b_n}$.

If $\langle \mathbf{a}, \mathbf{b} \rangle = 0$, we say that **a** and **b** are **orthogonal**.

The relationship between dot and inner products is that $\langle \mathbf{v}, \mathbf{w} \rangle = \mathbf{v} \cdot \bar{\mathbf{w}}$. So, when **w** is real, the dot and inner products of **v** and **w** are the same; and **v** and **w** are orthogonal if and only if **v** and $\bar{\mathbf{w}}$ are perpendicular.

Since $\langle \mathbf{v}, \mathbf{v} \rangle = 0$ if $\mathbf{v} = 0$ and $\langle \mathbf{v}, \mathbf{v} \rangle > 0$ if **v** is nonzero (prove), we can define the **length** $\|\mathbf{v}\|$ of $\mathbf{v} \in F^n$ as $\|\mathbf{v}\| = \sqrt{\langle \mathbf{v}, \mathbf{v} \rangle}$. (We can't use the dot product here because although $\langle \mathbf{v}, \mathbf{v} \rangle$ is positive, $\mathbf{v} \cdot \mathbf{v}$ may not be.) We refer to

$\|\mathbf{v}\|^2 = \langle \mathbf{v}, \mathbf{v} \rangle$ as the **squared length** of $\mathbf{v}$. When $\mathbf{v} \in \mathbb{R}^2$, this definition gives the same length for $\mathbf{v}$ as does the definition given in Chapter 1.

EXAMPLES

1. Let

$$\mathbf{v} = \begin{bmatrix} 3 \\ i \\ 2 \end{bmatrix} \quad \text{and} \quad \mathbf{w} = \begin{bmatrix} 3 \\ 1 \\ 2 \end{bmatrix} + i \begin{bmatrix} 2 \\ -3 \\ 2 \end{bmatrix}.$$

Then

$$\langle \mathbf{v}, \mathbf{w} \rangle = \mathbf{v} \cdot \bar{\mathbf{w}} = \begin{bmatrix} 3 \\ i \\ 2 \end{bmatrix} \cdot \left(\begin{bmatrix} 3 \\ 1 \\ 2 \end{bmatrix} - i \begin{bmatrix} 2 \\ -3 \\ 2 \end{bmatrix} \right)$$

$$= 9 + i + 4 - 6i - 3 - 8i = 10 - 13i.$$

2. Let

$$\mathbf{v} = \begin{bmatrix} a+bi \\ 0 \\ c+di \end{bmatrix} \quad \text{and} \quad \mathbf{w} = \begin{bmatrix} -c+bi \\ 0 \\ a-bi \end{bmatrix}.$$

Then

$$\langle \mathbf{v}, \mathbf{w} \rangle = \mathbf{v} \cdot \bar{\mathbf{w}} = \begin{bmatrix} a+bi \\ 0 \\ c+di \end{bmatrix} \cdot \begin{bmatrix} -(c+bi) \\ 0 \\ a+bi \end{bmatrix} = 0,$$

so that $\mathbf{v}$ and $\mathbf{w}$ are orthogonal.

3. The squared length of $\begin{bmatrix} 3 \\ i \\ 2 \end{bmatrix}$ is $9 + 1 + 4 = 14$.

Properties of vector operations

The basic properties of vector operations in the plane hold in F^n as well. The proofs for $n = 2$ given in Chapter 1 adapt easily to the general case. We leave the details to the reader.

Theorem 2.1. *Properties of Vector Operations.*
Let $a_r, b_r, c_r \in F$ for $1 \le r \le n$ and $s, t \in F$. Then

1. $$\left(\begin{bmatrix} a_1 \\ \vdots \\ a_n \end{bmatrix} + \begin{bmatrix} b_1 \\ \vdots \\ b_n \end{bmatrix} \right) + \begin{bmatrix} c_1 \\ \vdots \\ c_n \end{bmatrix} = \begin{bmatrix} a_1 \\ \vdots \\ a_n \end{bmatrix} + \left(\begin{bmatrix} b_1 \\ \vdots \\ b_n \end{bmatrix} + \begin{bmatrix} c_1 \\ \vdots \\ c_n \end{bmatrix} \right);$$

2. $\begin{bmatrix} a_1 \\ \vdots \\ a_n \end{bmatrix} + 0 = \begin{bmatrix} a_1 \\ \vdots \\ a_n \end{bmatrix}$ and $\begin{bmatrix} a_1 \\ \vdots \\ a_n \end{bmatrix} + \begin{bmatrix} b_1 \\ \vdots \\ b_n \end{bmatrix} = \begin{bmatrix} b_1 \\ \vdots \\ b_n \end{bmatrix} + \begin{bmatrix} a_1 \\ \vdots \\ a_n \end{bmatrix}$;

3. $\begin{bmatrix} a_1 \\ \vdots \\ a_n \end{bmatrix} + \mathbf{w} = \begin{bmatrix} b_1 \\ \vdots \\ b_n \end{bmatrix}$ has a unique solution $\mathbf{w}$, namely, $\mathbf{w} = \begin{bmatrix} b_1 \\ \vdots \\ b_n \end{bmatrix} - \begin{bmatrix} a_1 \\ \vdots \\ a_n \end{bmatrix}$;

4. $t\left(\begin{bmatrix} a_1 \\ \vdots \\ a_n \end{bmatrix} + \begin{bmatrix} b_1 \\ \vdots \\ b_n \end{bmatrix}\right) = t\begin{bmatrix} a_1 \\ \vdots \\ a_n \end{bmatrix} + t\begin{bmatrix} b_1 \\ \vdots \\ b_n \end{bmatrix}$;

5. $(s + t)\begin{bmatrix} a_1 \\ \vdots \\ a_n \end{bmatrix} = s\begin{bmatrix} a_1 \\ \vdots \\ a_n \end{bmatrix} + t\begin{bmatrix} a_1 \\ \vdots \\ a_n \end{bmatrix}$ and $(st)\begin{bmatrix} a_1 \\ \vdots \\ a_n \end{bmatrix} = s\left(t\begin{bmatrix} a_1 \\ \vdots \\ a_n \end{bmatrix}\right)$;

6. $0\begin{bmatrix} a_1 \\ \vdots \\ a_n \end{bmatrix} = \mathbf{0}$ and $1\begin{bmatrix} a_1 \\ \vdots \\ a_n \end{bmatrix} = \begin{bmatrix} a_1 \\ \vdots \\ a_n \end{bmatrix}$.

These operations enable us to calculate with vectors much as we do with numbers. Note that the associative law (Property 1) for sums enables us to drop parentheses in sums. And, by defining

$$-\begin{bmatrix} a_1 \\ \vdots \\ a_n \end{bmatrix} = 0 - \begin{bmatrix} a_1 \\ \vdots \\ a_n \end{bmatrix} = \begin{bmatrix} -a_1 \\ \vdots \\ -a_n \end{bmatrix},$$

if $\mathbf{v} = \begin{bmatrix} a_1 \\ \vdots \\ a_n \end{bmatrix}$, then $-\mathbf{v} = -\begin{bmatrix} a_1 \\ \vdots \\ a_n \end{bmatrix}$ is the solution

$$\mathbf{w} = \begin{bmatrix} -a_1 \\ \vdots \\ -a_n \end{bmatrix}$$

to the equation $\mathbf{v} + \mathbf{w} = 0$. We also have

$$-\begin{bmatrix} a_1 \\ \vdots \\ a_n \end{bmatrix} = (-1)\begin{bmatrix} a_1 \\ \vdots \\ a_n \end{bmatrix};$$

that is, $-\mathbf{v} = (-1)\mathbf{v}$. (Verify!)

If $a \in F$ and $\mathbf{v}, \mathbf{w} \in F^n$ with $a\mathbf{v} = \mathbf{w}$, then $\mathbf{v} = 1\mathbf{v} = ((1/a)a)\mathbf{v} = (1/a)(a\mathbf{v}) = (1/a)\mathbf{w}$, using (5) and (6). It follows that if $a\mathbf{v} = a'\mathbf{v}'$, with a nonzero, then $\mathbf{v} = (1/a)(a'\mathbf{v}') = (a'/a)\mathbf{v}'$, by (5). And if $a\mathbf{v} = a\mathbf{v}'$ with a nonzero, then $\mathbf{v} = 1\mathbf{v}' = \mathbf{v}'$, so $\mathbf{v} = \mathbf{v}'$. (Thus, when $a\mathbf{v} = a\mathbf{v}'$ with a nonzero, *we can get* $\mathbf{v} = \mathbf{v}'$ *by cancellation by* a.)

EXAMPLE

Using the preceding theorem, we can simplify the expression

$$2\left(\begin{bmatrix}3\\2\\3\end{bmatrix}+\left(\left(\begin{bmatrix}2\\0\\5\end{bmatrix}+\begin{bmatrix}1\\2\\3\end{bmatrix}\right)+\mathbf{v}\right)\right)=\begin{bmatrix}3\\1\\3\end{bmatrix}$$

and solve for $\mathbf{v}$ as follows:

a. Drop inside parentheses (by (1)) and add to get

$$2\left(\begin{bmatrix}6\\4\\11\end{bmatrix}+\mathbf{v}\right)=\begin{bmatrix}3\\1\\3\end{bmatrix}.$$

b. Reduce the left-hand side (by (3)) and solve for

$$2\mathbf{v}=\begin{bmatrix}3\\1\\3\end{bmatrix}-2\begin{bmatrix}6\\4\\11\end{bmatrix}=\begin{bmatrix}-9\\-7\\-19\end{bmatrix}.$$

c. We then get

$$2\mathbf{v}=\begin{bmatrix}3\\1\\3\end{bmatrix}-2\begin{bmatrix}6\\4\\11\end{bmatrix}=\begin{bmatrix}-9\\-7\\-19\end{bmatrix},\qquad \mathbf{v}=\begin{bmatrix}-9/2\\-7/2\\-19/2\end{bmatrix}.$$

The properties of dot product for $n = 2$ transfer to n dimensions without difficulty.

Theorem 2.2. *Properties of the Dot Product.*
The dot product for vectors $\mathbf{u}$, $\mathbf{v}$, $\mathbf{w}$ in F^n satisfies the following properties.

1. $\mathbf{v}\cdot\mathbf{v}$ is 0 if $\mathbf{v}$ is 0 and it is positive if $\mathbf{v}\in\mathbb{R}^n$ and $\mathbf{v}$ is nonzero.
2. $\mathbf{v}\cdot\mathbf{w}=\mathbf{w}\cdot\mathbf{v}$.
3. $\mathbf{u}\cdot(\mathbf{v}+\mathbf{w})=\mathbf{u}\cdot\mathbf{v}+\mathbf{u}\cdot\mathbf{w}$ and $(\mathbf{u}+\mathbf{v})\cdot\mathbf{w}=\mathbf{u}\cdot\mathbf{w}+\mathbf{v}\cdot\mathbf{w}$.
4. $(r\mathbf{v})\cdot\mathbf{w}=r(\mathbf{v}\cdot\mathbf{w})=\mathbf{v}\cdot(r\mathbf{w})$ for $r\in F$.

When $F = \mathbb{C}$, addition, subtraction and scalar multiplication relate to conjugation of vectors as follows.

Theorem 2.3. *Properties of Complex Conjugation of Vectors.*
For vectors $\mathbf{v}, \mathbf{w}\in\mathbb{C}^n$ and scalars $z\in\mathbb{C}$, we have $\overline{\mathbf{v}+\mathbf{w}}=\overline{\mathbf{v}}+\overline{\mathbf{w}}$, $\overline{\mathbf{v}-\mathbf{w}}=\overline{\mathbf{v}}-\overline{\mathbf{w}}$, and $\overline{z\mathbf{v}}=\overline{z}\,\overline{\mathbf{v}}$.

Proof. To verify these equations amounts to writing out each side, performing the indicated operations, and then comparing the results. We do this now in the case of addition as an example, the other cases being similar.

$$\overline{\mathbf{v}+\mathbf{w}} = \overline{\begin{bmatrix} v_1 + w_1 \\ \vdots \\ v_n + w_n \end{bmatrix}} = \begin{bmatrix} \overline{v_1 + w_1} \\ \vdots \\ \overline{v_n + w_n} \end{bmatrix} = \begin{bmatrix} \overline{v_1} + \overline{w_1} \\ \vdots \\ \overline{v_n} + \overline{w_n} \end{bmatrix}$$

$$\overline{\mathbf{v}} + \overline{\mathbf{w}} = \begin{bmatrix} \overline{v_1} \\ \vdots \\ \overline{v_n} \end{bmatrix} + \begin{bmatrix} \overline{w_1} \\ \vdots \\ \overline{w_n} \end{bmatrix} = \begin{bmatrix} \overline{v_1} + \overline{w_1} \\ \vdots \\ \overline{v_n} + \overline{w_n} \end{bmatrix}. \quad \blacksquare$$

EXAMPLE

By the theorem,

$$\overline{(1+2i)\begin{bmatrix} 6+i \\ 4 \\ 11 \end{bmatrix}} = (1-2i)\begin{bmatrix} 6-i \\ 4 \\ 11 \end{bmatrix}.$$

To check this, we note that the left-hand side is

$$\overline{\begin{bmatrix} 4+13i \\ 4+8i \\ 11+22i \end{bmatrix}} = \begin{bmatrix} 4-13i \\ 4-8i \\ 11-22i \end{bmatrix}$$

and the right-hand side is

$$\begin{bmatrix} 4-13i \\ 4-8i \\ 11-22i \end{bmatrix}.$$

Because $\langle \mathbf{v}, \mathbf{w} \rangle = \mathbf{v} \cdot \overline{\mathbf{w}}$, the properties of dot product translate directly into properties for inner products.

Theorem 2.4. *Properties of the Inner Product.*
The inner product for vectors $\mathbf{u}$, $\mathbf{v}$, $\mathbf{w}$ in $\mathbb{C}$ satisfies the following properties.

1. $\langle \mathbf{v}, \mathbf{v} \rangle$ is 0 if $\mathbf{v}$ is 0 and is positive if $\mathbf{v} \in \mathbb{C}$ and $\mathbf{v}$ is nonzero.
2. $\overline{\langle \mathbf{v}, \mathbf{w} \rangle} = \langle \mathbf{w}, \mathbf{v} \rangle$.
3. $\langle \mathbf{u}, \mathbf{v} + \mathbf{w} \rangle = \langle \mathbf{u}, \mathbf{v} \rangle + \langle \mathbf{u}, \mathbf{w} \rangle$ and $\langle \mathbf{u} + \mathbf{v}, \mathbf{w} \rangle = \langle \mathbf{u}, \mathbf{w} \rangle + \langle \mathbf{v}, \mathbf{w} \rangle$.
4. $\langle a\mathbf{v}, \mathbf{w} \rangle = a\langle \mathbf{v}, \mathbf{w} \rangle = \langle \mathbf{v}, \bar{a}\mathbf{w} \rangle$ for $a \in \mathbb{C}$.

Proof. Property (1) follows directly from the definition

$$\langle \mathbf{v}, \mathbf{v} \rangle = v_1\overline{v_1} + \cdots + v_n\overline{v_n}$$

of the inner product in terms of the entries $\mathbf{v}_s$ of $\mathbf{v}$. For if $\mathbf{v}$ is 0, its entries are 0 and the inner product is 0. And if some entry or entries are not zero, the inner product is a sum of nonnegative numbers, some of which are positive.

Property (2) follows from the equalities

$$\langle \mathbf{w}, \mathbf{v} \rangle = w_1\overline{v_1} + \cdots + w_n\overline{v_n}$$

$$\overline{\langle \mathbf{v}, \mathbf{w} \rangle} = \overline{v_1\overline{w}_1 + \cdots + v_n\overline{w}_n} = \overline{v}_1 w_1 + \cdots + \overline{v}_n w_n.$$

For (3), note that

$$\langle \mathbf{u}, \mathbf{v} + \mathbf{w} \rangle = \mathbf{u} \cdot \overline{(\mathbf{v} + \mathbf{w})} = \mathbf{u} \cdot (\overline{\mathbf{v}} + \overline{\mathbf{w}}) = \mathbf{u} \cdot \overline{\mathbf{v}} + \mathbf{u} \cdot \overline{\mathbf{w}} = \langle \mathbf{u}, \mathbf{v} \rangle + \langle \mathbf{u}, \mathbf{w} \rangle$$

$$\langle \mathbf{u} + \mathbf{v}, \mathbf{w} \rangle = (\mathbf{u} + \mathbf{v}) \cdot \overline{\mathbf{w}} = \mathbf{u} \cdot \overline{\mathbf{w}} + \mathbf{v} \cdot \overline{\mathbf{w}} = \langle \mathbf{u}, \mathbf{w} \rangle + \langle \mathbf{v}, \mathbf{w} \rangle.$$

Finally, for (4), note that

$$\langle a\mathbf{v}, \mathbf{w} \rangle = (a\mathbf{v}) \cdot \overline{\mathbf{w}} = a(\mathbf{v} \cdot \overline{\mathbf{w}}) = a\langle \mathbf{v}, \mathbf{w} \rangle$$

$$\langle \mathbf{v}, \bar{a}\mathbf{w} \rangle = \mathbf{v} \cdot \overline{(\bar{a}\mathbf{w})} = \mathbf{v} \cdot (a\overline{\mathbf{w}}) = a(\mathbf{v} \cdot \overline{\mathbf{w}}) = a\langle \mathbf{v}, \mathbf{w} \rangle. \quad \blacksquare$$

PROBLEMS

NUMERICAL PROBLEMS

1. Perform the indicated operations.

(a) $\begin{bmatrix} 2 \\ 3 \\ 3 \end{bmatrix} + \begin{bmatrix} 3 \\ 4 \\ 1 \end{bmatrix}$ **(b)** $\begin{bmatrix} 2-3i \\ 4-8i \\ 3 \end{bmatrix} + \begin{bmatrix} 3-4i \\ 2+i \\ 1 \end{bmatrix}$ **(c)** $\begin{bmatrix} 2 \\ 3 \\ 3 \end{bmatrix} - \begin{bmatrix} 3 \\ 4 \\ 1 \end{bmatrix}$

(d) $\begin{bmatrix} 2-3i \\ 4-8i \\ 3 \end{bmatrix} - \begin{bmatrix} 3-4i \\ 2+i \\ 1 \end{bmatrix}$ **(e)** $4\begin{bmatrix} 2 \\ 3 \\ 3 \end{bmatrix}$ **(f)** $(1+i)\begin{bmatrix} 2-3i \\ 4-8i \\ 3 \end{bmatrix}$

(g) $\begin{bmatrix} 1-i \\ 3+i \\ 3 \end{bmatrix} + \begin{bmatrix} i \\ 4 \\ 1 \end{bmatrix}$ **(h)** $\begin{bmatrix} 2-2i \\ 1+8i \\ 3-i \end{bmatrix} + \begin{bmatrix} 3-4i \\ i \\ 1-i \end{bmatrix}$ **(i)** $\begin{bmatrix} 1 \\ 3 \\ 3 \end{bmatrix} - \begin{bmatrix} 1 \\ 4i \\ 1 \end{bmatrix}$

(j) $\begin{bmatrix} 3i \\ 8-8i \\ 1 \end{bmatrix} - \begin{bmatrix} 4i \\ 2+i \\ 1-3i \end{bmatrix}$ **(k)** $5\begin{bmatrix} 2 \\ 1 \\ 3 \end{bmatrix}$

2. Compute the following.

(a) $\overline{(2-3i)\begin{bmatrix} 2+2i \\ 2+4i \\ 3 \end{bmatrix}}$ **(b)** $\overline{(5+4i)\begin{bmatrix} 6+i \\ 2 \\ 11 \end{bmatrix} + (3-6i)\begin{bmatrix} 6-i \\ 7i \\ 11 \end{bmatrix}}$

3. Express each of the following vectors as a sum of its real and pure imaginary parts.

(a) $\begin{bmatrix} 2-4i \\ 2-2i \\ 3+i \end{bmatrix}$ **(b)** $\begin{bmatrix} 3-3i \\ 1-3i \\ 2+3i \end{bmatrix}$ **(c)** $\begin{bmatrix} 2-1i \\ 1-4i \\ 3-3i \end{bmatrix}$

(d) $\begin{bmatrix} 2-i \\ 1-i \\ 3+i \end{bmatrix}$ (e) $\begin{bmatrix} 5-i \\ 1-i \\ 3+i \end{bmatrix}$ (f) $\begin{bmatrix} 2-i \\ 2-i \\ 5-i \end{bmatrix}$

4. Give the conjugate of each of the vectors in Problem 3.
5. Compute the dot product $\mathbf{v} \cdot \mathbf{w}$ in each of the following cases.

(a) $\mathbf{v} = \begin{bmatrix} 1 \\ 2 \\ 3 \end{bmatrix}, \mathbf{w} = \begin{bmatrix} 2 \\ 1 \\ -3 \end{bmatrix}$ (b) $\mathbf{v} = \begin{bmatrix} 1 \\ 2 \\ 0 \end{bmatrix}, \mathbf{w} = \begin{bmatrix} -2 \\ 1 \\ 0 \end{bmatrix}$

(c) $\mathbf{v} = \begin{bmatrix} 1+i \\ 2+i \end{bmatrix}, \mathbf{w} = \begin{bmatrix} -2-i \\ 1+i \end{bmatrix}$ (d) $\mathbf{v} = \begin{bmatrix} 1+i \\ 2+i \end{bmatrix}, \mathbf{w} = \begin{bmatrix} -2+i \\ 1-i \end{bmatrix}$

6. Compute the inner product $\langle \mathbf{v}, \mathbf{w} \rangle$ for each of the pairs of vectors listed in Problem 5. In which cases does the inner product equal the dot product?
7. Solve the following equations for $\mathbf{x}$.

(a) $4\left(\begin{bmatrix} 2 \\ 2 \\ 1 \end{bmatrix} - \mathbf{x}\right) = 5\begin{bmatrix} 1 \\ 1 \\ 3 \end{bmatrix} - 3\begin{bmatrix} 2 \\ 0 \\ 3 \end{bmatrix}$

(b) $4\left(2\left(\begin{bmatrix} 2 \\ 2 \\ 1 \end{bmatrix} + \begin{bmatrix} 1 \\ 0 \\ 3 \end{bmatrix}\right) - \mathbf{x}\right) = 5\left(\begin{bmatrix} 1 \\ 1 \\ 3 \end{bmatrix} - \begin{bmatrix} 2 \\ 0 \\ 3 \end{bmatrix}\right)$

(c) $\frac{1}{5}\left(\begin{bmatrix} 3 \\ 2 \\ 3 \end{bmatrix} - \left(2\left(\begin{bmatrix} 2 \\ 0 \\ 5 \end{bmatrix} + \begin{bmatrix} 1 \\ 2 \\ 3 \end{bmatrix}\right) + 3\mathbf{x}\right)\right) = 5\left(\begin{bmatrix} 3 \\ 1 \\ 3 \end{bmatrix} - \begin{bmatrix} 3 \\ 1 \\ 4 \end{bmatrix}\right)$

THEORETICAL PROBLEMS

8. If

$$\mathbf{e}_1 = \begin{bmatrix} 1 \\ 0 \\ 0 \end{bmatrix}, \quad \mathbf{e}_2 = \begin{bmatrix} 0 \\ 1 \\ 0 \end{bmatrix}, \quad \mathbf{e}_3 = \begin{bmatrix} 0 \\ 0 \\ 1 \end{bmatrix},$$

show that

$$\begin{bmatrix} a \\ b \\ c \end{bmatrix} = a\mathbf{e}_1 + b\mathbf{e}_2 + c\mathbf{e}_3.$$

9. In Problem 8, show that $a\mathbf{e}_1 + b\mathbf{e}_2 + c\mathbf{e}_3 = a'\mathbf{e}_1 + b'\mathbf{e}_2 + c'\mathbf{e}_3$ if and only if $a = a'$, $b = b'$, and $c = c'$.
10. Show that $\langle i\mathbf{v}, i\mathbf{v} \rangle = \|\mathbf{v}\|^2$.

11. Show that $\overline{-\mathbf{v}} = -\overline{\mathbf{v}}$.
12. Show that $\overline{a\mathbf{v} + b\mathbf{w}} = \bar{a}\overline{\mathbf{v}} + \bar{b}\overline{\mathbf{v}}$ for $a, b \in \mathbb{C}$ and $\mathbf{v}, \mathbf{w} \in \mathbb{C}^n$.
13. Show that z is real if and only if $z = \bar{z}$.
14. Show that the real part of z is $(z + \bar{z})/2$.
15. Show that the pure imaginary part of z is $(z - \bar{z})/2$.
16. Show that $(a + b)(\mathbf{v} + \mathbf{w}) = a\mathbf{v} + a\mathbf{w} + b\mathbf{v} + b\mathbf{w}$ for $a, b \in F$ and $\mathbf{v}, \mathbf{w} \in F^n$.
17. Find a nonzero complex vector $\mathbf{v}$ such that $\mathbf{v} \cdot \mathbf{v} = 0$.
18. Prove the properties of vector operations in Theorem 2.1, following the proofs given in Chapter 1 for $n = 2$.

2.4 DIRECTED SEGMENTS. TRANSLATIONS

Segments and directed segments

For any $\mathbf{v}, \mathbf{w} \in F^n$, we let $\overrightarrow{\mathbf{v}\,\mathbf{w}}$ denote the **directed segment** leading from $\mathbf{v}$ to $\mathbf{w}$. As in the Cartesian plane, designating $\overrightarrow{\mathbf{v}\,\mathbf{w}}$ amounts to designating its base $\mathbf{v}$ and tip $\mathbf{w}$. These determine the **segment** $\overline{\mathbf{v}\,\mathbf{w}} = \{(1 - t)\mathbf{v} + t\mathbf{w} \mid 0 \leq t \leq 1\}$ between $\mathbf{v}$ and $\mathbf{w}$ (Figure 2.4). Note that

1. $(1 - t)\mathbf{v} + t\mathbf{w}$ is $\mathbf{v}$ for $t = 0$ and $\mathbf{w}$ for $t = 1$;
2. $(1 - t)\mathbf{v} + t\mathbf{w} = \mathbf{v} + t(\mathbf{w} - \mathbf{v})$.

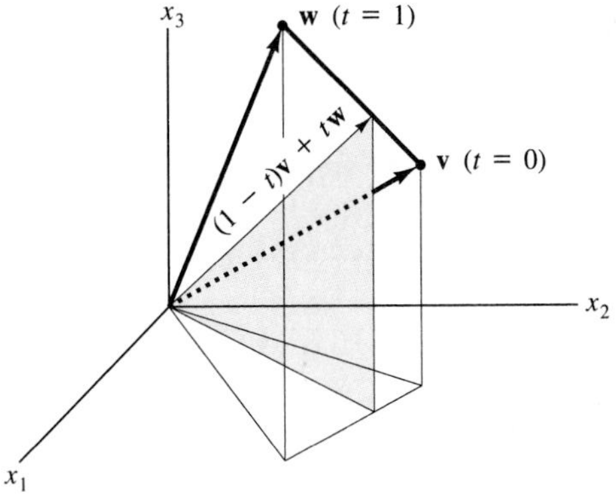

Figure 2.4 The point $\mathbf{x} = (1 - t)\mathbf{v} + t\mathbf{w}$ on the segment between $\mathbf{v}$ and $\mathbf{w}$.

If $\mathbf{v}$ and $\mathbf{w}$ are not necessarily real, the real parts of the points on the segment $\overline{\mathbf{v}\,\mathbf{w}}$ form the segment joining the real part of $\mathbf{v}$ to the real part of $\mathbf{w}$ (Figure 2.5). (Prove!)

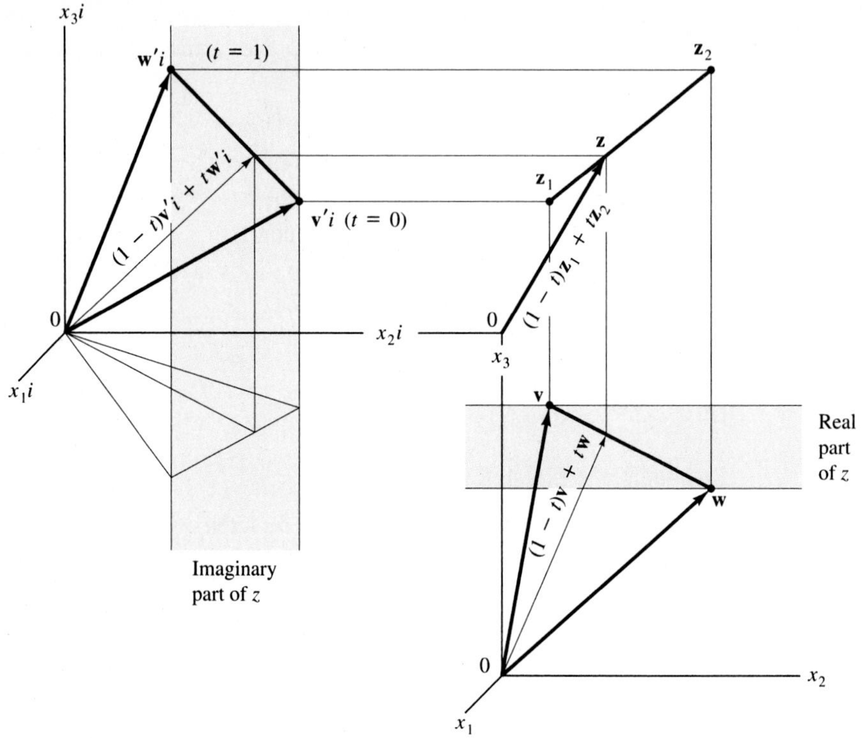

Figure 2.5 Real and pure imaginary parts of $\mathbf{z} = (1-t)\mathbf{z}_1 + t\mathbf{z}_2$, where $\mathbf{z}_1 = \mathbf{v} + \mathbf{v}'i$, $\mathbf{z}_2 = \mathbf{w} + \mathbf{w}'i$. (Six axes are needed for the three coordinates of $\mathbf{z} \in \mathbb{C}^3$.)

Translation of directed segments

Following the lead taken in Chapter 1:

1. We can move $\overrightarrow{\mathbf{v}\,\mathbf{w}}$ to $\overrightarrow{\mathbf{u}+\mathbf{v}\ \mathbf{u}+\mathbf{w}}$ by translation by $\mathbf{u}$.
2. So, we can move $\overrightarrow{\mathbf{v}\,\mathbf{w}}$ by translation by $-\mathbf{v}$ to the corresponding directed segment whose base is 0, namely, $\overrightarrow{0\ \mathbf{w}-\mathbf{v}}$.
3. We regard the directed segment $\overrightarrow{0\ \mathbf{w}-\mathbf{v}}$ with base 0 as the same as the point $\mathbf{w} - \mathbf{v}$. So, we can *always represent a directed segment* $\overrightarrow{\mathbf{v}\,\mathbf{w}}$ *with base* $\mathbf{v}$ *by the vector* $\mathbf{w} - \mathbf{v}$. In particular, the vector $\mathbf{v}$ represents $\overrightarrow{0\,\mathbf{v}}$, so we equate $\mathbf{v} = \overrightarrow{0\,\mathbf{v}}$ (Figure 2.6).
4. Since $\overrightarrow{\mathbf{u}+\mathbf{v}\ \mathbf{u}+\mathbf{w}}$ is then represented by $\mathbf{u} + \mathbf{w} - (\mathbf{u} + \mathbf{v}) = \mathbf{w} - \mathbf{v}$, this means that *all the directed segments obtained from* $\overrightarrow{\mathbf{v}\,\mathbf{w}}$ *by translation are represented by the vector* $\mathbf{w} - \mathbf{v}$.

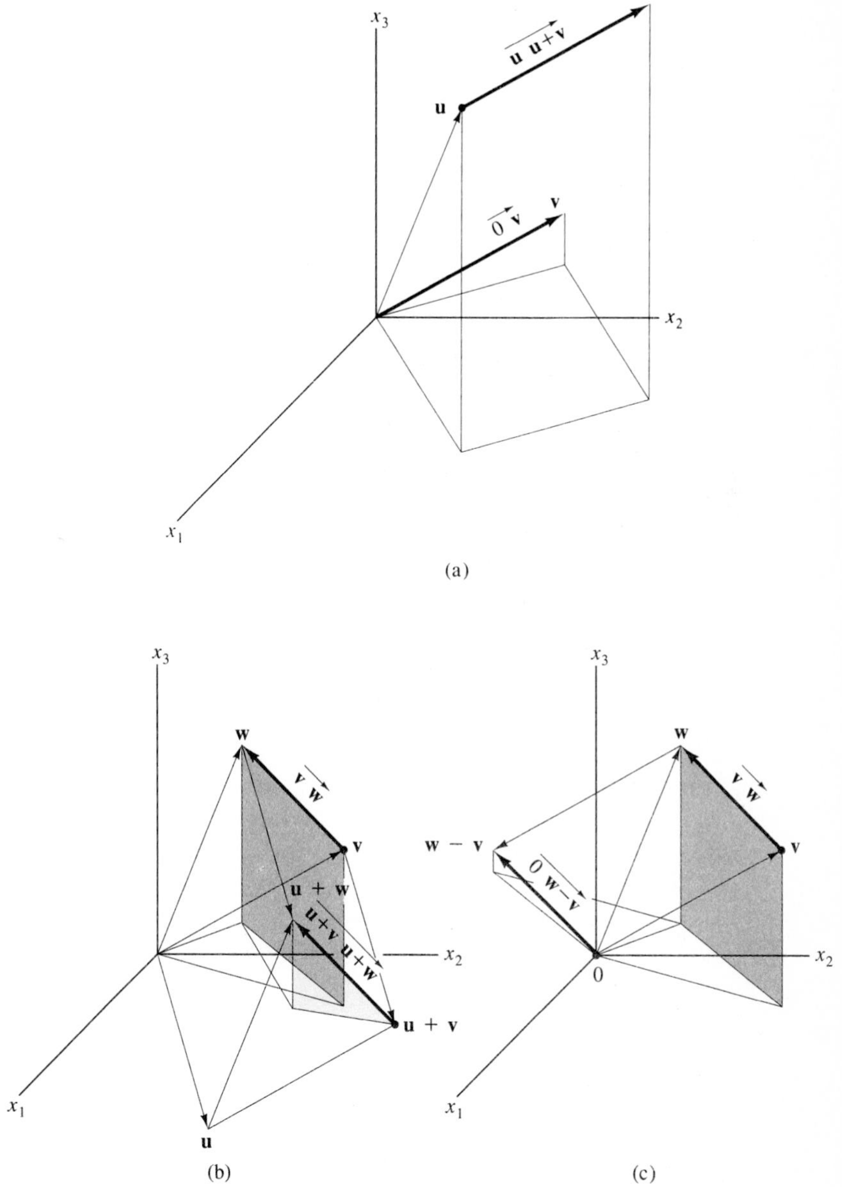

Figure 2.6 (a) Translating $\mathbf{v} = \overrightarrow{\mathbf{0}\,\mathbf{v}}$ by $\mathbf{u}$ to get $\overrightarrow{\mathbf{u}\;\mathbf{u}+\mathbf{v}}$. (b) Translating $\overrightarrow{\mathbf{v}\,\mathbf{w}}$ by $\mathbf{u}$ to get $\overrightarrow{\mathbf{u}+\mathbf{v}\;\mathbf{u}+\mathbf{w}}$. (c) Translating $\overrightarrow{\mathbf{v}\,\mathbf{w}}$ by $-\mathbf{v}$ to get $\overrightarrow{\mathbf{0}\;\mathbf{w}-\mathbf{v}} = \mathbf{w} - \mathbf{v}$.

EXAMPLE

The directed segment $\overrightarrow{\mathbf{v}\,\mathbf{w}}$, where

$$\mathbf{v} = \begin{bmatrix} 2 \\ -3 \\ 1 \end{bmatrix} \quad \text{and} \quad \mathbf{w} = \begin{bmatrix} 3 \\ 1 \\ 2 \end{bmatrix}$$

is represented by

$$\mathbf{w} - \mathbf{v} = \begin{bmatrix} 3 \\ 1 \\ 2 \end{bmatrix} - \begin{bmatrix} 2 \\ -3 \\ 1 \end{bmatrix} = \begin{bmatrix} 1 \\ 4 \\ 1 \end{bmatrix}.$$

If $\mathbf{u} = \begin{bmatrix} 2 \\ 1 \\ 1 \end{bmatrix}$, then $\overrightarrow{\mathbf{u}+\mathbf{v}\;\mathbf{u}+\mathbf{w}}$ is represented by

$$\mathbf{u} + \mathbf{w} - (\mathbf{u} + \mathbf{v}) = \begin{bmatrix} 5 \\ 2 \\ 3 \end{bmatrix} - \begin{bmatrix} 4 \\ -2 \\ 2 \end{bmatrix},$$

which is also $\begin{bmatrix} 1 \\ 4 \\ 1 \end{bmatrix}$.

As in the plane, this leads us to the following definition.

Definition. *Directed Segments Parallel to a Given Vector.*
A directed segment $\overrightarrow{\mathbf{v}\,\mathbf{w}}$ is **parallel** to a given nonzero vector if $\mathbf{w} - \mathbf{v}$ is a multiple of it. Two directed segments are **parallel** if they are parallel to the same nonzero vector (Figure 2.7).

EXAMPLE

The directed segments $\overrightarrow{\mathbf{v}\,\mathbf{w}}$ and $\overrightarrow{\mathbf{v}'\,\mathbf{w}'}$, where

$$\mathbf{v} = \begin{bmatrix} 2 \\ -3 \\ 1 \end{bmatrix} \quad \mathbf{w} = \begin{bmatrix} 3 \\ 1 \\ 2 \end{bmatrix} \quad \mathbf{v}' = \begin{bmatrix} 1 \\ 2 \\ 3 \end{bmatrix} \quad \mathbf{w}' = \begin{bmatrix} 3 \\ 10 \\ 5 \end{bmatrix}$$

are parallel since they are both parallel to $\begin{bmatrix} 3 \\ 12 \\ 3 \end{bmatrix}$. (Verify!)

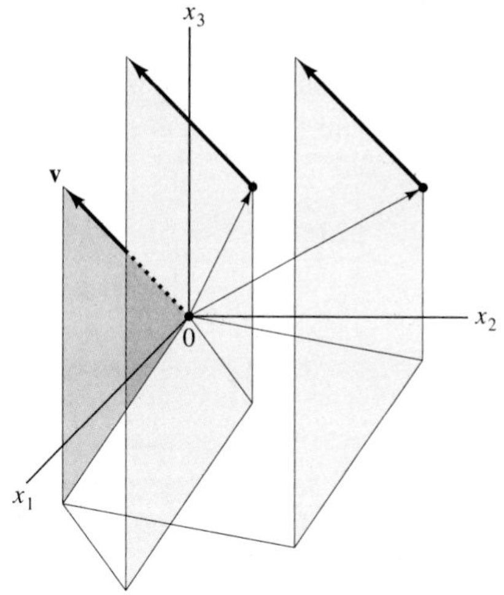

Figure 2.7 The directed segments $\overrightarrow{\mathbf{u}\,\mathbf{u}+\mathbf{v}}$ parallel to a given nonzero vector **v**.

Translation of vectors is a very useful tool for simplifying the geometric representation of a vector expression. In Figure 2.8, we translate vectors freely to give a geometric proof of the associative law for addition of vectors.

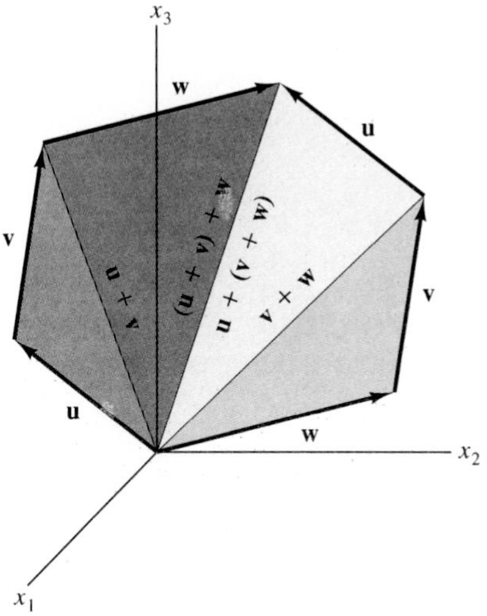

Figure 2.8 Geometric proof of $(\mathbf{u} + \mathbf{v}) + \mathbf{w} = \mathbf{u} + (\mathbf{v} + \mathbf{w})$.

PROBLEMS

NUMERICAL PROBLEMS

1. Find a point $\mathbf{u}$ on the segment between

$$\mathbf{v} = \begin{bmatrix} 2 \\ 3 \\ 1 \end{bmatrix} \quad \text{and} \quad \mathbf{w} = \begin{bmatrix} 5 \\ 3 \\ 5 \end{bmatrix}$$

such that

(a) Its distance from $\mathbf{v}$ is 6 times its distance from $\mathbf{w}$;

(b) The product of its distance from $\mathbf{v}$ and its distance from $\mathbf{w}$ is $\frac{1}{2}$.

2. For each of the following sets $\mathbf{v}$, $\mathbf{w}$, $\mathbf{v}'$, and $\mathbf{w}'$ of vectors, determine whether $\overrightarrow{\mathbf{v}\,\mathbf{w}}$ and $\overrightarrow{\mathbf{v}'\,\mathbf{w}'}$ are parallel. If so, give a nonzero vector to which they are both parallel.

(a) $\mathbf{v} = \begin{bmatrix} 1 \\ 2 \\ 3 \end{bmatrix}, \mathbf{w} = \begin{bmatrix} 4 \\ 3 \\ 5 \end{bmatrix}, \mathbf{v}' = \begin{bmatrix} 2 \\ 3 \\ 3 \end{bmatrix}, \mathbf{w}' = \begin{bmatrix} 8 \\ 5 \\ 7 \end{bmatrix}$

(b) $\mathbf{v} = \begin{bmatrix} 2 \\ 1 \\ 1 \end{bmatrix}, \mathbf{w} = \begin{bmatrix} 8 \\ 1 \\ 9 \end{bmatrix}, \mathbf{v}' = \begin{bmatrix} 1 \\ 4 \\ 3 \end{bmatrix}, \mathbf{w}' = \begin{bmatrix} 4 \\ 4 \\ 7 \end{bmatrix}$

(c) $\mathbf{v} = \begin{bmatrix} 1 \\ 2 \\ 3 \end{bmatrix}, \mathbf{w} = \begin{bmatrix} 4 \\ 2 \\ 5 \end{bmatrix}, \mathbf{v}' = \begin{bmatrix} 2 \\ 2 \\ 3 \end{bmatrix}, \mathbf{w}' = \begin{bmatrix} 8 \\ 2 \\ 7 \end{bmatrix}$

THEORETICAL PROBLEMS

3. Show that the directed segments $\overrightarrow{\mathbf{v}\,\mathbf{w}}$ and $\overrightarrow{\mathbf{v}'\,\mathbf{w}'}$ are parallel if $\mathbf{v} \neq \mathbf{w}$ and $\mathbf{w}' - \mathbf{v}'$ is a multiple of $\mathbf{w} - \mathbf{v}$.

Hard

4. Show for $\mathbf{v}, \mathbf{w} \in \mathbb{C}^n$ that the real parts of the points on the segment $\overline{\mathbf{v}\,\mathbf{w}}$ form the segment joining the real part of $\mathbf{v}$ to the real part of $\mathbf{w}$.

2.5 SUBSPACES OF n-SPACE

Whereas Cartesian n-space F^n is a set of vectors together with operations on them, certain subsets of F^n have similar operations.

Definition. *Subspaces.*

A subspace of F^n is a subset V of F^n containing 0 such that if $\mathbf{v}, \mathbf{w} \in V$ and $\mathbf{a} \in F$, then $\mathbf{v} + \mathbf{w}, a\mathbf{v} \in V$.

Right away, we see the following.

1. A subspace V of F^n is, like F^n itself, a set of vectors with operations of addition, subtraction, and scalar multiplication. The subtraction operation is expressed in terms of the other operations as $\mathbf{v} - \mathbf{w} = \mathbf{v} + (-\mathbf{w})$, where $-\mathbf{w}$ denotes $(-1)\mathbf{w}$.
2. A subspace V of F^n inherits from F^n all of the properties of Theorem 2.1.
3. F^n is a subspace of itself.
4. $\{\mathbf{0}\}$ is a subspace of F^n called the **zero subspace**.
5. For any vector $\mathbf{v} \in F^n$, $F\mathbf{v} = \{a\mathbf{v} \mid a \in F\}$ is a subspace called the **span** of $\mathbf{v}$.
6. If V and W are subspaces of F^n, then $V + W = \{\mathbf{v} + \mathbf{w} \mid \mathbf{v} \in V, \mathbf{w} \in \mathbf{W}\}$ is a subspace of F^n, called the **sum** of V and W. To see this, just note that if $\mathbf{v} + \mathbf{w}$ and $\mathbf{v}' + \mathbf{w}'$ are in $V + W$, then
   (a) $(\mathbf{v} + \mathbf{w}) + (\mathbf{v}' + \mathbf{w}') = (\mathbf{v} + \mathbf{v}') + (\mathbf{w} + \mathbf{w}')$ is in $V + W$;
   (b) $(\mathbf{v} + \mathbf{w}) - (\mathbf{v}' + \mathbf{w}') = (\mathbf{v} - \mathbf{v}') + (\mathbf{w} - \mathbf{w}')$ is in $V + W$;
   (c) $a(\mathbf{v} + \mathbf{w}) = a\mathbf{v} + a\mathbf{w}$ is in $V + W$ for all $a \in F$.
7. For any k subspaces $V_1, \ldots, V_k$ of F^n, the *sum*

$$V_1 + \cdots + V_k = \{\mathbf{v}_1 + \cdots + \mathbf{v}_k \mid a_1 \in V_1, \ldots, a_k \in V_k\}$$

   is a subspace of F^n, by repeated application of (6).
8. In particular, for elements $\mathbf{v}_1, \ldots, \mathbf{v}_k$ of F^n,

$$F\mathbf{v}_1 + \cdots + F\mathbf{v}_k = \{a_1\mathbf{v}_1 + \cdots + a_k\mathbf{v}_k \mid a_1, \ldots, a_k \in F\}$$

   is a subspace of F^n called the **span** of $\mathbf{v}_1, \ldots, \mathbf{v}_k$. Calling element $a_1\mathbf{v}_1 + \cdots + a_k\mathbf{v}_k$ a **linear combination** of $\mathbf{v}_1, \ldots, \mathbf{v}_k$, the span of k vectors is just the set of all linear combinations of them (Figure 2.9).
9. For any two subspaces V and W of F^n, the intersection $V \cap W$ is a subspace of F^n. To see this, just note that if $\mathbf{v}$ and $\mathbf{w}$ are in $V \cap W$, then they are also in V and W, so that $\mathbf{v} + \mathbf{w}$, $\mathbf{v} - \mathbf{w}$ and $a\mathbf{v}$ are in V and W, hence in $V \cap W$, for all $a \in F$.
10. In fact, the intersection of any collection of subspaces of F^n is a subspace, by the same reasoning. (Prove!)

Since a subspace V of F^n contains the span $F\mathbf{v}_1 + \cdots + F\mathbf{v}_k$ of any set $\mathbf{v}_1, \ldots, \mathbf{v}_k$ of elements contained in it, $F\mathbf{v}_1 + \cdots + F\mathbf{v}_k$ is a subset of $F\mathbf{w}_1 + \cdots + F\mathbf{w}_n$ if and only if each $\mathbf{v}_j$ can be expressed in the form $\mathbf{v}_j = W\mathbf{x}_j$ where W is the matrix $W = [\mathbf{w}_1 \ \ldots \ \mathbf{w}_n]$ whose columns are the $\mathbf{w}$'s and $\mathbf{x}_j$ is a vector. When this is possible, taking X to be the matrix $X = [\mathbf{x}_1 \ \ldots \ \mathbf{x}_k]$ gives $[\mathbf{v}_1 \ \ldots \ \mathbf{v}_k] = [\mathbf{w}_1 \ \ldots \ \mathbf{w}_n]X$. This proves Theorem 2.5.

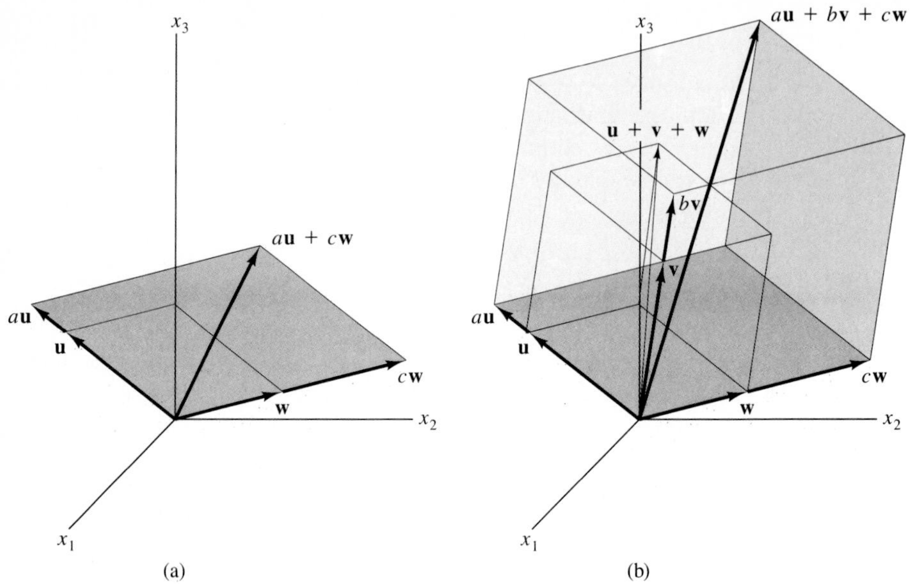

Figure 2.9 (a) The linear combination $a\mathbf{u} + c\mathbf{w}$ of the vectors $\mathbf{u}$ and $\mathbf{w}$. (b) The linear combinations $a\mathbf{u} + b\mathbf{v} + c\mathbf{w}$ of the vectors $\mathbf{u}, \mathbf{v}, \mathbf{w}$.

Theorem 2.5. *Inclusion of Subspaces vis-à-vis Matrix Products.* $F\mathbf{v}_1 + \cdots + F\mathbf{v}_k \subseteq F\mathbf{w}_1 + \cdots + F\mathbf{w}_n$ if and only if there is a matrix X such that $[\mathbf{v}_1 \ \ldots \ \mathbf{v}_k] = [\mathbf{w}_1 \ \ldots \ \mathbf{w}_n]X$.

If X in this theorem is invertible, the two spans are equal. (Prove!)

EXAMPLES

1. Since

$$\begin{bmatrix} -2 & -2 \\ 7 & 10 \\ 4 & 6 \end{bmatrix} = \begin{bmatrix} 1 & -1 \\ 1 & 2 \\ 1 & 1 \end{bmatrix} \begin{bmatrix} 1 & 2 \\ 3 & 4 \end{bmatrix}, \qquad F\begin{bmatrix} -2 \\ 7 \\ 4 \end{bmatrix} + F\begin{bmatrix} -2 \\ 10 \\ 6 \end{bmatrix} \subseteq F\begin{bmatrix} 1 \\ 1 \\ 1 \end{bmatrix} + F\begin{bmatrix} -1 \\ 2 \\ 1 \end{bmatrix}.$$

For instance,

$$\begin{bmatrix} -2 \\ 7 \\ 4 \end{bmatrix} = 1\begin{bmatrix} 1 \\ 1 \\ 1 \end{bmatrix} + 3\begin{bmatrix} -1 \\ 2 \\ 1 \end{bmatrix} \quad \text{and} \quad \begin{bmatrix} -2 \\ 10 \\ 6 \end{bmatrix} = 2\begin{bmatrix} 1 \\ 1 \\ 1 \end{bmatrix} + 4\begin{bmatrix} -1 \\ 2 \\ 1 \end{bmatrix}.$$

2. Since

$$\begin{bmatrix} -2 & -2 \\ 7 & 10 \\ 4 & 6 \end{bmatrix} \begin{bmatrix} 1 & 2 \\ 3 & 4 \end{bmatrix}^{-1} = \begin{bmatrix} 1 & -1 \\ 1 & 2 \\ 1 & 1 \end{bmatrix}, \qquad F\begin{bmatrix} -2 \\ 7 \\ 4 \end{bmatrix} + F\begin{bmatrix} -2 \\ 10 \\ 6 \end{bmatrix} \supseteq F\begin{bmatrix} 1 \\ 1 \\ 1 \end{bmatrix} + F\begin{bmatrix} -1 \\ 2 \\ 1 \end{bmatrix}.$$

By (1), it follows that the two spans are the same.

Lines and planes through the origin

The smallest subspaces other than the zero subspace are lines and planes through **0**.

Definition. *Lines and Planes through the Origin.*
A **line** through **0** is a subspace of the form $F\mathbf{v}$ where $\mathbf{v}$ is nonzero. **A plane** through **0** is a subspace of the form $F\mathbf{v} + F\mathbf{w}$ where $\mathbf{v}$ is nonzero and $\mathbf{w}$ is not in the line $F\mathbf{v}$ (Figures 2.9(a) and 2.10).

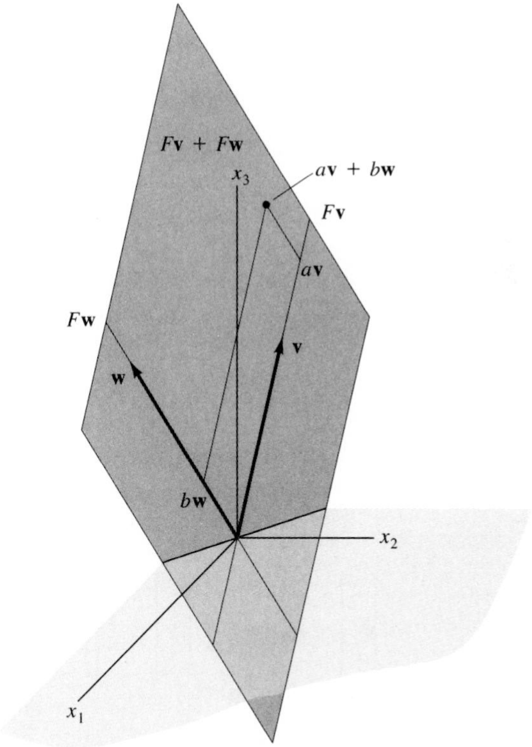

Figure 2.10 The lines $F\mathbf{v}$ and $F\mathbf{w}$ and the plane $F\mathbf{v} + F\mathbf{w}$.

EXAMPLE

If

$$\mathbf{v} = \begin{bmatrix} 1 \\ 5 \\ 3 \end{bmatrix} \quad \text{and} \quad \mathbf{w} = \begin{bmatrix} 2 \\ 1 \\ 4 \end{bmatrix},$$

then

$$\mathbb{R}\mathbf{v} = \left\{ \begin{bmatrix} 1s \\ 5s \\ 3s \end{bmatrix} \middle| s \in \mathbb{R} \right\}$$

is the line through $\mathbf{0}$ and $\mathbf{v}$ and

$$\mathbb{R}\mathbf{v} + \mathbb{R}\mathbf{w} = \left\{ \begin{bmatrix} 1s+2t \\ 5s+1t \\ 3s+4t \end{bmatrix} \middle| s, t \in \mathbb{R} \right\}$$

is the plane through 0, $\mathbf{v}$, and $\mathbf{w}$.

Elementary operations on pairs of vectors

Any plane $F\mathbf{v} + F\mathbf{w}$ through $\mathbf{0}$ can be expressed as $F\mathbf{v}' + F\mathbf{w}'$, where $\mathbf{v}'$ and $\mathbf{w}'$ are obtained from $\mathbf{v}$ and $\mathbf{w}$ by one or several of the following **elementary operations** on pairs of vectors.

1. Add a multiple of $\mathbf{v}$ or $\mathbf{w}$ to the other.
2. Multiply $\mathbf{v}$ or $\mathbf{w}$ by a nonzero scalar $a \in F$.
3. Interchange $\mathbf{v}$ and $\mathbf{w}$.

Since these operations change only $\mathbf{v}$ and $\mathbf{w}$ but not the plane $F\mathbf{v} + F\mathbf{w}$ (prove), they can be performed any number of times without changing the plane.

EXAMPLES

1.

$$F\begin{bmatrix} 2 \\ 3 \\ 1 \end{bmatrix} + F\begin{bmatrix} 6 \\ 8 \\ 5 \end{bmatrix} = F\begin{bmatrix} 2 \\ 3 \\ 1 \end{bmatrix} + F\begin{bmatrix} 0 \\ -1 \\ 2 \end{bmatrix} = F\begin{bmatrix} 2 \\ 0 \\ 7 \end{bmatrix} + F\begin{bmatrix} 0 \\ -1 \\ 2 \end{bmatrix}$$

$$= F\begin{bmatrix} 1 \\ 0 \\ 7/2 \end{bmatrix} + F\begin{bmatrix} 0 \\ -1 \\ 2 \end{bmatrix} = F\begin{bmatrix} 1 \\ 0 \\ 7/2 \end{bmatrix} + F\begin{bmatrix} 0 \\ 1 \\ -2 \end{bmatrix}.$$

2. If $F\mathbf{v} + F\mathbf{w}$ is a plane through $\mathbf{0}$ and $v_1 = w_1 = 0$, then $F\mathbf{v} + F\mathbf{w}$ equals the plane

$$F\begin{bmatrix} 0 \\ 1 \\ 0 \end{bmatrix} + F\begin{bmatrix} 0 \\ 0 \\ 1 \end{bmatrix}.$$

(Prove!)

3. Suppose that v_1 or w_1 is nonzero, and interchange $\mathbf{v}$ and $\mathbf{w}$ (one of the elementary operations), if necessary, to ensure that v_1 is nonzero. Then replace $\mathbf{v}$ by $\mathbf{v}' = v_1^{-1}\mathbf{v}$, so that

$$\mathbf{v}' = \begin{bmatrix} 1 \\ d \\ e \end{bmatrix}$$

for some d, e. Letting $\mathbf{w}' = \mathbf{w} - w_1\mathbf{v}'$, we have

$$\mathbf{w}' = \begin{bmatrix} 0 \\ f \\ g \end{bmatrix}$$

for some f, g. Now

$$F\mathbf{v} + F\mathbf{w} = F\mathbf{v}' + F\mathbf{w}' = F\begin{bmatrix} 1 \\ d \\ e \end{bmatrix} + F\begin{bmatrix} 0 \\ f \\ g \end{bmatrix},$$

where either f or g is nonzero. (Why?) If f is nonzero, replace $\mathbf{w}'$ by

$$\mathbf{w}'' = f^{-1}\mathbf{w}' = \begin{bmatrix} 0 \\ 1 \\ b \end{bmatrix},$$

where $b = f^{-1}g$, and $\mathbf{v}'$ by

$$\mathbf{v}'' = \mathbf{v}' - d\mathbf{w}'' = \begin{bmatrix} 1 \\ 0 \\ a \end{bmatrix},$$

where $a = e - db$. Then

$$F\mathbf{v} + F\mathbf{w} = F\begin{bmatrix} 1 \\ 0 \\ a \end{bmatrix} + F\begin{bmatrix} 0 \\ 1 \\ b \end{bmatrix}.$$

On the other hand, if f is 0, replace $\mathbf{w}'$ by

$$\mathbf{w}'' = \begin{bmatrix} 0 \\ 0 \\ 1 \end{bmatrix}$$

and $\mathbf{v}'$ by

$$\mathbf{v}' - e\mathbf{w}'' = \begin{bmatrix} 1 \\ a \\ 0 \end{bmatrix},$$

where $a = d$. In this case,

$$F\mathbf{v} + F\mathbf{w} = F\begin{bmatrix} 1 \\ a \\ 0 \end{bmatrix} + F\begin{bmatrix} 0 \\ 0 \\ 1 \end{bmatrix}.$$

Examples (2) and (3) show that *any plane in* $\mathbb{R}^3$ *through* $\mathbf{0}$ *is one of*

$$F\begin{bmatrix} 0 \\ 1 \\ 0 \end{bmatrix} + F\begin{bmatrix} 0 \\ 0 \\ 1 \end{bmatrix}, \quad F\begin{bmatrix} 1 \\ 0 \\ a \end{bmatrix} + F\begin{bmatrix} 0 \\ 1 \\ b \end{bmatrix}, \quad F\begin{bmatrix} 1 \\ a \\ 0 \end{bmatrix} + F\begin{bmatrix} 0 \\ 0 \\ 1 \end{bmatrix},$$

as illustrated in Figure 2.11. In other words, *any plane through* $\mathbf{0}$ *not containing the* x_3 *axis is*

$$F\begin{bmatrix} 1 \\ a \\ 0 \end{bmatrix} + F\begin{bmatrix} 0 \\ 0 \\ 1 \end{bmatrix} \qquad \text{for some } a \neq 0.$$

The equation of a plane

The set of solutions to an equation $ax_1 + bx_2 + cx_3 = 0$ (a or b or c nonzero) is a plane. For instance, if c is nonzero, it is the plane

$$F\begin{bmatrix} 1 \\ 0 \\ p \end{bmatrix} + F\begin{bmatrix} 0 \\ 1 \\ q \end{bmatrix},$$

where $a1 + b0 + cp = 0$ and $a0 + b1 + cq = 0$. (Prove!) Similar descriptions correspond to the other cases of b or a nonzero. Conversely, every plane $F\mathbf{v} + F\mathbf{w}$ through $\mathbf{0}$ is the set of solutions to an equation $ax_1 + bx_2 + cx_3 = 0$ (a or b or c nonzero). To find it, simply solve the system of linear equations

$$av_1 + bv_2 + cv_3 = 0$$

$$aw_1 + bw_2 + cw_3 = 0$$

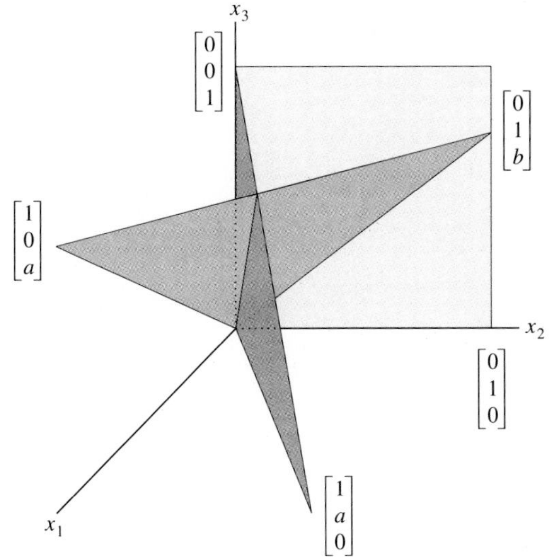

Figure 2.11 The three kinds of planes $F\mathbf{v} + F\mathbf{w}$ through $\mathbf{0}$ in $\mathbb{R}^3$.

for a, b, c. There is a solution with a or b or c nonzero, since there are fewer equations than there are unknowns a, b, and c. This proves the following theorem.

Theorem 2.6. *The Equation of a Plane through* $\mathbf{0}$.
For any plane $F\mathbf{v} + F\mathbf{w}$ through $\mathbf{0}$ in $\mathbb{R}^3$, there are real numbers a, b, c (a or b or c nonzero) such that the set of solutions x to $ax_1 + bx_2 + cx_3 = 0$ is the plane $F\mathbf{v} + F\mathbf{w}$. Conversely, the set of solutions to such an equation is a plane $F\mathbf{v} + F\mathbf{w}$ through $\mathbf{0}$ for some $\mathbf{v}$ and $\mathbf{w}$.

The vector $\begin{bmatrix}a\\b\\c\end{bmatrix}$ is called the **normal** to the plane $ax_1 + bx_2 + cx_3 = 0$ (Figure 2.12) and will be discussed later.

EXAMPLES

1. The equation of the plane

$$F\begin{bmatrix}1\\0\\a\end{bmatrix} + F\begin{bmatrix}0\\1\\b\end{bmatrix}$$

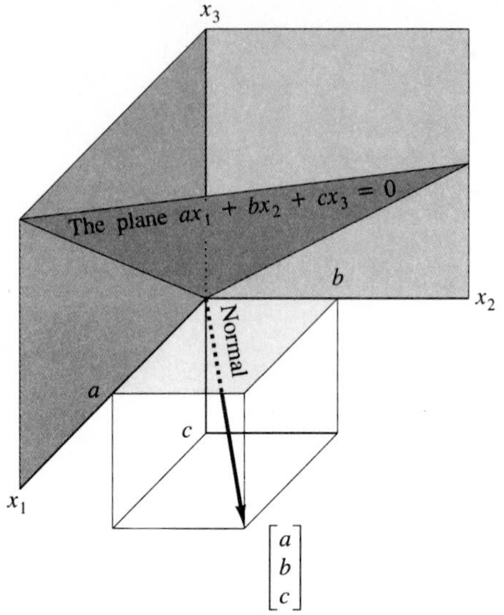

Figure 2.12 The plane $ax_1 + bx_2 + cx_3 = 0$ and its normal $\begin{bmatrix} a \\ b \\ c \end{bmatrix}$.

is $ax_1 + bx_2 - x_3 = 0$, since the vectors satisfying the equation are

$$r\begin{bmatrix} 1 \\ 0 \\ a \end{bmatrix} + s\begin{bmatrix} 0 \\ 1 \\ b \end{bmatrix} = \begin{bmatrix} r \\ s \\ ra+sb \end{bmatrix}.$$

2. Similarly, the equation of

$$F\begin{bmatrix} 1 \\ a \\ 0 \end{bmatrix} + F\begin{bmatrix} 0 \\ 0 \\ 1 \end{bmatrix}$$

is $ax_1 - x_2 = 0$ and that of

$$F\begin{bmatrix} 0 \\ 1 \\ 0 \end{bmatrix} + F\begin{bmatrix} 0 \\ 0 \\ 1 \end{bmatrix}$$

is $x_1 = 0$. (Prove!)

PROBLEMS

NUMERICAL PROBLEMS

1. Is the set V of vectors $\begin{bmatrix} 1 \\ r \\ s \end{bmatrix}$ $(r, s \in F)$ a subspace of F^3?

2. Is the set V of vectors $\begin{bmatrix} s+3r+1 \\ r \\ s \end{bmatrix}$ $(r, s \in F)$ a subspace of F^3?

3. Is the set V of vectors $\begin{bmatrix} 4s+r \\ r \\ s \end{bmatrix}$ $(r, s \in F)$ a subspace of F^3?

4. Is the set V of vectors $\begin{bmatrix} 2t \\ 2s+r+4t \\ r-s \end{bmatrix}$ $(r, s, t \in F)$ a subspace of F^3?

5. Is the set V of vectors $\begin{bmatrix} t \\ r^3-s^3 \\ s^3 \end{bmatrix}$ $(r, s, t \in \mathbb{R})$ a subspace of $\mathbb{R}^3$?

6. Are the two planes $F\mathbf{v} + F\mathbf{w}$ and $F\mathbf{v}' + F\mathbf{w}'$ equal if

(a) $\mathbf{v} = \begin{bmatrix} 1 \\ 3 \\ 3 \end{bmatrix}$, $\mathbf{w} = \begin{bmatrix} 2 \\ 2 \\ 3 \end{bmatrix}$, $\mathbf{v}' = \begin{bmatrix} 1 \\ 3 \\ 3 \end{bmatrix}$, and $\mathbf{w}' = \begin{bmatrix} 3 \\ 5 \\ 6 \end{bmatrix}$;

(b) $\mathbf{v} = \begin{bmatrix} 1 \\ 3 \\ 3 \end{bmatrix}$, $\mathbf{w} = \begin{bmatrix} 2 \\ 2 \\ 3 \end{bmatrix}$, $\mathbf{v}' = \begin{bmatrix} 1 \\ -1 \\ 0 \end{bmatrix}$, and $\mathbf{w}' = \begin{bmatrix} 3 \\ 5 \\ 6 \end{bmatrix}$;

(c) $\mathbf{v} = \begin{bmatrix} 1 \\ 3 \\ 3 \end{bmatrix}$, $\mathbf{w} = \begin{bmatrix} 2 \\ 2 \\ 3 \end{bmatrix}$, $\mathbf{v}' = \begin{bmatrix} 1 \\ -1 \\ 0 \end{bmatrix}$, and $\mathbf{w}' = \begin{bmatrix} 4 \\ 4 \\ 6 \end{bmatrix}$?

7. Find the equation of the plane in each case.

(a) $F\begin{bmatrix} 2 \\ 3 \\ 3 \end{bmatrix} + F\begin{bmatrix} 8 \\ 12 \\ 17 \end{bmatrix}$ **(b)** $F\begin{bmatrix} 2 \\ 0 \\ 2 \end{bmatrix} + F\begin{bmatrix} 1 \\ 1 \\ 2 \end{bmatrix}$

(c) $F\begin{bmatrix} 3 \\ 3 \\ 3 \end{bmatrix} + F\begin{bmatrix} 1 \\ 3 \\ 5 \end{bmatrix}$ **(d)** $F\begin{bmatrix} 2 \\ 4 \\ 1 \end{bmatrix} + F\begin{bmatrix} 3 \\ 7 \\ 1 \end{bmatrix}$

THEORETICAL PROBLEMS

8. For

$$\mathbf{e}_1 = \begin{bmatrix} 1 \\ 0 \\ \vdots \\ 0 \end{bmatrix}, \quad \mathbf{e}_2 = \begin{bmatrix} 0 \\ 1 \\ \vdots \\ 0 \end{bmatrix}, \quad \ldots, \quad \mathbf{e}_n = \begin{bmatrix} 0 \\ 0 \\ \vdots \\ 1 \end{bmatrix},$$

show that $F\mathbf{e}_1 + \cdots + F\mathbf{e}_n = \mathbb{R}^n$.

9. For the $\mathbf{e}_1, \mathbf{e}_2, \ldots, \mathbf{e}_n$ defined in Problem 8, show that $a_1\mathbf{e}_1 + \cdots + a_n\mathbf{e}_n = 0$ if and only if $a_1 = 0, \ldots, a_n = 0$.

10. Show that $F\mathbf{v} + F\mathbf{w} = F\mathbf{v} + F(\mathbf{w} + a\mathbf{v})$ for any $a \in F$.

11. Using Problem 10, show that $F\mathbf{v} + F\mathbf{w} = F\mathbf{v}' + F\mathbf{w}'$ if the pair of vectors $\mathbf{v}'$ and $\mathbf{w}'$ is obtained from $\mathbf{v}$ and $\mathbf{w}$ by a sequence of elementary operations on pairs of vectors.

12. Show that there is a plane $\mathbb{C}\mathbf{v} + \mathbb{C}\mathbf{w}$ in $\mathbb{C}^3$ which contains an element $a\mathbf{v} + b\mathbf{w}$ whose conjugate is not in $\mathbb{C}\mathbf{v} + \mathbb{C}\mathbf{w}$.

13. Show that the conjugate of every element of

$$\mathbb{C}\begin{bmatrix} 2 \\ 6 \\ 3 \end{bmatrix} + \mathbb{C}\begin{bmatrix} 2 \\ 1 \\ 3 \end{bmatrix}$$

is contained in

$$\mathbb{C}\begin{bmatrix} 2 \\ 6 \\ 3 \end{bmatrix} + \mathbb{C}\begin{bmatrix} 2 \\ 1 \\ 3 \end{bmatrix}.$$

14. Show that any subspace V inherits from F^n all the properties of Theorem 2.1.

15. For any vector $\mathbf{v}$, $F\mathbf{v} = \{a\mathbf{v} \mid a \in F\}$ is a subspace.

16. Suppose that $\mathbf{u}, \mathbf{v}, \mathbf{w} \in F^n$, $\mathbf{u}$ is nonzero, and $\mathbf{v}$ and $\mathbf{w}$ are in the line $F\mathbf{u}$. Show that $V = F\mathbf{u} + F\mathbf{v} + F\mathbf{w}$ is just the line $F\mathbf{u}$ and the mapping from F to V sending a to $a\mathbf{u}$ is 1-1 and onto.

17. Suppose that $\mathbf{u}, \mathbf{v}, \mathbf{w} \in F^n$, $\mathbf{u}$ is nonzero, $\mathbf{v}$ is not in the line $F\mathbf{u}$, and $\mathbf{w}$ is in the plane $F\mathbf{u} + F\mathbf{v}$. Show that

(a) $V = F\mathbf{u} + F\mathbf{v} + F\mathbf{w}$ is just the plane $F\mathbf{u} + F\mathbf{v}$;

(b) The mapping from F^2 to V sending $\begin{bmatrix} a \\ b \end{bmatrix}$ to $a\mathbf{u} + b\mathbf{v}$ is 1-1 and onto.

18. Find the normals to the following three planes in F^3.

(a) $F\begin{bmatrix} 1 \\ 0 \\ a \end{bmatrix} + F\begin{bmatrix} 0 \\ 1 \\ b \end{bmatrix}$ **(b)** $F\begin{bmatrix} 1 \\ c \\ 0 \end{bmatrix} + F\begin{bmatrix} 0 \\ 0 \\ 1 \end{bmatrix}$ **(c)** $F\begin{bmatrix} 0 \\ 1 \\ 0 \end{bmatrix} + F\begin{bmatrix} 0 \\ 0 \\ 1 \end{bmatrix}$

19. In Problem 18, show that any two of the three normals are perpendicular if and only if $a = b = c = 0$, that is, if and only if the three planes are the planes containing two of the three coordinate axes.

20. The intersection of any nonempty collection of subspaces of F^n is a subspace.

21. For $\mathbf{u}, \mathbf{v}, \mathbf{w} \in F^n$, suppose that $\mathbf{u}$ is nonzero, $\mathbf{v}$ is not in the line $F\mathbf{u}$, and $\mathbf{w}$ is not in the plane $F\mathbf{u} + F\mathbf{v}$. Show that the mapping from F^3 to $V = F\mathbf{u} + F\mathbf{v} + F\mathbf{w}$ sending

$$\begin{bmatrix} a \\ b \\ c \end{bmatrix}$$

to $a\mathbf{u} + b\mathbf{v} + c\mathbf{w}$ is 1-1 and onto.

22. Show that if the conjugate of every element of a plane $\mathbb{C}\mathbf{v} + \mathbb{C}\mathbf{w}$ is also contained in $\mathbb{C}\mathbf{v} + \mathbb{C}\mathbf{w}$, then there are real vectors $\mathbf{v}'$ and $\mathbf{w}'$ such that $\mathbb{C}\mathbf{v} + \mathbb{C}\mathbf{w} = \mathbb{C}\mathbf{v}' + \mathbb{C}\mathbf{w}'$.

23. Let

$$\mathbf{e}_1 = \begin{bmatrix} 1 \\ 0 \\ 0 \end{bmatrix}, \qquad \mathbf{e}_2 = \begin{bmatrix} 0 \\ 1 \\ 0 \end{bmatrix}, \qquad \mathbf{e}_3 = \begin{bmatrix} 0 \\ 0 \\ 1 \end{bmatrix},$$

so that we can write

$$\begin{bmatrix} a \\ b \\ c \end{bmatrix} = a\mathbf{e}_1 + b\mathbf{e}_2 + c\mathbf{e}_3.$$

Define

$$\begin{bmatrix} a \\ b \\ c \end{bmatrix} \times \begin{bmatrix} d \\ e \\ f \end{bmatrix} = \begin{vmatrix} \mathbf{e}_1 & a & d \\ \mathbf{e}_2 & b & e \\ \mathbf{e}_3 & c & f \end{vmatrix}$$

where

$$\begin{vmatrix} \mathbf{e}_1 & a & d \\ \mathbf{e}_2 & b & e \\ \mathbf{e}_3 & c & f \end{vmatrix} = \begin{vmatrix} b & e \\ c & f \end{vmatrix}\mathbf{e}_1 - \begin{vmatrix} a & d \\ c & f \end{vmatrix}\mathbf{e}_2 + \begin{vmatrix} a & d \\ b & e \end{vmatrix}\mathbf{e}_3.$$

Show that

(a) $\begin{bmatrix} a \\ b \\ c \end{bmatrix} \times \begin{bmatrix} d \\ e \\ f \end{bmatrix} = \begin{bmatrix} bf - ce \\ cd - af \\ ae - bd \end{bmatrix};$

(b) $\begin{bmatrix} a \\ b \\ c \end{bmatrix} \times \begin{bmatrix} d \\ e \\ f \end{bmatrix}$ is perpendicular to $\begin{bmatrix} a \\ b \\ c \end{bmatrix}$ and $\begin{bmatrix} d \\ e \\ f \end{bmatrix}$;

(c) $\begin{bmatrix} a \\ b \\ c \end{bmatrix} \times \begin{bmatrix} d \\ e \\ f \end{bmatrix}$ is nonzero if $\begin{bmatrix} a \\ b \\ c \end{bmatrix}$ and $\begin{bmatrix} d \\ e \\ f \end{bmatrix}$ are nonzero and $F\begin{bmatrix} a \\ b \\ c \end{bmatrix} \neq F\begin{bmatrix} d \\ e \\ f \end{bmatrix}$;

(d) A normal for the plane $F\begin{bmatrix} a \\ b \\ c \end{bmatrix} + F\begin{bmatrix} d \\ e \\ f \end{bmatrix}$ is $\begin{bmatrix} a \\ b \\ c \end{bmatrix} \times \begin{bmatrix} d \\ e \\ f \end{bmatrix}$.

24. Compute the normals.

(a) $\begin{bmatrix} 1 \\ 0 \\ a \end{bmatrix} \times \begin{bmatrix} 0 \\ 1 \\ b \end{bmatrix}$ for $F\begin{bmatrix} 1 \\ 0 \\ a \end{bmatrix} + F\begin{bmatrix} 0 \\ 1 \\ b \end{bmatrix}$ **(b)** $\begin{bmatrix} 1 \\ c \\ 0 \end{bmatrix} \times \begin{bmatrix} 0 \\ 0 \\ 1 \end{bmatrix}$ for $F\begin{bmatrix} 1 \\ c \\ 0 \end{bmatrix} + F\begin{bmatrix} 0 \\ 0 \\ 1 \end{bmatrix}$

(c) $\begin{bmatrix} 0 \\ 1 \\ 0 \end{bmatrix} \times \begin{bmatrix} 0 \\ 0 \\ 1 \end{bmatrix}$ for $F\begin{bmatrix} 0 \\ 1 \\ 0 \end{bmatrix} + F\begin{bmatrix} 0 \\ 0 \\ 1 \end{bmatrix}$

25. Show that the equation for the plane

$$F\begin{bmatrix} a \\ b \\ c \end{bmatrix} + F\begin{bmatrix} d \\ e \\ f \end{bmatrix} \quad \text{is} \quad \begin{bmatrix} bf-ce \\ cd-af \\ ae-bd \end{bmatrix} \cdot \begin{bmatrix} x_1 \\ x_2 \\ x_3 \end{bmatrix} = 0.$$

26. The *determinant*

$$\begin{vmatrix} r & a & d \\ s & b & e \\ t & c & f \end{vmatrix}$$

is defined to be the scalar

$$\begin{vmatrix} r & a & d \\ s & b & e \\ t & c & f \end{vmatrix} = \begin{bmatrix} bf-ce \\ cd-af \\ ae-bd \end{bmatrix} \cdot \begin{bmatrix} r \\ s \\ t \end{bmatrix}.$$

Show that the determinant

$$\begin{vmatrix} r & a & d \\ s & b & e \\ t & c & f \end{vmatrix}$$

is nonzero if and only if the following conditions are met.

(a) No column is a multiple of another column.

(b) No column is in the plane through $\mathbf{0}$ containing the other two columns.

2.6 TRANSLATION OF SUBSPACES

Given a subspace V of F^n and a vector $\mathbf{u}$, we get the **translate** $\mathbf{u} + V = \{\mathbf{u} + \mathbf{v} \mid \mathbf{v} \in V\}$ of V by $\mathbf{u}$. This is the image of V under the translation mapping $T_{\mathbf{u}}$, which we now define.

Definition. *Translations.*
For $\mathbf{u} \in F^n$, $T_{\mathbf{u}}$ is the mapping from F^n to itself defined by $T_u(\mathbf{v}) = \mathbf{u} + \mathbf{v}$. We call $T_{\mathbf{u}}$ a **translation** by $\mathbf{u}$.

Lines and planes through a point

Translations are used to move lines and planes through one point to lines and planes through another point. Note the following facts.

1. Translation by $\mathbf{u}$ maps a line $F\mathbf{v}$ through $\mathbf{0}$ and $\mathbf{v}$ to the *line* $\mathbf{u} + F\mathbf{v}$ *through* $\mathbf{u}$ and $\mathbf{u} + \mathbf{v}$. The line $\mathbf{u} + F\mathbf{v}$ is also called the line through $\mathbf{u}$ *parallel* to $F\mathbf{v}$.
2. Translation by $\mathbf{u}$ maps a plane $F\mathbf{v} + F\mathbf{w}$ through $\mathbf{0}$, $\mathbf{v}$, and $\mathbf{w}$ to the *plane* $\mathbf{u} + (F\mathbf{v} + F\mathbf{w})$ *through* $\mathbf{u}$, $\mathbf{u} + \mathbf{v}$, and $\mathbf{u} + \mathbf{w}$. The plane $\mathbf{u} + (F\mathbf{v} + F\mathbf{w})$ is also called the plane through $\mathbf{u}$ *parallel* to $F\mathbf{v} + F\mathbf{w}$ (Figure 2.13).

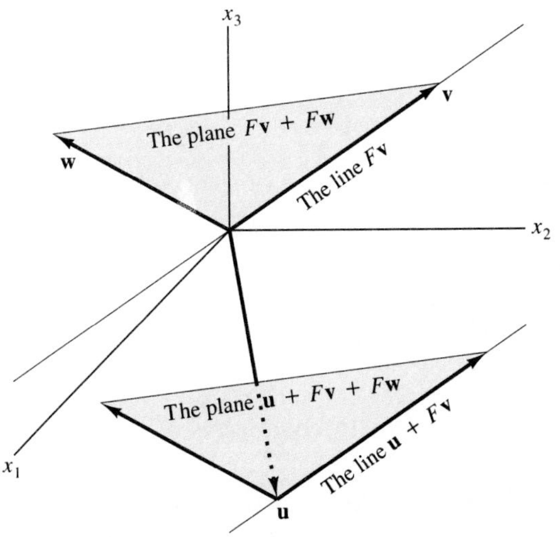

Figure 2.13 Translation by $\mathbf{u}$. The line $\mathbf{u} + F\mathbf{v}$ and plane $\mathbf{u} + F\mathbf{v} + F\mathbf{w}$.

The general point $\mathbf{x}$ on the line $\mathbf{u} + F\mathbf{v}$ is $\mathbf{x} = \mathbf{u} + s\mathbf{v}$ $(s \in F)$, whereas the general point $\mathbf{x}$ on the plane $\mathbf{u} + (F\mathbf{v} + F\mathbf{w})$ is $\mathbf{x} = \mathbf{u} + s\mathbf{v} + t\mathbf{w}$ $(s, t \in F)$. The equation $\mathbf{x} = \mathbf{u} + s\mathbf{v}$ is the *parametric equation* of the line $\mathbf{u} + F\mathbf{v}$, the parameter being s; and the equation $\mathbf{x} = \mathbf{u} + s\mathbf{v} + t\mathbf{w}$ is the *parametric equation* of the plane $\mathbf{u} + F\mathbf{v} + F\mathbf{w}$, the parameters being s and t.

EXAMPLES

1. If $\mathbf{v} = \begin{bmatrix} 1 \\ 5 \\ 3 \end{bmatrix}$ and $\mathbf{u} = \begin{bmatrix} 2 \\ 6 \\ 3 \end{bmatrix}$, then the line

$$\mathbf{u} + \mathbb{R}\mathbf{v} = \begin{bmatrix} 2 \\ 6 \\ 3 \end{bmatrix} + \mathbb{R}\begin{bmatrix} 1 \\ 5 \\ 3 \end{bmatrix}$$

is the set

$$\mathbf{u} + \mathbb{R}\mathbf{v} = \left\{ \begin{bmatrix} 2+1s \\ 6+5s \\ 3+3s \end{bmatrix} \middle| \, s \in \mathbb{R} \right\}$$

and its parametric equation is

$$\mathbf{x} = \begin{bmatrix} 2 \\ 6 \\ 3 \end{bmatrix} + s\begin{bmatrix} 1 \\ 5 \\ 3 \end{bmatrix} \qquad (s \in F).$$

2. Similarly, if

$$\mathbf{v} = \begin{bmatrix} 1 \\ 5 \\ 3 \end{bmatrix}, \qquad \mathbf{w} = \begin{bmatrix} 2 \\ 1 \\ 4 \end{bmatrix}, \qquad \text{and} \qquad \mathbf{u} = \begin{bmatrix} 2 \\ 6 \\ 3 \end{bmatrix},$$

the plane $\mathbf{u} + (\mathbb{R}\mathbf{v} + \mathbb{R}\mathbf{w})$ is the set

$$\mathbf{u} + (\mathbb{R}\mathbf{v} + \mathbb{R}\mathbf{w}) = \left\{ \begin{bmatrix} 2+1s+2t \\ 6+5s+1t \\ 3+3s+4t \end{bmatrix} \middle| \, s, t \in \mathbb{R} \right\}$$

and its parametric equation is

$$\mathbf{x} = \begin{bmatrix} 2 \\ 6 \\ 3 \end{bmatrix} + s\begin{bmatrix} 1 \\ 5 \\ 3 \end{bmatrix} + t\begin{bmatrix} 2 \\ 1 \\ 4 \end{bmatrix} \qquad (s, t \in F).$$

The equation of a plane in F^3

Let $F\mathbf{v} + F\mathbf{w}$ be the set of solutions

$$\mathbf{x} = \begin{bmatrix} x_1 \\ x_2 \\ x_3 \end{bmatrix}$$

to $ax_1 + bx_2 + cx_3 = 0$, and let

$$\mathbf{u} = \begin{bmatrix} u_1 \\ u_2 \\ u_3 \end{bmatrix}.$$

Then the set of solutions to $a(x_1 - u_1) + b(x_2 - u_2) + c(x_3 - u_3) = 0$ is the plane $\mathbf{u} + F\mathbf{v} + F\mathbf{w} = \{\mathbf{u} + s\mathbf{v} + t\mathbf{w} \mid s, t \in F\}$. The reason for this is that $\mathbf{x} = s\mathbf{v} + t\mathbf{w}$ satisfies $ax_1 + bx_2 + cx_3 = 0$ if and only if $\mathbf{x} = \mathbf{u} + s\mathbf{v} + t\mathbf{w}$ satisfies $a(x_1 - u_1) + b(x_2 - u_2) + c(x_3 - u_3) = 0$. (Verify!) This proves the following.

Theorem 2.7. *Equation of a Plane Parallel to a Given Plane through a Given Point.*
The equation of a plane $\mathbf{u} + F\mathbf{v} + F\mathbf{w}$ through $\mathbf{u}$ is

$$a(x_1 - u_1) + b(x_2 - u_2) + c(x_3 - u_3) = 0,$$

where $ax_1 + bx_2 + cx_3 = 0$ is the equation of the parallel plane $F\mathbf{v} + F\mathbf{w}$ through $\mathbf{0}$.

Since

$$\begin{bmatrix} a \\ b \\ c \end{bmatrix}$$

is a normal to the plane $ax_1 + bx_2 + cx_3 = 0$, it is also called a *normal* to the plane $a(x_1 - u_1) + b(x_2 - u_2) + c(x_3 - u_3) = 0$ obtained by translation by u (Figure 2.14).

Corollary. If not all of a, b, c are 0 and if

$$\mathbf{u} = \begin{bmatrix} u_1 \\ u_2 \\ u_3 \end{bmatrix}$$

is a solution to $ax_1 + bx_2 + cx_3 = p$, then the set of solutions of $ax_1 + bx_2 + cx_3 = p$ is the plane through $\mathbf{u}$ parallel to the plane $ax_1 + bx_2 + cx_3 = 0$.

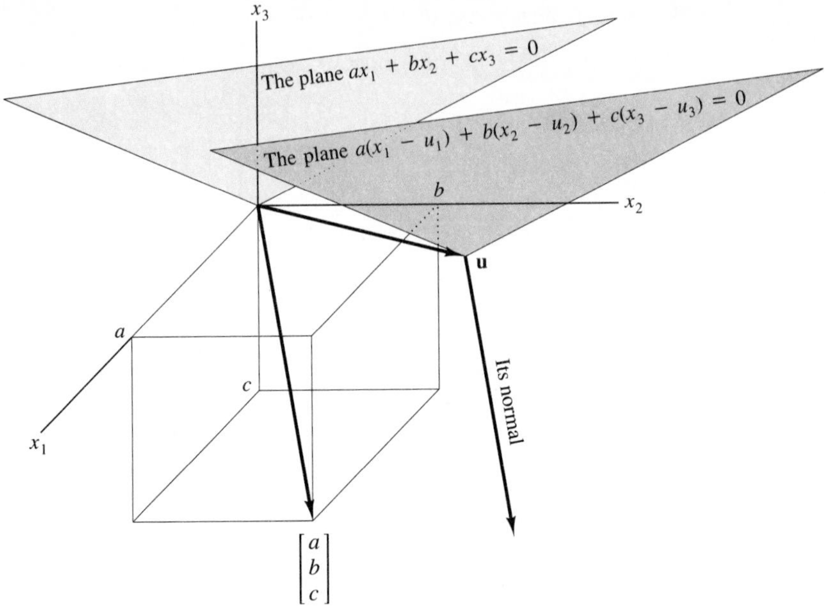

Figure 2.14 The plane $a(x_1 - u_1) + b(x_2 - u_2) + c(x_3 - u_3) = 0$ and its normal

$$\mathbf{v} = \begin{bmatrix} a \\ b \\ c \end{bmatrix}.$$

Proof. Assume that $au_1 + bu_2 + cu_3 = p$. Then subtracting this equation from the equation $ax_1 + bx_2 + cx_3 = p$ results in the equation

$$a(x_1 - u_1) + b(x_2 - u_2) + c(x_3 - u_3) = 0.$$

So, the set of solutions to $ax_1 + bx_2 + cx_3 = p$ is the same as the set of solutions to $a(x_1 - u_1) + b(x_2 - u_2) + c(x_3 - u_3) = 0$. ■

EXAMPLE

The set of solutions to $3x_1 - 2x_2 + 2x_3 = 3$ is a plane which passes through the point

$$\begin{bmatrix} 1 \\ 1 \\ 1 \end{bmatrix},$$

so its equation is $3(x_1 - 1) - 2(x_2 - 1) + 2(x_3 - 1) = 0$. The vector

$$\begin{bmatrix} 3 \\ -2 \\ 2 \end{bmatrix}$$

is a normal to the plane.

PROBLEMS

NUMERICAL PROBLEMS

1. Give the parametric equation for the line through $\mathbf{0}$ and $\begin{bmatrix} 2 \\ 3 \\ 3 \end{bmatrix}$.

2. Give the parametric equation for the line through $\begin{bmatrix} 5 \\ 4 \\ 4 \end{bmatrix}$ and $\begin{bmatrix} 42 \\ 3 \\ 3 \end{bmatrix}$.

3. Give the parametric equation for the line through $\mathbf{0}$ and $\begin{bmatrix} 1 \\ 5 \\ 3 \end{bmatrix}$.

4. Give the parametric equation for the line through $\begin{bmatrix} 1 \\ 1 \\ 2 \end{bmatrix}$ and $\begin{bmatrix} 33 \\ 1 \\ 2 \end{bmatrix}$.

5. Determine whether $\mathbf{u}$ is in the segment $\overline{\mathbf{v}\,\mathbf{w}}$ in the following cases. If so, what is the description of $\mathbf{u}$ in terms of $\mathbf{v}$ and $\mathbf{w}$?

   (a) $\mathbf{u} = \begin{bmatrix} 3 \\ 2 \\ 3 \end{bmatrix}, \mathbf{v} = \begin{bmatrix} 1 \\ 1 \\ 2 \end{bmatrix}, \mathbf{w} = \begin{bmatrix} 5 \\ 3 \\ 4 \end{bmatrix}$ (b) $\mathbf{u} = \begin{bmatrix} 3 \\ 2 \\ 3 \end{bmatrix}, \mathbf{v} = \begin{bmatrix} 4 \\ -1 \\ 5 \end{bmatrix}, \mathbf{w} = \begin{bmatrix} 5 \\ 5 \\ 4 \end{bmatrix}$

   (c) $\mathbf{u} = \begin{bmatrix} 6 \\ 4 \\ 6 \end{bmatrix}, \mathbf{v} = \begin{bmatrix} 1 \\ 1 \\ 2 \end{bmatrix}, \mathbf{w} = \begin{bmatrix} 5 \\ 3 \\ 4 \end{bmatrix}$

6. Find the equation of each of the following planes.

   (a) $\begin{bmatrix} 2 \\ 1 \\ 3 \end{bmatrix} + F\begin{bmatrix} 2 \\ 3 \\ 3 \end{bmatrix} + F\begin{bmatrix} 0 \\ 1 \\ 2 \end{bmatrix}$ (b) $\begin{bmatrix} 5 \\ 2 \\ 5 \end{bmatrix} + F\begin{bmatrix} -1 \\ 0 \\ 1 \end{bmatrix} + F\begin{bmatrix} 2 \\ 3 \\ 1 \end{bmatrix}$

   (c) $\begin{bmatrix} 5 \\ 3 \\ 4 \end{bmatrix} + F\begin{bmatrix} 2 \\ 3 \\ 3 \end{bmatrix} + F\begin{bmatrix} 8 \\ 12 \\ 17 \end{bmatrix}$

7. Express the following equations in the form

$$a(x_1 - r) - b(x_2 - s) + s(x_3 - t) = 0.$$

(a) $5x_1 - 2x_2 + 2x_3 = 10$ (b) $3x_1 - 3x_2 + 2x_3 = 2$
(c) $3x_1 - 4x_2 + 5x_3 = 7$

8. Express the plane of solutions to the following equations in $\mathbb{R}^3$ in the form $\mathbf{u} + \mathbb{R}\mathbf{v} + \mathbb{R}\mathbf{w}$.

(a) $1x_1 - 1x_2 + 2x_3 = 3$ (b) $2x_1 - 2x_2 + 3x_3 = 5$
(c) $3x_1 - 2x_2 + 1x_3 = 5$

9. Find a parametric equation for the plane of solutions to each of the equations in Problem 8.

THEORETICAL PROBLEMS

10. Show that the line $F\begin{bmatrix} a \\ b \end{bmatrix} + \begin{bmatrix} c \\ d \end{bmatrix}$ is the set of solutions $\begin{bmatrix} x_1 \\ x_2 \end{bmatrix}$ to the equation $-b(x_1 - c) + a(x_2 - d) = 0$.

11. Show that the set of solutions $\begin{bmatrix} x_1 \\ x_2 \end{bmatrix}$ to $ax_1 + bx_2 = p$ is the line $F\begin{bmatrix} b \\ -a \end{bmatrix} + F\begin{bmatrix} c \\ d \end{bmatrix}$, where $\begin{bmatrix} c \\ d \end{bmatrix}$ is a point which satisfies $ax_1 + bx_2 = p$.

12. Show that for two distinct points $\mathbf{v}, \mathbf{w} \in \mathbb{R}^n$, the line segment $\overline{\mathbf{v}\,\mathbf{w}} = \{(1 - t)\mathbf{v} + t\mathbf{w} \mid 0 \le t \le 1\}$ is a subset of the line $\mathbf{v} + F(\mathbf{w} - \mathbf{v})$ through the points $\mathbf{v}$ and $\mathbf{w}$.

2.7 LINEAR EQUATIONS. HYPERPLANES

Linear functions and linear equations

A **linear function** from F^n to F is a function $y = f(\mathbf{x})$ where

$$\mathbf{x} = \begin{bmatrix} x_1 \\ \vdots \\ x_n \end{bmatrix} \in F$$

and $f(\mathbf{x}) = a_1x_1 + \cdots + a_nx_n$, the a_s's $(1 \le s \le n)$ being constants. Often, we write the function simply as $y = a_1x_1 + \cdots + a_nx_n$. For example, $y = 3x_1 - 2x_2 + 2x_3$ is a linear function that maps

$$\begin{bmatrix} 1 \\ 3 \\ 2 \end{bmatrix}$$

to $3 \cdot 1 - 2 \cdot 3 + 2 \cdot 2 = 1$.

Linear functions f satisfy the following properties.

Theorem 2.8. *Linearity Properties.*
Let f be a linear function from F^n to F. Then f satisfies the following properties.

1. $f(\mathbf{x}+\mathbf{y}) = f(\mathbf{x}) + f(\mathbf{y})$ and $f(\mathbf{x}-\mathbf{y}) = f(\mathbf{x}) - f(\mathbf{y})$ for all $\mathbf{x}, \mathbf{y} \in F^n$.
2. $f(t\mathbf{x}) = tf(\mathbf{x})$ and $f(-\mathbf{x}) = -f(\mathbf{x})$ for all $t \in F$ and all $\mathbf{x} \in F^n$.
3. $f(\mathbf{0}) = 0$.

Proof. Let $f(\mathbf{x}) = a_1x_1 + \cdots + a_nx_n$ be the linear function. Replacing $\mathbf{x}$ by $\mathbf{x}+\mathbf{y}$, we get

$$\begin{aligned} f(\mathbf{x}+\mathbf{y}) &= a_1(x_1+y_1) + \cdots + a_n(x_n+y_n) \\ &= a_1x_1 + \cdots + a_nx_n + a_1y_1 + \cdots + a_ny_n \\ &= f(\mathbf{x}) + f(\mathbf{y}). \end{aligned}$$

Replacing $\mathbf{x}$ by $t\mathbf{x}$, we get

$$\begin{aligned} f(t\mathbf{x}) &= a_1(tx_1) + \cdots + a_n(tx_n) \\ &= ta_1(x_1) + \cdots + ta_n(x_n) \\ &= tf(\mathbf{x}). \end{aligned}$$

Taking $t = -1$, we get

$$f(-\mathbf{x}) = f((-1)\mathbf{x}) = (-1)f(\mathbf{x}) = -f(\mathbf{x}).$$

Putting these together, we get

$$f(\mathbf{x}-\mathbf{y}) = f(\mathbf{x}+(-\mathbf{y})) = f(\mathbf{x}) + f(-\mathbf{y}) = f(\mathbf{x}) - f(\mathbf{y}).$$

Since $f(\mathbf{x}) = a_1x_1 + \cdots + a_nx_n$, we have $f(\mathbf{0}) = a_10 + \cdots + a_n0 = 0$. ■

If $p \in F$, the linear function $f(\mathbf{x}) = a_1x_1 + \cdots + a_nx_n$ gives us a corresponding *linear equation* $f(\mathbf{x}) = p$, which we write simply as

$$a_1x_1 + \cdots + a_nx_n = p.$$

For example, if $a_1 = 3$, $a_2 = -2$, $a_3 = 4$, and $p = -3$, we get the linear equation $3x_1 - 2x_2 + 4x_3 = -3$.

Hyperplanes

The set of points

$$\mathbf{x} = \begin{bmatrix} x_1 \\ \vdots \\ x_n \end{bmatrix}$$

in F^n satisfying a linear equation $a_1x_1 + \cdots + a_nx_n = p$, where not all of the a_s's are 0, is called a **hyperplane**. We sometimes refer to this hyperplane as *the set of solutions*, or as the *locus of points*, of the equation $a_1x_1 + \cdots + a_nx_n = p$.

A hyperplane in F^n is said to be of dimension $n - 1$, indicating that if a_s is a nonzero coefficient of its equation $a_1x_1 + \cdots + a_nx_n = p$, x_s can be regarded expressed as a variable *dependent* on the $n - 1$ *independent variables* $x_1, \ldots, x_{s-1}, x_{s+1}, \ldots, x_n$.

EXAMPLES

1. The hyperplanes in $\mathbb{R} = \mathbb{R}^1$ are just points, since the equation $a_1x_1 = p$ is satisfied only by the point $x_1 = p/a_1$ of $\mathbb{R} = \mathbb{R}^1$.
2. The hyperplanes in F^2 are just the lines $\mathbf{u} + F\mathbf{v}$ introduced in Section 2.5. (Prove!)
3. The hyperplanes in F^3 are just the planes $\mathbf{u} + F\mathbf{v} + F\mathbf{w}$ introduced in Section 2.5. (Verify, using Theorem 2.7 and its corollary.)
4. The hyperplane in F^3 of solutions to $3x_1 + 2x_2 + 2x_3 = 6$ is of dimension $3 - 1 = 2$, and we can write $x_2 = 3 - \frac{3}{2}x_1 - x_3$, where x_1 and x_3 are independent variables. It consists of the vectors of the form

$$\begin{bmatrix} x_1 \\ 3 - \frac{3}{2}x_1 - x_3 \\ x_3 \end{bmatrix}.$$

By (3), we can regard our results on planes in F^3 as a kind of model to follow for hyperplanes in F^n. When $p = 0$, we get the *homogeneous* linear equation

$$a_1x_1 + \cdots + a_nx_n = 0.$$

Since $a_1x_1 + \cdots + a_nx_n$ is just the dot product

$$\begin{bmatrix} a_1 \\ \vdots \\ a_n \end{bmatrix} \cdot \begin{bmatrix} x_1 \\ \vdots \\ x_n \end{bmatrix},$$

the hyperplane of solutions of this equation is the set of vectors perpendicular to

$$\begin{bmatrix} a_1 \\ \vdots \\ a_n \end{bmatrix}.$$

As for planes, we therefore refer to

$$\begin{bmatrix} a_1 \\ \vdots \\ a_n \end{bmatrix}$$

as a *normal* to the hyperplane $a_1x_1 + \cdots + a_nx_n = 0$. For a homogeneous equation, we have the following.

Theorem 2.9. *Hyperplanes through* **0** *Are Subspaces.*
The hyperplane of solutions of $a_1x_1 + \cdots + a_nx_n = 0$ is a subspace of F^n.

Proof. Let $f(\mathbf{x}) = a_1x_1 + \cdots + a_nx_n$, so that the hyperplane is the set V of solutions $\mathbf{x}$ to the equation $f(\mathbf{x}) = 0$. Using Theorem 2.8:

1. If $\mathbf{x}, \mathbf{y} \in V$, then $f(\mathbf{x} + \mathbf{y}) = f(\mathbf{x}) + f(\mathbf{y}) = 0 + 0 = 0$, so that $\mathbf{x} + \mathbf{y} \in V$;
2. If $\mathbf{x} \in V$ and $t \in F$, then $f(t\mathbf{x}) = tf(\mathbf{x}) = t0 = 0$, so that $t\mathbf{x} \in V$;
3. $f(\mathbf{0}) = 0$.

But then V is a subspace of F^n. ■

EXAMPLE

The hyperplane of solutions of $2x_1 + 3x_2 + 2x_3 + 4x_4 = 0$ in F^4 is a subspace, by our theorem.

For a nonhomogeneous equation, we have Theorem 2.10.

Theorem 2.10. *Translation of a Hyperplane.*
If H is the set of solutions to $a_1x_1 + \cdots + a_nx_n = p$ and u is any point in H, then H is also the set of solutions of $a_1(x_1 - u_1) + \cdots + a_n(x_n - u_n) = 0$ and $H = \mathbf{u} + V$, where V is the hyperplane of solutions to the homogeneous equation $a_1x_1 + \cdots + a_nx_n = 0$.

Proof. Let $f(\mathbf{x})$ be the linear function $f(\mathbf{x}) = a_1x_1 + \cdots + a_nx_n$. Then $\mathbf{x}$ is in H if and only if $f(\mathbf{x}) = p$. In particular, $f(\mathbf{u}) = p$, since $\mathbf{u}$ is in H. Since $f(\mathbf{x} - \mathbf{u}) = f(\mathbf{x}) - f(\mathbf{u}) = f(\mathbf{x}) - p$, it follows that $\mathbf{x}$ is in H if and only if $f(\mathbf{x} - \mathbf{u}) = 0$. So, $\mathbf{x}$ is in H if and only if $\mathbf{x} - \mathbf{u}$ is in V, which implies that $\mathbf{H} = \mathbf{u} + V$. (Prove!) ■

EXAMPLE

The hyperplane of solutions of $2x_1 + 3x_2 + 2x_3 + 4x_4 = 7$ in F^4 contains

$$\begin{bmatrix} 1 \\ 1 \\ 1 \\ 0 \end{bmatrix},$$

so it is also the set

$$\begin{bmatrix} 1 \\ 1 \\ 1 \\ 0 \end{bmatrix} + V$$

of solutions to $2(x_1 - 1) + 3(x_2 - 1) + 2(x_3 - 1) + 4(x_4 - 0) = 0$, where V is the set of solutions to $2x_1 + 3x_2 + 2x_3 + 4x_4 = 0$.

Since

$$\begin{bmatrix} a_1 \\ \vdots \\ a_n \end{bmatrix}$$

is a normal to the hyperplane $a_1x_1 + \cdots + a_nx_n = 0$, it is also called a *normal* to the hyperplane $a_1(x_1 - u_1) + \cdots + a_n(x_n - u_n) = 0$ obtained by translation by $\mathbf{u}$.

Half-spaces

As in the case of the Cartesian plane, the equation $a_1x_1 + \cdots + a_nx_n = p$ of a hyperplane divides $\mathbb{R}^n$ into three parts:

1. The hyperplane $\left\{ \begin{bmatrix} x_1 \\ \vdots \\ x_n \end{bmatrix} \middle| \, a_1x_1 + \cdots + a_nx_n = p \right\}$ itself;
2. The *positive half-space*
$$\left\{ \begin{bmatrix} x_1 \\ \vdots \\ x_n \end{bmatrix} \middle| \, a_1x_1 + \cdots + a_nx_n > p \right\};$$
3. The *negative half-space*
$$\left\{ \begin{bmatrix} x_1 \\ \vdots \\ x_n \end{bmatrix} \middle| \, a_1x_1 + \cdots + a_nx_n < p \right\}.$$

See Figure 2.15.

Parallel vectors and hyperplanes. Intersection of hyperplanes

We say that two hyperplanes *intersect* if they have a point in common. Two hyperplanes that are equal or do not intersect are said to be *parallel*. Two nonzero vectors $\mathbf{v}$ and $\mathbf{w}$ are parallel if the lines $F\mathbf{v}$ and $F\mathbf{w}$ are equal.

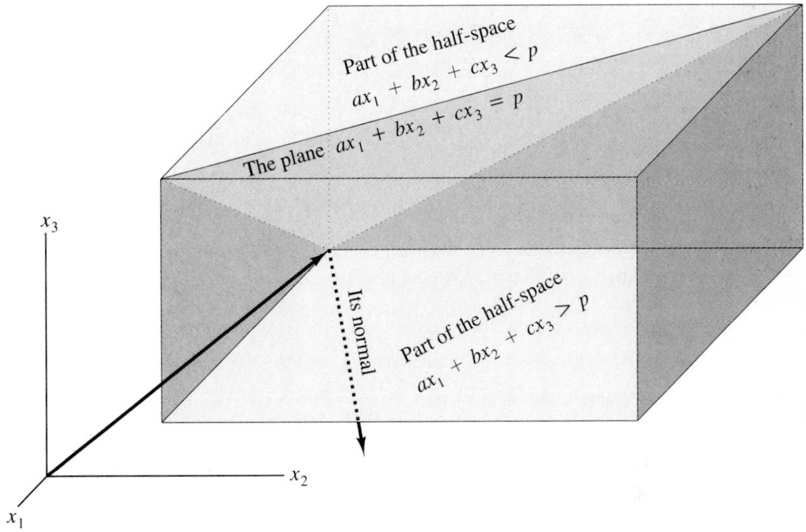

Figure 2.15 Plane $ax_1 + bx_2 + cx_3 = p$ and half-spaces $ax_1 + bx_2 + cx_3 < p$, $ax_1 + bx_2 + cx_3 > p$.

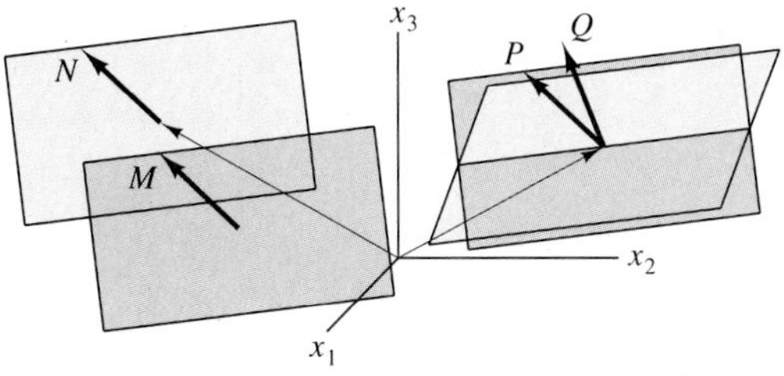

Figure 2.16 (a) Parallel planes $ax_1 + bx_2 + cx_3 = p$, $ax_1 + bx_2 + cx_3 = q$, and their normals M and N. (b) Intersecting planes $ax_1 + bx_2 + cx_3 = r$, $dx_1 + ex_2 + fx_3 = s$, and their normals P and Q.

From these definitions, we get the following criteria, illustrated in Figure 2.16.

Theorem 2.11. *Criteria for Parallel Hyperplanes.*
Two hyperplanes are parallel if and only if their normals are parallel.

Proof. Consider two hyperplanes corresponding to equations

$$a_1x_1 + \cdots + a_nx_n = p \quad \text{and} \quad b_1x_1 + \cdots + b_nx_n = q.$$

If

$$\begin{bmatrix} b_1 \\ \vdots \\ b_n \end{bmatrix} = t \begin{bmatrix} a_1 \\ \vdots \\ a_n \end{bmatrix} \qquad (t \text{ nonzero}),$$

then any solution to $a_1x_1 + \cdots + a_nx_n = p$ is also a solution to $b_1x_1 + \cdots + b_nx_n = tp$ and conversely. If $q = tp$, this implies that the two hyperplanes are equal; and if not, it implies that they don't intersect. (Explain!) This proves one direction. The other direction is obvious. ■

EXAMPLES

1. The intersection of two hyperplanes (lines) in F^2 is a line, point, or the empty set. Similarly, the intersection of two hyperplanes (planes) in F^3 is a plane, line, or the empty set. (Prove!)
2. The hyperplanes $2x_1 + 3x_2 + 2x_3 + 3x_4 = 7$ and $4x_1 + 6x_2 + 4x_3 + 6x_4 = 1$ in F^4 are parallel.
3. The intersection of the hyperplanes $0x_1 + 3x_2 + 2x_3 + 3x_4 = 8$ and $0x_1 + 6x_2 - 4x_3 - 6x_4 = -4$ in F^4 is the plane

$$\begin{bmatrix} 0 \\ 1 \\ 1 \\ 1 \end{bmatrix} + F\begin{bmatrix} 1 \\ 0 \\ 0 \\ 0 \end{bmatrix} + F\begin{bmatrix} 0 \\ 1 \\ -2 \\ 3 \end{bmatrix}.$$

(Verify!)

4. The intersection of any two hyperplanes in F^4 is a hyperplane, a plane, or the empty set. (Prove!)

PROBLEMS

NUMERICAL PROBLEMS

1. Let $f(\mathbf{x}) = 3x_1 + 2x_2 + x_3 + 30$ and $g(\mathbf{x}) = 2x_1 + 5x_2 + x_3 + 20$. Show that the set of $\mathbf{x}$ for which $f(\mathbf{x}) = g(\mathbf{x})$ is a plane.
2. Find the normal to the plane in Problem 1.
3. Find the equation for the plane through the origin parallel to the plane in Problem 1.
4. Find a point $\mathbf{u}$ such that translation $T_{\mathbf{u}}$ maps the plane in Problem 3 to the plane in Problem 1.
5. Separate each of the following sets of points into those on the plane $1x_1 + 2x_2 + 4x_3 = 7$, those in its positive half-space, and those in its negative half-space.

(a) The points on the segment $\overline{\mathbf{v}\,\mathbf{w}}$, where

$$\mathbf{v} = -\begin{bmatrix} 2 \\ 1 \\ 3 \end{bmatrix} \quad \text{and} \quad \mathbf{w} = \begin{bmatrix} 2 \\ 1 \\ 3 \end{bmatrix}$$

(b) The plane $1x_1 + 2x_2 + 4x_3 = 6$

(c) The plane $1x_1 + 2x_2 + 4x_3 = 8$

(d) The plane $2x_1 + 0x_2 + 0x_3 = 4$

6. Show that the intersection of the hyperplanes $0x_1 + 3x_2 + 2x_3 + 3x_4 = 8$ and $0x_1 + 6x_2 - 4x_3 - 6x_4 = -4$ in F^4 is the plane

$$\begin{bmatrix} 0 \\ 1 \\ 1 \\ 1 \end{bmatrix} + F\begin{bmatrix} 1 \\ 0 \\ 0 \\ 0 \end{bmatrix} + F\begin{bmatrix} 0 \\ 0 \\ -3 \\ 2 \end{bmatrix}.$$

7. Find the normals of the following planes.

(a) $F\begin{bmatrix} -1 \\ 1 \\ -1 \\ 1 \end{bmatrix} + F\begin{bmatrix} -1 \\ -1 \\ 1 \\ 1 \end{bmatrix} + F\begin{bmatrix} 1 \\ 1 \\ -3 \\ 1 \end{bmatrix}$ **(b)** $F\begin{bmatrix} 0 \\ -3 \\ 0 \\ 1 \end{bmatrix} + F\begin{bmatrix} -1 \\ 0 \\ 3 \\ -2 \end{bmatrix} + F\begin{bmatrix} 1 \\ 0 \\ 0 \\ 0 \end{bmatrix}$

THEORETICAL PROBLEMS

8. Show that the hyperplanes in F^2 are just the lines $\mathbf{u} + F\mathbf{v}$ introduced in Section 2.3.

9. Suppose that the (nonzero) vectors

$$\begin{bmatrix} a \\ b \\ c \end{bmatrix} \quad \text{and} \quad \begin{bmatrix} d \\ e \\ f \end{bmatrix}$$

are the normals to planes V and W in $\mathbb{R}^3$ through the origin. Assuming that the normals to V and W are perpendicular, show that the following points are in $V \cap W$.

$$\mathbf{p} = \begin{bmatrix} 1 \\ 0 \\ 0 \end{bmatrix} - \frac{a}{a^2 + b^2 + c^2}\begin{bmatrix} a \\ b \\ c \end{bmatrix} - \frac{d}{d^2 + e^2 + f^2}\begin{bmatrix} d \\ e \\ f \end{bmatrix}$$

$$\mathbf{q} = \begin{bmatrix} 0 \\ 1 \\ 0 \end{bmatrix} - \frac{b}{a^2 + b^2 + c^2}\begin{bmatrix} a \\ b \\ c \end{bmatrix} - \frac{e}{d^2 + e^2 + f^2}\begin{bmatrix} d \\ e \\ f \end{bmatrix}$$

$$\mathbf{r} = \begin{bmatrix} 0 \\ 0 \\ 1 \end{bmatrix} - \frac{c}{a^2 + b^2 + c^2}\begin{bmatrix} a \\ b \\ c \end{bmatrix} - \frac{f}{d^2 + e^2 + f^2}\begin{bmatrix} d \\ e \\ f \end{bmatrix}$$

10. In Problem 9, show that one of **p**, **q**, and **r** is nonzero.

11. In Problem 9, show that if **r** is nonzero, then $F\mathbf{r}$ contains $F\mathbf{p}$ and $F\mathbf{q}$.

Hard

12. Show that the intersection of two hyperplanes in F^4 is a hyperplane, a plane, or the empty set.

13. Show that the intersection of two or more hyperplanes in F^4 is a hyperplane, a plane, a line, a point or the empty set.

14. Show that every line in F^4 can be expressed as the intersection of a plane and a hyperplane.

2.8 SYSTEMS OF LINEAR EQUATIONS

A **system of *m* linear equations** in n variables is

$$\begin{aligned} a_{11}x_1 + \cdots + a_{1n}x_n &= p_1, \\ &\vdots \\ a_{m1}x_1 + \cdots + a_{mn}x_n &= p_m. \end{aligned}$$

The a_{rs}'s are called the **coefficients**, and the p_r's are the **constants** of the system. A **solution** to the system is any

$$\mathbf{x} = \begin{bmatrix} x_1 \\ \vdots \\ x_n \end{bmatrix}$$

which satisfies (is a solution to) each equation in the system.

Since the set of solutions to a single equation in this system is a hyperplane (if some coefficient is nonzero), all n-space, or the empty set (if the equation is $0x_1 + \cdots + 0x_n = p$ with p nonzero), this gives the following theorem.

Theorem 2.12. *Set of All Solutions to a System of Linear Equations.* The set of simultaneous solutions to a system of linear equations in n variables is an intersection of hyperplanes, all of n space or the empty set.

Corollary. The set of simultaneous solutions to a set of linear equations in three variables is a point, a line, a plane, all 3-space, or the empty set.

Proof. An intersection of hyperplanes in F^3 is just an intersection of planes, which is a point, a line, a plane, or the empty set. Given this, we can simply invoke the preceding theorem. ■

EXAMPLES

1. The set of simultaneous solutions to the system

$$\begin{aligned} 1x_1 + 2x_2 - 1x_3 &= 2 \\ -1x_1 + 1x_2 + 1x_3 &= 1 \end{aligned}$$

is the intersection of two planes. To find the intersection, we pass from the given system to the "equivalent system" (concept soon to be made precise)

$$\begin{aligned} 1x_1 + 2x_2 - 1x_3 &= 2 \\ 0x_1 + 1x_2 + 0x_3 &= 1 \end{aligned}$$

obtained by replacing the second equation by the sum of the two equations and then multiplying it by $\frac{1}{3}$. From the second equation, we solve for $x_2 = 1$. Then, solving for x_1 in terms of x_3 in the first equation, we get the general solution

$$\begin{bmatrix} x_1 \\ x_2 \\ x_3 \end{bmatrix} = \begin{bmatrix} x_3 \\ 1 \\ x_3 \end{bmatrix} = \begin{bmatrix} 0 \\ 1 \\ 0 \end{bmatrix} + x_3 \begin{bmatrix} 1 \\ 0 \\ 1 \end{bmatrix},$$

where x_3 is an **independent**, or **free**, variable (one that can be chosen freely). The set of solutions is the line $\mathbf{u} + F\mathbf{v}$, where

$$\mathbf{u} = \begin{bmatrix} 0 \\ 1 \\ 0 \end{bmatrix} \quad \text{and} \quad \mathbf{v} = \begin{bmatrix} 1 \\ 0 \\ 1 \end{bmatrix}.$$

2. The set of simultaneous solutions to the system

$$\begin{aligned} 1x_1 + 2x_2 - 1x_3 &= 2, \\ -1x_1 + 1x_2 + 1x_3 &= 1, \\ 2x_1 + 4x_2 + 6x_3 &= 12 \end{aligned}$$

is the intersection of three planes. To find the solution, we pass to the equivalent system

$$\begin{aligned} 1x_1 + 2x_2 - 1x_3 &= 2, \\ 0x_1 + 3x_2 + 0x_3 &= 3, \\ 0x_1 + 0x_2 + 8x_3 &= 8, \end{aligned}$$

where the second equation is replaced by the sum of the first two and the third is then replaced by the third plus -2 times the first. Multiplying the second and third equation by nonzero constants, we get the system

$$\begin{aligned} 1x_1 + 2x_2 - 1x_3 &= 2, \\ 0x_1 + 1x_2 + 0x_3 &= 1, \\ 0x_1 + 0x_2 + 1x_3 &= 1. \end{aligned}$$

Solving for $x_3 = 1$, $x_2 = 1$, and $x_1 = 2 - 2x_2 + x_3 = 2 - 2 + 1 = 1$, we find that the only solution is the point

$$\begin{bmatrix} 1 \\ 1 \\ 1 \end{bmatrix}.$$

3. The set of simultaneous solutions to the system

$$\begin{aligned} 0x_1 + 2x_2 - 4x_3 &= 2, \\ -2x_1 + 2x_2 + 2x_3 &= 2 \end{aligned}$$

is the intersection of two planes. To find the solution, we pass to the equivalent system

$$\begin{aligned} 1x_1 - 1x_2 - 1x_3 &= -1, \\ 0x_1 + 1x_2 - 2x_3 &= 1, \end{aligned}$$

where the first two equations are interchanged and each is multiplied by a nonzero constant. Solving the last equation for x_2, substituting the result in the first, and then solving for x_1, we get the general solution

$$\begin{bmatrix} x_1 \\ x_2 \\ x_3 \end{bmatrix} = \begin{bmatrix} 0+3x_3 \\ 1+2x_3 \\ x_3 \end{bmatrix} = \begin{bmatrix} 0 \\ 1 \\ 0 \end{bmatrix} + x_3 \begin{bmatrix} 3 \\ 2 \\ 1 \end{bmatrix},$$

expressed in terms of the free variable x_3. This is the line

$$\begin{bmatrix} 0 \\ 1 \\ 0 \end{bmatrix} + F \begin{bmatrix} 3 \\ 2 \\ 1 \end{bmatrix}.$$

4. The set of simultaneous solutions to the system

$$\begin{aligned} 2x_1 + 2x_2 - 4x_3 &= 2, \\ -2x_1 - 2x_2 + 4x_3 &= 3 \end{aligned}$$

is empty, since an equivalent system is

$$\begin{aligned} 1x_1 + 1x_2 - 2x_3 &= 1, \\ 0x_1 + 0x_2 + 0x_3 &= 5. \end{aligned}$$

Gaussian elimination. Back-substitution

The preceding examples illustrate what is involved in solving systems of linear equations. The key concept is equivalence, which is formalized as follows.

Definition. *Equivalent Systems of Linear Equations.*
Two systems of linear equations are **equivalent** if one can be obtained from the other by a sequence of 0 (no change is made) or more of the following **elementary operations**.

1. Replace an equation in the system by the same equation plus some multiple of another equation in the system.
2. Multiply some equation in the system by a nonzero scalar.
3. Interchange two equations in the system.

To clarify the kind of system we want to get using elementary operations, we need appropriate terminology. The **leading term** of an equation $a_1x_1 + \cdots + a_nx_n = p$ is a_kx_k if the equation is $0x_{k-1} + \cdots + 0x_{k-1} + a_kx_k + \cdots + a_nx_n = p$, where a_k is nonzero. The coefficient a_k of the leading term is called the **leading coefficient**, and the corresponding variable x_k is called the **leading variable**. Any given system of linear equations can be reduced to an **echelon** system—one where each leading coefficient is 1 and the leading term of each equation lies to the right of the leading terms of the preceding equations. Any equations for which all coefficients of the variables are 0 are put at the end.

EXAMPLES

In the earlier examples, the original systems were reduced to the following echelon systems.

1. $$\begin{aligned} 1x_1 + 2x_2 - 1x_3 &= 2 \\ 0x_1 + 1x_2 + 0x_3 &= 1 \end{aligned}$$

2. $$\begin{aligned} 1x_1 + 2x_2 - 1x_3 &= 2 \\ 0x_1 + 1x_2 + 0x_3 &= 1 \\ 0x_1 + 0x_2 + 1x_3 &= 1 \end{aligned}$$

3. $$\begin{aligned} 1x_1 - 1x_2 - 1x_3 &= -1 \\ 0x_1 + 1x_2 - 2x_3 &= 1 \end{aligned}$$

4. $$\begin{aligned} 1x_1 + 1x_2 - 2x_3 &= 1 \\ 0x_1 + 0x_2 + 0x_3 &= 5 \end{aligned}$$

In each case, the echelon system was solved by **back-substitution**.

1. The last equation was used to solve for the leading variable.
2. That variable was substituted into the preceding equations.
3. This process was repeated for each of the other equations, working backward from the last equation.

In view of these examples, the following theorem is evident. It says that we can always reduce the problem of solving a system of linear equations to that of solving a corresponding echelon system. This is the method of **Gaussian elimination**, sometimes referred to as **forward elimination**.

Theorem 2.13. *Invariance of the Solution Set under Equivalence.* The set of solutions of a system of linear equations is the same as the set of solutions of any equivalent system of linear equations. Any system of linear equations is equivalent to an echelon system.

Homogeneous systems

A **homogeneous** system of m equations in n variables is a system

$$\begin{aligned} a_{11}x_1 + \cdots + a_{1n}x_n &= 0, \\ &\vdots \\ a_{m1}x_1 + \cdots + a_{mn}x_n &= 0, \end{aligned}$$

where the right-hand-side values are all 0. The set of solutions to a single equation in this system is a hyperplane through $\mathbf{0}$ (if some coefficient is nonzero) or all of n-space (if all coefficients are 0). So, we have the following theorem.

Theorem 2.14. *Set of All Solutions to a System of Linear Equations.* The set of simultaneous solutions to a system of linear equations in n variables is an intersection of hyperplanes through $\mathbf{0}$ or all n-space.

Since hyperplanes through $\mathbf{0}$ are subspaces and since intersections of subspaces are subspaces, this gives us a corollary.

Corollary. The set of simultaneous solutions to a homogeneous system of linear equations is a subspace.

The next theorem establishes an important difference between F^m and F^n when m and n are different.

Theorem 2.15. *Homogeneous Systems with More Variables than Equations.* If $n > m$, then any homogeneous system

$$\begin{aligned} a_{11}x_1 + \cdots + a_{1n}x_n &= 0, \\ &\vdots \\ a_{m1}x_1 + \cdots + a_{mn}x_n &= 0 \end{aligned}$$

has a nonzero solution x.

Proof. By Theorem 2.13, we can replace such a system by an equivalent homogeneous echelon system. It has a nonzero solution, found by back-substitution, since the number n of variables is greater than the number of equations. ■

EXAMPLES

1. The set of simultaneous solutions to the homogeneous system

$$\begin{aligned} 1x_1 + 2x_2 - 1x_3 &= 0, \\ -1x_1 + 1x_2 + 1x_3 &= 0 \end{aligned}$$

is the intersection of two planes through $\mathbf{0}$. To find the intersection, proceed as before and pass from the given system to the equivalent system

$$\begin{aligned} 1x_1 + 2x_2 - 1x_3 &= 0, \\ 0x_1 + 1x_2 + 0x_3 &= 0. \end{aligned}$$

It is no longer necessary to keep track of the right-hand-side values, since they are always 0. Take $x_2 = 0$, and solve for x_1 in terms of x_3. This results in the general solution

$$\begin{bmatrix} x_1 \\ x_2 \\ x_3 \end{bmatrix} = \begin{bmatrix} x_3 \\ 0 \\ x_3 \end{bmatrix} = x_3 \begin{bmatrix} 1 \\ 0 \\ 1 \end{bmatrix},$$

where x_3 is a free variable. The set of solutions is therefore the line

$$F \begin{bmatrix} 1 \\ 0 \\ 1 \end{bmatrix}.$$

2. The set of simultaneous solutions to the system

$$\begin{aligned} 1x_1 + 2x_2 - 1x_3 &= 0, \\ -1x_1 + 1x_2 + 1x_3 &= 0, \\ 2x_1 + 4x_2 + 6x_3 &= 0 \end{aligned}$$

is the intersection of three planes through $\mathbf{0}$. To find the solution, we pass to the equivalent system

$$\begin{aligned} 1x_1 + 2x_2 - 1x_3 &= 0, \\ 0x_1 + 1x_2 + 0x_3 &= 0, \\ 0x_1 + 0x_2 + 1x_3 &= 0. \end{aligned}$$

The only solution is the point $\mathbf{0}$.

Nonhomogeneous systems

When the system is nonhomogeneous, there need not be a simultaneous solution. When there is, however, the set of solutions is easy to describe.

Theorem 2.16. *Set of Solutions to a Nonhomogeneous System of Linear Equations.*

Let $u = \begin{bmatrix} u_1 \\ \vdots \\ u_n \end{bmatrix}$ be a simultaneous solution to the system

$$\begin{aligned} a_{11}x_1 + \cdots + a_{1n}x_n &= p_1, \\ &\vdots \\ a_{m1}x_1 + \cdots + a_{mn}x_n &= p_m \end{aligned}$$

of linear equations. Then the set of all solutions is $u + V$, where V is the subspace of solutions to the corresponding homogeneous system

$$\begin{aligned} a_{11}x_1 + \cdots + a_{1n}x_n &= 0, \\ &\vdots \\ a_{m1}x_1 + \cdots + a_{mn}x_n &= 0. \end{aligned}$$

Proof. We know that the equation $a_{r1}x_1 + \cdots + a_{rn}x_n = p_r$ has the same set of solutions as the equation $a_{r1}(x_1 - u_1) + \cdots + a_{rn}(x_n - u_n) = 0$ for all r, by Theorem 2.10. So, $\mathbf{x}$ is a solution to the given system if and only if $\mathbf{x} - \mathbf{u}$ is a solution to the corresponding homogeneous system. This means that $\mathbf{x}$ is a solution to the given system if and only if $\mathbf{x} = \mathbf{u} + \mathbf{v}$, where $\mathbf{v} \in V$. ■

Let's take another look at our two examples in the light of this theorem.

EXAMPLES

1. Since $\begin{bmatrix} 0 \\ 1 \\ 0 \end{bmatrix}$ is a solution to the system

$$\begin{aligned} 1x_1 + 2x_2 - 1x_3 &= 2, \\ -1x_1 + 1x_2 + 1x_3 &= 1 \end{aligned}$$

and $F\begin{bmatrix} 1 \\ 0 \\ 1 \end{bmatrix}$ is the set of solutions to the homogeneous system

$$\begin{aligned} 1x_1 + 2x_2 - 1x_3 &= 0, \\ -1x_1 + 1x_2 + 1x_3 &= 0, \end{aligned}$$

the set of all solutions to the original system is the line

$$\begin{bmatrix} 0 \\ 1 \\ 0 \end{bmatrix} + F \begin{bmatrix} 1 \\ 0 \\ 1 \end{bmatrix}.$$

2. Since $\begin{bmatrix} 1 \\ 1 \\ 1 \end{bmatrix}$ is a solution to the system

$$\begin{aligned} 1x_1 + 2x_2 - 1x_3 &= 2, \\ -1x_1 + 1x_2 + 1x_3 &= 1, \\ 2x_1 + 4x_2 + 6x_3 &= 12, \end{aligned}$$

and 0 is the only solution to the corresponding homogeneous system,

$$\begin{bmatrix} 1 \\ 1 \\ 1 \end{bmatrix}$$

is the only solution.

Nonsingular systems of linear equations

We now apply our results to an important special class of linear equations.

Definition. *Nonsingular System of Linear Equations.*
A system of n linear equations in n unknowns is said to be **nonsingular** if it has one and only one solution.

The system in the second of the last examples is nonsingular and illustrates part of Theorem 2.17.

Theorem 2.17. *Conditions for Nonsingular Systems of Linear Equations.*
The following conditions are equivalent.

1. The following system is nonsingular:

$$\begin{aligned} a_{11}x_1 + \cdots + a_{1n}x_n &= p_1, \\ &\vdots \\ a_{n1}x_1 + \cdots + a_{nn}x_n &= p_n. \end{aligned}$$

2. $x = 0$ is the only solution to the corresponding homogeneous system

$$\begin{aligned} a_{11}x_1 + \cdots + a_{1n}x_n &= 0, \\ &\vdots \\ a_{n1}x_1 + \cdots + a_{nn}x_n &= 0. \end{aligned}$$

3. The corresponding homogeneous system is equivalent to an echelon system of the form

$$\begin{aligned} 1x_1 + \cdots + b_{1n}x_n &= 0 \qquad \text{(leading term } 1x_1\text{)}, \\ &\vdots \qquad\qquad\qquad \vdots \\ 0x_1 + \cdots + \quad 1x_n &= 0 \qquad \text{(leading term } 1x_n\text{)}. \end{aligned}$$

4. The homogeneous system is equivalent to the *identity* system

$$\begin{aligned} 1x_1 + \cdots + 0x_n &= 0, \\ &\vdots \\ 0x_1 + \cdots + 1x_n &= 0. \end{aligned}$$

Proof. The condition that the homogeneous system has 0 as its only solution does not change if we replace it by an equivalent echelon system. The condition that a square echelon system has 0 as its only solution means that it has the form

$$\begin{aligned} 1x_1 + \cdots + b_{1n}x_n &= 0, \\ &\vdots \\ 0x_1 + \cdots + \quad 1x_n &= 0, \end{aligned}$$

where the leading term of the kth equation is $1x_k$ for all k. (Prove!) So, Conditions 2 and 3 are equivalent. Condition 1 implies Condition 2 by Theorem 2.16. Conversely, Condition 2 implies Condition 1. For this, note that using the same elementary operations, the original system becomes

$$\begin{aligned} 1x_1 + \cdots + b_{1n}x_n &= q_1, \\ &\vdots \\ 0x_1 + \cdots + \quad 1x_n &= q_n. \end{aligned}$$

This can be solved by back-substitution, giving a solution $\mathbf{x}$ to the original system of linear equations:

$$\begin{aligned} x_n &= q_n, \\ x_{n-1} &= q_{n-1} - b_{n-1n}x_n, \\ &\vdots \\ x_1 &= q_1 - b_{12}x_2 - \cdots - b_{1n}x_n. \end{aligned}$$

Thus, Conditions 1–3 are equivalent.

Certainly Condition 4 implies Condition 2. Conversely, Condition 2 implies Condition 4. First replace the homogeneous system by the equivalent echelon system

$$\begin{aligned} 1x_1 + \cdots + b_{1n}x_n &= 0, \\ &\vdots \\ 0x_1 + \cdots + \quad 1x_n &= 0. \end{aligned}$$

Then add $-b_{rn}$ times equation n to equation r for $r = 1$ to $r = n - 1$. Similarly, add $-b_{rn-k}$ times equation $n - k$ to equation r for $r = 1$ to $n - k$. Doing this for $k = 1$ to $n - 1$, we get system (4). ■

PROBLEMS

NUMERICAL PROBLEMS

1. Find an echelon system equivalent to each of the following systems.

(a)
$$\begin{aligned} 1x_1 + 2x_2 - 4x_3 &= 0 \\ -5x_1 + 2x_2 + 5x_3 &= 0 \end{aligned}$$

(b)
$$\begin{aligned} 3x_1 + 2x_2 - 1x_3 &= 0 \\ -3x_1 + 1x_2 + 2x_3 &= 0 \\ 3x_1 + 2x_2 + 6x_3 &= 0 \end{aligned}$$

(c)
$$\begin{aligned} 3x_1 + 3x_2 + 3x_3 &= 0 \\ -1x_1 + 1x_2 + 1x_3 &= 0 \\ 2x_1 + 2x_2 + 3x_3 &= 0 \\ 2x_1 + 2x_2 + 3x_3 &= 0 \end{aligned}$$

2. Find the set of solutions for each of the homogeneous systems in Problem 1.

3. Find an echelon system equivalent to each of the following nonhomogeneous systems.

(a)
$$\begin{aligned} 1x_1 + 2x_2 - 4x_3 &= -2 \\ -5x_1 + 2x_2 + 5x_3 &= 7 \end{aligned}$$

(b)
$$\begin{aligned} 3x_1 + 2x_2 - 1x_3 &= 5 \\ -3x_1 + 1x_2 + 2x_3 &= -2 \\ 3x_1 + 2x_2 + 6x_3 &= 5 \end{aligned}$$

(c)
$$\begin{aligned} 3x_1 + 3x_2 + 3x_3 &= 6 \\ -1x_1 + 1x_2 + 1x_3 &= 0 \\ 2x_1 + 2x_2 + 3x_3 &= 5 \\ 2x_1 + 2x_2 + 3x_3 &= 4 \end{aligned}$$

4. Find the set of solutions for each of the nonhomogeneous systems given in Problem 3. Verify Theorem 2.16 in each case.

THEORETICAL PROBLEMS

5. Show for $m < n$ that any homogeneous system of m linear equations in n variables has infinitely many solutions.

6. Show for $m > n$ that for any homogeneous system

$$\begin{gathered} a_{11}x_1 + \cdots + a_{1n}x_n = 0, \\ \vdots \\ a_{m1}x_1 + \cdots + a_{mn}x_n = 0, \end{gathered}$$

there are values $p_1, \ldots, p_m$ for which the system

$$\begin{gathered} a_{11}x_1 + \cdots + a_{1n}x_n = p_1 \\ \vdots \\ a_{m1}x_1 + \cdots + a_{mn}x_n = p_m \end{gathered}$$

has no solution.

7. Show that the set of solutions to a homogeneous system of linear equations of rank r is the intersection of r hyperplanes, where r is the number of nonzero equations of an equivalent echelon system.

SUGGESTED READING

P. R. Halmos, *Finite Dimensional Vector Spaces*, Van Nostrand-Reinhold, New York, 1958. [One of the classics in the subject. Very enjoyable reading.]

CHAPTER 3

LINEAR TRANSFORMATIONS OF n-SPACE

3.1 LINEAR TRANSFORMATIONS

In Chapter 1, we discussed the linear transformations of $\mathbb{R}^2$. Now, we move on to discuss linear transformations from F^n to F^m for any positive integers m and n. Although much of what we do here is parallel to what was done before, there are two important differences. First, the field F can be either $\mathbb{R}$ or $\mathbb{C}$. Second, when m and n are not equal, F^n is mapped to F^m rather than to itself. On the other hand, when m and n are equal, we are working with linear transformations of F^n, and the product of any two of them is again a linear transformation of F^n. In this case, there are far-reaching consequences, which are discussed in Chapter 5, "The Algebra of $n \times n$ Matrices."

Definition. *Linear Transformations.*

A **linear transformation** from F^n to F^m is a mapping R from F^n to F^m of the form

$$R\begin{bmatrix} x_1 \\ \vdots \\ x_n \end{bmatrix} = \begin{bmatrix} a_{11}x_1 + \cdots + a_{1n}x_n \\ \vdots \qquad\qquad \vdots \\ a_{m1}x_1 + \cdots + a_{mn}x_n \end{bmatrix},$$

where the coefficients a_{rs} are scalars. We say that the **size** of R is $m \times n$. The set of linear transformations from F^n to F^m is denoted by $L(F^n, F^m)$.

EXAMPLES

1. Since $F = F^1$ (we don't distinguish between a 1×1 matrix $[c]$ and the scalar c itself), the linear transformations from F^n to F^1 are just the linear functions introduced in Chapter 1.

2. More generally, if we write a function R from F^n to F^m in the form

$$R(\mathbf{x}) = \begin{bmatrix} f_1(\mathbf{x}) \\ \vdots \\ f_m(\mathbf{x}) \end{bmatrix},$$

the **coordinate functions** $f_r(\mathbf{x})$ are linear functions for $1 \le r \le m$ if and only if R is a linear transformation. (Explain!)

3.
$$R\begin{bmatrix} x_1 \\ x_2 \\ x_3 \end{bmatrix} = \begin{bmatrix} 3x_1+2x_2+4x_3 \\ 2x_1-5x_2+2x_3 \end{bmatrix}$$

is a linear transformation from F^3 to F^2 of size 2×3.

Systems of linear equations

Note that for any linear transformation

$$R\begin{bmatrix} x_1 \\ \vdots \\ x_n \end{bmatrix} = \begin{bmatrix} a_{11}x_1+\cdots+a_{1n}x_n \\ \vdots \qquad\qquad \vdots \\ a_{m1}x_1+\cdots+a_{mn}x_n \end{bmatrix}$$

and any $\mathbf{p} \in F^m$, the equation $R(\mathbf{x}) = \mathbf{p}$ is equivalent to the system of linear equations

$$\begin{aligned} a_{11}x_1 + \cdots + a_{1n}x_n &= p_1, \\ &\vdots \\ a_{m1}x_1 + \cdots + a_{mn}x_n &= p_m. \end{aligned}$$

For this reason, *we sometimes refer to the equation* $R(\mathbf{x}) = \mathbf{p}$ *as a system of linear equations.*

Standard unit vectors

We call

$$\mathbf{e}_1 = \begin{bmatrix} 1 \\ 0 \\ \vdots \\ 0 \end{bmatrix}, \quad \mathbf{e}_2 = \begin{bmatrix} 0 \\ 1 \\ \vdots \\ 0 \end{bmatrix}, \ldots, \quad \mathbf{e}_n = \begin{bmatrix} 0 \\ 0 \\ \vdots \\ 1 \end{bmatrix}$$

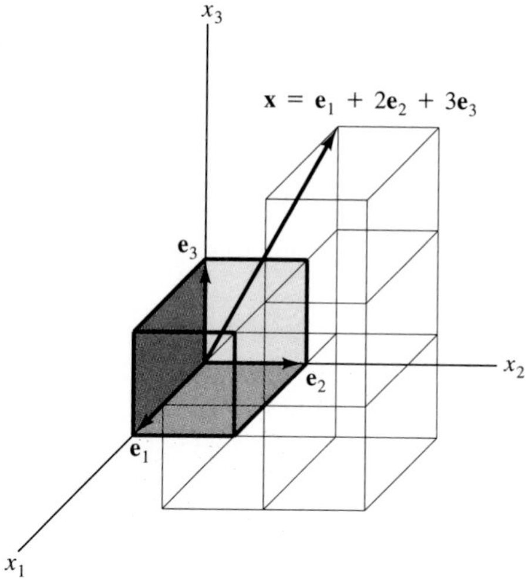

Figure 3.1 The standard unit vectors $\mathbf{e}_1$, $\mathbf{e}_2$, and $\mathbf{e}_3$, the unit cube in $\mathbb{R}^3$, and $\mathbf{x} = \mathbf{e}_1 + 2\mathbf{e}_2 + 3\mathbf{e}_3$.

the **standard unit vectors** (or *directions*) for F^n. (See Figure 3.1.) Any

$$\mathbf{x} = \begin{bmatrix} x_1 \\ \vdots \\ x_n \end{bmatrix}$$

can be expressed in terms of the $\mathbf{e}_s$ as $\mathbf{x} = x_1\mathbf{e}_1 + \cdots + x_n\mathbf{e}_n$. Letting the x_s take on all possible values between 0 and 1, $\mathbf{x}$ ranges throughout the unit cube

$$\{x_1\mathbf{e}_1 + \cdots + x_n\mathbf{e}_n \mid 0 \le x_s \le 1 \text{ for } 1 \le s \le n\}$$

in F^n.

The effect of

$$R\begin{bmatrix} x_1 \\ \vdots \\ x_n \end{bmatrix} = \begin{bmatrix} a_{11}x_1 + \cdots + a_{1n}x_n \\ \vdots \qquad\qquad \vdots \\ a_{m1}x_1 + \cdots + a_{mn}x_n \end{bmatrix}$$

can be understood by looking at what it does to the $\mathbf{e}_s$. It maps $\mathbf{e}_s$ to the sth column of coefficients for all s—that is,

$$R(\mathbf{e}_1) = \begin{bmatrix} a_{11} \\ \vdots \\ a_{m1} \end{bmatrix}, \ldots, R(\mathbf{e}_n) = \begin{bmatrix} a_{1n} \\ \vdots \\ a_{mn} \end{bmatrix}.$$

Also, it maps $\mathbf{x} = x_1\mathbf{e}_1 + \cdots + x_n\mathbf{e}_n$ to

$$R\begin{bmatrix} x_1 \\ \vdots \\ x_n \end{bmatrix} = \begin{bmatrix} a_{11}x_1 + \cdots + a_{1n}x_n \\ \vdots \qquad\qquad \vdots \\ a_{m1}x_1 + \cdots + a_{mn}x_n \end{bmatrix} = x_1\begin{bmatrix} a_{11} \\ \vdots \\ a_{m1} \end{bmatrix} + \cdots + x_n\begin{bmatrix} a_{1n} \\ \vdots \\ a_{mn} \end{bmatrix}.$$

So, we need only know where R maps $\mathbf{e}_1, \ldots, \mathbf{e}_n$ to find where it maps $\mathbf{x} = x_1\mathbf{e}_1 + \cdots + x_n\mathbf{e}_n$. (See Figure 3.2.)

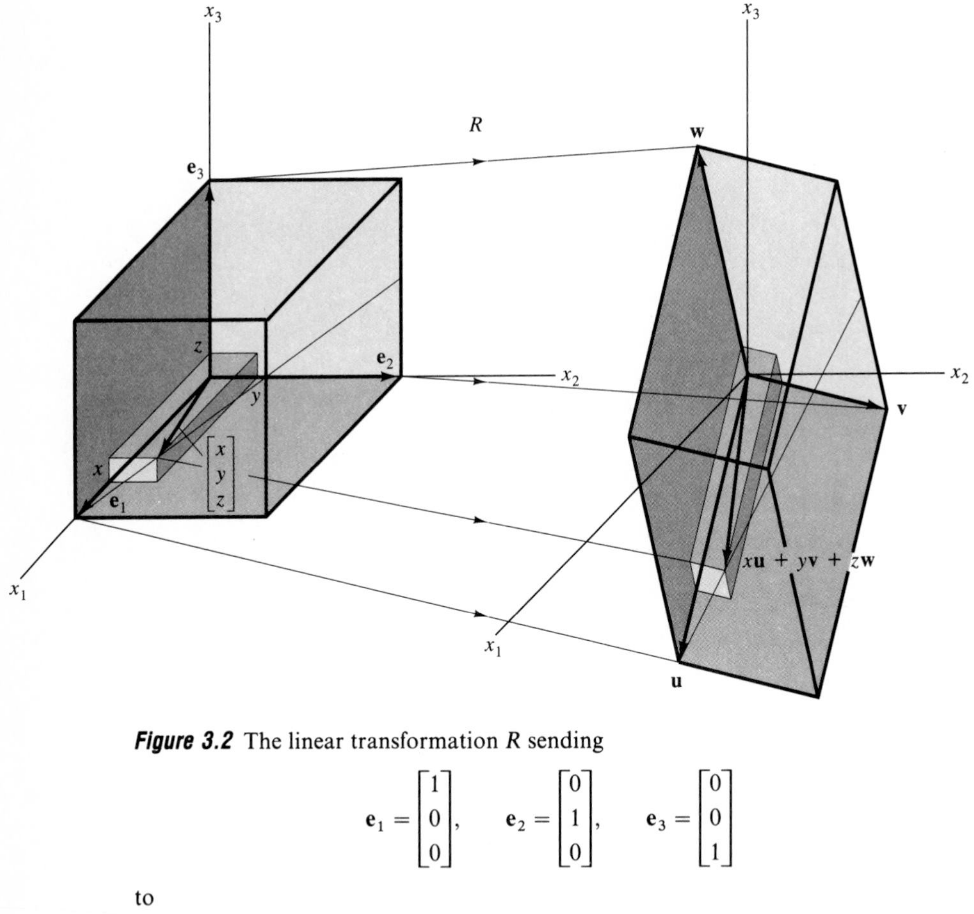

Figure 3.2 The linear transformation R sending

$$\mathbf{e}_1 = \begin{bmatrix} 1 \\ 0 \\ 0 \end{bmatrix}, \qquad \mathbf{e}_2 = \begin{bmatrix} 0 \\ 1 \\ 0 \end{bmatrix}, \qquad \mathbf{e}_3 = \begin{bmatrix} 0 \\ 0 \\ 1 \end{bmatrix}$$

to

$$\mathbf{u} = \begin{bmatrix} a \\ b \\ c \end{bmatrix}, \qquad \mathbf{v} = \begin{bmatrix} d \\ e \\ f \end{bmatrix}, \qquad \mathbf{w} = \begin{bmatrix} g \\ h \\ i \end{bmatrix}$$

maps $x\mathbf{e}_1 + y\mathbf{e}_2 + z\mathbf{e}_3 = \begin{bmatrix} x \\ y \\ z \end{bmatrix}$ to $x\mathbf{u} + y\mathbf{v} + z\mathbf{w} = \begin{bmatrix} xa + yd + zg \\ xb + ye + zh \\ xc + yf + zi \end{bmatrix}$.

EXAMPLE

The linear transformation

$$R\begin{bmatrix} x_1 \\ x_2 \\ x_3 \end{bmatrix} = \begin{bmatrix} 3x_1 + 2x_2 + 4x_3 \\ 2x_1 - 5x_2 + 2x_3 \end{bmatrix}$$

maps $\mathbf{x} = \begin{bmatrix} x_1 \\ x_2 \\ x_3 \end{bmatrix}$ to $x_1\begin{bmatrix} 3 \\ 2 \end{bmatrix} + x_2\begin{bmatrix} 2 \\ -5 \end{bmatrix} + x_3\begin{bmatrix} 4 \\ 2 \end{bmatrix}$.

Existence and uniqueness of a linear transformation

From knowing what a linear transformation R does to the standard unit vectors $\mathbf{e}_s$ and any $\mathbf{x} = x_1\mathbf{e}_1 + \cdots + x_n\mathbf{e}_n$, we get the following two theorems on existence and uniqueness of linear transformations.

Theorem 3.1. *Existence of Linear Transformations with Prescribed Images.* Given any n vectors $\mathbf{v}_1, \ldots, \mathbf{v}_n$ in F^m, we can find a linear transformation R from F^n to F^m such that

$$R(\mathbf{e}_1) = \mathbf{v}_1, \ldots, R(\mathbf{e}_n) = \mathbf{v}_n.$$

Proof. Take the coefficients for R to be the entries in the $\mathbf{v}_s$ column by column. ■

Theorem 3.2. *Uniqueness of a Linear Transformation with Prescribed Images.* Two linear transformations R, S from F^n to F^m are equal if and only if $R(\mathbf{e}_1) = S(\mathbf{e}_1), \ldots, R(\mathbf{e}_n) = S(\mathbf{e}_n)$.

Proof. We have seen that the images of the $\mathbf{e}_s$ are just the coefficients of the linear transformation, column by column, so they are the same. ■

EXAMPLE

To get a linear transformation R which maps

$$\begin{bmatrix} 1 \\ 0 \\ 0 \end{bmatrix} \text{ to } \begin{bmatrix} 3 \\ 4 \end{bmatrix}, \quad \begin{bmatrix} 0 \\ 1 \\ 0 \end{bmatrix} \text{ to } \begin{bmatrix} 5 \\ 6 \end{bmatrix}, \quad \begin{bmatrix} 0 \\ 0 \\ 1 \end{bmatrix} \text{ to } \begin{bmatrix} 7 \\ 8 \end{bmatrix},$$

take

$$R\begin{bmatrix} x_1 \\ x_2 \\ x_3 \end{bmatrix} = \begin{bmatrix} 3x_1 + 5x_2 + 7x_3 \\ 4x_1 + 6x_2 + 8x_3 \end{bmatrix}.$$

Conditions for a linear transformation

We now give very important criteria for when a function is a linear transformation.

Theorem 3.3. *Criteria for R to Be a Linear Transformation.*
A function R from F^n to F^m is a linear transformation if and only if it satisfies the properties

1. $R(\mathbf{x} + \mathbf{y}) = R(\mathbf{x}) + R(\mathbf{y})$ for all $\mathbf{x}, \mathbf{y} \in F^n$;
2. $R(a\mathbf{x}) = aR(\mathbf{x})$ for all $\mathbf{x} \in F^n$, $a \in F$.

Proof. Suppose first that R is the linear transformation

$$R\begin{bmatrix} x_1 \\ \vdots \\ x_n \end{bmatrix} = \begin{bmatrix} a_{11}x_1 + \cdots + a_{1n}x_n \\ \vdots \\ a_{m1}x_1 + \cdots + a_{mn}x_n \end{bmatrix},$$

and let $f_r(\mathbf{x})$ be the coordinate function $f_r(\mathbf{x}) = a_{r1}x_1 + \cdots + a_{rn}x_n$. Since

$$f_r(\mathbf{x} + \mathbf{y}) = f_r(\mathbf{x}) + f_r(\mathbf{y}) \qquad \text{for all } \mathbf{x}, \mathbf{y} \in F^n,$$

$$f_r(a\mathbf{x}) = af_r(\mathbf{x}) \qquad \text{for all } \mathbf{x} \in F^n,\ a \in F,$$

for $1 \le r \le m$, by Theorem 2.8, we get

$$R(\mathbf{x} + \mathbf{y}) = \begin{bmatrix} f_1(\mathbf{x}+\mathbf{y}) \\ \vdots \\ f_m(\mathbf{x}+\mathbf{y}) \end{bmatrix} = \begin{bmatrix} f_1(\mathbf{x})+f_1(\mathbf{y}) \\ \vdots \\ f_m(\mathbf{x})+f_m(\mathbf{y}) \end{bmatrix} = \begin{bmatrix} f_1(\mathbf{x}) \\ \vdots \\ f_m(\mathbf{x}) \end{bmatrix} + \begin{bmatrix} f_1(\mathbf{y}) \\ \vdots \\ f_m(\mathbf{y}) \end{bmatrix} = R(\mathbf{x}) + R(\mathbf{y}),$$

$$R(a\mathbf{x}) = \begin{bmatrix} f_1(a\mathbf{x}) \\ \vdots \\ f_m(a\mathbf{x}) \end{bmatrix} = \begin{bmatrix} af_1(\mathbf{x}) \\ \vdots \\ af_m(\mathbf{x}) \end{bmatrix} = a\begin{bmatrix} f_1(\mathbf{x}) \\ \vdots \\ f_m(\mathbf{x}) \end{bmatrix} = aR(\mathbf{x}).$$

Conversely, suppose that R satisfies the given properties. Then R maps the standard unit vectors to certain vectors, say

$$R(\mathbf{e}_1) = \begin{bmatrix} a_{11} \\ \vdots \\ a_{m1} \end{bmatrix}, \ldots, R(\mathbf{e}_n) = \begin{bmatrix} a_{1n} \\ \vdots \\ a_{mn} \end{bmatrix}.$$

Letting S be the linear transformation

$$S\begin{bmatrix} x_1 \\ \vdots \\ x_n \end{bmatrix} = \begin{bmatrix} a_{11}x_1 + \cdots + a_{1n}x_n \\ \vdots \\ a_{m1}x_1 + \cdots + a_{mn}x_n \end{bmatrix},$$

we know that

$$S(\mathbf{x}) = x_1\begin{bmatrix} a_{11} \\ \vdots \\ a_{m1} \end{bmatrix} + \cdots + x_n = \begin{bmatrix} a_{1n} \\ \vdots \\ a_{mn} \end{bmatrix}$$

for all **x**. By Properties 1 and 2, we also have

$$R(\mathbf{x}) = x_1 \begin{bmatrix} a_{11} \\ \vdots \\ a_{m1} \end{bmatrix} + \cdots + x_n = \begin{bmatrix} a_{1n} \\ \vdots \\ a_{mn} \end{bmatrix}.$$

(Verify!) So, $R = S$ and R is a linear transformation. ■

EXAMPLE

$R(\mathbf{x}) = \begin{bmatrix} x_2 + 1 \\ x_1 \end{bmatrix}$ is not a linear transformation because

$$R\left(\begin{bmatrix} 1 \\ 0 \end{bmatrix} + \begin{bmatrix} 0 \\ 1 \end{bmatrix}\right) = \begin{bmatrix} 2 \\ 1 \end{bmatrix} \quad \text{and} \quad R\begin{bmatrix} 1 \\ 0 \end{bmatrix} + R\begin{bmatrix} 0 \\ 1 \end{bmatrix} = \begin{bmatrix} 1 \\ 1 \end{bmatrix} + \begin{bmatrix} 2 \\ 0 \end{bmatrix} = \begin{bmatrix} 3 \\ 1 \end{bmatrix}.$$

(Verify!)

The inverse of a linear transformation

An important example of how to use Theorem 3.3 is the next corollary, illustrated in Figure 3.3.

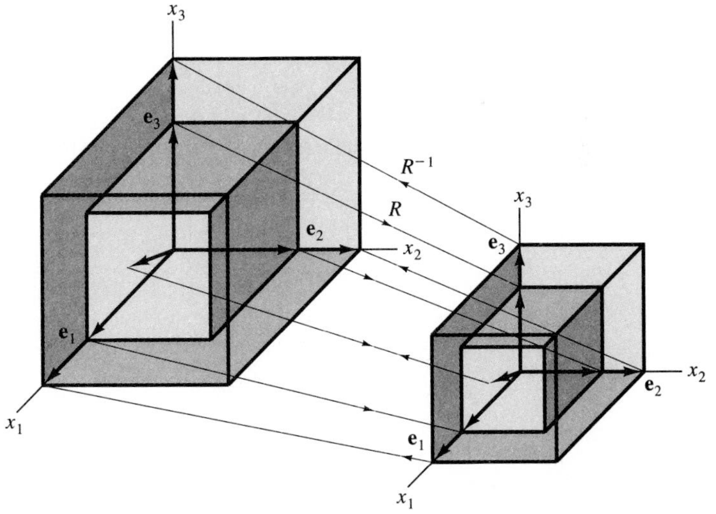

Figure 3.3 The inverse of a linear transformation R from $\mathbb{R}^3$ to itself.

Corollary. If a linear transformation R from F^n to F^m is an invertible function, then its inverse is a linear transformation.

Proof. The inverse S of R maps F^m to F^n. Typical elements of F^m are $\mathbf{x}' = R(\mathbf{x})$ and $\mathbf{y}' = R(\mathbf{y})$, which get mapped by S to $S(\mathbf{x}') = \mathbf{x}$ and $S(\mathbf{y}') = \mathbf{y}$.

To verify Properties 1 and 2 of the theorem amounts to observing that

$$S(\mathbf{x}' + \mathbf{y}') = S(R(\mathbf{x}) + R(\mathbf{y})) = S(R(\mathbf{x} + \mathbf{y})) = \mathbf{x} + \mathbf{y} = S(\mathbf{x}') + S(\mathbf{y}')$$

$$S(a\mathbf{x}') = S(aR(\mathbf{x})) = S(R(a\mathbf{x})) = a\mathbf{x} = aS(\mathbf{x}'). \quad \blacksquare$$

EXAMPLE

The linear transformation R mapping $\begin{bmatrix}1\\0\end{bmatrix}$ to $\begin{bmatrix}1\\2\end{bmatrix}$ and $\begin{bmatrix}0\\1\end{bmatrix}$ to $\begin{bmatrix}3\\5\end{bmatrix}$ is invertible. (Verify!) So, its inverse R^{-1} is a linear transformation. It can be gotten by finding the linear transformation R^{-1} which maps $\begin{bmatrix}1\\2\end{bmatrix}$ to $\begin{bmatrix}1\\0\end{bmatrix}$ and $\begin{bmatrix}3\\5\end{bmatrix}$ to $\begin{bmatrix}0\\1\end{bmatrix}$. This is $R^{-1}(\mathbf{x}) = \begin{bmatrix}-5x_1+3x_2\\2x_1-1x_2\end{bmatrix}$. (Verify!)

You may ask yourself whether m must equal n if there exists an invertible linear transformation from F^n to F^m. The answer is "yes," which is of great importance. This is proved in the next theorem and its corollary.

Theorem 3.4. *Condition for Existence of a 1-1 Linear Transformation. If there exists a 1-1 linear transformation from F^n to F^m, then $n \leq m$.*

Proof. Suppose that there exists a 1-1 linear transformation

$$R\begin{bmatrix}x_1\\\vdots\\x_n\end{bmatrix} = \begin{bmatrix}a_{11}x_1+\cdots+a_{1n}x_n\\\vdots \qquad \vdots\\a_{m1}x_1+\cdots+a_{mn}x_n\end{bmatrix}$$

from F^n to F^m. If $n > m$, then the homogeneous system of linear equations

$$\begin{bmatrix}a_{11}x_1+\cdots+a_{1n}x_n\\\vdots \qquad \vdots\\a_{m1}x_1+\cdots+a_{mn}x_n\end{bmatrix} = 0$$

has a nonzero solution $\begin{bmatrix}x_1\\\vdots\\x_n\end{bmatrix}$, so that

$$R\begin{bmatrix}x_1\\\vdots\\x_n\end{bmatrix} = 0 = R(0).$$

But this is not possible, since R is 1-1. So, $n \leq m$. $\blacksquare$

EXAMPLE

The linear transformation $R(\mathbf{x}) = \begin{bmatrix}-5x_1+3x_2+x_3\\2x_1-1x_2\end{bmatrix}$ from $\mathbb{R}^3$ to $\mathbb{R}^2$ is not 1-1 since $n = 3 > m = 2$.

Corollary. If there exists an invertible linear transformation from F^n to F^m, then $n = m$.

Proof. Suppose that R is such a linear transformation and let R^{-1} be its inverse. Then R^{-1} is a linear transformation, by the corollary to Theorem 3.3. But then $n \le m$, since R is 1-1, and $m \le n$, since R^{-1} is 1-1. So $m = n$. ■

EXAMPLE

The linear transformation

$$R(\mathbf{x}) = \begin{bmatrix} x_1 - x_2 \\ x_2 - x_1 \\ x_1 + x_2 \end{bmatrix}$$

from $\mathbb{R}^2$ to $\mathbb{R}^3$ is not invertible since $2 \neq 3$.

Some special linear transformations

By specifying the coefficients a_{rs}, we can come up with a useful array of various and sundry linear transformations

$$R\begin{bmatrix} x_1 \\ \vdots \\ x_n \end{bmatrix} = \begin{bmatrix} a_{11}x_1 + \cdots + a_{1n}x_n \\ \vdots \qquad\qquad \vdots \\ a_{m1}x_1 + \cdots + a_{mn}x_n \end{bmatrix}.$$

Some important ones are listed here.

1. The zero linear transformation

$$R\begin{bmatrix} x_1 \\ \vdots \\ x_n \end{bmatrix} = \begin{bmatrix} 0x_1 + \cdots + 0x_n \\ \vdots \qquad\qquad \vdots \\ 0x_1 + \cdots + 0x_n \end{bmatrix}$$

   maps every vector to $\mathbf{0}$. It is denoted simply by $0(\mathbf{x})$ or $\mathbf{0}$.

2. The **identity** linear transformation

$$R\begin{bmatrix} x_1 \\ \vdots \\ x_n \end{bmatrix} = \begin{bmatrix} 1x_1 + \cdots + 0x_n \\ \vdots \qquad\qquad \vdots \\ 0x_1 + \cdots + 1x_n \end{bmatrix},$$

   where the coefficient a_{rs} is 1 if $r = s$ and 0 otherwise, maps every vector $\mathbf{x}$ to itself. It is denoted by $I(\mathbf{x})$ or I. Note that $m = n$.

3. **Scalar multiplication by** a is the linear transformation

$$R\begin{bmatrix} x_1 \\ \vdots \\ x_n \end{bmatrix} = \begin{bmatrix} ax_1 + \cdots + 0x_n \\ \vdots \qquad\qquad \vdots \\ 0x_1 + \cdots + ax_n \end{bmatrix},$$

where the coefficient a_{rs} is a if $r = s$ and 0 otherwise. It maps every vector $\mathbf{x}$ to $a\mathbf{x}$. Note that $m = n$ and that $R = I$ when $a = 1$ and $R = 0$ when $a = 0$.

4. A **diagonal** linear transformation

$$R\begin{bmatrix} x_1 \\ \vdots \\ x_n \end{bmatrix} = \begin{bmatrix} d_1x_1 + \cdots + 0x_n \\ \vdots \qquad\qquad \vdots \\ 0x_1 + \cdots + d_nx_n \end{bmatrix}$$

maps $\mathbf{e}_s$ to $d_s\mathbf{e}_s$ for all s. It is denoted by $\text{Diag}(d_1, \ldots, d_n)(\mathbf{x})$ or $\text{Diag}(d_1, \ldots, d_n)$. Note that $m = n$. When $d_1 = \cdots = d_n = a$, it is scalar multiplication by a. The linear transformations R, R^{-1} illustrated in Figure 3.3 are diagonal. (Explain!) See also Figure 3.4.

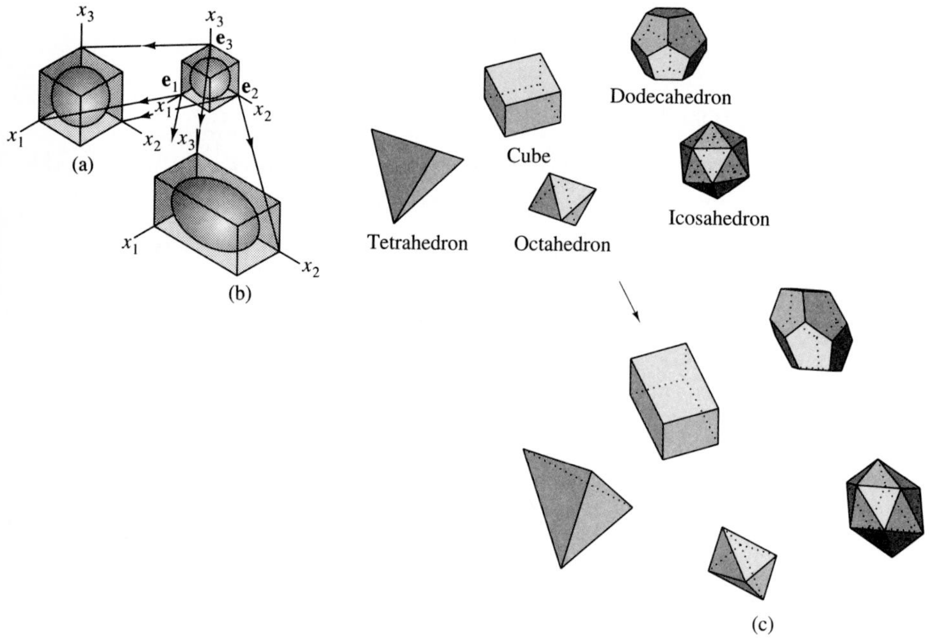

Figure 3.4 Image of a sphere under (a) scalar and (b) diagonal linear transformations R of $\mathbb{R}^3$. (c) Image of the Platonic solids under a diagonal linear transformation.

5. The linear transformation

$$R\begin{bmatrix} x_1 \\ \vdots \\ x_n \end{bmatrix} = \begin{bmatrix} 0x_1 + \cdots + 1x_n \\ \vdots \qquad\qquad \vdots \\ 0x_1 + \cdots + 0x_n \end{bmatrix},$$

where the coefficient a_{rs} is 1 if $r = 1$ and $s = n$ and 0 otherwise, maps $\mathbf{e}_n$ to $\mathbf{e}_1$ and $\mathbf{e}_s$ to $\mathbf{0}$ for $s < n$. It is denoted by $E_{1n}(\mathbf{x})$ or E_{1n}.

6. The linear transformation $E_{ij}(\mathbf{x})$, whose coefficient a_{rs} is 1 if $r = i$ and $s = j$ and 0 otherwise, maps $\mathbf{e}_j$ to $\mathbf{e}_i$ and $\mathbf{e}_s$ to $\mathbf{0}$ for $s \neq j$. The linear transformations $E_{ij}(\mathbf{x})$ $(1 \leq i \leq m,\ 1 \leq j \leq n)$ are called the **standard unit transformations**. When $i = j$, we get the projection $E_{ii}(\mathbf{x})$ of $\mathbb{R}^n$ on $F\mathbf{e}_i$ (Figure 3.5).

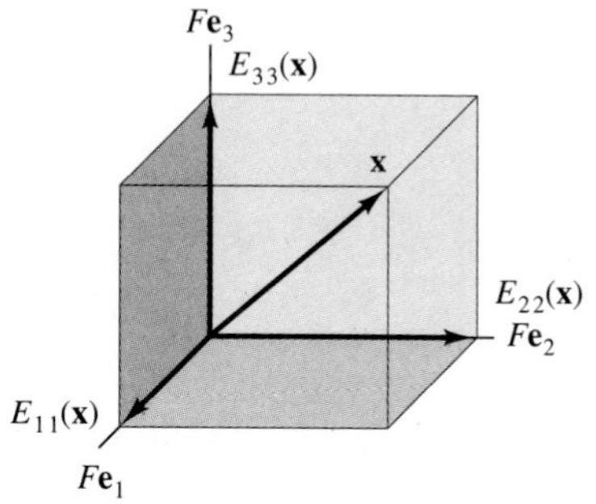

Figure 3.5 The projection $E_{ii}(\mathbf{x})$ of F^3 on $F\mathbf{e}_i$ for $i = 1, 2, 3$ and $F = \mathbb{R}$.

7. The **shear** linear transformation $A_{ij}(a)(\mathbf{x})$ $(i \neq j)$, where a_{rr} is 1 for all r, $a_{rs} = a$ if $r = i$ and $s = j$ and 0 otherwise, maps $\mathbf{e}_j$ to $\mathbf{e}_j + a\mathbf{e}_i$ and $\mathbf{e}_s$ to $\mathbf{e}_s$ for $s \neq j$. We assume here that $m = n$ (Figure 3.6).

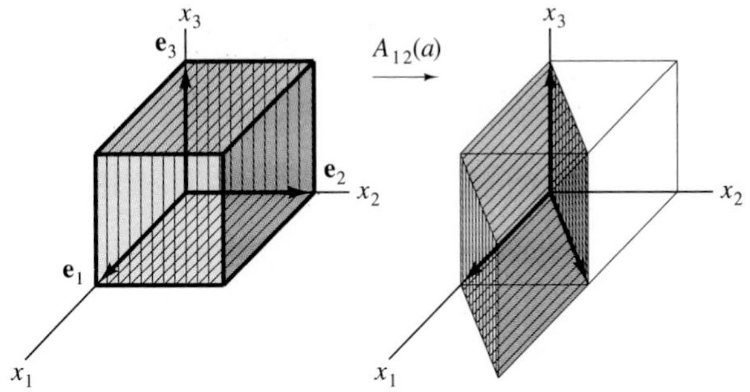

Figure 3.6 The shear $A_{12}(a)(\mathbf{x})$ maps $\mathbf{e}_1$ to $\mathbf{e}_1$, $\mathbf{e}_2$ to $a\mathbf{e}_1 + \mathbf{e}_2$, and $\mathbf{e}_3$ to $\mathbf{e}_3$.

8. The linear transformation $I_{ij}(\mathbf{x})$ $(i \neq j)$, where $a_{rr} = 1$ for all r except i and j, $a_{ij} = a_{ji} = 1$, and all other coefficients are 0 maps $\mathbf{e}_i$ to $\mathbf{e}_j$, $\mathbf{e}_j$ to $\mathbf{e}_i$, and $\mathbf{e}_s$ to $\mathbf{e}_s$ for $s \neq i, j$. It is called **interchange** of the directions $\mathbf{e}_i$ and $\mathbf{e}_j$, or **reflection** across the hyperplane $x_i = x_j$. We assume here that $m = n$ (Figure 3.7).

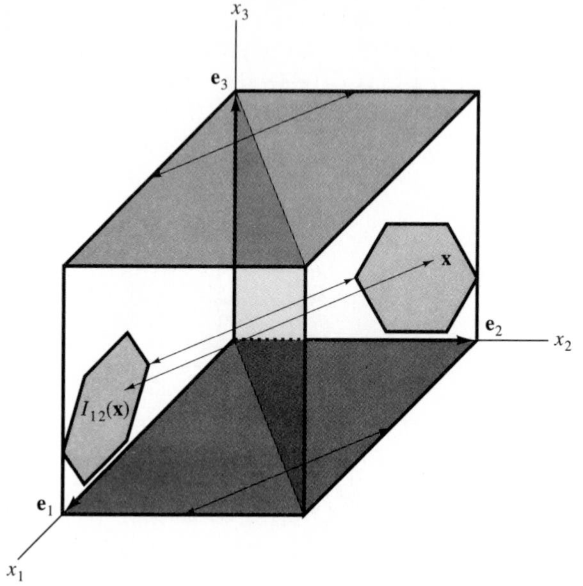

Figure 3.7 Reflection $I_{12}(\mathbf{x})$ across the plane $x_1 = x_2$ in $\mathbb{R}^3$.

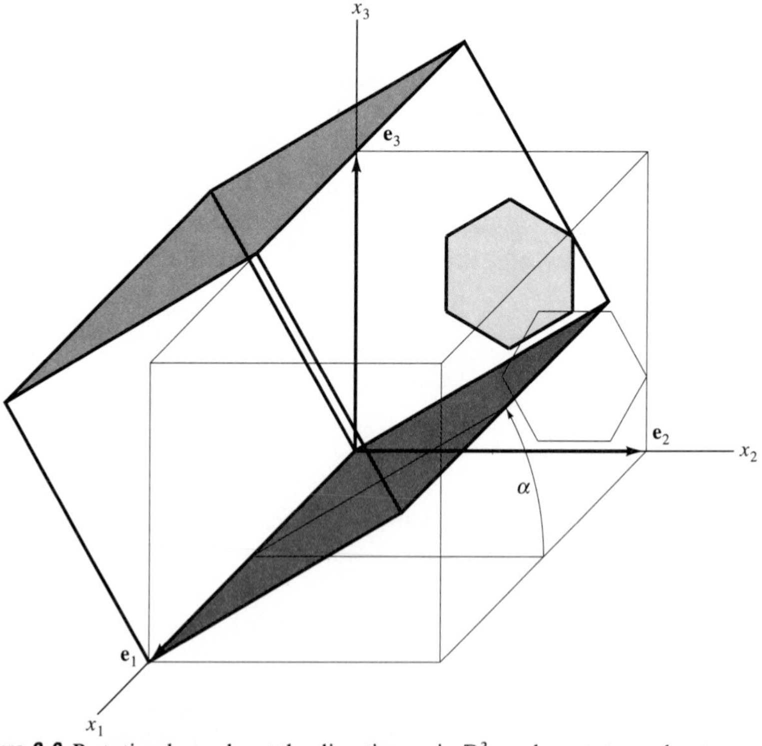

Figure 3.8 Rotation by α about the direction $\mathbf{e}_1$ in $\mathbb{R}^3$ sends $\mathbf{e}_1$ to $\mathbf{e}_1$ and $\mathbf{e}_2$ to $(\cos\alpha)\mathbf{e}_2 + (\sin\alpha)\mathbf{e}_3$.

9. The linear transformation

$$R\begin{bmatrix} x_1 \\ \vdots \\ x_n \end{bmatrix} = \begin{bmatrix} (\cos\alpha)x_1 - (\sin\alpha)x_2 + \cdots + 0x_n \\ (\sin\alpha)x_1 + (\cos\alpha)x_2 + \cdots + 0x_n \\ \vdots \qquad\qquad \vdots \qquad\qquad \vdots \\ 0x_1 + \qquad 0x_2 + \cdots + 1x_n \end{bmatrix}$$

sends $\mathbf{e}_1$ to $(\cos\alpha)\mathbf{e}_1 + (\sin\alpha)\mathbf{e}_2$, $\mathbf{e}_2$ to $-(\sin\alpha)\mathbf{e}_1 + (\cos\alpha)\mathbf{e}_2$ and $\mathbf{e}_s$ to $\mathbf{e}_s$ for $s > 2$. It is **rotation by α about the directions $\mathbf{e}_2, \ldots, \mathbf{e}_n$** (Figure 3.8).

EXAMPLES

1. The zero linear transformation of size 2×3 is

$$R\begin{bmatrix} x_1 \\ x_2 \\ x_3 \end{bmatrix} = \begin{bmatrix} 0x_1 + 0x_2 + 0x_3 \\ 0x_1 + 0x_2 + 0x_3 \end{bmatrix},$$

which can also be written $R(\mathbf{x}) = \mathbf{0}$.

2. The identity of size 3×3 is

$$R\begin{bmatrix} x_1 \\ x_2 \\ x_3 \end{bmatrix} = \begin{bmatrix} 1x_1 & 0x_1 & 0x_1 \\ 0x_2 & 1x_2 & 0x_2 \\ 0x_3 & 0x_3 & 1x_3 \end{bmatrix},$$

which can also be written $R(\mathbf{x}) = \mathbf{x}$.

3. Scalar multiplication by a of size 3×3 is

$$R\begin{bmatrix} x_1 \\ x_2 \\ x_3 \end{bmatrix} = \begin{bmatrix} ax_1 & 0x_1 & 0x_1 \\ 0x_2 & ax_2 & 0x_2 \\ 0x_3 & 0x_3 & ax_3 \end{bmatrix},$$

which can also be written $R(\mathbf{x}) = a\mathbf{x}$. It maps $\mathbf{e}_i$ to $a\mathbf{e}_i$ for $i = 1, 2, 3$.

4. The linear transformation

$$R\begin{bmatrix} x_1 \\ x_2 \\ x_3 \end{bmatrix} = \begin{bmatrix} ax_1 & 0x_1 & 0x_1 \\ 0x_2 & bx_2 & 0x_2 \\ 0x_3 & 0x_3 & cx_3 \end{bmatrix}$$

is the diagonal linear transformation Diag(a, b, c). It maps $\mathbf{e}_1$ to $a\mathbf{e}_1$, $\mathbf{e}_2$ to $b\mathbf{e}_2$, and $\mathbf{e}_3$ to $c\mathbf{e}_3$. (Verify!)

5. The standard unit transformation E_{32} of size 3×4 is the linear transformation

$$R\begin{bmatrix} x_1 \\ x_2 \\ x_3 \end{bmatrix} = \begin{bmatrix} 0x_1 & 0x_1 & 0x_1 & 0x_1 \\ 0x_2 & 0x_2 & 0x_2 & 0x_2 \\ 0x_3 & 1x_3 & 0x_3 & 0x_3 \end{bmatrix}.$$

6. The shear $R(\mathbf{x}) = A_{23}(a)(\mathbf{x})$ of size 3×3 is the linear transformation

$$R\begin{bmatrix} x_1 \\ x_2 \\ x_3 \end{bmatrix} = \begin{bmatrix} 1x_1 & 0x_1 & 0x_1 \\ 0x_2 & 1x_2 & ax_2 \\ 0x_3 & 0x_3 & 1x_3 \end{bmatrix}.$$

It maps $\begin{bmatrix} 0 \\ 0 \\ 1 \end{bmatrix}$ to $\begin{bmatrix} 0 \\ 0 \\ 1 \end{bmatrix} + a\begin{bmatrix} 0 \\ 1 \\ 0 \end{bmatrix}$.

7. The interchange I_{23} of size 3×3 is

$$R\begin{bmatrix} x_1 \\ x_2 \\ x_3 \end{bmatrix} = \begin{bmatrix} 1x_1 & 0x_1 & 0x_1 \\ 0x_2 & 0x_2 & 1x_2 \\ 0x_3 & 1x_3 & 0x_3 \end{bmatrix}.$$

8. Rotation by α about $\mathbf{e}_3$ is the linear transformation

$$R\begin{bmatrix} x_1 \\ x_2 \\ x_3 \end{bmatrix} = \begin{bmatrix} (\cos\alpha)x_1 - (\sin\alpha)x_2 + 0x_3 \\ (\sin\alpha)x_1 + (\cos\alpha)x_2 + 0x_3 \\ 0x_1 + \quad 0x_1 + 1x_3 \end{bmatrix}.$$

PROBLEMS

NUMERICAL PROBLEMS

1. Find the image of $\mathbf{u}$ under $R\begin{bmatrix} x_1 \\ x_2 \\ x_3 \end{bmatrix} = \begin{bmatrix} 3x_1 + 2x_2 + 4x_3 \\ 2x_1 - 5x_2 + 2x_3 \end{bmatrix}$ for:

(a) $\mathbf{u} = \begin{bmatrix} 1 \\ 3 \\ 4 \end{bmatrix}$; **(b)** $\mathbf{u} = \begin{bmatrix} 4 \\ 2 \\ 3 \end{bmatrix}$; **(c)** $\mathbf{u} = \begin{bmatrix} 5 \\ 1 \\ 2 \end{bmatrix}$; **(d)** $\mathbf{u} = \begin{bmatrix} 2 \\ 4 \\ 2 \end{bmatrix}$.

2. Express $R(\mathbf{x}) = \mathbf{p}$ as a system of two linear equations in three variables if

$$R\begin{bmatrix} x_1 \\ x_2 \\ x_3 \end{bmatrix} = \begin{bmatrix} 3x_1 - 2x_2 + 4x_3 \\ 3x_1 - 5x_2 + 1x_3 \end{bmatrix}$$

and $\mathbf{p}$ is as described in the following cases.

(a) $\mathbf{p} = \begin{bmatrix} 3 \\ 3 \end{bmatrix}$ **(b)** $\mathbf{p} = \begin{bmatrix} -2 \\ -5 \end{bmatrix}$ **(c)** $\mathbf{p} = \begin{bmatrix} 4 \\ 1 \end{bmatrix}$ **(d)** $\mathbf{p} = \begin{bmatrix} 7 \\ 4 \end{bmatrix}$

3. Find all $\begin{bmatrix} x_1 \\ x_2 \\ x_3 \end{bmatrix}$ for which $R\begin{bmatrix} x_1 \\ x_2 \\ x_3 \end{bmatrix} = \mathbf{p}$ for

$$R\begin{bmatrix} x_1 \\ x_2 \\ x_3 \end{bmatrix} = \begin{bmatrix} 3x_1 - 2x_2 + 4x_3 \\ 3x_1 - 5x_2 + 1x_3 \end{bmatrix}$$

in the cases given in Problem 2.

4. Describe the linear transformation which maps $\mathbf{e}_1 \in F^3$ to $\mathbf{f}_1$, $\mathbf{e}_2 \in F^3$ to $\mathbf{f}_2$, and $\mathbf{e}_3 \in F^3$ to $\mathbf{f}_3$ in the following cases.

(a) $\mathbf{f}_1 = \begin{bmatrix} 1 \\ 0 \end{bmatrix}, \mathbf{f}_2 = \begin{bmatrix} 0 \\ 1 \end{bmatrix}, \mathbf{f}_3 = \begin{bmatrix} 0 \\ 0 \end{bmatrix}$ **(b)** $\mathbf{f}_1 = \begin{bmatrix} 1 \\ 1 \end{bmatrix}, \mathbf{f}_2 = \begin{bmatrix} 1 \\ 1 \end{bmatrix}, \mathbf{f}_3 = \begin{bmatrix} 1 \\ 1 \end{bmatrix}$

(c) $\mathbf{f}_1 = \begin{bmatrix} 2 \\ 3 \end{bmatrix}, \mathbf{f}_2 = \begin{bmatrix} 3 \\ 1 \end{bmatrix}, \mathbf{f}_3 = \begin{bmatrix} 4 \\ 3 \end{bmatrix}$ **(d)** $\mathbf{f}_1 = \begin{bmatrix} 0 \\ 1 \end{bmatrix}, \mathbf{f}_2 = \begin{bmatrix} 1 \\ 4 \end{bmatrix}, \mathbf{f}_3 = \begin{bmatrix} 0 \\ 5 \end{bmatrix}$

(e) $\mathbf{f}_1 = \begin{bmatrix} 1 \\ 0 \\ 0 \end{bmatrix}, \mathbf{f}_2 = \begin{bmatrix} 0 \\ 1 \\ 0 \end{bmatrix}, \mathbf{f}_3 = \begin{bmatrix} 0 \\ 0 \\ 1 \end{bmatrix}$ **(f)** $\mathbf{f}_1 = \begin{bmatrix} 0 \\ 0 \\ 1 \end{bmatrix}, \mathbf{f}_2 = \begin{bmatrix} 1 \\ 0 \\ 0 \end{bmatrix}, \mathbf{f}_3 = \begin{bmatrix} 0 \\ 1 \\ 0 \end{bmatrix}$

(g) $\mathbf{f}_1 = \begin{bmatrix} a \\ 0 \\ 0 \end{bmatrix}, \mathbf{f}_2 = \begin{bmatrix} 0 \\ b \\ 0 \end{bmatrix}, \mathbf{f}_3 = \begin{bmatrix} 0 \\ 0 \\ c \end{bmatrix}$ **(h)** $\mathbf{f}_1 = \begin{bmatrix} 0 \\ 0 \\ c \end{bmatrix}, \mathbf{f}_2 = \begin{bmatrix} a \\ 0 \\ 0 \end{bmatrix}, \mathbf{f}_3 = \begin{bmatrix} 0 \\ b \\ 0 \end{bmatrix}$

5. Write out the following linear transformations.

(a) $E_{43}(\mathbf{x})$ of size 5×4 **(b)** $A_{43}(20)(\mathbf{x})$ of size 5×5
(c) $I_{42}(\mathbf{x})$ of size 5×5 **(d)** $\text{Diag}(1, 3, 4, 0, 6, 92, 123)(\mathbf{x})$
(e) $E_{42}(\mathbf{x})$ of size 6×3 **(f)** $A_{46}(-5)(\mathbf{x})$ of size 6×6
(g) $I_{34}(\mathbf{x})$ of size 4×4 **(h)** $\text{Diag}(\pi, 3, 9, 66, i + 1, 2, 2)(\mathbf{x})$

Hard

6. Find the images of the following vectors under the projections E_{11}, E_{22}, and E_{33}.

(a) $\begin{bmatrix} 3 \\ 1 \\ c \end{bmatrix}$ **(b)** $\begin{bmatrix} 1 \\ 4 \\ 5 \end{bmatrix}$ **(c)** $\begin{bmatrix} 2 \\ 1 \\ a \end{bmatrix}$

7. Find the images of the vectors in Problem 6 under the unit transformations E_{13}, E_{32}, and E_{23}.

8. Does the mapping R from $\mathbb{C}^2$ to itself defined by $R(\mathbf{v}) = \overline{\mathbf{v}}$ (conjugate of $\mathbf{v}$) satisfy

(a) $R(\mathbf{x} + \mathbf{y}) = R(\mathbf{x}) + R(\mathbf{y})$ for all $\mathbf{x}, \mathbf{y} \in \mathbb{C}^2$?

(b) $R(a\mathbf{x}) = aR(\mathbf{x})$ for all $\mathbf{x} \in \mathbb{C}^2$ and $a \in \mathbb{C}$?
(c) $R(a\mathbf{x}) = aR(\mathbf{x})$ for all $\mathbf{x} \in \mathbb{C}^2$ and $a \in \mathbb{R}$?

9. Is the mapping R in Problem 8 a linear transformation from $\mathbb{C}^2$ to itself?

THEORETICAL PROBLEMS

10. Express $\text{Diag}(d_1, \ldots, d_n)(\mathbf{x})$ as a sum of multiples of the images $E_{11}(\mathbf{x}), \ldots, E_{nn}(\mathbf{x})$ of $\mathbf{x}$ under the projections E_{ii}.
11. Suppose that R is a linear transformation from $\mathbb{C}^n$ to $\mathbb{C}^m$. Let $\bar{R}$ be the mapping from $\mathbb{C}^n$ to $\mathbb{C}^m$ defined by $\bar{R}(\mathbf{v} + i\mathbf{w}) = \overline{R(\mathbf{v}) + iR(\mathbf{w})}$ for all $\mathbf{v}$, $\mathbf{w} \in \mathbb{R}^n$. Is $\bar{R}$ a linear transformation? If so, describe its coefficients in terms of those of R.
12. Show that the linear transformation

$$R\begin{bmatrix} x_1 \\ \vdots \\ x_n \end{bmatrix} = \begin{bmatrix} a_{11}x_1 + \cdots + a_{1n}x_n \\ \vdots \qquad\qquad \vdots \\ a_{m1}x_1 + \cdots + a_{mn}x_n \end{bmatrix}$$

satisfies the equations $R(\mathbf{e}_s) = a_{1s}\mathbf{e}_1 + a_{2s}\mathbf{e}_2 + \cdots + a_{ms}\mathbf{e}_m$ for $1 \leq s \leq n$.

13. Show that a function f from F^n to F is a linear function if it satisfies the properties $f(\mathbf{v} + \mathbf{w}) = f(\mathbf{v}) + f(\mathbf{w})$, $f(a\mathbf{v}) = af(\mathbf{v})$ for all $a \in F$ and all $\mathbf{v}, \mathbf{w} \in F^n$.

3.2 ALGEBRAIC OPERATIONS ON LINEAR TRANSFORMATIONS

The linear transformations from F^n to F^m can be combined algebraically in many ways. In addition, given linear transformations S from F^t to F^s and R from F^s to F^r, we get the **product** RS (composite of functions), defined by $(RS)(\mathbf{x}) = R(S(\mathbf{x}))$ for $\mathbf{x} \in F^t$. Although defined as a function, this product RS turns out to be a linear transformation from F^t to F^r. This makes it possible to work with linear transformations algebraically and to build algebraic expressions for desired transformations or vectors, later to be simplified and computed or otherwise used.

Addition, subtraction, and scalar multiplication

We can add, subtract and scalar multiply linear transformations from F^n to F^m just as we did when $m = n = 2$.

Definition. *Sums, Differences, and Scalar Products.*
For two linear transformations R and S given by

$$R\begin{bmatrix} x_1 \\ \vdots \\ x_n \end{bmatrix} = \begin{bmatrix} a_{11}x_1 + \cdots + a_{1n}x_n \\ \vdots \qquad\qquad \vdots \\ a_{m1}x_1 + \cdots + a_{mn}x_n \end{bmatrix}, \qquad S\begin{bmatrix} x_1 \\ \vdots \\ x_n \end{bmatrix} = \begin{bmatrix} b_{11}x_1 + \cdots + b_{1n}x_n \\ \vdots \qquad\qquad \vdots \\ b_{m1}x_1 + \cdots + b_{mn}x_n \end{bmatrix},$$

the sum $R + S$, difference $R - S$, and scalar product rR (r real) are the linear transformations given by the formulas

1. $$(R + S)\begin{bmatrix} x_1 \\ \vdots \\ x_n \end{bmatrix} = \begin{bmatrix} (a_{11}+b_{11})x_1 + \cdots + (a_{1n}+b_{1n})x_n \\ \vdots \qquad\qquad \vdots \\ (a_{m1}+b_{m1})x_1 + \cdots + (a_{mn}+b_{mn})x_n \end{bmatrix};$$
2. $$(R - S)\begin{bmatrix} x_1 \\ \vdots \\ x_n \end{bmatrix} = \begin{bmatrix} (a_{11}-b_{11})x_1 + \cdots + (a_{1n}-b_{1n})x_n \\ \vdots \qquad\qquad \vdots \\ (a_{m1}-b_{m1})x_1 + \cdots + (a_{mn}-b_{mn})x_n \end{bmatrix};$$
3. $$(rR)\begin{bmatrix} x_1 \\ \vdots \\ x_n \end{bmatrix} = \begin{bmatrix} ra_{11}x_1 + \cdots + ra_{1n}x_n \\ \vdots \qquad\qquad \vdots \\ ra_{m1}x_1 + \cdots + ra_{mn}x_n \end{bmatrix}.$$

EXAMPLES

If R and S are given by

$$R\begin{bmatrix} x_1 \\ x_2 \\ x_3 \end{bmatrix} = \begin{bmatrix} 3x_1 + 4x_2 - 1x_3 \\ 1x_1 + 2x_2 + 3x_3 \end{bmatrix}, \qquad S\begin{bmatrix} x_1 \\ x_2 \\ x_3 \end{bmatrix} = \begin{bmatrix} 1x_1 + 1x_2 + 2x_3 \\ 2x_1 + 1x_2 - 2x_3 \end{bmatrix},$$

the sum $R + S$, difference $R - S$, and scalar product rR (r real) are the linear transformations given by the formulas

1. $$(R + S)\begin{bmatrix} x_1 \\ x_2 \\ x_3 \end{bmatrix} = \begin{bmatrix} (3+1)x_1 + (4+1)x_2 + (-1+2)x_3 \\ (1+2)x_1 + (2+1)x_2 + \quad (3-2)x_3 \end{bmatrix};$$
2. $$(R - S)\begin{bmatrix} x_1 \\ x_2 \\ x_3 \end{bmatrix} = \begin{bmatrix} (3-1)x_1 + (4-1)x_2 + (-1-2)x_3 \\ (1-2)x_1 + (2-1)x_2 + \quad (3+2)x_3 \end{bmatrix};$$
3. $$(rR)\begin{bmatrix} x_1 \\ x_2 \\ x_3 \end{bmatrix} = \begin{bmatrix} r3x_1 + r4x_2 - r1x_3 \\ r1x_1 + r2x_2 + r3x_3 \end{bmatrix}.$$

See Figure 3.9.

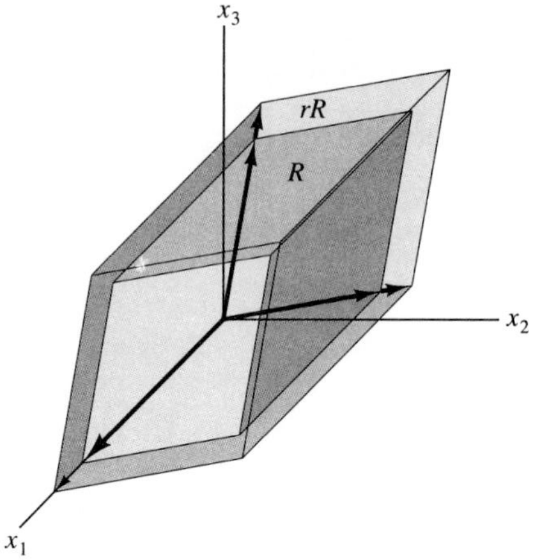

Figure 3.9 Images of the unit cube I under linear transformations R and rR.

The product of two linear transformations

Given linear transformations S from F^t to F^s and R from F^s to F^r, the product RS defined by

$$(RS)(\mathbf{x}) = R(S(\mathbf{x})) \qquad \text{for } \mathbf{x} \in F^t$$

is a linear transformation from F^t to F^r (Figure 3.10). To see this, we simply unwind the equation $(RS)(\mathbf{x}) = R(S(\mathbf{x}))$ using explicit descriptions

$$R\begin{bmatrix} x_1 \\ \vdots \\ x_s \end{bmatrix} = \begin{bmatrix} a_{11}x_1 + \cdots + a_{1s}x_s \\ \vdots \qquad\qquad \vdots \\ a_{r1}x_1 + \cdots + a_{rs}x_s \end{bmatrix}, \qquad S\begin{bmatrix} x_1 \\ \vdots \\ x_t \end{bmatrix} = \begin{bmatrix} b_{11}x_1 + \cdots + b_{1t}x_t \\ \vdots \qquad\qquad \vdots \\ b_{s1}x_1 + \cdots + b_{st}x_t \end{bmatrix},$$

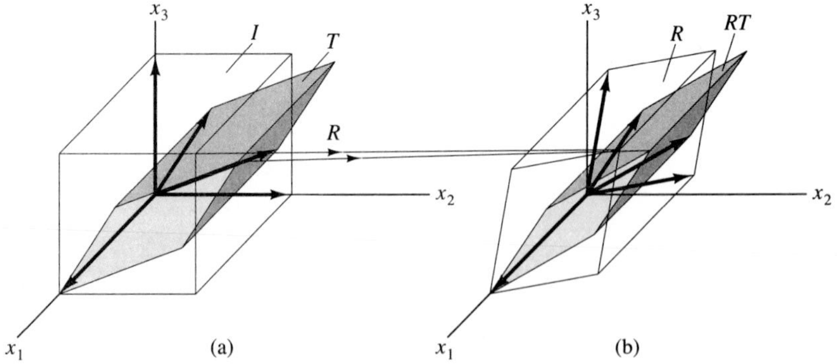

Figure 3.10 Images of the unit cube under the linear transformations (a) I and T and (b) R and RT.

just as we did in Chapter 1 when $m = n = 2$. We see that

$$(RS)\begin{bmatrix} x_1 \\ \vdots \\ x_t \end{bmatrix} = R\left(S\begin{bmatrix} x_1 \\ \vdots \\ x_t \end{bmatrix}\right) = R\begin{bmatrix} b_{11}x_1 + \cdots + b_{1t}x_t \\ \vdots \qquad\qquad \vdots \\ b_{s1}x_1 + \cdots + b_{st}x_t \end{bmatrix} = R\begin{bmatrix} y_1 \\ \vdots \\ y_s \end{bmatrix}$$

$$= \begin{bmatrix} a_{11}y_1 + \cdots + a_{1s}y_s \\ \vdots \qquad\qquad \vdots \\ a_{r1}y_1 + \cdots + a_{rs}y_s \end{bmatrix} = \begin{bmatrix} c_{11}x_1 + \cdots + c_{1t}x_t \\ \vdots \qquad\qquad \vdots \\ c_{r1}x_1 + \cdots + c_{rt}x_t \end{bmatrix},$$

where

$$\begin{bmatrix} y_1 \\ \vdots \\ y_s \end{bmatrix} = \begin{bmatrix} b_{11}x_1 + \cdots + b_{1t}x_t \\ \vdots \qquad\qquad \vdots \\ b_{s1}x_1 + \cdots + b_{st}x_t \end{bmatrix}.$$

Replacing the y's by their expressions in terms of the x's, we find that the typical c_{ik} is the dot product

$$\begin{bmatrix} a_{i1} \\ \vdots \\ a_{is} \end{bmatrix} \cdot \begin{bmatrix} b_{1k} \\ \vdots \\ b_{sk} \end{bmatrix} = a_{i1}b_{1k} + a_{i2}b_{2k} + \cdots + a_{is}b_{sk}$$

for $1 \le i \le r$ and $1 \le k \le t$. (Verify!) Note that i is a *row* subscript (we go along row i in R) and k is a *column* subscript (we go along column k in S) for the coefficients.

EXAMPLE

If

$$R\begin{bmatrix} x_1 \\ x_2 \\ x_3 \end{bmatrix} = \begin{bmatrix} 3x_1 + 4x_2 - 1x_3 \\ 1x_1 + 2x_2 + 3x_3 \end{bmatrix} \quad \text{and} \quad S\begin{bmatrix} x_1 \\ x_2 \\ x_3 \end{bmatrix} = \begin{bmatrix} 1x_1 + 2x_2 \\ 2x_1 + 1x_2 \\ 4x_1 + 3x_2 \end{bmatrix},$$

then

$$(RS)\begin{bmatrix} x_1 \\ x_2 \\ x_3 \end{bmatrix} = \begin{bmatrix} (3\cdot1 + 4\cdot2 - 1\cdot4)x_1 & (3\cdot2 + 4\cdot1 - 1\cdot3)x_2 \\ (1\cdot1 + 2\cdot2 + 3\cdot4)x_1 & (1\cdot2 + 2\cdot1 + 3\cdot3)x_2 \end{bmatrix}.$$

From the corollaries to Theorems 3.3 and 3.4, we get criteria for invertibility in terms of the product.

Theorem 3.5. *Criteria for Invertibility of a Linear Transformation R.*
A linear transformation R from F^n to F^m is invertible if and only if $m = n$ and there is a linear transformation S from F^m to F^n such that $RS = SR = I$.

EXAMPLE

Since the linear transformation sending $\begin{bmatrix} 1 \\ 0 \end{bmatrix}$ to $\begin{bmatrix} 1 \\ 1 \end{bmatrix}$ and $\begin{bmatrix} 0 \\ 1 \end{bmatrix}$ to $\begin{bmatrix} 1 \\ -1 \end{bmatrix}$ sends $\frac{1}{2}\begin{bmatrix} 1 \\ 1 \end{bmatrix}$ to $\begin{bmatrix} 1 \\ 0 \end{bmatrix}$ and $\frac{1}{2}\begin{bmatrix} 1 \\ -1 \end{bmatrix}$ to $\begin{bmatrix} 0 \\ 1 \end{bmatrix}$ (verify), its inverse is the linear transformation sending $\begin{bmatrix} 1 \\ 0 \end{bmatrix}$ to $\frac{1}{2}\begin{bmatrix} 1 \\ 1 \end{bmatrix}$ and $\begin{bmatrix} 0 \\ 1 \end{bmatrix}$ to $\frac{1}{2}\begin{bmatrix} 1 \\ -1 \end{bmatrix}$. (Explain!)

Basic properties

We collect the basic properties of linear transformations and these operations in the following theorem.

Theorem 3.6. *Properties of Linear Transformations.*
Linear transformations R, S, T and scalars $a, b \in F$ satisfy the following properties, where 0 and I denote the zero and identity linear transformations of the appropriate size.

1. $(R + S) + T = R + (S + T)$ if R, S, T are of the same size $m \times n$.
2. $R + 0 = 0 + R = R$, where 0 is the zero of the same size as R.
3. If R, S, T are of the same size, $R + S = T$ has a unique solution S for any R and T, namely, $S = T - R$.
4. $IR = RI = R$ and $0R = R0 = 0$ (the first 0, I are of size $m \times m$, the second 0, I of size $n \times n$, and the third 0 of size $m \times n$, where R has size $m \times n$).
5. $(RS)T = R(ST)$, where R has size $r \times s$, S has size $s \times t$, and T has size $t \times u$.
6. $(R + S)T = RT + ST$, where R and S have size $r \times s$ and T has size $s \times t$.
7. $R(S + T) = RS + RT$, where R has size $r \times s$ and S and T have size $s \times t$.
8. $(a + b)R = aR + bR$.
9. $R + S = S + R$, where R and S have the same size.
10. $a(RS) = (aR)S = R(aS)$, where R has size $r \times s$ and S has size $s \times t$.
11. $IR = R$ and $0R = 0$ (where the first 0 is real and the second is the 0 linear transformation).

Proof. As in the case $m = n = 2$, the fifth property follows from the associative law for functions, and the others are easy to prove by calculating each side of the equation and verifying equality. We illustrated this in Chapter 1 for $m = n = 2$ by proving $R + S = S + R$. Here, we illustrate it for $m = 2$ and $n = 3$ by proving a distributive law. The same proof works for any m and n by keeping track of subscripts.

$$\begin{bmatrix} r & s \\ t & u \end{bmatrix}\left(\begin{bmatrix} a & b & c \\ d & e & f \end{bmatrix}+\begin{bmatrix} g & h & i \\ j & k & l \end{bmatrix}\right)$$
$$= \begin{bmatrix} r & s \\ t & u \end{bmatrix}\begin{bmatrix} a+g & b+h & c+i \\ d+j & e+k & f+l \end{bmatrix}$$
$$= \begin{bmatrix} ra+rg+sd+sj+rb+rh+se+sk+rc+ri+sf+sl \\ ta+tg+ud+uj+tb+th+ue+uk+tc+ti+uf+ul \end{bmatrix}$$

$$\begin{bmatrix} r & s \\ t & u \end{bmatrix}\begin{bmatrix} a & b & c \\ d & e & f \end{bmatrix}+\begin{bmatrix} r & s \\ t & u \end{bmatrix}\begin{bmatrix} g & h & i \\ j & k & l \end{bmatrix}$$
$$= \begin{bmatrix} ra+sd+rb+se+rc+sf \\ ta+ud+tb+ue+tc+uf \end{bmatrix} + \begin{bmatrix} rg+sj+rhsk+ri+sl \\ tg+uj+thuk+ti+ul \end{bmatrix}$$

The two expressions are equal by the definition of addition. ■

A few simple observations are in order.

1. When $m = n$, any two linear transformations R, S of size $n \times n$ can be multiplied to get RS and to get SR. However, even when $n = 2$, we saw that
   - **(a)** RS and SR are not always equal;
   - **(b)** $RS = I$ does not have a solution R for every nonzero S.
2. The linear transformation $S = 0 - R$ is the unique solution to $R + S = 0$ (Property 3). Since $R + (-1)R = 0$ as well, we have $0 - R = (-1)R$. Denoting them both by $-R$, we have $0 - R = (-1)R = -R$.
3. The distributive laws over addition imply corresponding distributive laws over subtraction. For example, $(R - S)T = RT - ST$ can be proved using (1).
4. The scalar linear transformations can now be represented as aI.

EXAMPLE

$T = (R^{-1}(a(RS) + R(bS))R)^2$ can be computed algebraically as follows, where some shortcuts are taken for the reader to fill in:

$$T = (R^{-1}(a(RS) + R(bS))R)^2 = \cdots = (R^{-1}a(RS)R + R^{-1}R(bs)R)^2$$
$$= (aR^{-1}RSR + I(bS)R)^2 = (aISR + bSR)^2$$
$$= \cdots = ((a + b)SR)^2 = \cdots = (a + b)^2(SR)^2.$$

So, to compute T efficiently, simply perform the multiplication SR, square the result, and multiply by the scalar $(a + b)^2$.

Kernel and image

Associated with any linear transformation R from F^n to F^m are two very important subspaces, the **kernel** and the **image** of R. These are defined as follows:

$$\text{Kernel } R = \{\mathbf{x} \in F^n \mid R(\mathbf{x}) = \mathbf{0}\};$$

$$\text{Image } R = \{\mathbf{x}' \in F^m \mid \mathbf{x}' = R(\mathbf{x}) \quad \text{for some } \mathbf{x} \in F^n\} = \{R(\mathbf{x}) \mid \mathbf{x} \in F^n\}.$$

To see that Kernel R is a subspace, just take $\mathbf{x}, \mathbf{y} \in$ Kernel R and note that

$$R(\mathbf{x} + \mathbf{y}) = R(\mathbf{x}) + R(\mathbf{y}) = \mathbf{0} + \mathbf{0} = \mathbf{0},$$

$$R(a\mathbf{x}) = aR(\mathbf{x}) = a\mathbf{0} = \mathbf{0} \text{ for } a \in F.$$

So, $\mathbf{x} + \mathbf{y}$ and $a\mathbf{x}$ are in Kernel R. To see that Image R is a subspace, just take $\mathbf{x}' = R(\mathbf{x})$, $\mathbf{y}' = R(\mathbf{y}) \in$ Image R and note that

$$\mathbf{x}' + \mathbf{y}' = R(\mathbf{x}) + R(\mathbf{y}) = R(\mathbf{x} + \mathbf{y}) \in \text{Image } R,$$

$$a\mathbf{x}' = aR(\mathbf{x}) = R(a\mathbf{x}) \in \text{Image } R.$$

This proves the following.

Theorem 3.7. *Kernel and Image.*
The kernel and image of a linear transformation are subspaces.

We can put these subspaces to good use in the following two theorems.

Theorem 3.8. *Kernel when R Is 1-1.*
A linear transformation R from F^n to F^m is 1-1 if and only if Kernel $R = \{\mathbf{0}\}$.

Proof. Suppose first that R is 1-1. If $R(\mathbf{x}) = \mathbf{0}$, then $R(\mathbf{x}) = R(\mathbf{0})$, which implies that $\mathbf{x} = \mathbf{0}$. So, Kernel $R = \{\mathbf{0}\}$.

Suppose, conversely, that Kernel $R = \{\mathbf{0}\}$. If $R(\mathbf{x}) = R(\mathbf{y})$, then

$$R(\mathbf{x} - \mathbf{y}) = R(\mathbf{x}) - R(\mathbf{y}) = \mathbf{0},$$

so that $\mathbf{x} - \mathbf{y}$ is in the set Kernel $R = \{\mathbf{0}\}$. This implies that $\mathbf{x} - \mathbf{y} = \mathbf{0}$, so that $\mathbf{x} = \mathbf{y}$. Since this is true for all $\mathbf{x}, \mathbf{y}$, R is 1-1. ■

Theorem 3.9. *Kernel and Image When R Is Invertible.*
A linear transformation R from F^n to F^m is invertible if and only if Kernel $R = \{\mathbf{0}\}$ and Image $R = F^m$.

Proof. If R is invertible, then it is 1-1 and onto. Since it is 1-1, its kernel is $\{\mathbf{0}\}$, as just shown. Since it is onto, Image $R = F^n$. Conversely, if R has kernel $\{\mathbf{0}\}$ and image F^n, then it is 1-1 and onto, by the preceding theorem. So, it is an invertible mapping. ■

EXAMPLES

1. In Chapter 1, we computed the inverse for

$$R\begin{bmatrix} x_1 \\ x_2 \end{bmatrix} = \begin{bmatrix} ax_1 + bx_2 \\ cx_1 + dx_2 \end{bmatrix},$$

which exists if and only if the determinant $ad - bc$ is nonzero. The inverse was found to be

$$S\begin{bmatrix} x_1 \\ x_2 \end{bmatrix} = \frac{1}{ad - bc}\begin{bmatrix} dx_1 - bx_2 \\ -cx_1 + ax_2 \end{bmatrix}.$$

This is just a disguised form of *Cramer's rule*, since it enables one to solve the system of equations

$$R\begin{bmatrix} x_1 \\ x_2 \end{bmatrix} = \begin{bmatrix} ax_1 + bx_2 \\ cx_1 + dx_2 \end{bmatrix} = \begin{bmatrix} p_1 \\ p_2 \end{bmatrix}$$

by

$$\begin{bmatrix} x_1 \\ x_2 \end{bmatrix} = R^{-1}R\begin{bmatrix} x_1 \\ x_2 \end{bmatrix} = R^{-1}\begin{bmatrix} p_1 \\ p_2 \end{bmatrix} = \frac{1}{ad - bc}\begin{bmatrix} dp_1 - bp_2 \\ -cp_1 + ap_2 \end{bmatrix}.$$

2. Since the linear transformation $R = \text{Diag}(d_1, \ldots, d_n)$ maps $\mathbf{e}_s$ to $d_s\mathbf{e}_s$ for all s, it is invertible with inverse $S = \text{Diag}(d_1^{-1}, \ldots, d_n^{-1})$, provided that the d_s are all nonzero. To prove this, simply note that SR and RS both map $\mathbf{e}_s$ to $\mathbf{e}_s$ for all s, which implies that $SR = RS = I$. If some d_s is 0, R is not invertible. (Prove!) See Figure 3.11(b).

3. The linear transformation $R = A_{ij}(a)$ $(i \neq j)$ is invertible with inverse $S = A_{ij}(-a)$, since SR and RS both map $\mathbf{e}_s$ to $\mathbf{e}_s$ for all s. (Verify!) See Figure 3.11(a).

4. The linear transformation $R = I_{ij}$ $(i \neq j)$ is invertible with inverse R, since R^2 maps $\mathbf{e}_s$ to itself for all s. (Verify!) See Figure 3.11(c).

5. The linear transformation

$$R\begin{bmatrix} x_1 \\ x_2 \\ x_3 \end{bmatrix} = \begin{bmatrix} 1x_1 + 2x_2 + 3x_3 \\ 0x_1 + 1x_2 + 1x_3 \\ 0x_1 + 0x_2 + 1x_3 \end{bmatrix}$$

is invertible with inverse

$$S\begin{bmatrix} x_1 \\ x_2 \\ x_3 \end{bmatrix} = \begin{bmatrix} 1x_1 - 2x_2 - 1x_3 \\ 0x_1 + 1x_2 - 1x_3 \\ 0x_1 + 0x_2 + 1x_3 \end{bmatrix},$$

since RS and SR both map $\mathbf{e}_s$ to itself for $s = 1, 2, 3$. (Verify!)

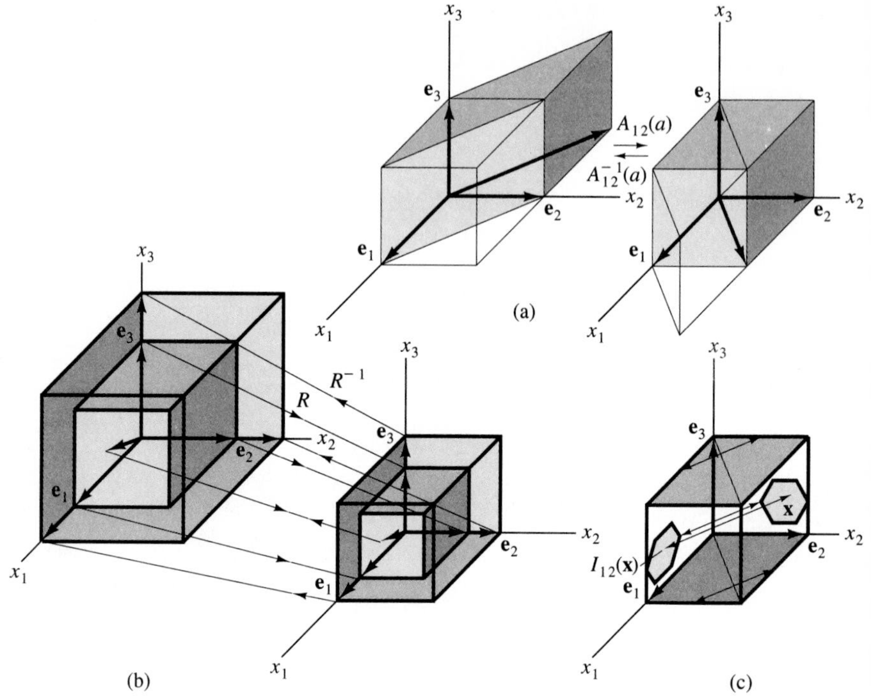

Figure 3.11 The inverses of (a) $A_{ij}(a)(\mathbf{x})$, (b) $R(\mathbf{x}) = \text{Diag}(r, s, t)(\mathbf{x})$, and (c) $I_{ij}(\mathbf{x}) = I_{ij}^{-1}(\mathbf{x})$.

PROBLEMS

NUMERICAL PROBLEMS

1. For the linear transformations

$$R\begin{bmatrix} x_1 \\ x_2 \end{bmatrix} = \begin{bmatrix} 1x_1 + x_2 + x_3 \\ 0x_1 + x_2 + x_3 \end{bmatrix}, \qquad S\begin{bmatrix} x_1 \\ x_2 \end{bmatrix} = \begin{bmatrix} 1x_1 + 2x_2 + \ x_3 \\ 0x_1 - \ x_2 + 2x_3 \end{bmatrix},$$

$$T\begin{bmatrix} x_1 \\ x_2 \end{bmatrix} = \begin{bmatrix} 2x_1 + x_2 \\ 0x_1 + x_2 \end{bmatrix},$$

compute the following linear transformations.

(a) $(2T)(R + 3S)$ **(b)** $T^{-1}R$ **(c)** $T^{-1}(R - S)$

(d) TS **(e)** TR

2. Find all values r such that the linear transformation $rI + T$ is not invertible, where T is as defined in Problem 1.

3. Compute $(rI + T)^{-1}$ in terms of r, where T is as defined in Problem 1.

4. Find the inverse of T, as defined in Problem 1. Use it to solve the equation $T(\mathbf{x}) = \begin{bmatrix} 2 \\ 3 \end{bmatrix}$ for $\mathbf{x}$.

5. For

$$R\begin{bmatrix} x_1 \\ x_2 \\ x_3 \end{bmatrix} = \begin{bmatrix} 1x_1 + 2x_2 + 3x_3 \\ 0x_1 + 1x_2 + 1x_3 \\ 0x_1 + 0x_2 + 1x_3 \end{bmatrix},$$

show that

$$S\begin{bmatrix} x_1 \\ x_2 \\ x_3 \end{bmatrix} = \begin{bmatrix} 1x_1 - 2x_2 - 1x_3 \\ 0x_1 + 1x_2 - 1x_3 \\ 0x_1 + 0x_2 + 1x_3 \end{bmatrix}$$

is the inverse of R.

THEORETICAL PROBLEMS

6. Show that $R + (-1)R = 0$ for any R.
7. Show that $(R - S)T = RT - ST$ for any R, S, T of size 2×2.
8. If R is a linear transformation of size 3×3 and $RS = SR$ for all linear transformations S, show that R is a scalar $R = aI$ for some a.
9. Show that if R and S are invertible linear transformations of the same size, then RS is invertible and its inverse is $S^{-1}R^{-1}$. (See Appendix A, Section A.2.)
10. Show that if R is a linear transformation and $R(\mathbf{u}) = \mathbf{p}$, then the set of all solutions to $R(\mathbf{x}) = \mathbf{p}$ is $\mathbf{u}$ + Kernel R. Compare this with a corresponding theorem on systems of linear equations.
11. Show that $\text{Diag}(d_1, \ldots, d_n)(\mathbf{x}) = d_1 E_{11}(\mathbf{x}) + \cdots + d_n E_{nn}(\mathbf{x})$ for all $\mathbf{x}$.
12. Show that $A_{ij}(a)(\mathbf{x}) = \mathbf{x} + aE_{ij}(\mathbf{x})$ for all $\mathbf{x}$.
13. Show that $\text{Diag}(d_1, \ldots, d_n)$ is not invertible if any of the d_s are zero.
14. Show for $i \neq j$ that $A_{ij}(a)A_{ij}(b) = A_{ij}(a + b)$.
15. Show that the inverse of $A_{ij}(a)$ $(i \neq j)$ is $S = A_{ij}(-a)$.
16. Show that the inverse of $I_{ij} (i \neq j)$ is I_{ij}.

3.3 MATRICES AND THEIR PROPERTIES

You've seen 2×2 matrices modeled after linear transformations of $\mathbb{R}^2$ and read about linear transformations from F^n to F^m. Therefore, much of what we now say about $m \times n$ matrices will seem familiar.

Matrices

The first order of business is to define matrices in general and set forth the criteria for when two of them are equal.

Definition. *$m \times n$ Matrix.*
An $m \times n$ **matrix** over F is an array

$$A = \begin{bmatrix} a_{11} & \cdots & a_{1n} \\ \vdots & & \vdots \\ a_{m1} & \cdots & a_{mn} \end{bmatrix}$$

of scalars a_{rs}. The scalar a_{rs} located in **row** r and **column** s is the (r, s)-**entry** of A, and (r, s) is called its **position**.

We call m the **row degree**, n the **column degree**, and $m \times n$ the **size** of an $m \times n$ matrix A. For an $n \times n$ matrix A, n is called the **degree** of A. The set of $m \times n$ matrices over F is denoted by $M_{m \times n}F$, and the set of $n \times n$ matrices over F is denoted by M_nF.

Definition. *Equality of Two Matrices.*
Two matrices A and B are **equal** if they have the same size and the same (r, s)-entry for all rows r and columns s.

The matrix of a linear transformation

As for linear transformations of $\mathbb{R}^2$, any linear transformation R can be represented by a corresponding matrix $m(R)$. To understand this representation properly, we need the following matrix vector product.

Definition. *The Product of a Matrix and a Vector.*

The **product** $A\mathbf{x}$ of the matrix $A = \begin{bmatrix} a_{11} & \cdots & a_{1n} \\ \vdots & & \vdots \\ a_{m1} & \cdots & a_{mn} \end{bmatrix}$ and vector $\mathbf{x} = \begin{bmatrix} x_1 \\ \vdots \\ x_n \end{bmatrix}$ is

$$\begin{bmatrix} a_{11} & \cdots & a_{1n} \\ \vdots & & \vdots \\ a_{m1} & \cdots & a_{mn} \end{bmatrix} \begin{bmatrix} x_1 \\ \vdots \\ x_n \end{bmatrix} = \begin{bmatrix} a_{11}x_1 + \cdots + a_{1n}x_n \\ \vdots \qquad\qquad \vdots \\ a_{m1}x_1 + \cdots + a_{mn}x_n \end{bmatrix}.$$

EXAMPLE

For

$$A = \begin{bmatrix} 1 & 3 & 1 \\ 2 & 1 & 1 \end{bmatrix} \quad \text{and} \quad \mathbf{x} = \begin{bmatrix} c \\ d \\ 4 \end{bmatrix},$$

$$A\mathbf{x} = \begin{bmatrix} 1c + 3d + 4 \\ 2c + 1d + 4 \end{bmatrix}.$$

Note that for any matrix

$$A = \begin{bmatrix} a_{11} & \dots & a_{1n} \\ \vdots & & \vdots \\ a_{m1} & \dots & a_{mn} \end{bmatrix}$$

and any $\mathbf{p} \in F^m$, the equation $A\mathbf{x} = \mathbf{p}$ is equivalent to the system of linear equations

$$\begin{aligned} a_{11}x_1 + \cdots + a_{1n}x_n &= p_1, \\ &\vdots \\ a_{m1}x_1 + \cdots + a_{mn}x_n &= p_m. \end{aligned}$$

For instance, the equation

$$\begin{bmatrix} 1 & 3 & 1 \\ 2 & 1 & 1 \end{bmatrix} \begin{bmatrix} c \\ d \\ 4 \end{bmatrix} = \begin{bmatrix} 3 \\ 7 \end{bmatrix}$$

is equivalent to the system

$$\begin{aligned} 1c + 3d + 1(4) &= 3, \\ 2c + 1d + 1(4) &= 7. \end{aligned}$$

The mapping $R(\mathbf{x}) = A\mathbf{x}$ is a linear transformation, and the equation $A\mathbf{x} = \mathbf{p}$ is just the equation $R(\mathbf{x}) = \mathbf{p}$. So, we sometimes refer to the equation $A\mathbf{x} = \mathbf{p}$ as a system of linear equations, just as we do the equation $R(\mathbf{x}) = \mathbf{p}$.

Definition. *The Matrix $m(R)$ of a Linear Transformation R.*
The **matrix (of coefficients)** of

$$R \begin{bmatrix} x_1 \\ \vdots \\ x_n \end{bmatrix} = \begin{bmatrix} a_{11}x_1 + \cdots + a_{1n}x_n \\ \vdots \\ a_{m1}x_1 + \cdots + a_{mn}x_n \end{bmatrix}$$

is

$$m(R) = \begin{bmatrix} a_{11} & \dots & a_{1n} \\ \vdots & & \vdots \\ a_{m1} & \dots & a_{mn} \end{bmatrix},$$

so that $R(\mathbf{x}) = m(R)\mathbf{x}$ for all $\mathbf{x}$.

EXAMPLE

The matrix of $R(\mathbf{x}) = \begin{bmatrix} 1x_1 + 3x_2 + 1x_3 \\ 2x_1 + 1x_2 + 1x_3 \end{bmatrix}$ is $m(R) = \begin{bmatrix} 1 & 3 & 1 \\ 2 & 1 & 1 \end{bmatrix}$.

For any matrix A and linear transformation R, it follows that

1. The columns of A are the vectors $A\mathbf{e}_n, \ldots, A\mathbf{e}_n$;
2. The matrix $m(R)$ of R is the matrix whose columns are $R(\mathbf{e}_1), \ldots, R(\mathbf{e}_n)$;
3. $R(\mathbf{x}) = m(R)\mathbf{x}$ for all vectors $\mathbf{x}$.

EXAMPLES

1. $\begin{bmatrix} 1 & 3 & 1 \\ 2 & 1 & 1 \end{bmatrix}\mathbf{e}_2 = \begin{bmatrix} 3 \\ 1 \end{bmatrix}$.

2. For $R(\mathbf{x}) = \begin{bmatrix} 1x_1 + 3x_2 + 1x_3 \\ 2x_1 + 1x_2 + 1x_3 \end{bmatrix}$, $R(\mathbf{e}_2) = \begin{bmatrix} 3 \\ 1 \end{bmatrix}$.

By (3), the matrix $m(R)$ of R completely determines R. From this, it follows that the function $m(R)$ is a 1-1 function from the set of linear transformations R to the set of matrices. On the other hand, for any matrix A, the linear transformation $R(\mathbf{x}) = A\mathbf{x}$ has matrix $m(R) = A$. So, m is also onto, and we have proved the following basic theorem.

Theorem 3.10. *Matrix Correspondence Theorem.*
$m(R)$ is a 1-1 and onto (invertible) function from the set of linear transformations R from F^n to F^m to the set of $m \times n$ matrices A.

Some special matrices

The matrices $m(R)$ of the special linear transformations R listed in Section 2.1 are listed here. Note the importance of the **main diagonal** consisting of the entries a_{ij} for which $i = j$. When the entries a_{ij} $(i < j)$ above it are all zero, A is said to be **lower triangular**. And when the entries a_{ij} $(i > j)$ below it are all zero, A is said to be **upper triangular**.

1. The *zero* matrix

$$m(0) = \begin{bmatrix} 0 & \ldots & 0 \\ \vdots & & \vdots \\ 0 & \ldots & 0 \end{bmatrix}.$$

   It, too, is denoted simply by 0.

2. The *identity* matrix

$$m(I) = \begin{bmatrix} 1 & \ldots & 0 \\ \vdots & & \vdots \\ 0 & \ldots & 1 \end{bmatrix},$$

   also denoted by I.

3. The *scalar* matrix

$$m(aI) = \begin{bmatrix} a & \dots & 0 \\ \vdots & & \vdots \\ 0 & \dots & a \end{bmatrix}.$$

4. The *diagonal*

$$m(\operatorname{Diag}(d_1, \dots, d_n)) = \begin{bmatrix} d_1 & \dots & 0 \\ \vdots & & \vdots \\ 0 & \dots & d_n \end{bmatrix},$$

also denoted by $\operatorname{Diag}(d_1, \dots, d_n)$.

5. The *standard unit matrix* $m(E_{ij})$, whose (r, s)-entry a_{rs} is 1 if $r = i$ and $s = j$ and 0 otherwise. It is also denoted by E_{ij}. For example, the 3×4 matrix E_{23} is

$$\begin{bmatrix} 0 & 0 & 0 & 0 \\ 0 & 0 & 1 & 0 \\ 0 & 0 & 0 & 0 \end{bmatrix}.$$

6. The square matrix $m(A_{ij}(a))$ $(i \neq j)$, where a_{rr} is 1 for all r, $a_{rs} = a$ if $r = i$ and $s = j$, and 0 otherwise. It is also denoted by $A_{ij}(a)$. For example, the 3×3 matrix $A_{23}(3)$ is

$$\begin{bmatrix} 1 & 0 & 0 \\ 0 & 1 & a \\ 0 & 0 & 1 \end{bmatrix}.$$

Note that $A_{ij}(a)$ is upper triangular if $i < j$ and lower triangular otherwise. We refer to A_{ij} as a *shear matrix.*

7. The square matrix I_{ij} $(i \neq j)$, where $a_{ij} = a_{ji} = 1$ and all other coefficients are 0. It is also denoted by I_{ij}. We refer to I_{ij} as an *interchange matrix.*

8. The *rotation matrix*

$$\begin{bmatrix} (\cos\alpha) & -(\sin\alpha) & 0 \dots 0 \\ (\sin\alpha) & (\cos\alpha) & 0 \dots 0 \\ 0 & 0 & 1 \dots 0 \\ \vdots & \vdots & \vdots \quad\ \vdots \\ 0 & 0 & 0 \dots 1 \end{bmatrix}$$

about the directions $\mathbf{e}_s$ for $s > 2$.

Algebraic operations

Since we have an invertible mapping $m(R) = A$ between linear transformations $R(\mathbf{x}) = A\mathbf{x}$ from F^n to F^m and $m \times n$ matrices A, operations on linear transformations induce operations on matrices. Just as in the case of $m = n = 2$ in Chapter 1, we define the matrix operations of addition, subtraction, scalar multiplication, and product by

$$\begin{bmatrix} a_{11} & \dots & a_{1n} \\ \vdots & & \vdots \\ a_{m1} & \dots & a_{mn} \end{bmatrix} + \begin{bmatrix} b_{11} & \dots & b_{1n} \\ \vdots & & \vdots \\ b_{m1} & \dots & b_{mn} \end{bmatrix} = \begin{bmatrix} a_{11}+b_{11} & \dots & a_{1n}+b_{1n} \\ \vdots & & \vdots \\ a_{m1}+b_{m1} & \dots & a_{mn}+b_{mn} \end{bmatrix}$$

$$\begin{bmatrix} a_{11} & \dots & a_{1n} \\ \vdots & & \vdots \\ a_{m1} & \dots & a_{mn} \end{bmatrix} - \begin{bmatrix} b_{11} & \dots & b_{1n} \\ \vdots & & \vdots \\ b_{m1} & \dots & b_{mn} \end{bmatrix} = \begin{bmatrix} a_{11}-b_{11} & \dots & a_{1n}-b_{1n} \\ \vdots & & \vdots \\ a_{m1}-b_{m1} & \dots & a_{mn}-b_{mn} \end{bmatrix}$$

$$r\begin{bmatrix} a_{11} & \dots & a_{1n} \\ \vdots & & \vdots \\ a_{m1} & \dots & a_{mn} \end{bmatrix} = \begin{bmatrix} ra_{11} & \dots & ra_{1n} \\ \vdots & & \vdots \\ ra_{m1} & \dots & ra_{mn} \end{bmatrix}$$

$$\begin{bmatrix} a_{11} & \dots & a_{1s} \\ \vdots & & \vdots \\ a_{r1} & \dots & a_{rs} \end{bmatrix} \begin{bmatrix} b_{11} & \dots & b_{1t} \\ \vdots & & \vdots \\ b_{s1} & \dots & b_{st} \end{bmatrix} = \begin{bmatrix} c_{11} & \dots & c_{1t} \\ \vdots & & \vdots \\ c_{r1} & \dots & c_{rt} \end{bmatrix}$$

where the typical c_{ik} is the dot product

$$\begin{bmatrix} a_{i1} \\ \vdots \\ a_{is} \end{bmatrix} \cdot \begin{bmatrix} b_{1k} \\ \vdots \\ b_{sk} \end{bmatrix} = a_{i1}b_{1k} + a_{i2}b_{2k} + \cdots + a_{is}b_{sk}$$

The matrix product $AB = C$ is built entry by entry, taking a row i of A and a column k of B and computing c_{ik} as the sums of products. For instance:

$$\begin{bmatrix} a & b & c \\ \boxed{d \;\; e \;\; f} \\ g & h & i \\ j & k & l \end{bmatrix} \begin{bmatrix} m & \boxed{n} & o \\ p & \boxed{q} & r \\ s & \boxed{t} & u \end{bmatrix} = \begin{bmatrix} A & B & C \\ D & \boxed{E} & F \\ G & H & I \\ J & K & L \end{bmatrix}, \qquad E = dn + eq + ft.$$

$$\begin{bmatrix} \boxed{a \;\; b} \\ c \;\; d \end{bmatrix} \begin{bmatrix} e & \boxed{f} \\ g & \boxed{h} \end{bmatrix} = \begin{bmatrix} ae+bg & \boxed{af+bh} \\ ce+dg & cf+dh \end{bmatrix}.$$

EXAMPLES

1. All our examples of operations on 2×2 matrices give corresponding examples of operations on 3×3 matrices if we add a third row and column of zeros. That is,

$$\begin{bmatrix} a & b & 0 \\ c & d & 0 \\ 0 & 0 & 0 \end{bmatrix} + \begin{bmatrix} e & f & 0 \\ f & g & 0 \\ 0 & 0 & 0 \end{bmatrix} = \begin{bmatrix} h & i & 0 \\ j & k & 0 \\ 0 & 0 & 0 \end{bmatrix}$$

if $\begin{bmatrix} a & b \\ c & d \end{bmatrix} + \begin{bmatrix} e & f \\ f & g \end{bmatrix} = \begin{bmatrix} h & i \\ j & k \end{bmatrix}$; the same is true for subtraction and multiplication.

2. All the examples of operations on linear transformations have counterparts here. (Find them!)
3. When we add, subtract, or multiply A and B, where A and B are diagonal $n \times n$ matrices, the product is a diagonal $n \times n$ matrix. (Verify!)
4. When we add, subtract or multiply A and B, where A and B are upper triangular $n \times n$ matrices, the product is an upper triangular $n \times n$ matrix. (Verify!) The same is true if we say *lower* rather than *upper*.

Our definitions for these operations on matrices are designed to correspond to the operations for linear transformations.

Theorem 3.11. *Linear Transformations and Their Matrices.* $m(R + S) = m(R) + m(S)$, $m(R - S) = m(R) - m(S)$, and $m(rR) = rm(R)$ for any linear transformations R and S of the same size and any scalar r. If R is of size $r \times s$ and S is of size $s \times t$, then $m(R)$ is of size $r \times s$, $m(S)$ is of size $s \times t$, and we have $m(RS) = m(R)m(S)$.

Proof. Let

$$A = m(R) = \begin{bmatrix} a_{11} & \dots & a_{1n} \\ \vdots & & \vdots \\ a_{m1} & \dots & a_{mn} \end{bmatrix}, \qquad B = M(S) = \begin{bmatrix} b_{11} & \dots & b_{1n} \\ \vdots & & \vdots \\ b_{m1} & \dots & b_{mn} \end{bmatrix}.$$

Since $R(\mathbf{x}) = m(R)\mathbf{x}$ and $S(\mathbf{x}) = m(S)\mathbf{x}$, we have $R(\mathbf{x}) = A\mathbf{x}$ and $S(\mathbf{x}) = B\mathbf{x}$—that is,

$$R\begin{bmatrix} x_1 \\ \vdots \\ x_n \end{bmatrix} = \begin{bmatrix} a_{11}x_1 + \cdots + a_{1n}x_n \\ \vdots \\ a_{m1}x_1 + \cdots + a_{mn}x_n \end{bmatrix}, \qquad S\begin{bmatrix} x_1 \\ \vdots \\ x_n \end{bmatrix} = \begin{bmatrix} b_{11}x_1 + \cdots + b_{1n}x_n \\ \vdots \\ b_{m1}x_1 + \cdots + b_{mn}x_n \end{bmatrix}.$$

So, we have

$$(R + S)\begin{bmatrix} x_1 \\ \vdots \\ x_n \end{bmatrix} = \begin{bmatrix} (a_{11} + b_{11})x_1 + \cdots + (a_{1n} + b_{1n})x_n \\ \vdots \\ (a_{m1} + b_{m1})x_1 + \cdots + (a_{mn} + b_{mn})x_n \end{bmatrix},$$

whose matrix is

$$m(R + S) = \begin{bmatrix} a_{11} + b_{11} & \dots & a_{1n} + b_{1n} \\ \vdots & & \vdots \\ a_{m1} + b_{m1} & \dots & a_{mn} + b_{mn} \end{bmatrix} = A + B = m(R) + m(B).$$

The other operations can be done the same way. ■

By this theorem, we now transfer the algebraic properties of linear transformations to matrices in the following theorem. As in the counterpart of this theorem for linear transformations, the various matrices in the theorem must be of appropriate sizes. Having spelled this out for linear transformations, we can omit the size constraints, since they are clear from context.

Theorem 3.12. *Properties of Matrices.*
Matrices A, B, and C and real numbers a and b satisfy the following properties, where 0 and I denote the zero and identity matrices.

1. $(A + B) + C = A + (B + C)$.
2. $A + 0 = 0 + A = A$.
3. $A + B = C$ has a unique solution B for any A and C, namely, $B = C - A$.
4. $IA = AI = A$ and $0A = A0 = 0$.
5. $(AB)C = A(BC)$.
6. $(A + B)C = AC + BC$.
7. $A(B + C) = AB + AC$.
8. $(a + b)A = aA + bA$.
9. $A + B = B + A$.
10. $a(AB) = (aA)B = A(aB)$.
11. $1A = A$ and $0A = 0$ (where the first 0 is real and the second is the 0 matrix).

Proof. Let $R(\mathbf{x}) = A\mathbf{x}$ and $S(\mathbf{x}) = B\mathbf{x}$. Then the property $R + S = S + R$ implies that

$$A + B = m(R) + m(S) = m(R + S) = m(S + R) = m(S) + m(R) = B + A.$$

The other properties can be shown the same way. ■

We also have the following.

Theorem 3.13. *Properties of Products of Matrices and Vectors.*
Let A be an $r \times s$ matrix and B be an $s \times t$ matrix. Suppose that $\mathbf{x}, \mathbf{x}' \in F^t$ and $r \in F$. Then

1. $B(\mathbf{x} + \mathbf{x}') = B\mathbf{x} + B\mathbf{x}'$ and $B(\mathbf{x} - \mathbf{x}') = B\mathbf{x} - B\mathbf{x}'$;
2. $B(r\mathbf{x}) = r(B\mathbf{x})$;
3. $A(B\mathbf{x}) = (AB)\mathbf{x}$.

Proof. Let $R(\mathbf{x}) = A\mathbf{x}$ and $S(\mathbf{x}) = B\mathbf{x}$. Then $B(\mathbf{x} + \mathbf{x}') = S(\mathbf{x} + \mathbf{x}') = S(\mathbf{x}) + S(\mathbf{x}') = B\mathbf{x} + B\mathbf{x}'$. Similarly, $B(\mathbf{x} - \mathbf{x}') = B\mathbf{x} - B\mathbf{x}'$ and $B(r\mathbf{x}) = r(B\mathbf{x})$. Finally, $A(B\mathbf{x}) = R(S(\mathbf{x})) = (RS)(\mathbf{x}) = m(RS)\mathbf{x} = (m(R)m(S))\mathbf{x} = (AB)\mathbf{x}$. ■

As before, the matrix $B = 0 - A$ is the unique solution to $A + B = 0$, $0 - A = (-1)A$, which we denote $-A$, and $0 - A = (-1)A = -A$. We also have $m(-R) = -m(R)$. And, as before, scalar matrices can now be represented as aI.

EXAMPLE

If $\mathbf{x} = 3\begin{bmatrix}1\\2\end{bmatrix} + C\begin{bmatrix}a\\b\end{bmatrix}$, then $A\mathbf{x} = 3A\begin{bmatrix}1\\2\end{bmatrix} + 4(AC)\begin{bmatrix}a\\b\end{bmatrix}$ (prove), A and C being any given 2×2 matrices.

Invertible matrices

In order to carry over the concept of an invertible linear transformation to matrices, we introduce them as follows.

Definition. *Invertible Linear Transformations and Their Inverses.*
The matrix A is **invertible** if the linear transformation $R(\mathbf{x}) = A\mathbf{x}$ is invertible. If A is invertible, its **inverse** is the matrix $A^{-1} = m(R^{-1})$ of the inverse of the linear transformation $R(\mathbf{x}) = A\mathbf{x}$.

From Theorem 3.5, we then get the following.

Theorem 3.14. *Criteria for Invertibility of a Matrix.*
An $n \times n$ matrix A is invertible if and only if there is a $n \times n$ matrix B such that $AB = BA = I$. When A is invertible, any such B is $B = A^{-1}$.

Proof. We know that a linear transformation R of F^n is invertible if and only if there is a linear transformation S of F^n such that $RS = SR = I$. Apply m to get the corresponding matrices $A = m(R)$, $B = m(S)$ and the corresponding equation $m(RS) = m(SR) = m(I) = I$. Note that the A and B are typical $n \times n$ matrices, since the mapping $A = m(R)$ is 1-1 and onto. Since $m(RS) = m(R)m(S) = AB$ and $m(SR) = m(S)m(R) = BA$, this is just the equation $AB = BA = I$. Since A is invertible if and only if R is invertible, we conclude that an $n \times n$ matrix A is invertible if and only if $AB = BA = I$ for some $n \times n$ matrix B.

When $A = m(R)$ is invertible, R is invertible and the S such that $RS = SR = I$ is $S = R^{-1}$, by Theorem 3.5. So, $B = m(S) = m(R^{-1})$ is the inverse of A. ■

EXAMPLE

$\begin{bmatrix}1 & 2\\3 & 5\end{bmatrix}^{-1} = \begin{bmatrix}-5 & 2\\3 & -1\end{bmatrix}$, since

$$\begin{bmatrix}-5 & 2\\3 & -1\end{bmatrix}\begin{bmatrix}1 & 2\\3 & 5\end{bmatrix} = \begin{bmatrix}1 & 2\\3 & 5\end{bmatrix}\begin{bmatrix}-5 & 2\\3 & -1\end{bmatrix} = I.$$

Nullspace and column space

Let A be an $m \times n$ matrix. Then the kernel of the linear transformation $R(\mathbf{x}) = A\mathbf{x}$ is called the **nullspace** of A, denoted by $n(A)$ (see Figure 3.12):

$$n(A) = \{\mathbf{x} \in F^n \mid A\mathbf{x} = 0\}.$$

The image of the linear transformation $R(\mathbf{x}) = A\mathbf{x}$ is called the **column space** of A, denoted by $c(A)$ (see Figure 3.13):

$$c(A) = \{A\mathbf{x} \mid \mathbf{x} \in F^n\}.$$

If

$$\mathbf{x} = \begin{bmatrix} x_1 \\ \vdots \\ x_n \end{bmatrix} \quad \text{and} \quad A = \begin{bmatrix} a_{11} & \dots & a_{1n} \\ \vdots & & \vdots \\ a_{m1} & \dots & a_{mn} \end{bmatrix} = [A_{*1} \quad \dots \quad A_{*n}]$$

where

$$A_{*1} = \begin{bmatrix} a_{11} \\ \vdots \\ a_{m1} \end{bmatrix}, \dots, A_{*n} = \begin{bmatrix} a_{1n} \\ \vdots \\ a_{mn} \end{bmatrix},$$

then we have

$$A\mathbf{x} = A(x_1\mathbf{e}_1 + \cdots + x_n\mathbf{e}_n) = x_1 A\mathbf{e}_1 + \cdots + x_n A\mathbf{e}_n,$$
$$A\mathbf{x} = x_1 A_{*1} + \cdots + x_n A_{*n}.$$

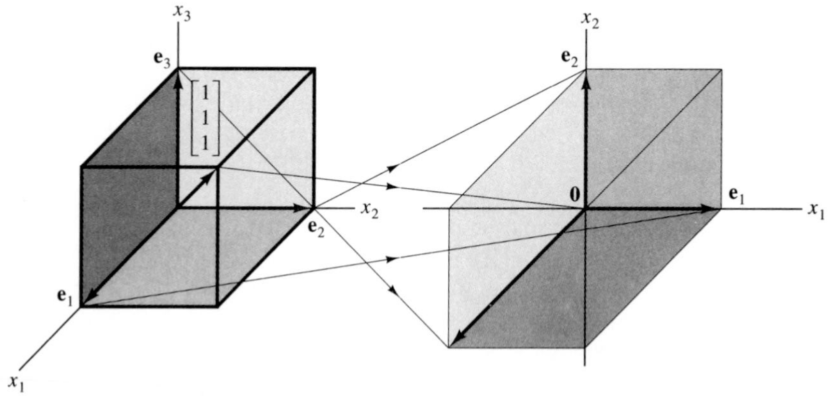

Figure 3.12 The nullspace

$$F\begin{bmatrix} 1 \\ 1 \\ 1 \end{bmatrix}$$

of $A = \begin{bmatrix} 1 & 0 & -1 \\ 0 & 1 & -1 \end{bmatrix}$ is the kernel of $R(\mathbf{x}) = \begin{bmatrix} 1x_1 & 0x_2 & -1x_3 \\ 0x_1 & 1x_2 & -1x_3 \end{bmatrix}$.

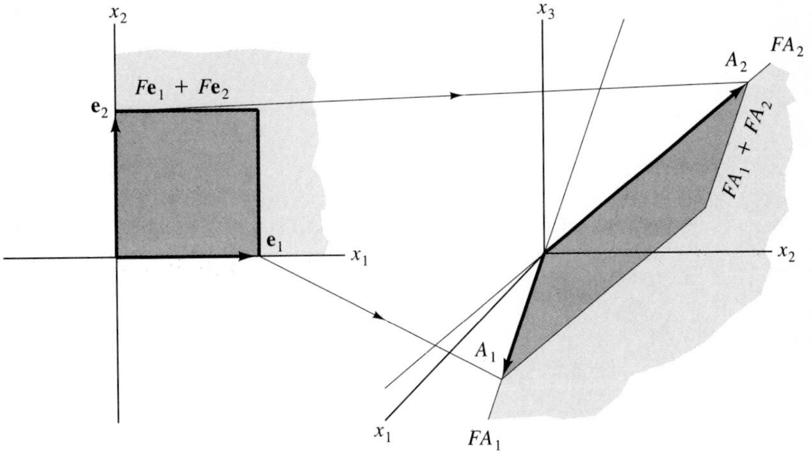

Figure 3.13 The column space of $A = [A_1 \quad A_2]$ is the image $FA_1 + FA_2$ of $R(\mathbf{x}) = A\mathbf{x}$.

So,

$$c(A) = \{x_1 A_{*1} + \cdots + x_n A_{*n} \,|\, x_1, \ldots, x_n \in F\},$$
$$c(A) = FA_{*1} + \cdots + FA_{*n},$$

and $c(A)$ is the span of the columns $A_{*1}, \ldots, A_{*n}$ of A.

EXAMPLES

1. The column space of

$$A = \begin{bmatrix} 1 & 2 \\ 2 & 3 \\ 1 & 1 \end{bmatrix} \quad \text{is} \quad F\begin{bmatrix} 1 \\ 2 \\ 1 \end{bmatrix} + F\begin{bmatrix} 2 \\ 3 \\ 1 \end{bmatrix}.$$

The nullspace of A is $\{0\}$, since $A\mathbf{x} = 0$ implies that $\mathbf{x} = 0$. (Verify!)

2. For

$$A = \begin{bmatrix} 1 & 2 & 1 \\ 2 & 3 & 1 \end{bmatrix} \quad \text{and} \quad \mathbf{x} = \begin{bmatrix} x_1 \\ x_2 \\ x_3 \end{bmatrix},$$

$$A\mathbf{x} = x_1\begin{bmatrix} 1 \\ 2 \end{bmatrix} + x_2\begin{bmatrix} 2 \\ 3 \end{bmatrix} + x_3\begin{bmatrix} 1 \\ 1 \end{bmatrix}.$$

The nullspace of A is

$$n(A) = F\begin{bmatrix} 1 \\ -1 \\ 1 \end{bmatrix},$$

and the column space of A is

$$c(A) = F\begin{bmatrix}1\\2\end{bmatrix} + F\begin{bmatrix}2\\3\end{bmatrix} + F\begin{bmatrix}1\\1\end{bmatrix} = F^2.$$

(Verify!)

Transpose of a matrix. Symmetric matrices

The **main diagonal** of an $m \times n$ matrix A is the diagonal containing the entries $a_{11}, a_{22}, \ldots, a_{dd}$, where d is the smaller of m and n. We can *transpose* A by rotating it about its main diagonal or by exchanging rows and columns. If A is unchanged under this operation, it is said to be *symmetric*.

Definition. *The Transpose of a Matrix A.*
If

$$A = \begin{bmatrix} a_{11} & \ldots & a_{1n} \\ \vdots & & \vdots \\ a_{m1} & \ldots & a_{mn} \end{bmatrix},$$

its **transpose** is

$$A^T = \begin{bmatrix} a_{11} & \ldots & a_{m1} \\ \vdots & & \vdots \\ a_{1n} & \ldots & a_{mn} \end{bmatrix}.$$

If $A = A^T$, we say that A is **symmetric**.

EXAMPLES

1. The main diagonal of $\begin{bmatrix} a & b & c \\ d & e & f \end{bmatrix}$ is the diagonal consisting of a and e. Rotating $\begin{bmatrix} \boxed{a} & b & c \\ d & \boxed{e} & f \end{bmatrix}$ about this diagonal gives

$$\begin{bmatrix} \boxed{a} & d \\ b & \boxed{e} \\ c & f \end{bmatrix},$$

its transpose.

2. Similarly, the main diagonal of

$$\begin{bmatrix} a & d \\ b & e \\ c & f \end{bmatrix}$$

is the diagonal consisting of a and e, and the transpose of

$$\begin{bmatrix} a & d \\ b & e \\ c & f \end{bmatrix} \quad \text{is} \quad \begin{bmatrix} a & b & c \\ d & e & f \end{bmatrix}.$$

3. The matrix $\begin{bmatrix} a & b \\ d & e \end{bmatrix}$ is symmetric if and only if $b = d$.

4. The matrix $\begin{bmatrix} a & b & c \\ b & e & f \end{bmatrix}$ is not symmetric, since it is not square.

By the correspondence between linear transformations and matrices, we can transfer the concept of transpose of a matrix to that of a linear transformation. Later, in Section 6.9, it takes on geometric meaning when we bring quadratic equations to normal form by an orthogonal transformation. (See Section 1.7.)

Definition. *The Transpose of a Linear Transformation R.*
The **transpose** of a linear transformation $R(\mathbf{x})$ is the linear transformation $R^T(\mathbf{x}) = m(R)^T\mathbf{x}$. If $R = R^T$, then we say that R is **symmetric**.

By the very nature of our definition, we have

1. $m(R^T) = m(R)^T$;
2. R is symmetric if and only if $m(R)$ is symmetric.

EXAMPLE

The transpose of the linear transformation $R(\mathbf{x}) = \begin{bmatrix} a & b & c \\ d & e & f \end{bmatrix}\mathbf{x}$ is the linear transformation

$$R^T(\mathbf{x}) = \begin{bmatrix} a & d \\ b & e \\ c & f \end{bmatrix}\mathbf{x}.$$

Again, we get the following properties, when the sizes of the matrices are compatible.

Theorem 3.15. *Properties of the Transpose Operation.*
The transpose operation satisfies

1. $(A + B)^T = A^T + B^T, (A - B)^T = A^T - B^T, (rA)^T = rA^T$;
2. $(AB)^T = B^TA^T$.

Proof. The (r, s)-entry of $A^T + B^T$ is the sum $a_{sr} + b_{sr}$ of the (s, r)-entries of A and B. That, in turn, is the (s, r)-entry of $A + B$, so it is the (r, s)-entry of $(A + B)^T$. The other properties go much the same way. ■

EXAMPLE

For $A = \begin{bmatrix} 1 & 1 \\ 0 & 1 \end{bmatrix}$ and $B = \begin{bmatrix} 2 & 0 \\ 0 & 3 \end{bmatrix}$, $AB = \begin{bmatrix} 2 & 3 \\ 0 & 3 \end{bmatrix}$ is the transpose of $B^T A^T = \begin{bmatrix} 2 & 0 \\ 0 & 3 \end{bmatrix} \begin{bmatrix} 1 & 0 \\ 1 & 1 \end{bmatrix} = \begin{bmatrix} 2 & 0 \\ 3 & 3 \end{bmatrix}$.

Corollary. If A and B are symmetric, then so are $A + B$, $A - B$, and rA. And if A and B are symmetric and $AB = BA$, then AB is symmetric.

EXAMPLES

1. The matrices $A = \begin{bmatrix} 1 & 2 \\ 2 & 3 \end{bmatrix}$ and $B = \begin{bmatrix} -1 & 1 \\ 1 & 3 \end{bmatrix}$ are symmetric. Their product is $\begin{bmatrix} 1 & 2 \\ 2 & 3 \end{bmatrix} \begin{bmatrix} -1 & 1 \\ 1 & 3 \end{bmatrix} = \begin{bmatrix} 1 & 7 \\ 1 & 11 \end{bmatrix}$, which is not symmetric. By the corollary, this implies that $AB \neq BA$. (Confirm!)
2. For $A = \begin{bmatrix} 1 & 3 \\ 3 & 1 \end{bmatrix}$ and $B = \begin{bmatrix} 2 & 1 \\ 1 & 3 \end{bmatrix}$, $A + B = \begin{bmatrix} 3 & 4 \\ 4 & 4 \end{bmatrix}$ is symmetric.

Of course, using the mapping $m(R)$ and property $m(R^T) = m(R)^T$, we can derive the corresponding basic properties of the transpose operation for linear transformations.

Row and column n-spaces F^n and F_n

Having introduced matrices and operations on them, a quick review will show that the vectors in F^m and their operations of addition, subtraction, and scalar multiplication are just $m \times 1$ matrices with matrix addition, subtraction, and scalar multiplication. So, the following definition is compatible with what was said before.

Definition. *Row Space and Column Space.*
A **column vector** is an $n \times 1$ matrix and a **row vector** is a $1 \times n$ matrix. We denote the set of $n \times 1$ column vectors by F^n, called **column n-space**, and the set of $1 \times n$ row vectors by F_n, called **row n-space**.

Everything that we said about F^n and its elements and operations remains true with this new definition. By the operation of transpose, all that we did in the column space F^n has its transposed counterpart in the row space F_n. Note that matrix multiplications can be performed between elements $\mathbf{w} \in F^n$ and elements $\mathbf{v}^T \in F_n$ in either order, but with very different results. The product $\mathbf{v}^T\mathbf{w}$ is just the dot product of $\mathbf{v}$ and $\mathbf{w}$, since $\mathbf{v}^T\mathbf{w} = v_1 w_1 + \cdots + v_n w_n$, whereas the product $\mathbf{w}\mathbf{v}^T$ is an $n \times n$ matrix.

EXAMPLE

The product $\begin{bmatrix} c \\ d \end{bmatrix}[a \quad b]$ is $\begin{bmatrix} ca & cb \\ da & db \end{bmatrix}$, which has determinant 0. The product $[a \quad b]\begin{bmatrix} c \\ d \end{bmatrix}$ is $ac + bd$.

Row space

The transpose operation is a symmetry underlying the whole of matrix algebra. Features of a matrix expressed in terms of rows and columns can be recast, by transposing, as features of its transpose expressed in terms of columns and rows. For example, if the third column of a matrix A is the sum of the first two, then the third row of A^T is the sum of the first two rows of A^T. (Verify!)

Virtually every column concept has a row counterpart. We now give an important instance of this. Whereas the column space of a matrix A is the span of the columns $A_{*1}, \ldots, A_{*n}$ of A, we now define the row space $r(A)$ of an $m \times n$ matrix A to be the span $FA_{1*} + \cdots + FA_{m*}$ of the rows $A_{1*}, \ldots, A_{m*}$ of A. Then the row space $r(A)$ of A^T consists of the transposes of the vectors in the column space of A and the column space of A^T consists of the transposes of the vectors in the row space of A.

EXAMPLES

1. For $A = \begin{bmatrix} 1 & 2 & 1 \\ 2 & 3 & 1 \end{bmatrix}$, the row space of A is

$$r(A) = F[1 \quad 2 \quad 1] + F[1 \quad 3 \quad 1] = \{[r+s \quad 2r+3s \quad r+s] \mid r, s \in F\}.$$

2. A vector is in the column space of $\begin{bmatrix} 1 & 2 & 1 \\ 2 & 3 & 1 \end{bmatrix}$ if and only if its transpose is in the row space of $\begin{bmatrix} 1 & 2 & 1 \\ 2 & 3 & 1 \end{bmatrix}^T$.

Row space, column space, and quadratic functions

We will use column n-spaces F^n and row m-spaces F_m both individually and conjointly. To illustrate their conjoint use, whenever an $m \times n$ matrix A is given, we get the **bilinear form** $\mathbf{v}^T A\mathbf{w}$ ($\mathbf{v} \in F^m$, $\mathbf{w} \in F^n$). (See Problem 19.) Also, whenever an $n \times n$ matrix A is given, we get the **quadratic form** $\mathbf{w}^T A\mathbf{w}$ ($\mathbf{w} \in F^n$). (See Problem 20.) These are discussed in Chapter 7.

EXAMPLES

1. The **row variable vector** $[y_1 \quad y_2]$ and **column variable vector**

$$\begin{bmatrix} x_1 \\ x_2 \\ x_3 \end{bmatrix}$$

come together in a single expression

$$[y_1 \quad y_2]\begin{bmatrix} 1 & 0 & 2 \\ 4 & 5 & 6 \end{bmatrix}\begin{bmatrix} x_1 \\ x_2 \\ x_3 \end{bmatrix} = 1y_1x_1 + 2y_1x_3 + 4y_2x_1 + 5y_2x_2 + 6y_2x_3,$$

enabling us to represent such forms in vector notation.

2. The quadratic form $ax_1^2 + cx_1x_2 + dx_2^2$ is $[x_1 \quad x_2]\begin{bmatrix} a & b/2 \\ b/2 & d \end{bmatrix}\begin{bmatrix} x_1 \\ x_2 \end{bmatrix}$.

3. For row vectors A_{i*} in F_s and column vectors B_{*j} in F^s, let

$$A = \begin{bmatrix} A_{1*} \\ \vdots \\ A_{r*} \end{bmatrix} \quad \text{and} \quad B = [B_{*1} \quad \dots \quad B_{*t}].$$

Then we have

$$AB = [AB_{*1} \quad \dots \quad AB_{*t}] = \begin{bmatrix} A_{1*}B \\ \vdots \\ A_{r*}B \end{bmatrix} = \begin{bmatrix} A_{1*} \\ \vdots \\ A_{r*} \end{bmatrix} [B_{*1} \quad \dots \quad B_{*t}]$$

$$= \begin{bmatrix} A_{1*}B_{*1} & \dots & A_{1*}B_{*t} \\ \vdots & & \vdots \\ A_{r*}B_{*1} & \dots & A_{r*}B_{*t} \end{bmatrix}.$$

(Prove!) For example, if $A = \begin{bmatrix} a & b \\ c & d \end{bmatrix}$ and $B = \begin{bmatrix} e & f \\ g & h \end{bmatrix}$, then

$$AB = \left(A\begin{bmatrix} e \\ g \end{bmatrix} A\begin{bmatrix} f \\ h \end{bmatrix}\right) = \begin{bmatrix} [a \quad b]B \\ [c \quad d]B \end{bmatrix} = \begin{bmatrix} a & b \\ c & d \end{bmatrix}\begin{bmatrix} e & f \\ g & h \end{bmatrix}$$

$$= \begin{bmatrix} [a \quad b]\begin{bmatrix} e \\ g \end{bmatrix} & [a \quad b]\begin{bmatrix} f \\ h \end{bmatrix} \\ [c \quad d]\begin{bmatrix} e \\ g \end{bmatrix} & [c \quad d]\begin{bmatrix} f \\ h \end{bmatrix} \end{bmatrix}.$$

PROBLEMS

NUMERICAL PROBLEMS

1. For the following linear transformations R, find the matrix $m(R)$.

(a) $R(\mathbf{x}) = \begin{bmatrix} 3x_1+4x_2+2x_3 \\ 3x_1+4x_2+2x_3 \end{bmatrix}$ **(b)** $R(\mathbf{x}) = \begin{bmatrix} 3x_1+7x_2+3x_3 \\ 3x_1+5x_2+5x_3 \\ 4x_1+2x_2+9x_3 \end{bmatrix}$

(c) $R(\mathbf{x}) = \begin{bmatrix} 6x_1+7x_2+8x_3+4x_4 \\ 5x_1+4x_2+3x_3+2x_4 \\ 3x_1+4x_2+5x_3+6x_4 \end{bmatrix}$

2. For the matrices

$$A = \begin{bmatrix} 2 & 2 & 2 \\ 4 & 1 & 2 \end{bmatrix}, \quad B = \begin{bmatrix} 4 & 3 & 1 \\ 2 & 1 & 1 \end{bmatrix}, \quad C = \begin{bmatrix} 3 & 0 \\ 1 & 2 \end{bmatrix},$$

compute the following linear transformations.

(a) $C(3B + 2A)$ **(b)** $C(B - A)$ **(c)** CB **(d)** $C^{-1}B$

3. Compute the following.

(a) $3\begin{bmatrix} 1 & 2 \\ 0 & 1 \end{bmatrix}\begin{bmatrix} 1 \\ 3 \end{bmatrix} - \begin{bmatrix} 1 \\ 2 \end{bmatrix}$ **(b)** $\begin{bmatrix} 1 & 3 \\ 0 & 1 \end{bmatrix}\begin{bmatrix} 1+3a \\ 1-b \end{bmatrix}$

(c) $3\begin{bmatrix} 1 & 2 \\ 0 & 1 \end{bmatrix}\begin{bmatrix} 1 & 1 & 3 \\ 0 & 0 & 1 \end{bmatrix} - \begin{bmatrix} 1 & 3 & 0 \\ 1 & 0 & 2 \end{bmatrix}$

(d) $4\left(\begin{bmatrix} 1 & 2 \\ 0 & 1 \end{bmatrix}\left(3\begin{bmatrix} 1 & 1 & 3 \\ 1 & 1 & 1 \end{bmatrix}\right) + 7\begin{bmatrix} 1 & 1 & 0 \\ 1 & 3 & 2 \end{bmatrix}\right)$

(e) $\left(\begin{bmatrix} 1 & 2 \\ 0 & 1 \end{bmatrix}\begin{bmatrix} 1 & 3 \\ 0 & 1 \end{bmatrix}\right)\begin{bmatrix} 1 & 0 \\ 1 & 2 \end{bmatrix}\begin{bmatrix} 1 \\ 1 \end{bmatrix}$ and $\begin{bmatrix} 1 & 2 \\ 0 & 1 \end{bmatrix}\left(\begin{bmatrix} 1 & 3 \\ 0 & 1 \end{bmatrix}\begin{bmatrix} 1 & 0 \\ 1 & 2 \end{bmatrix}\right)\begin{bmatrix} 1 \\ 1 \end{bmatrix}$

4. Find all values r such that the linear transformation $rI + C$ is not invertible, where

$$C = \begin{bmatrix} 1 & 2 & 1 \\ 0 & 2 & 2 \\ 0 & 0 & 3 \end{bmatrix}.$$

5. Verify that the linear transformations $R(\mathbf{x})$ and $S(\mathbf{x})$ are inverses of each other for

(a) $R(\mathbf{x}) = \begin{bmatrix} 1 & 2 \\ 3 & 5 \end{bmatrix}\mathbf{x}$, $S(\mathbf{x}) = \begin{bmatrix} -5 & 2 \\ 3 & -1 \end{bmatrix}\mathbf{x}$;

(b) $R(\mathbf{x}) = \begin{bmatrix} 3 & 4 \\ 4 & 5 \end{bmatrix}\mathbf{x}$, $S(\mathbf{x}) = \begin{bmatrix} -5 & 4 \\ 4 & -3 \end{bmatrix}\mathbf{x}$.

6. Compute the inverse of the matrix C in Problem 4. Then solve the following equations for x.

(a) $C\mathbf{x} = \begin{bmatrix} 1 \\ 1 \\ 4 \end{bmatrix}$ **(b)** $C\mathbf{x} = \begin{bmatrix} 2 \\ 1 \\ 3 \end{bmatrix}$ **(c)** $C\mathbf{x} = \begin{bmatrix} 5 \\ 2 \\ 3 \end{bmatrix}$ **(d)** $C\mathbf{x} = \begin{bmatrix} 2 \\ 3 \\ 5 \end{bmatrix}$

7. Determine the nullspace of A for

(a) $A = \begin{bmatrix} 2 & 2 \\ 1 & 1 \end{bmatrix}$; **(b)** $A = \begin{bmatrix} 2 & 3 & 2 \\ 1 & 0 & 1 \end{bmatrix}$; **(c)** $A = \begin{bmatrix} 2 & 3 & 2 \\ 1 & 1 & 1 \end{bmatrix}$.

8. Describe the column space of A for the matrices in Problem 7.

9. Compute the transposes of

(a) $\begin{bmatrix} 2 & 2 \\ 1 & 1 \end{bmatrix}$; **(b)** $\begin{bmatrix} 3 & 1 & 1 \\ 0 & 3 & 1 \end{bmatrix}$; **(c)** $\begin{bmatrix} 4 & 3 & 0 \\ 1 & 4 & 2 \end{bmatrix}$;

(d) $\begin{bmatrix} 3 & 1 \\ 0 & 3 \end{bmatrix}\begin{bmatrix} 4 & 3 & 0 \\ 1 & 4 & 2 \end{bmatrix}$; **(e)** $\begin{bmatrix} 3 & 1 & 1 \\ 0 & 3 & 1 \end{bmatrix} + \begin{bmatrix} 4 & 3 & 0 \\ 1 & 4 & 2 \end{bmatrix}$.

10. Express the following quadratic equations in vector form.

(a) $3x^2 + 2xy + 4y^2 = 1$ **(b)** $3x^2 - 3xy + 2y^2 = 4$

(c) $2x^2 + 1xy + 5y^2 = 6$

Hard

11. For $B = \begin{bmatrix} 5 & 4 & 0 & 0 \\ 4 & 5 & 0 & 0 \\ 0 & 0 & 5 & 4 \\ 0 & 0 & 4 & 5 \end{bmatrix}$, find a matrix C such that $C^2 = B$.

12. If A is a 4×4 matrix and $AB = BA$, where

$$B = \begin{bmatrix} 2 & 1 & 0 & 0 \\ 1 & 2 & 0 & 0 \\ 0 & 0 & 2 & 1 \\ 0 & 0 & 1 & 2 \end{bmatrix}, \quad \text{then} \quad A = \begin{bmatrix} a & c & d & e \\ c & a & e & d \\ f & g & b & h \\ g & f & h & b \end{bmatrix}$$

for some a, b, c, d, e, f, g, h.

THEORETICAL PROBLEMS

13. Show that if A is an $r \times s$ matrix and the columns of an $s \times t$ matrix B are $B_{*1}, \ldots, B_{*t}$, then the columns of AB are $AB_{*1}, \ldots, AB_{*t}$. In other words, adopting the notation $B = [B_{*1} \quad \cdots \quad B_{*t}]$, $AB = [AB_{*1} \quad \cdots \quad AB_{*t}]$.

14. If B is an $s \times t$ matrix and the rows of an $r \times s$ matrix A are $A_{1*}, \ldots, A_{r*}$, then the rows of AB are $A_{1*}B, \ldots, A_{r*}B$. In other words, adopting the notation $A = \begin{bmatrix} A_{1*} \\ \vdots \\ A_{r*} \end{bmatrix}$,

$$AB = \begin{bmatrix} A_{1*}B \\ \vdots \\ A_{r*}B \end{bmatrix}.$$

15. Show that the properties of the transpose operation can be used to obtain either of the results in Problem 13 and 14 from the other.

16. Following the notation in Problems 14 and 15, show that the product

$$AB = \begin{bmatrix} A_{1*} \\ \vdots \\ A_{r*} \end{bmatrix} [B_{*1} \quad \dots \quad B_{*t}]$$

with the A_{i*} in F_s and the B_{*j} in F^s is

$$AB = \begin{bmatrix} A_{1*} \\ \vdots \\ A_{r*} \end{bmatrix} [B_{*1} \quad \dots \quad B_{*t}] = \begin{bmatrix} A_{1*}B_{*1} \dots A_{1*}B_{*t} \\ \vdots \qquad\qquad \vdots \\ A_{r*}B_{*1} \dots A_{r*}B_{*t} \end{bmatrix}$$

17. If A is a 4×4 matrix and $AB = BA$ for all matrices B of the form

$$B = \begin{bmatrix} a & b & 0 & 0 \\ c & d & 0 & 0 \\ 0 & 0 & e & f \\ 0 & 0 & g & h \end{bmatrix}, \quad \text{then} \quad A = \begin{bmatrix} r & 0 & 0 & 0 \\ 0 & r & 0 & 0 \\ 0 & 0 & s & 0 \\ 0 & 0 & 0 & s \end{bmatrix}$$

for some r and s.

18. Show that if A and B are invertible matrices, then AB is invertible and its inverse is $B^{-1}A^{-1}$.

19. Verify the following property of **bilinearity** for $\mathbf{v}^T A\mathbf{w}$:

$(a\mathbf{v} + a'\mathbf{v}')^T A\mathbf{w} = a(\mathbf{v}^T A\mathbf{w}) + a'(\mathbf{v}'^T A\mathbf{w})$ (a, a' scalars and $\mathbf{v}$, $\mathbf{v}'$, $\mathbf{w}$ vectors)

$\mathbf{v}^T A(a\mathbf{w} + a'\mathbf{w}') = a(\mathbf{v}^T A\mathbf{w}) + a'(\mathbf{v}^T A\mathbf{w}')$ (a, a' scalars and $\mathbf{v}$, $\mathbf{w}$, $\mathbf{w}'$ vectors)

20. Writing $\mathbf{w} = x_1\mathbf{e}_1 + \cdots + x_n\mathbf{e}_n$, express the quadratic form $\mathbf{w}^T A\mathbf{w}$ as a quadratic function in the x's.

3.4 COMPUTATIONAL METHODS

In order to tap the vast power of the theory of matrices, we need computational tools to solve systems of linear equations, find inverses of matrices, and factor them. In this and the remaining sections of this chapter, we develop such tools.

The problem

Before developing computational tools, we should discuss the problem, which, simply stated, is this:

Given matrices A and P, find the set of solutions X to $AX = P$.

Note the following.

1. For $AX = P$ to have a solution X, the number m of rows of A must equal the number of rows of P.
2. If X is a solution, it must be of size $n \times k$, where n is the number of columns of A and k is the number of columns of P. So, X and P have the same number of columns.
3. If P is just a column vector, then X is just a column vector, and the problem is simply to find the set of solutions to the system
$$\begin{bmatrix} a_{11} & \cdots & a_{1n} \\ \vdots & & \vdots \\ a_{m1} & \cdots & a_{mn} \end{bmatrix} \begin{bmatrix} x_1 \\ \vdots \\ x_n \end{bmatrix} = \begin{bmatrix} p_1 \\ \vdots \\ p_n \end{bmatrix}$$
of linear equations. We already have methods to do this, namely, Gaussian elimination and back-substitution.
4. If P has k columns $P_1, \ldots, P_k$, then X has k columns $X_1, \ldots, X_k$. Writing $X = [X_1 \ \ldots \ X_k]$ and $P = [P_1 \ \ldots \ P_k]$, the problem $AX = P$ becomes $[AX_1 \ \ldots \ AX_k] = [P_1 \ \ldots \ P_k]$. So,
$$AX = P \quad \textit{if and only if} \quad AX_1 = P_1, \ldots, AX_k = P_k.$$
We solve the systems $AX_i = P_i$ by choosing elementary operations on equations to reduce the systems to echelon systems. Since the choices depend only on the left-hand sides AX_i and don't involve the X_i, they depend only on A. So, we make the same choices for each of the systems $AX_1 = P_1, \ldots, AX_k = P_k$. In other words, we can solve the problem $AX = P$ by solving the k problems $AX_1 = P_1, \ldots, AX_k = P_k$ *in parallel*.
5. If A is an invertible matrix, then $AX = P$ has exactly one solution, namely, $X = A^{-1}P$ (P must have the same number of rows as A).
6. In particular, if A is an invertible matrix and $P = I$, then the solution to $AX = I$ is $X = A^{-1}$. So, we now have a method to compute A^{-1}, when it exists.

By (4), we have proved the following theorem.

Theorem 3.16. *Solving $AX = P$ Column by Column.*

The set of solutions X to $AX = P$ can be found by the method of Gaussian elimination and back-substitution, performed in parallel for all the columns of P.

EXAMPLES

1. To solve the equation

$$\begin{bmatrix} 1 & 1 & 1 \\ 2 & 3 & 1 \end{bmatrix} X = \begin{bmatrix} 1 & 4 \\ 3 & 5 \end{bmatrix} \quad \text{for} \quad X = \begin{bmatrix} x_{11} & x_{12} \\ x_{21} & x_{22} \\ x_{31} & x_{32} \end{bmatrix},$$

subtract -2 times the equation $[1 \quad 1 \quad 1]X = [1 \quad 4]$ from the equation $[2 \quad 3 \quad 1]X = [3 \quad 5]$ to get the equation $[0 \quad 1 \quad -1]X = [1 \quad -3]$. The new equation is

$$\begin{bmatrix} 1 & 1 & 1 \\ 0 & 1 & -1 \end{bmatrix} X = \begin{bmatrix} 1 & 4 \\ 1 & -3 \end{bmatrix},$$

which further reduces to the equation

$$\begin{bmatrix} 1 & 0 & 2 \\ 0 & 1 & -1 \end{bmatrix} X = \begin{bmatrix} 0 & 7 \\ 1 & -3 \end{bmatrix}.$$

(Explain!) This system is equivalent to the two echelon systems

$$\begin{bmatrix} 1 & 0 & 2 \\ 0 & 1 & -1 \end{bmatrix} X_1 = \begin{bmatrix} 0 \\ 1 \end{bmatrix},$$

$$\begin{bmatrix} 1 & 0 & 2 \\ 0 & 1 & -1 \end{bmatrix} X_2 = \begin{bmatrix} 7 \\ -3 \end{bmatrix}.$$

Solving these for X_1, X_2 and putting the result in $X = [X_1 \quad X_2]$, we get

$$X_1 = \begin{bmatrix} 0 - 2a \\ 1 + 1a \\ 0 + 1a \end{bmatrix}, \qquad X_2 = \begin{bmatrix} 7 - 2b \\ -3 + 1b \\ 0 + 1b \end{bmatrix},$$

$$X = [X_1 \quad X_2] = \begin{bmatrix} 0 - 2a & 7 - 2b \\ 1 + 1a & -3 + 1b \\ 0 + 1a & 0 + 1b \end{bmatrix}$$

where a and b can be any scalars. (Check!) Note that

$$\mathbf{x} = \begin{bmatrix} -2a \\ 1a \\ 1a \end{bmatrix}$$

is the general solution to the homogeneous system $\begin{bmatrix} 1 & 1 & 1 \\ 2 & 3 & 1 \end{bmatrix} \mathbf{x} = 0$.

2. If we know that a matrix such as $A = \begin{bmatrix} 1 & 1 \\ 2 & 3 \end{bmatrix}$ is invertible, we find its inverse as the solution X to $AX = I$ in the same way. But this is now much easier since the final step is trivial! Let's see why.

To solve the equation

$$\begin{bmatrix} 1 & 1 \\ 2 & 3 \end{bmatrix} X = \begin{bmatrix} 1 & 0 \\ 0 & 1 \end{bmatrix} \quad \text{for} \quad X = \begin{bmatrix} x_{11} & x_{12} \\ x_{21} & x_{22} \end{bmatrix},$$

subtract -2 times the equation $[1 \quad 1]X = [1 \quad 0]$ from the equation $[2 \quad 3]X = [0 \quad 1]$ to get the equation $[0 \quad 1]X = [-2 \quad 1]$. The new equation is

$$\begin{bmatrix} 1 & 1 \\ 0 & 1 \end{bmatrix} X = \begin{bmatrix} 1 & 0 \\ -2 & 1 \end{bmatrix},$$

which further reduces to

$$\begin{bmatrix} 1 & 0 \\ 0 & 1 \end{bmatrix} X = \begin{bmatrix} 3 & -1 \\ -2 & 1 \end{bmatrix}$$

(explain)—that is, to $IX = \begin{bmatrix} 3 & -1 \\ -2 & 1 \end{bmatrix}$. Since $X = IX$, the answer falls in our lap as $A^{-1} = \begin{bmatrix} 3 & -1 \\ -2 & 1 \end{bmatrix}$!

The method for its solution

As nicely as the method just described works, we can abbreviate it. The method of Gaussian elimination and back-substitution is based on elementary operations on linear equations. These do not alter the variables in any way. Rather, they affect only the coefficients and right-hand-side values, one equation at a time.

So, we can discard X, which provides no data needed for the computation, and pass from the equation $AX = P$ to the matrix $B = A \mid P$ (read *A join P*) obtained by placing P after A. (Remember that A and P have the same number of rows.) The bar ($\mid$) indicates where A joins P. It is not really part of the new matrix B. Rather, it divides B into the **submatrices** A and P, so that $EB = E[A \mid P]$ can be expressed as $EA \mid EP$.

We now can pass from the elementary operations on equations in the system $AX = P$ to **elementary row operations** on the matrix $B = A \mid P$.

The Elementary Row Operations.

1. Add a times row j of B to row i of B ($i \neq j$).
2. Multiply row i of B by a nonzero scalar a.
3. Interchange rows i and j of B.

These are operations performed on a matrix, and we use them in the following definition.

Definition. *Row Equivalence and Row Reduction.*
A matrix B' is **row equivalent** to a matrix B if B' can be obtained from B by zero or more elementary row operations. The process whereby this is done is **row reduction**.

The fundamental properties of row equivalence are given in the following theorem. We refer to them as the **equivalence relation properties** of row equivalence. Other *relations*, such as the relation "A has the same age as B" between people, also satisfy these properties. We will come upon several relations of this kind between matrices (column equivalence, similarity, orthogonal similarity, and unitary similarity).

Theorem 3.17. *The Equivalence Relation Properties.*
Let A, B, and C be $m \times n$ matrices.

1. A is row equivalent to A.
2. If A is row equivalent to B, then B is row equivalent to A.
3. If A is row equivalent to B and B is row equivalent to C, then A is row equivalent to C.

Proof. In the definition of row equivalence, (1) and (3) are virtually built right into the definition. So, we prove only (2). Suppose that A is row equivalent to B. Then A can be obtained from B by a sequence of elementary row operations. However, each of these operations has an inverse:

1. The inverse of adding a times row j to row i is adding $-a$ times row j to row i.
2. The inverse of multiplying row i by a (nonzero) is multiplying row i by a^{-1}.
3. The inverse of interchanging rows i and j is to interchange rows i and j.

So, we can perform the inverse operations in reverse order, starting with A, to end up with B. So, B is row equivalent to A. ■

EXAMPLES

Let's redo the preceding examples in abbreviated form.

1. To solve the equation

$$\begin{bmatrix} 1 & 1 & 1 \\ 2 & 3 & 1 \end{bmatrix} X = \begin{bmatrix} 1 & 4 \\ 3 & 5 \end{bmatrix} \quad \text{for} \quad X = \begin{bmatrix} x_{11} & x_{12} \\ x_{21} & x_{22} \\ x_{31} & x_{32} \end{bmatrix},$$

we perform the reductions

$$\left[\begin{array}{ccc|cc} 1 & 1 & 1 & 1 & 4 \\ 2 & 3 & 1 & 3 & 5 \end{array}\right] \to \left[\begin{array}{ccc|cc} 1 & 1 & 1 & 1 & 4 \\ 0 & 1 & -1 & 1 & -3 \end{array}\right]$$

$$\to \left[\begin{array}{ccc|cc} 1 & 0 & 2 & 0 & 7 \\ 0 & 1 & -1 & 1 & -3 \end{array}\right]$$

by the elementary row operations of adding -2 times row 1 to row 2, and then adding -1 times row 2 to row 1. Then we can solve $\begin{bmatrix} 1 & 0 & 2 \\ 0 & 1 & -1 \end{bmatrix} X = \begin{bmatrix} 0 & 7 \\ 1 & -3 \end{bmatrix}$ instead, again getting

$$X = \begin{bmatrix} 0-2a & 7-2b \\ 1+1a, & -3+1b \\ 0+1a & 0+1b \end{bmatrix}.$$

2. To solve the equation

$$\begin{bmatrix} 1 & 1 \\ 2 & 3 \end{bmatrix} X = \begin{bmatrix} 1 & 0 \\ 0 & 1 \end{bmatrix} \quad \text{for} \quad X = \begin{bmatrix} x_{11} & x_{12} \\ x_{21} & x_{22} \end{bmatrix},$$

we perform the reductions

$$\left[\begin{array}{cc|cc} 1 & 1 & 1 & 0 \\ 2 & 3 & 0 & 1 \end{array}\right] \to \left[\begin{array}{cc|cc} 1 & 1 & 1 & 0 \\ 0 & 1 & -2 & 1 \end{array}\right] \to \left[\begin{array}{cc|cc} 1 & 0 & 3 & -1 \\ 0 & 1 & -2 & 1 \end{array}\right]$$

by the elementary row operations of adding -2 times row 1 to row 2 and then adding -1 times row 2 to row 1. So, we solve $\begin{bmatrix} 1 & 0 \\ 0 & 1 \end{bmatrix} X = \begin{bmatrix} 3 & -1 \\ -2 & 1 \end{bmatrix}$ instead. As before, the answer falls in our laps as

$$X = \begin{bmatrix} 3 & -1 \\ -2 & 1 \end{bmatrix}.$$

Echelon matrices

When the system $AX = P$ is reduced to an echelon system $A'X = P'$, the matrix A' is an echelon matrix in the sense defined below.

Definition. *The Leading Entry of a Row.*

Given an $m \times n$ matrix A, the **leading position** of row i is the position (i, j) if row i is $[0 \quad \ldots \quad 0 \quad a_{ij} \quad \ldots \quad a_{in}]$, where a_{ij} is nonzero. (Zero rows have no leading position.) The **leading entry** of a nonzero row is the entry a_{ij} in the position (i, j).

Definition. *Conditions for an Echelon Matrix.*
A is an **echelon matrix** if

1. No nonzero row lies below a zero row;
2. For each nonzero row, its leading entry is 1 and this entry lies to the right of the leading entries of the rows above it.

In an echelon matrix, the leading entries together with their positions are called **pivots**.

If $A'X = P'$ is an echelon system, it can be further reduced to a system $A''X = P''$, where A'' is a reduced echelon matrix in the sense of the following definition.

Definition. *Conditions for a Reduced Echelon Matrix.*
A matrix A is a **reduced echelon matrix** if it is an echelon matrix such that each leading entry is the only nonzero entry of its column.

EXAMPLES

In the following examples, pivots in echelon matrices are marked in boldface.

1. We encountered the echelon matrices

$$\begin{bmatrix} \mathbf{1} & 1 & 1 \\ 0 & \mathbf{1} & -1 \end{bmatrix}, \quad \begin{bmatrix} \mathbf{1} & 0 & 2 \\ 0 & \mathbf{1} & -1 \end{bmatrix}, \quad \begin{bmatrix} \mathbf{1} & 1 \\ 0 & \mathbf{1} \end{bmatrix}, \quad \begin{bmatrix} \mathbf{1} & 0 \\ 0 & \mathbf{1} \end{bmatrix}$$

in the preceding examples. The first reduces further to the second, which is a reduced echelon matrix. The third reduces further to the fourth, which is a reduced echelon matrix.

2. The matrix

$$\begin{bmatrix} 1 & 0 & 2 \\ 0 & 0 & 0 \\ 0 & 1 & -1 \end{bmatrix}$$

is not echelon but

$$\begin{bmatrix} \mathbf{1} & 0 & 2 \\ 0 & 0 & \mathbf{1} \\ 0 & 0 & 0 \end{bmatrix}$$

is.

PROBLEMS

NUMERICAL PROBLEMS

1. Find the matrix $A|P$ corresponding to the following systems $AX = P$.

(a) $\begin{bmatrix} 1 & 1 & 1 \\ 3 & 4 & 2 \end{bmatrix} X = \begin{bmatrix} 1 & 2 & 3 & 4 \\ 5 & 6 & 7 & 8 \end{bmatrix}$

(b) $\begin{bmatrix} 1 & 1 & 2 \\ 2 & 2 & -1 \end{bmatrix} X = \begin{bmatrix} 1 & 2 & 3 & 4 \\ 2 & 4 & 6 & 8 \end{bmatrix}$

(c) $\begin{bmatrix} 3 & 4 \\ 4 & 5 \end{bmatrix} X = \begin{bmatrix} 3 & 2 \\ 4 & 4 \end{bmatrix}$

2. Solve $AX = P$ in the following cases by finding A^{-1}.

(a) $\begin{bmatrix} 1 & 3 \\ 1 & 4 \end{bmatrix} X = \begin{bmatrix} 1 & 3 & 2 & 1 \\ 2 & 2 & 3 & 1 \end{bmatrix}$ (b) $\begin{bmatrix} 2 & 3 \\ 3 & 4 \end{bmatrix} X = \begin{bmatrix} 2 & 1 & 3 & 4 \\ 3 & 3 & 3 & 3 \end{bmatrix}$

(c) $\begin{bmatrix} 3 & 4 \\ 4 & 5 \end{bmatrix} X = \begin{bmatrix} 3 & 2 & 3 & 2 \\ 4 & 3 & 3 & 4 \end{bmatrix}$

3. Reduce $A|P$ to $A'|P'$, where A' is a reduced echelon matrix, in each part of Problems 1 and 2.
4. Solve the system $A'X = P'$ for all X in each part of Problem 1.

THEORETICAL PROBLEMS

5. Show that $E[A|B] = EA|EB$ if A and B both have the same number of rows as the number of columns of E.
6. Show that the inverse of any elementary operation is also an elementary row operation by verifying assertions (1), (2), and (3) made in the proof of Theorem 3.17.

Hard

7. If A is invertible and A is row equivalent to B, show that B is invertible. (***Hint:*** Do this first when B is obtained from A by one elementary row operation.)
8. A is invertible if and only if A^T is invertible.
9. If a reduced echelon $n \times n$ matrix R is invertible, show that $R = I$. (***Hint:*** If R is not I, show that its image is not F^n.)
10. If A is invertible, show that A is row equivalent to I.
11. If A is not invertible, show that A is not row equivalent to I. (***Hint:*** Use the results of some of the above problems.)

3.5 ELEMENTARY MATRICES

What began in Section 2.4 as a scheme for abbreviation is destined to have some important mathematical consequences as well. The elementary row operations can be interpreted algebraically if we perform them on the identity matrix I to get the elementary matrices.

Definition. *The Elementary Matrices.*
The **elementary matrices** $A_{ij}(a)$, $M_i(a)$, and I_{ij} are constructed as follows.

1. Add a times row j of I to row i of I $(i \neq j)$ to get $A_{ij}(a)$.
2. Multiply row i of I by a nonzero scalar a to get $M_i(a)$.
3. Interchange rows i and j of I to get I_{ij} $(i \neq j)$.

The results are as follows.

1. The entries of $A_{ij}(a)$ are 1 on the main diagonal, the entry in row i and column j is a, and the other entries are 0.
2. The ith diagonal entry of $M_i(a)$ is a, the other diagonal entries are 1s, and the off-diagonal entries are 0.
3. I_{ij} is obtained from the identity matrix by interchanging the values 0 and 1 for the four entries located in rows and columns i and j.

EXAMPLES

1. The 2×2 elementary matrices are

$$A_{21}(a) = \begin{bmatrix} 1 & 0 \\ a & 1 \end{bmatrix}, \qquad A_{12}(a) = \begin{bmatrix} 1 & a \\ 0 & 1 \end{bmatrix}, \qquad I_{12} = \begin{bmatrix} 0 & 1 \\ 1 & 0 \end{bmatrix},$$

$$M_1(a) = \begin{bmatrix} a & 0 \\ 0 & 1 \end{bmatrix} \quad (a \neq 0), \qquad M_2(a) = \begin{bmatrix} 1 & 0 \\ 0 & a \end{bmatrix} \quad (a \neq 0).$$

2. Some 3×3 elementary matrices are

$$A_{13}(a) = \begin{bmatrix} 1 & 0 & a \\ 0 & 1 & 0 \\ 0 & 0 & 1 \end{bmatrix}, \qquad A_{32}(a) = \begin{bmatrix} 1 & 0 & 0 \\ 0 & 1 & 0 \\ 0 & a & 1 \end{bmatrix},$$

$$M_2(a) = \begin{bmatrix} 1 & 0 & 0 \\ 0 & a & 0 \\ 0 & 0 & 1 \end{bmatrix} \quad (a \neq 0), \qquad I_{13} = \begin{bmatrix} 0 & 0 & 1 \\ 0 & 1 & 0 \\ 1 & 0 & 0 \end{bmatrix}.$$

The elementary row operations can then be interpreted algebraically, as the following theorem shows.

Theorem 3.18. *Affect of Multiplying on the Left by Elementary Matrices.*
Performing elementary row operations has the following effects.

1. Adding a times row j to row i of B has the same effect as multiplying B by $A_{ij}(a)$ to get $A_{ij}(a)B$.

2. Multiplying a times row i of B has the same effect as multiplying B by the matrix $M_i(a)$, getting $M_i(a)B$.
3. Performing elementary row operation (3) on B has the same effect as multiplying B by the matrix I_{ij} to get $I_{ij}B$.

Proof. We briefly indicate two ways to prove this, leaving the details to the reader.

If we apply an elementary row operation to the product AB of matrices A and B, the result is the same as applying the same operation to A and multiplying by B. (Verify!) When $A = I$, this establishes our three assertions. For instance, adding a times row j to row i of $B = IB$ has the same effect as adding a times row j to row i of I, getting $A_{ij}(a)$, and then multiplying by B, getting $A_{ij}(a)B$.

A more direct proof of our three assertions is simply to compare the results. For example, adding a times row 2 to row 3 of

$$B = \begin{bmatrix} r & s \\ t & u \\ v & w \end{bmatrix}$$

gives

$$\begin{bmatrix} r & s \\ t & u \\ at+v & au+w \end{bmatrix},$$

whereas multiplying $A_{32}(a) = \begin{bmatrix} 1 & 0 & 0 \\ 0 & 1 & 0 \\ 0 & a & 1 \end{bmatrix}$ and B gives

$$\begin{bmatrix} 1 & 0 & 0 \\ 0 & 1 & 0 \\ 0 & a & 1 \end{bmatrix} \begin{bmatrix} r & s \\ t & u \\ v & w \end{bmatrix} = \begin{bmatrix} r & s \\ t & u \\ at+v & au+w \end{bmatrix}. \qquad \blacksquare$$

EXAMPLES

1. $A_{12}(a)\begin{bmatrix} 1 & 2 & 3 \\ 4 & 5 & 6 \end{bmatrix} = \begin{bmatrix} 1 & a \\ 0 & 1 \end{bmatrix}\begin{bmatrix} 1 & 2 & 3 \\ 4 & 5 & 6 \end{bmatrix} = \begin{bmatrix} 1+4a & 2+5a & 3+6a \\ 4 & 5 & 6 \end{bmatrix}$
2. $M_2(a)\begin{bmatrix} 1 & 2 & 3 \\ 4 & 5 & 6 \end{bmatrix} = \begin{bmatrix} 1 & 0 \\ 0 & a \end{bmatrix}\begin{bmatrix} 1 & 2 & 3 \\ 4 & 5 & 6 \end{bmatrix} = \begin{bmatrix} 1 & 2 & 3 \\ 4a & 5a & 6a \end{bmatrix}$
3. $I_{12}\begin{bmatrix} 1 & 2 & 3 \\ 4 & 5 & 6 \end{bmatrix} = \begin{bmatrix} 0 & 1 \\ 1 & 0 \end{bmatrix}\begin{bmatrix} 1 & 2 & 3 \\ 4 & 5 & 6 \end{bmatrix} = \begin{bmatrix} 4 & 5 & 6 \\ 1 & 2 & 3 \end{bmatrix}$

Among the examples of inverses of matrices given in Section 3.3 were $A_{ij}(a)^{-1} = A_{ij}(-a)$, $I_{ij}^{-1} = I_{ij}$ and $\operatorname{Diag}(d_1, \ldots, d_n)^{-1} = \operatorname{Diag}(d_1^{-1}, \ldots, d_n^{-1})$

when the d's are all nonzero. Since $M_i(a) = \text{Diag}(1, \ldots, a, \ldots, 1)$, where a is in the ith position, we now have the following.

Theorem 3.19. *The Inverses of the Elementary Matrices.*
The elementary matrices $A_{ij}(a)$, $M_i(a)$, and I_{ij} are invertible with inverses $A_{ij}(a)^{-1} = A_{ij}(-a)$, $M_i(a)^{-1} = M_i(a^{-1})$, and $I_{ij}^{-1} = I_{ij}$.

When we perform a row reduction going from a matrix B to a matrix B', the matrices encountered along the way can be obtained by successively multiplying by appropriate elementary matrices $E_1, \ldots, E_d$. So, we can express B' in *factored form* as $B' = E_d \cdots E_1 B$.

EXAMPLES

Let's see how our two examples look from this vantage point:

1. $\begin{bmatrix} 1 & 1 & 1 \\ 2 & 3 & 1 \end{bmatrix} X = \begin{bmatrix} 1 & 4 \\ 3 & 5 \end{bmatrix}$ is equivalent to

$$\begin{bmatrix} 1 & 0 & 2 \\ 0 & 1 & -1 \end{bmatrix} X = \begin{bmatrix} 0 & 7 \\ 1 & -3 \end{bmatrix}$$

since

$$\left[\begin{array}{ccc|cc} 1 & 1 & 1 & 1 & 4 \\ 2 & 3 & 1 & 3 & 5 \end{array}\right] \to \left[\begin{array}{ccc|cc} 1 & 1 & 1 & 1 & 4 \\ 0 & 1 & -1 & 1 & -3 \end{array}\right]$$
$$\to \left[\begin{array}{ccc|cc} 1 & 0 & 2 & 0 & 7 \\ 0 & 1 & -1 & 1 & -3 \end{array}\right]$$

by elementary row operations of adding -2 times row 1 to row 2 and then adding -1 times row 2 to row 1. Representing these operations by the elementary matrices $E_1 = \begin{bmatrix} 1 & 0 \\ -2 & 1 \end{bmatrix}$ and $E_2 = \begin{bmatrix} 1 & -1 \\ 0 & 1 \end{bmatrix}$, we get

$$\left[\begin{array}{ccc|cc} 1 & 0 & 2 & 0 & 7 \\ 0 & 1 & -1 & 1 & -3 \end{array}\right] = E_2 E_1 \left[\begin{array}{ccc|cc} 1 & 1 & 1 & 1 & 4 \\ 2 & 3 & 1 & 3 & 5 \end{array}\right].$$

This implies that

$$\begin{bmatrix} 1 & 0 & 2 \\ 0 & 1 & -1 \end{bmatrix} = E_2 E_1 \begin{bmatrix} 1 & 1 & 1 \\ 2 & 3 & 1 \end{bmatrix} \quad \text{and} \quad \begin{bmatrix} 0 & 7 \\ 1 & -3 \end{bmatrix} = E_2 E_1 \begin{bmatrix} 1 & 4 \\ 3 & 5 \end{bmatrix}.$$

So, the equation $\begin{bmatrix} 1 & 0 & 2 \\ 0 & 1 & -1 \end{bmatrix} X = \begin{bmatrix} 0 & 7 \\ 1 & -3 \end{bmatrix}$ is just

$$E_2 E_1 \begin{bmatrix} 1 & 1 & 1 \\ 2 & 3 & 1 \end{bmatrix} X = E_2 E_1 \begin{bmatrix} 1 & 4 \\ 3 & 5 \end{bmatrix},$$

that is, $E_2 E_1$ times the old equation.

2. $\begin{bmatrix} 1 & 1 \\ 2 & 3 \end{bmatrix} X = \begin{bmatrix} 1 & 0 \\ 0 & 1 \end{bmatrix}$ is equivalent to $\begin{bmatrix} 1 & 0 \\ 0 & 1 \end{bmatrix} X = \begin{bmatrix} 3 & -1 \\ -2 & 1 \end{bmatrix}$,
since

$$\left[\begin{array}{cc|cc} 1 & 1 & 1 & 0 \\ 2 & 3 & 0 & 1 \end{array}\right] \to \left[\begin{array}{cc|cc} 1 & 1 & 1 & 0 \\ 0 & 1 & -2 & 1 \end{array}\right] \to \left[\begin{array}{cc|cc} 1 & 0 & 3 & -1 \\ 0 & 1 & -2 & 1 \end{array}\right]$$

by elementary row operations of adding -2 times row 1 to row 2 and then adding -1 times row 2 to row 1. Representing these operations by the elementary matrices $E_1 = \begin{bmatrix} 1 & 0 \\ -2 & 1 \end{bmatrix}$ and $E_2 = \begin{bmatrix} 1 & -1 \\ 0 & 1 \end{bmatrix}$, we get

$$\left[\begin{array}{cc|cc} 1 & 0 & 3 & -1 \\ 0 & 1 & -2 & 1 \end{array}\right] = E_2 E_1 \left[\begin{array}{cc|cc} 1 & 1 & 1 & 0 \\ 2 & 3 & 0 & 1 \end{array}\right],$$

that is,

$$\begin{bmatrix} 1 & 0 \\ 0 & 1 \end{bmatrix} = E_2 E_1 \begin{bmatrix} 1 & 1 \\ 2 & 3 \end{bmatrix} \quad \text{and} \quad \begin{bmatrix} 3 & -1 \\ -2 & 1 \end{bmatrix} = E_2 E_1 \begin{bmatrix} 1 & 0 \\ 0 & 1 \end{bmatrix} = E_2 E_1.$$

In other words, by row reducing A to $E_2 E_1 A = I$, we end up with $A^{-1} = X = E_2 E_1$. Not only do we get A^{-1}, but it appears to us in a factored form!

The complete scenario now unfolds before us in the following theorem.

Theorem 3.20. *The Fundamental Consequences of Row Equivalence.* Suppose that the matrices A and P have the same number of rows, and suppose that $A \mid P$ is row equivalent to $A' \mid P'$.

1. For any X, $AX = P$ if and only if $A'X = P'$.
2. For any Y, $PY = A$ if and only if $P'Y = A'$.
3. If the elementary matrices corresponding to the steps in a row-reduction process going from $A \mid P$ to $A' \mid P'$ are $E_1, \ldots, E_d$, then $A' = E_d \cdots E_1 A$ and $P' = E_d \cdots E_1 P$.

Proof. We first prove (1) and (3). Let $B = A \mid P$ and $B' = A' \mid P'$. Since B and B' are row equivalent, there are elementary matrices $E_1, \ldots, E_d$ such that $B' = E_d \cdots E_1 B$—that is, $A' \mid P' = E_d \cdots E_1 A \mid E_d \cdots E_1 P$. But then the equation $A'X = P'$ can be written $E_d \cdots E_1 AX = E_d \cdots E_1 P$. So, if $AX = P$ holds, then $A'X = P'$ holds. Conversely, if $A'X = P'$ holds, then

$$E_d \cdots E_1 AX = E_d \cdots E_1 P$$

holds. Canceling the invertible E's, we see that $AX = P$ holds.

Next, we prove (2). Since $A \mid P$ and $A' \mid P'$ are row equivalent and since row operations have the same effect on an entry in a given row, regardless of its position, $P \mid A$ and $P' \mid A'$ are also row equivalent. By (1), it therefore follows that the set of solutions Y to $PY = A$ is the same as the set of solutions to $P'Y = A'$. ■

EXAMPLES

We can illustrate this by rephrasing (1) of the last example. Since

$$\left[\begin{array}{ccc|cc} 1 & 1 & 1 & 1 & 4 \\ 2 & 3 & 1 & 3 & 5 \end{array}\right] \to \left[\begin{array}{ccc|cc} 1 & 1 & 1 & 1 & 4 \\ 0 & 1 & -1 & 1 & -3 \end{array}\right] \to \left[\begin{array}{ccc|cc} 1 & 0 & 2 & 0 & 7 \\ 0 & 1 & -1 & 1 & -3 \end{array}\right],$$

we have

1. $\left[\begin{array}{ccc|cc} 1 & 1 & 1 & 1 & 4 \\ 2 & 3 & 1 & 3 & 5 \end{array}\right]$ is row equivalent to $\left[\begin{array}{ccc|cc} 1 & 0 & 2 & 0 & 7 \\ 0 & 1 & -1 & 1 & -3 \end{array}\right]$;
2. $\begin{bmatrix} 1 & 0 & 2 \\ 0 & 1 & -1 \end{bmatrix} = \begin{bmatrix} 1 & -1 \\ 0 & 1 \end{bmatrix}\begin{bmatrix} 1 & 0 \\ -2 & 1 \end{bmatrix}\begin{bmatrix} 1 & 1 & 1 \\ 2 & 3 & 1 \end{bmatrix}$;
3. $\begin{bmatrix} 0 & 7 \\ 1 & -3 \end{bmatrix} = \begin{bmatrix} 1 & -1 \\ 0 & 1 \end{bmatrix}\begin{bmatrix} 1 & 0 \\ -2 & 1 \end{bmatrix}\begin{bmatrix} 1 & 4 \\ 3 & 5 \end{bmatrix}$;
4. $\begin{bmatrix} 1 & 1 & 1 \\ 2 & 3 & 1 \end{bmatrix} X = \begin{bmatrix} 1 & 4 \\ 3 & 5 \end{bmatrix}$ if and only if $\begin{bmatrix} 1 & 0 & 2 \\ 0 & 1 & -1 \end{bmatrix} X = \begin{bmatrix} 0 & 7 \\ 1 & -3 \end{bmatrix}$;
5. $\begin{bmatrix} 1 & 4 \\ 3 & 5 \end{bmatrix} Y = \begin{bmatrix} 1 & 1 & 1 \\ 2 & 3 & 1 \end{bmatrix}$ if and only if $\begin{bmatrix} 0 & 7 \\ 1 & -3 \end{bmatrix} Y = \begin{bmatrix} 1 & 0 & 2 \\ 0 & 1 & -1 \end{bmatrix}$.

Corollary. If A and A' are row equivalent, then $n(A) = n(A')$.

Proof. We've really already proved this in Chapter 1. Here, it is the special case of the preceding theorem, where P is the 0 element of F^m, since $n(A)$ and $n(A')$ are then the sets of solutions of the equations $AX = 0$ and $A'X = 0$. ■

EXAMPLE

Since $\begin{bmatrix} 1 & 1 & 1 \\ 2 & 3 & 1 \end{bmatrix} \to \begin{bmatrix} 1 & 1 & 1 \\ 0 & 1 & -1 \end{bmatrix} \to \begin{bmatrix} 1 & 0 & 2 \\ 0 & 1 & -1 \end{bmatrix}$, the nullspace of $\begin{bmatrix} 1 & 1 & 1 \\ 2 & 3 & 1 \end{bmatrix}$ is just the nullspace of $\begin{bmatrix} 1 & 0 & 2 \\ 0 & 1 & -1 \end{bmatrix}$, which is

$$F\begin{bmatrix} -2 \\ 1 \\ 1 \end{bmatrix}.$$

(Verify!)

Theorem 3.20 is the key to many things, some of which are the remaining theorems of this section. The first of these gives a very important criteria for invertibility as well as a method for computing the inverse. First, however, we need the following lemma.

Lemma. Let J be a reduced echelon $n \times n$ matrix whose column space is F^n. Then $J = I$.

Proof. Since $c(J) = F^n$, the last row of J is nonzero. Since J is an $n \times n$ echelon matrix, it follows that the leading entries of the rows are the diagonal entries and all of them are 1. Since J is reduced echelon, each of these 1s is the only nonzero entry in its column. So, $J = I$. ■

Theorem 3.21. *Invertibility of an $n \times n$ Matrix A when $c(A) = F^n$.*
Let A be an $n \times n$ matrix whose column space is F^n. Then A is invertible, A is row equivalent to I and A can be expressed as a product of elementary matrices.

Proof. Take elementary matrices E_s such that $E_d \cdots E_1 A = J$ is a reduced echelon matrix. Then A is row equivalent to J. Since $c(A) = F^n$ and the elementary matrices E_s are invertible, $c(J) = c(E_d \cdots E_1 A) = F^n$. By the lemma, this implies that $J = I$. But then $E_d \cdots E_1 A = I$, and A is the product $A = E_1^{-1} \cdots E_d^{-1}$ of the elementary matrices E_s^{-1}. ■

Theorem 3.22. *Invertibility of the Factors of an Invertible Matrix.*
If A and B are $n \times n$ matrices, then AB is invertible if and only if A and B are invertible, the inverse being $B^{-1}A^{-1}$.

Proof. If A and B are invertible, then so is AB, and its inverse is $B^{-1}A^{-1}$. (Prove!) Suppose, conversely, that AB is invertible. Then $c(AB) = F^n$, from which it follows that $c(A) = F^n$. (Explain!) But then A is invertible, by Theorem 3.21. Since A^{-1} and AB are invertible, so is their product $A^{-1}AB = B$. ■

Corollary. If A and B are $n \times n$ matrices and $AB = I$, then A is invertible and $B = A^{-1}$.

Proof. Since $AB = I$ is invertible, A is invertible by the preceding theorem. Multiplying $AB = I$ by A^{-1} then gives $B = A^{-1}$. ■

EXAMPLE

Consider a matrix A whose columns are the sides of a unit square; that is, $A = \begin{bmatrix} a & b \\ c & d \end{bmatrix}$, where $a^2 + c^2 = 1$, $b^2 + d^2 = 1$, and $ab + cd = 0$. Such a matrix A is called an **orthogonal matrix**. (See Figure 3.14.) Then

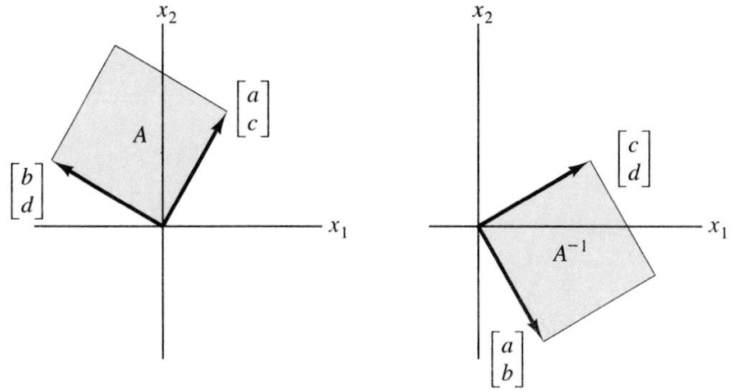

Figure 3.14 The inverse A^{-1} of $A = \begin{bmatrix} a & b \\ c & d \end{bmatrix}$ when $a^2 + c^2 = 1$, $b^2 + d^2 = 1$, and $ab + cd = 0$ is $A^T = \begin{bmatrix} a & c \\ b & d \end{bmatrix}$.

$AA^T = I$; that is, $\begin{bmatrix} a & c \\ b & d \end{bmatrix}\begin{bmatrix} a & b \\ c & d \end{bmatrix} = I$. (Verify!) By the last corollary, it follows that $\begin{bmatrix} a & b \\ c & d \end{bmatrix}$ is invertible with inverse $\begin{bmatrix} a & c \\ b & d \end{bmatrix}$.

Of course, we could also verify directly that $\begin{bmatrix} a & b \\ c & d \end{bmatrix}$ is invertible with inverse $\begin{bmatrix} a & c \\ b & d \end{bmatrix}$ by showing that $\begin{bmatrix} a & b \\ c & d \end{bmatrix}\begin{bmatrix} a & c \\ b & d \end{bmatrix} = I$. This amounts to showing that $a^2 + b^2 = 1$, $c^2 + d^2 = 1$, and $ac + cb = 0$. (Verify these equations by showing that $c = -b$ and $d = a$.)

Theorem 3.23. *Finding the Inverse by Row Reduction.*
The matrix A is invertible if and only if it is row equivalent to the identity I. If $A \mid I$ is row equivalent to $I \mid B$, then $B = A^{-1}$.

Proof. Suppose first that A is row equivalent to I. Certainly, then, $A \mid I$ is row equivalent to $I \mid B$ for some B. By Theorem 3.20 we have

1. For any X, $AX = I$ if and only if $IX = B$;
2. For any Y, $IY = A$ if and only if $BY = I$.

By (1), taking $X = B$, we have $AB = AX = I$. And by (2), taking Y to be A, we have $BA = BY = I$. But then $AB = BA = I$, so A is invertible and $B = A^{-1}$.

Conversely, suppose that A is invertible. Then $c(A) = F^n$ and A is row equivalent to I by Theorem 3.21. ■

EXAMPLE

By Theorem 3.23, we can find the inverse of $A = \begin{bmatrix} 1 & 2 \\ 3 & 5 \end{bmatrix}$ by a row reduction $A \mid I$ to $I \mid B$:

$$\left[\begin{array}{cc|cc} 1 & 2 & 1 & 0 \\ 3 & 5 & 0 & 1 \end{array}\right] \to \left[\begin{array}{cc|cc} 1 & 2 & 1 & 0 \\ 0 & -1 & -3 & 1 \end{array}\right] \to \left[\begin{array}{cc|cc} 1 & 0 & -5 & 2 \\ 0 & -1 & -3 & 1 \end{array}\right]$$
$$\to \left[\begin{array}{cc|cc} 1 & 0 & -5 & 2 \\ 0 & 1 & 3 & -1 \end{array}\right].$$

The inverse is then $B = \begin{bmatrix} -5 & 2 \\ 3 & -1 \end{bmatrix}$. (Verify!)

Theorem 3.24. *Invertibility and Products of Elementary Matrices.* The matrix A is invertible if and only if it can be expressed as a product $A = E_d \cdots E_1$ of elementary matrices.

Proof. If A is a product $A = E_d \cdots E_1$ of elementary matrices, then A is invertible, since the matrices E_s are invertible. Suppose, conversely, that A is invertible. Then A is a product of elementary matrices by Theorem 3.21. ■

EXAMPLE

The reduction

$$\left[\begin{array}{cc|cc} 1 & 2 & 1 & 0 \\ 3 & 5 & 0 & 1 \end{array}\right] \to \left[\begin{array}{cc|cc} 1 & 2 & 1 & 0 \\ 0 & -1 & -3 & 1 \end{array}\right] \to \left[\begin{array}{cc|cc} 1 & 0 & -5 & 2 \\ 0 & -1 & -3 & 1 \end{array}\right]$$
$$\to \left[\begin{array}{cc|cc} 1 & 0 & -5 & 2 \\ 0 & 1 & 3 & -1 \end{array}\right]$$

of $A \mid I$ corresponds to the factorizations

$$\begin{bmatrix} -5 & 2 \\ 3 & -1 \end{bmatrix} = \begin{bmatrix} 1 & 0 \\ 0 & -1 \end{bmatrix} \begin{bmatrix} 1 & 2 \\ 0 & 1 \end{bmatrix} \begin{bmatrix} 1 & 0 \\ -3 & 1 \end{bmatrix}$$
$$\begin{bmatrix} 1 & 2 \\ 3 & 5 \end{bmatrix} = \begin{bmatrix} 1 & 0 \\ 3 & 1 \end{bmatrix} \begin{bmatrix} 1 & -2 \\ 0 & 1 \end{bmatrix} \begin{bmatrix} 1 & 0 \\ 0 & -1 \end{bmatrix}$$

of A^{-1} and A. (Verify!)

PROBLEMS

NUMERICAL PROBLEMS

1. Write out the following 3×3 elementary matrices and their inverses.
   (a) $A_{23}(3)$ **(b)** $A_{21}(-5)$ **(c)** $M_2(\frac{1}{5})$ **(d)** I_{21}

2. Express the inverse of the following 3×3 matrices B as a product of elementary matrices.
   (a) $B = A_{12}(3)M_2(3)A_{13}(3)I_{12}A_{12}(3)$
   (b) $B = A_{23}(-\frac{3}{4})M_3(2)I_{31}A_{13}(5)$
   (c) $B = A_{12}(3)A_{13}(6)A_{12}(-3)$
3. Express the transpose of the matrices in Problem 2 as products of elementary matrices.
4. Factor the following matrices as products of elementary matrices.
   (a) $\begin{bmatrix} 1 & 2 \\ 3 & 7 \end{bmatrix}$ (b) $\begin{bmatrix} 3 & 2 \\ 4 & 3 \end{bmatrix}$ (c) $\begin{bmatrix} 3 & 4 \\ 4 & 5 \end{bmatrix}$
5. Find the inverses of the matrices listed in Problem 4 and factor them as products of elementary matrices.

THEORETICAL PROBLEMS

Problems 6–13 *can be done using parts* (1) *and* (2) *of Theorem* 3.20 *and little else. Try to do them using Theorem* 3.20 *and as little else as possible to give a self-contained theory of row reduction.*

6. Let $I \mid P$ be row equivalent to $I \mid Q$. Then $P = Q$. (***Hint:*** Use Theorem 3.20 with $X = P$.)
7. Let A be row equivalent to A'. Then $A \mid AM$ is row equivalent to $A' \mid A'M$ for all M of compatible size. (***Hint:*** $A \mid AM$ is row equivalent to $A' \mid R$ for some R. Show that $A'M = R$ by Theorem 3.20, taking $X = M$.)
8. Let $A \mid I$ be row equivalent to $I \mid B$. Then $AB = I$. (***Hint:*** Use Theorem 3.20, taking $X = B$.)
9. If A is row equivalent to I, we say A is **nonsingular**. If A is nonsingular, show that $AB = AC$ implies $B = C$. (***Hint:*** Show that $A \mid AB = A \mid AC$ is row equivalent to $I \mid B$ and to $I \mid C$.)
10. If A is nonsingular, show that $AB = I$ for exactly one B.
11. If A is nonsingular and $AB = I$, show that $BA = I$. (***Hint:*** Let $BA = J$. Then $AI = IA = ABA = AJ$, so $AI = AJ$.)
12. If A and B are $n \times n$ matrices and $AB = I$, then $BA = I$. (***Hint:*** It suffices to show that A is nonsingular, so let A be row equivalent to J, which is reduced echelon. Then $A \mid AB$ is row equivalent to $J \mid JB$, so JB is nonsingular. (Why?) But then $JBC = I$ for some C (why?), so that $J = I$ and A is nonsingular.)
13. A is nonsingular if and only if $AB = BA = I$ for some B.
14. If A is nonsingular, then A^T is nonsingular.
15. Prove that if we apply an elementary row operation to the product AB of matrices A and B, the result is the same as applying the same operation to A and multiplying by B.
16. Determine the effect of multiplying the general 3×3 matrix on the *right-hand side* by the matrices $A_{ij}(a)$, $M_i(a)$, I_{ij}.

17. Prove Theorem 3.18 for 3×3 matrices by direct comparison.

18. Show that if the determinant of a 2×2 matrix with integer entries is 1, then its inverse factors as a product of elementary matrices with integer entries.

Hard

19. Show that any invertible matrix A with integer entries factors as a product $A = E_k \cdots E_1 U$ of elementary matrices E_i with integer entries and an upper triangular matrix U with integer entries.

3.6 ROW REDUCTION. RANK AND NULLITY

Certain important features of a matrix are unchanged under row reduction. In this section, we describe some of these features, using some powerful theorems on row equivalence and echelon matrices.

Reduced echelon matrices

The first theorem amounts to comparing the pivots (leading entries together with their positions) of two related reduced echelon matrices. It may be helpful, while reading the proof, to interpret it for 3×3 matrices A and B, which should be sufficient to see how it works in general.

Theorem 3.25. *Each Reduced Echelon Matrix Is Determined by Its Own Row Space.*
Let A and B be reduced echelon $m \times n$ matrices whose row spaces $r(A)$ and $r(B)$ are equal. Then A and B are equal.

Proof. If necessary, reverse the roles of A and B so that the number r of nonzero rows of A is greater or equal to that of B. Denote the columns of A and B by $A_1, \ldots, A_n$ and $B_1, \ldots, B_n$. Let $A_{p(i)}$ be the column of A containing the pivot of A in row i for $1 \leq i \leq r$.

We first show that A and B have the same number of nonzero rows, their pivots are in the same locations, and, therefore, $A_{p(i)} = \mathbf{e}_i = B_{p(i)}$ for $1 \leq i \leq r$.

1. A_s is zero if and only if B_s is zero, since $r(A) = r(B)$.
2. By (1), the first nonzero columns of A and B are in the same position, which must be $p(1)$. Since A and B are reduced echelon, it follows that $A_{p(1)} = \mathbf{e}_1 = B_{p(1)}$.
3. $A_{p(2)} = \mathbf{e}_2$ is the first column that is not a multiple of $A_{p(1)} = \mathbf{e}_1$. Since $r(A) = r(B)$, it follows that $B_{p(2)}$ is the first column of B that is not a multiple of $B_{p(1)} = \mathbf{e}_1$. Since B is reduced echelon, it follows that $B_{p(2)} = \mathbf{e}_2 = A_{p(2)}$.
4. Continuing in this manner, we show that $B_{p(1)}, \ldots, B_{p(i)}$ are the columns containing the pivots of rows $1, \ldots, i$, so that they are the

standard unit vectors $\mathbf{e}_1, \ldots, \mathbf{e}_i$. If $i < r$, we can continue further, since $A_{p(i+1)}$ is the first column of A not contained in the span of $A_{p(1)} = \mathbf{e}_1, \ldots, A_{p(i)} = \mathbf{e}_i$. Since $r(A) = r(B)$, it follows that $B_{p(i+1)}$ is not in the span of $B_{p(1)} = \mathbf{e}_1, \ldots, B_{p(i)} = \mathbf{e}_i$. (Explain!) Since B is a reduced echelon matrix, it follows that $B_{p(i+1)} = \mathbf{e}_{i+1} = A_{p(i+1)}$. On the other hand, if $i = r$, we have already shown that the pivots of row j of A and B are in the same locations and $A_{p(j)} = \mathbf{e}_j = B_{p(j)}$ for $1 \leq j \leq r$.

5. By (4), the number r of nonzero rows of A is at most that of B. But, at the outset we picked A so that r is greater or equal to the number of nonzero rows of B. So, A and B have the same number of nonzero rows. But then A and B have all their pivots in the same rows and columns, $A_{p(i)} = \mathbf{e}_i = B_{p(i)}$ for $1 \leq i \leq r$, and the last $m - r$ rows of A and B are 0.

We have shown that A and B have the same columns $A_{p(i)} = \mathbf{e}_i = B_{p(i)}$ for $1 \leq i \leq r$ and the same last $m - r$ rows (all are 0 for both). It remains to show that the first r rows $A_{1*}, \ldots, A_{r*}$ and $B_{1*}, \ldots, B_{r*}$ of A and B are equal. Since the row spaces of A and B are the same, each B_{i*} is a linear combination

$$B_{i*} = c_{i1}A_{1*} + \cdots + c_{im}A_{r*} = [c_{i1} \quad \ldots \quad c_{im}]\begin{bmatrix} A_{1*} \\ \vdots \\ A_{r*} \end{bmatrix}.$$

But then

$$\begin{bmatrix} B_{1*} \\ \vdots \\ B_{r*} \end{bmatrix} = \begin{bmatrix} c_{11} & \ldots & c_{1r} \\ \vdots & & \vdots \\ c_{r1} & \ldots & c_{rr} \end{bmatrix}\begin{bmatrix} A_{1*} \\ \vdots \\ A_{r*} \end{bmatrix} = C\begin{bmatrix} A_{1*} \\ \vdots \\ A_{r*} \end{bmatrix}.$$

Since the $r \times r$ identity matrix I is obtained from both

$$\begin{bmatrix} B_{1*} \\ \vdots \\ B_{r*} \end{bmatrix} \quad \text{and} \quad \begin{bmatrix} A_{1*} \\ \vdots \\ A_{r*} \end{bmatrix}$$

the set of columns $p(1), \ldots, p(r)$, it follows that $I = CI$—that is, $C = I$. But then

$$\begin{bmatrix} B_{1*} \\ \vdots \\ B_{r*} \end{bmatrix} = \begin{bmatrix} A_{1*} \\ \vdots \\ A_{r*} \end{bmatrix}. \quad \blacksquare$$

Corollary. Let A and B be $m \times n$ matrices. Then the row spaces $r(A)$ and $r(B)$ are equal if and only if A and B are row equivalent.

Proof. Suppose first that A and B are row equivalent. Letting the rows of A be $A_1, \ldots, A_m$, we see that the following are true.

1. $FA_1 + \cdots + FA_m = FA'_1 + \cdots + FA'_m$ if the rows A'_r are obtained from the A_r by taking $A'_i = A_i + aA_j$ $(i \neq j)$ and $A'_r = A_r$ for r different from i. The reason for this is that the A'_r are expressed in terms of the A_r and we can express each A_r in terms of the A'_r by $A_i = A'_i - aA'_j$ and $A_r = A'_r$ for r different from i.
2. $FA_1 + \cdots + FA_m = FA'_1 + \cdots + FA'_m$ if the rows A'_r are obtained from the A_r by either interchanging two rows or by multiplying one row by a nonzero scalar.

By (1) and (2), any single elementary row operation, when applied to A, has no affect on $r(A)$. So, $r(A)$ is unchanged under any row reduction from A to B; that is, $r(A) = r(B)$.

Suppose, conversely, that $r(A) = r(B)$. Let A' be a row-reduced echelon matrix row equivalent to A and B' be a row-reduced echelon matrix row equivalent to B. Then $r(A) = r(A')$ and $r(B) = r(B')$ by what we have just shown. Since $r(A) = r(B)$, it follows that $r(A') = r(B')$. But then $A' = B'$ by Theorem 3.25. This, in turn, implies that A and B are row equivalent, since they are both row equivalent to $A' = B'$. ■

EXAMPLE

The matrices $\begin{bmatrix} 2 & 3 & 4 & 5 \\ 0 & 0 & 0 & 1 \end{bmatrix}$ and $\begin{bmatrix} 1 & 1 & 1 & 1 \\ 0 & 0 & 0 & 1 \end{bmatrix}$ are not row equivalent because they have different row spaces. (Verify!)

The following theorem is of great significance in the development of computational methods, since it is often necessary to know that A is row equivalent to exactly one reduced echelon matrix called its **reduced echelon form**.

Theorem 3.26. *The Reduced Echelon Form of A.*
A matrix A is row equivalent to only one reduced echelon matrix.

Proof. Let a given matrix be row equivalent to reduced echelon matrices A and B. Then A and B are row equivalent and, by the corollary to Theorem 3.25, $r(A) = r(B)$. But then $A = B$ by Theorem 3.25. ■

Pivot columns of a matrix. Rank

Since any echelon matrix is row equivalent to a row-reduced echelon matrix with the same number of pivots in the same positions, we get the following.

Corollary. Any two row equivalent echelon matrices have the same number of pivots, and they are located in the same positions.

Thanks to this corollary, we can introduce the following terms.

Definition. *The Pivot Columns of a Matrix.*

The **pivot columns** of a matrix A are the columns of A in the same positions as the columns containing the pivots of an echelon matrix A' row equivalent to A. The **rank** of a matrix A is the number of its pivot columns. It is denoted by Rank A.

The rank of A is also the number of nonzero rows in an echelon matrix A' row equivalent to A.

EXAMPLES

1. The echelon matrices

$$A = \begin{bmatrix} \mathbf{1} & 3 & 4 & 5 \\ 0 & 0 & \mathbf{1} & 2 \\ 0 & 0 & 0 & \mathbf{1} \end{bmatrix} \quad \text{and} \quad B = \begin{bmatrix} \mathbf{1} & 1 & 0 & 0 \\ 0 & 0 & \mathbf{1} & 7 \\ 0 & 0 & 0 & 0 \end{bmatrix}$$

cannot be row equivalent because their pivots are not the same.

2. Matrix A has pivot columns 1, 3, 4 and is of rank 3. Note that it has three nonzero rows.

3. Matrix B has pivot columns 1 and 3 and B is of rank 2. Note that B has two nonzero rows and the pivot columns 1 and 3 are e_1 and e_2.

4. Since

$$C = \begin{bmatrix} 1 & 3 & 4 & 5 \\ 1 & 3 & 5 & 7 \\ 1 & 3 & 4 & 6 \end{bmatrix}$$

is row equivalent to the echelon matrix A (verify), C has pivot columns 1, 3, 4 and is of rank 3.

For a reduced echelon matrix A', its rank r is the number of nonzero rows and its pivot columns are the standard unit vectors $\mathbf{e}_1, \ldots, \mathbf{e}_r$. This is used to describe the column space of A.

Theorem 3.27. *$c(A)$ and the Set of Pivot Columns for A.*

Let A be a matrix A whose pivot columns are $A_{p(1)}, \ldots, A_{p(r)}$.

1. The column space $c(A)$ is the span of the pivot columns of A, that is, $c(A) = \{x_1 A_{p(1)} + \cdots + x_r A_{p(r)} \mid x_1, \ldots, x_r \in F\}$.
2. The linear transformation

$$R\begin{bmatrix} x_1 \\ \vdots \\ x_r \end{bmatrix} = [A_{p(1)} \quad \cdots \quad A_{p(r)}] \begin{bmatrix} x_1 \\ \vdots \\ x_r \end{bmatrix}$$

is a 1-1 onto mapping from F^r to $c(A)$.

Proof. We claim that if $C \in c(A)$, then $C \in FA_{p(1)} + \cdots + FA_{p(r)}$. This then establishes that $c(A) = FA_{p(1)} + \cdots + FA_{p(r)}$, the span of the pivot columns of A, since $c(A)$ is the span of all of the columns of A. Letting $A' = E_d \cdots E_1 A$ be the reduced echelon matrix row equivalent to A, showing that $C = c_1 A_{p(1)} + \cdots + c_r A_{p(r)}$ amounts to showing that

$$C' = c_1 A'_{p(1)} + \cdots + c_r A'_{p(r)},$$

where $C' = E_d \cdots E_1 C$ and $A'_{p(i)} = E_d \cdots E_1 A_{p(i)}$ for $1 \le i \le r$. We can then multiply both sides by the inverse of $E_d \cdots E_1$ to get C back as $C = c_1 A_{p(1)} + \cdots + c_r A_{p(r)}$. But C' is in the column space of the matrix A' and the $A'_{p(1)}, \ldots, A'_{p(r)}$ are the pivot columns of A', which are just the standard unit vectors $\mathbf{e}_1, \ldots, \mathbf{e}_r$. So, letting the entries of C' be $c_1, \ldots, c_r, 0, \ldots, 0$, we have

$$C' = c_1 \mathbf{e}_1 + \cdots + c_r \mathbf{e}_r,$$

$$C' = c_1 A'_{p(1)} + \cdots + c_r A'_{p(r)},$$

$$C = c_1 A_{p(1)} + \cdots + c_r A_{p(r)}.$$

This proves (1).

By (1), Image $R = c(A)$ so that R maps F^r onto $c(A)$. To show that R is 1-1 amounts to showing that Kernel $R = 0$, by Theorem 3.8. If

$$\begin{bmatrix} c_1 \\ \vdots \\ c_r \end{bmatrix}$$

is in Kernel R, we have

$$0 = R \begin{bmatrix} c_1 \\ \vdots \\ c_r \end{bmatrix} = c_1 A_{p(1)} + \cdots + c_r A_{p(r)}.$$

Multiplying both sides by $E_d \cdots E_1$, we have

$$0 = c_1 \mathbf{e}_1 + \cdots + c_r \mathbf{e}_r = \begin{bmatrix} c_1 \\ \vdots \\ c_r \\ 0 \\ \vdots \\ 0 \end{bmatrix},$$

since $E_d \cdots E_1 A_{p(i)} = \mathbf{e}_i$ for $1 \le i \le r$. But then the typical $\begin{bmatrix} c_1 \\ \vdots \\ c_r \end{bmatrix}$ in Kernel R is 0, so that R is 1-1. This proves (2). ■

EXAMPLE

$$A = \begin{bmatrix} 1 & 3 & 4 & 5 \\ 1 & 3 & 5 & 6 \\ 1 & 3 & 4 & 5 \end{bmatrix}$$

has pivot columns 1 and 3, so its column space is the image

$$c(A) = F\begin{bmatrix}1\\1\\1\end{bmatrix} + F\begin{bmatrix}4\\5\\4\end{bmatrix}$$

of the linear transformation

$$R\begin{bmatrix}x_1\\x_2\end{bmatrix} = \begin{bmatrix}1 & 4\\1 & 5\\1 & 4\end{bmatrix}\begin{bmatrix}x_1\\x_2\end{bmatrix}.$$

A useful application is the following corollary.

Corollary. The column space of an $m \times n$ matrix A is F^m if and only if A has rank m.

Proof. Since the condition that the column space of A be F^m is not changed under row reduction, we may as well replace A by the reduced echelon matrix A' row equivalent to it. The column space of A' is the span of its pivot columns $\mathbf{e}_{p(1)}, \ldots, \mathbf{e}_{p(r)}$, which is F^m if and only if $r = m$. ■

EXAMPLE

A **Markov matrix** is a matrix such as $A = \begin{bmatrix}0.3 & 0.4\\0.7 & 0.6\end{bmatrix}$, whose entries are nonnegative and whose column sums are 1. For any $n \times n$ Markov matrix A, the column sums of $A - I$ are 0, so that the column space of $A - I$ is not all of F^n. (Explain!) By the preceding corollary, it follows that the rank of $A - I$ is less than n. (See Figure 3.15.)

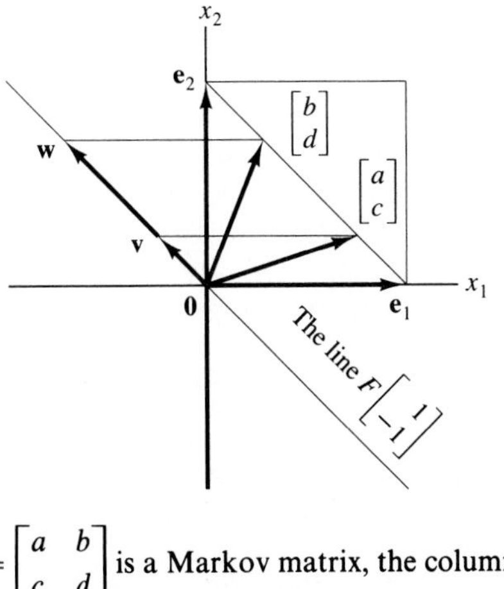

Figure 3.15 When $A = \begin{bmatrix}a & b\\c & d\end{bmatrix}$ is a Markov matrix, the columns $\mathbf{v} = \begin{bmatrix}a\\c\end{bmatrix} - \mathbf{e}_1$ and $\mathbf{w} = \begin{bmatrix}b\\d\end{bmatrix} - \mathbf{e}_2$ lie on the line $F\begin{bmatrix}1\\-1\end{bmatrix}$.

The rank of the transpose

Corollary. The ranks of a matrix A and its transpose A^T are equal.

Proof. Let the pivot columns of an $m \times n$ matrix A be $A_{p(1)}, \ldots, A_{p(r)}$. By Theorem 3.27, the row space of A^T equals the row space of the $n \times m$ matrix

$$B = \begin{bmatrix} (A_{p(1)})^T \\ \vdots \\ (A_{p(r)})^T \\ 0 \\ \vdots \\ 0 \end{bmatrix}.$$

By Theorem 3.25, this implies that A^T and B are row equivalent, so they have the same rank. Since B has only r nonzero rows, its rank is less or equal to $R = \text{Rank } A$. So, we conclude that $\text{Rank } A^T \leq \text{Rank } A$. Since this is true for any matrix A, we can apply it to the matrix A^T. We conclude that $\text{Rank } A^{TT} \leq \text{Rank } A^T$, that is, $\text{Rank } A \leq \text{Rank } A^T$. These inequalities imply that $\text{Rank } A = \text{Rank } A^T$. ■

EXAMPLE

The third row of the matrix

$$A = \begin{bmatrix} 1 & 2 & 3 \\ 2 & 2 & 2 \\ 1 & 0 & -1 \end{bmatrix}$$

is the difference of the first two. So, the rank of A^T is 2. But then the rank of A is 2, by the corollary.

Elementary column operations. Normal form

Knowing, as we do, that the rank of A equals that of its transpose makes computing the rank quite easy. Not only can we use elementary row operations in the reduction, but we can use the corresponding *elementary column operations.* Multiplication of A on the left by an elementary matrix E effects an elementary row operation $A \to EA$. So, multiplication of A^T on the right by E^T (also an elementary matrix) effects the corresponding elementary column operation $A^T \to A^T E^T = (EA)^T$ in the sense of the following definition.

Definition. *Elementary Column Operations.*

The following operations on the columns of a given matrix are called **elementary column operations.**

1. Add a scalar times one column to another.

2. Multiply one column by a nonzero scalar.
3. Interchange two columns.

Two matrices A and B are **column equivalent** if B can be obtained from A by zero or more elementary column operations. The process of going from A to B in this way is called **column reduction.**

The following theorem gives the **normal form** to which any $m \times n$ matrix can be reduced under elementary row and column operations. In it, the matrix in the upper left corner is the $r \times r$ identity matrix.

Theorem 3.28. *The Normal Form of a Matrix.*
Any matrix A can be reduced by elementary row and column operations to exactly one matrix of the form

$$\left[\begin{array}{ccc|ccc} 1 & \dots & 0 & 0 & \dots & 0 \\ \vdots & & \vdots & \vdots & & \vdots \\ 0 & \dots & 1 & 0 & \dots & 0 \\ \hline 0 & \dots & 0 & 0 & \dots & 0 \\ \vdots & & \vdots & \vdots & & \vdots \\ 0 & \dots & 0 & 0 & \dots & 0 \end{array}\right].$$

The number of pivots is Rank A.

Proof. To put A in this form, simply row-reduce A to a reduced echelon matrix A'. Since A'^T can be row-reduced to a reduced echelon matrix, A' can be *column-reduced* to the form described in the theorem. Since the rank is not changed by elementary column operations, by Theorem 3.27, the number of pivots equals the rank of A', which in turn equals Rank A. ■

EXAMPLES

1.
$$\begin{bmatrix} 1 & 3 & 4 & 5 \\ 1 & 3 & 5 & 7 \\ 1 & 3 & 4 & 6 \end{bmatrix} \to \begin{bmatrix} 1 & 3 & 4 & 5 \\ 0 & 0 & 1 & 2 \\ 0 & 0 & 0 & 1 \end{bmatrix} \to \begin{bmatrix} 1 & 0 & 0 & 0 \\ 0 & 1 & 0 & 0 \\ 0 & 0 & 1 & 0 \end{bmatrix}$$

is a two-stage reduction, where the first stage is row reduction and the second is column reduction. The rank is 3.

2.
$$\begin{bmatrix} 1 & 3 & 4 & 5 \\ 1 & 3 & 5 & 7 \\ 1 & 3 & 4 & 6 \end{bmatrix} \to \begin{bmatrix} 1 & 0 & 0 & 0 \\ 1 & 0 & 1 & 2 \\ 1 & 0 & 0 & 1 \end{bmatrix} \to \begin{bmatrix} 1 & 0 & 0 & 0 \\ 0 & 0 & 1 & 0 \\ 0 & 0 & 0 & 1 \end{bmatrix} \to \begin{bmatrix} 1 & 0 & 0 & 0 \\ 0 & 1 & 0 & 0 \\ 0 & 0 & 1 & 0 \end{bmatrix}$$

is a mixed reduction using row and column operations in any order.

3. The normal form of any nonzero matrix of the form

$$[a_1 \quad \ldots \quad a_n]\begin{bmatrix} b_1 \\ \vdots \\ b_n \end{bmatrix} \quad \text{is} \quad \left[\begin{array}{c|c} 1 & 0 \ldots 0 \\ \hline 0 & 0 \ldots 0 \\ \vdots & \vdots \quad \vdots \\ 0 & 0 \ldots 0 \end{array}\right],$$

since its rank is 1. (Explain!)

Nullity

Just as important as the pivot columns of a matrix A are the remaining columns.

Definition. *Nullity and the Nonpivot Columns.*
The **nonpivot columns** of a matrix A are the columns of A which are not pivot columns. The **nullity** of a matrix A is the number of its nonpivot columns.

The set of columns of A is now divided into the set of pivot columns and the set of nonpivot columns. From this, we get the following rule:

If A has n columns, then rank plus nullity equals n.

If A has rank r, it has nullity $n - r$. We have already expressed the column space $c(A)$ of A in terms of the pivot columns $A_{p(1)}, \ldots, A_{p(r)}$ of A. We now express the nullspace $n(A)$ of A in terms of the **nonpivot variables** $x_{q(1)}, \ldots, x_{q(n-r)}$ corresponding to the nonpivot columns $A_{q(1)}, \ldots, A_{q(n-r)}$ of A.

Theorem 3.29. *Getting the Nullspace from the Back-Substitution Equations.* Let A be a matrix of rank r and nullity $n - r$ and let A' be any echelon matrix row equivalent to A. Let the pivot columns of A be $A_{p(1)}, \ldots, A_{p(r)}$ and let the nonpivot columns be $A_{q(1)}, \ldots, A_{q(n-r)}$. Then:

The nullspace of A is the set

$$n(A) = \left\{ \begin{bmatrix} x'_1 \\ \vdots \\ x'_n \end{bmatrix} \middle| \; x_{q(1)}, \ldots, x_{q(n-r)} \in F \right\}$$

where the x's are defined by the **back-substitution equations**

$x'_j = x_{q(i)}$ if $j = q(i)$ ($n - r$ independent variables),

$x'_j = 0 - a'_{ij+1} - \cdots - a'_{in}x'_n$ if $j = p(i)$ (r dependent variables).

The mapping

$$R\begin{bmatrix} x_{q(1)} \\ \vdots \\ x_{q(n-r)} \end{bmatrix} = \begin{bmatrix} x'_1 \\ \vdots \\ x'_n \end{bmatrix}$$

defined by the back-substitution equations given here is a linear transformation from F^{n-r} to F^n which is a 1-1 onto mapping from F^{n-r} to $n(A)$.

Proof. Since A and A' are row equivalent, they have the same pivot columns and the same nullspaces. To compute the nullspace $n(A) = n(A')$, observe that the dot product of the transpose of row i of A' and

$$\begin{bmatrix} x'_1 \\ \vdots \\ x'_n \end{bmatrix}$$

is $x'_j + a'_{ij+1}x'_{j+1} + \cdots + a'_{in}x'_n$, where $j = p(i)$. Setting this to 0 for all i, we find that the independent variables are $x_{q(1)}, \ldots, x_{q(n-r)}$. Then, for $j = p(i)$, back-substitution leads to the given expression for x'_j in terms of $x'_{j+1}, \ldots, x'_n$, which have already been expressed in terms of the independent variables. This proves (1).

By (1), R maps F^{n-r} onto $n(A)$. Since $x'_{p(i)} = x_{q(i)}$ for $1 \leq i \leq r$, the image

$$\begin{bmatrix} x'_1 \\ \vdots \\ x'_n \end{bmatrix} \text{ of } \begin{bmatrix} x_{q(1)} \\ \vdots \\ x_{q(n-r)} \end{bmatrix}$$

under R determines

$$\begin{bmatrix} x_{q(1)} \\ \vdots \\ x_{q(n-r)} \end{bmatrix}.$$

This shows that R is 1-1. So, R is a 1-1 and onto mapping from F^{n-r} to $n(A)$. Since the coordinates x'_j defined in terms of the $x_{q(i)}$ by the back-substitution equations are linear functions in the $x_{q(i)}$ (explain), R is a linear transformation. ■

EXAMPLE

$$C = \begin{bmatrix} 1 & 3 & 4 & 5 & 0 \\ 1 & 3 & 5 & 7 & 0 \\ 1 & 3 & 4 & 6 & 4 \end{bmatrix}$$

is row equivalent to the echelon matrix

$$C' = \begin{bmatrix} \mathbf{1} & 3 & 4 & 5 & 0 \\ 0 & 0 & \mathbf{1} & 2 & 0 \\ 0 & 0 & 0 & \mathbf{1} & 4 \end{bmatrix},$$

whose pivot columns are 1, 3, and 4. So, its nullspace is

$$n(C) = \left\{ \begin{bmatrix} a \\ b \\ c \\ d \\ e \end{bmatrix} \middle| \ b, e \in F \right\},$$

where d, c, and a are obtained by back-substitution as $d = 0 - 4e$, $c = 0 - 2d$, and $a = -3b - 4c - 5d$. Expressing the dependent d, c, and a in terms of the independent b and e, we get $d = -4e$, $c = 8e$, and $a = -3b - 12e$ and

$$n(C) = \left\{ \begin{bmatrix} -3b - 12e \\ b \\ 8e \\ -4e \\ e \end{bmatrix} \middle| \ b, e \in F \right\} = F \begin{bmatrix} -3 \\ 1 \\ 0 \\ 0 \\ 0 \end{bmatrix} + F \begin{bmatrix} -12 \\ 0 \\ 8 \\ -4 \\ 1 \end{bmatrix}.$$

The linear transformation

$$R \begin{bmatrix} a \\ b \end{bmatrix} = \begin{bmatrix} -3b - 12e \\ b \\ 8e \\ -4e \\ e \end{bmatrix}$$

is an invertible mapping from F^2 to $n(C)$, whose matrix is

$$m(R) = \begin{bmatrix} -3 & -12 \\ 1 & 0 \\ 0 & 8 \\ 0 & -4 \\ 0 & 1 \end{bmatrix}.$$

Theorem 3.29 has the following geometric consequence (Figure 3.16).

Corollary. The nullspace of a matrix A of rank r and nullity $n - r$ is the intersection of r hyperplanes of F^n.

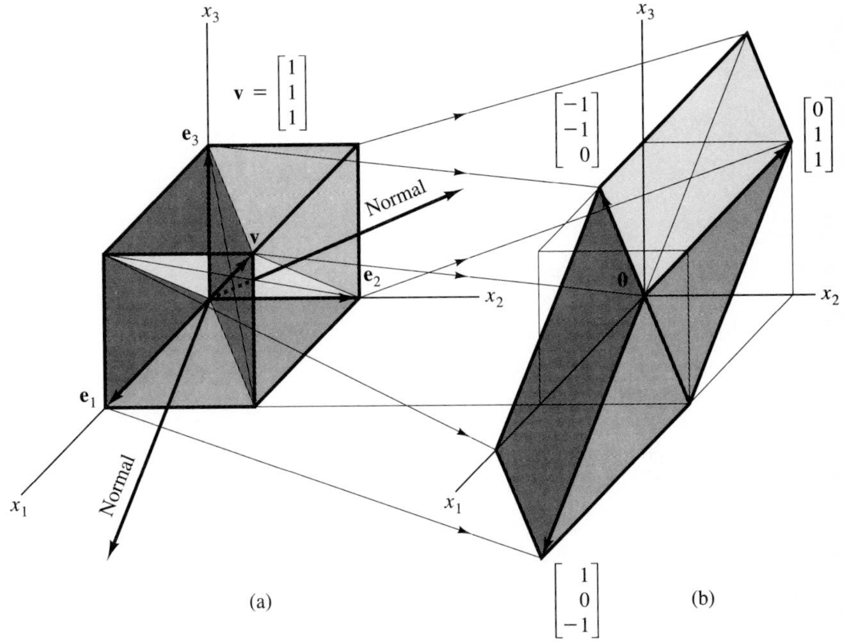

Figure 3.16 (a) The nullspace $F\mathbf{v}$ of a 3×3 matrix

$$\begin{bmatrix} 1 & 0 & -1 \\ 0 & 1 & -1 \\ -1 & 1 & 0 \end{bmatrix}$$

of rank 2 is the intersection of two planes. (b) The image is a plane.

Proof. In the notation of the preceding theorem, the nullspace $n(A)$ is just the intersection of the hyperplanes $H_1, \ldots, H_r$, where H_i is the hyperplane of solutions to $x_j + a'_{ij+1}x_{j+1} + \cdots + a'_{in}x_n = 0$ for $j = p(i)$. ■

EXAMPLE

In the preceding example, the nullspace

$$F\begin{bmatrix} -3 \\ 1 \\ 0 \\ 0 \\ 0 \end{bmatrix} + F\begin{bmatrix} -12 \\ 0 \\ 8 \\ -4 \\ 1 \end{bmatrix} \quad \text{of} \quad C = \begin{bmatrix} 1 & 3 & 4 & 5 & 0 \\ 1 & 3 & 5 & 7 & 0 \\ 1 & 3 & 4 & 6 & 4 \end{bmatrix}$$

is the set of solutions

$$\begin{bmatrix} a \\ b \\ c \\ d \\ e \end{bmatrix}$$

to the three equations $d = -4e$, $c = 8e$, and $a = -3b - 12e$. So, it is the intersection of the three corresponding hyperplanes.

The next corollary is a very useful application.

Corollary. An $m \times n$ matrix A has nullspace $\{0\}$ if and only if Rank $A = n$.

Proof. The rank plus nullity is $n = r + n - r$. So, $n - r$ is 0 if and only if $n = r$. ∎

EXAMPLE

We saw in an earlier example that if A is an $n \times n$ Markov matrix, the rank of $A - I$ is less than n. From this, it follows that the nullity of $A - I$ is not 0 and there is a nonzero vector $\mathbf{v}$ such that $A\mathbf{v} = \mathbf{v}$. (See Problem 20.)

Since rank plus nullity is the number of columns and since the rank of a matrix and its transpose are equal, we get the following.

Theorem 3.30. *The Nullity of a Square Matrix and Its Transpose.* The nullity of a square matrix and its transpose are equal.

EXAMPLE

For

$$A = \begin{bmatrix} 1 & 2 & 3 \\ 2 & 2 & 2 \\ 1 & 0 & -1 \end{bmatrix},$$

the nullspace of A^T contains

$$\begin{bmatrix} 1 \\ -1 \\ 1 \end{bmatrix}.$$

So, by the corollary, the nullspace of A is nonzero. From this, it follows that the columns of

$$\begin{bmatrix} 1 & 2 & 1 \\ 2 & 2 & 0 \\ 3 & 2 & -1 \end{bmatrix}$$

lie in some plane through 0. (Find it!)

PROBLEMS

NUMERICAL PROBLEMS

1. For each of the following pairs of matrices, determine whether they are row equivalent.

(a) $\begin{bmatrix} 2 & 1 & 3 \\ 4 & 3 & 1 \end{bmatrix}, \begin{bmatrix} 1 & 1 & 3 \\ 0 & 1 & 5 \end{bmatrix}$ **(b)** $\begin{bmatrix} 1 & 2 & 1 \\ 0 & 1 & 3 \end{bmatrix}, \begin{bmatrix} 1 & 2 & 1 \\ 0 & 0 & 1 \end{bmatrix}$

(c) $\begin{bmatrix} 3 & 3 & 1 & 3 \\ 3 & 2 & 1 & 2 \\ 6 & 5 & 2 & 5 \end{bmatrix}, \begin{bmatrix} 6 & 6 & 2 & 6 \\ 3 & 2 & 1 & 2 \\ 6 & 5 & 2 & 5 \end{bmatrix}$

(d) $\begin{bmatrix} 1 & 2 & 3 & 4 \\ 5 & 6 & 7 & 8 \end{bmatrix}, \begin{bmatrix} 2 & 3 & 4 & 5 \\ 6 & 7 & 8 & 9 \end{bmatrix}$

2. For each of the matrices in Problem 1, determine a corresponding echelon form.

3. Determine the rank and nullity for each of the matrices in Problem 1.

4. Verify that the Rank A = Rank A^T for the matrices listed in Problem 1.

5. Find the normal forms for the matrices listed in Problem 1.

6. Determine the pivot columns for each of the matrices in Problem 1.

7. Determine the column space for each of the matrices in Problem 1, expressed in terms of the pivot columns.

8. Determine the nullspace for each of the matrices A in Problem 1, expressed by giving the matrix of a linear transformation R from F^{n-r} to $n(A)$ and also expressed as a span.

9. Determine the row space of the matrix

$$A = \begin{bmatrix} 3 & 3 & 1 & 3 \\ 8 & 7 & 2 & 2 \\ 2 & 2 & 2 & 2 \\ 6 & 5 & 2 & 5 \end{bmatrix},$$

expressed in terms of the transposes of the pivot columns of A^T.

10. Show that

$$\begin{bmatrix} 1 & 4 & 5 \\ 1 & -1 & -2 \\ -2 & -3 & -3 \end{bmatrix}$$

has rank 2 by finding a plane through 0 containing its columns.

11. Show that

$$\begin{bmatrix} 1 & 1 & -2 \\ 4 & -1 & -3 \\ 5 & -2 & -3 \end{bmatrix}$$

has rank 2 by any method.

12. For each of the following matrices A, let m be the nullity of A and find a linear transformation R from F^m to $n(A)$.

(a) $A = \begin{bmatrix} 1 & 1 & 1 & 1 & 1 \\ 2 & 2 & 2 & 2 & 2 \\ 3 & 3 & 3 & 3 & 3 \end{bmatrix}$ **(b)** $A = \begin{bmatrix} 1 & 2 & 3 \\ 4 & 5 & 6 \\ 7 & 8 & 9 \end{bmatrix}$

(c) $A = \begin{bmatrix} 1 & 4 & 5 \\ 1 & -1 & -2 \\ -2 & -3 & -3 \end{bmatrix}$

Hard

13. For $A = \begin{bmatrix} 0 & 1 & 2 & 3 & 4 \\ 5 & 6 & 7 & 8 & 9 \end{bmatrix}$, do the following.

(a) Find the matrix $m(R)$ of a linear transformation R from F^3 to F^5 which has image $n(A)$ and kernel 0.

(b) Can $n(A)$ be expressed as the intersection of two hyperplanes? If so, give their equations. If not, explain why not.

(c) Can $n(A)$ be expressed as a single hyperplane? If so, give its equation.

14. In one of our examples, we learned that the columns of

$$\begin{bmatrix} 1 & 2 & 1 \\ 2 & 2 & 0 \\ 3 & 2 & -1 \end{bmatrix}$$

lie in some plane through 0. Find the equation of such a plane.

THEORETICAL PROBLEMS

15. For any $\mathbf{v}, \mathbf{w} \in F^n$, show that the matrix $\mathbf{v}^T\mathbf{w}$ has rank 0 or 1.

16. For any $m \times n$ matrix A, show the following.

(a) If $c(A) = F^m$, then $n \geq m$.

(b) If $n(A) = 0$, then $m \geq n$. (***Hint:*** First, show that to prove (a) and (b) for A, it suffices to prove them for the reduced echelon matrix A' row equivalent to A.)

17. Suppose that S is a subspace of F^n which is the intersection of r hyperplanes but cannot be expressed as the intersection of $r - 1$ hyperplanes. Show that $S = n(A)$ for some $r \times n$ matrix A of rank r.

18. Let $A = \begin{bmatrix} a & b \\ c & d \end{bmatrix}$ be a Markov matrix. Show by direct methods that the rows of $A - I$ are parallel and the columns of $A - I$ are parallel.

19. Give the equation of a plane in $\mathbb{R}^3$ which contains the columns of any 3×3 Markov matrix.

20. Let B be the matrix of the linear transformation

$$R \begin{bmatrix} x_{q(1)} \\ \vdots \\ x_{q(n-r)} \end{bmatrix} = \begin{bmatrix} x'_1 \\ \vdots \\ x'_n \end{bmatrix}$$

described in Theorem 3.29. Let $B_1, \ldots, B_{n-r}$ be the columns of B. Show

(a) $n(A)$ is the span of $B_1, \ldots, B_{n-r}$;

(b) $x_1 B_1 + \cdots + x_{n-r} B_{n-r} = y_1 B_1 + \cdots + y_{n-r} B_{n-r}$ only if $x_s = y_s$ for all s.

Hard

21. Let $A = \begin{bmatrix} a & b \\ c & d \end{bmatrix}$ be a Markov matrix. Find a vector $\mathbf{v}$, expressed in terms of a and b, whose entries are nonnegative and add up to 1 such that $A\mathbf{v} = \mathbf{v}$.

22. A country is divided into two states, S and T. Statistics show that, every 4 years, 0.4 of those having resided in S move to T and 0.3 of those having resided in T move to S. Letting $\begin{bmatrix} p \\ q \end{bmatrix}$ represent the current probabilities p of residing in S and q of residing in T for a resident of this country, these statistics lead one to predict that $\begin{bmatrix} p \\ q \end{bmatrix}$ will change to $\begin{bmatrix} 0.6 & 0.3 \\ 0.4 & 0.7 \end{bmatrix} \begin{bmatrix} p \\ q \end{bmatrix}$ in 4 years. Using Problem 21, find the **stable probability distribution** $\begin{bmatrix} p \\ q \end{bmatrix}$ which is unchanged upon passage to $\begin{bmatrix} 0.6 & 0.3 \\ 0.4 & 0.7 \end{bmatrix} \begin{bmatrix} p \\ q \end{bmatrix}$. See Figure 3.17.

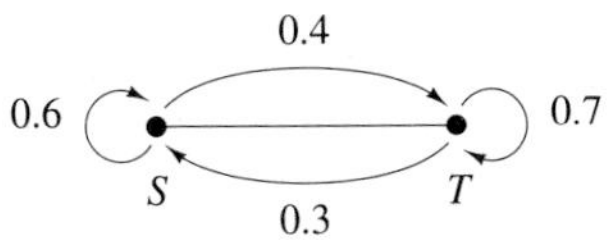

Figure 3.17 The transition diagram for the Markov matrix $A = \begin{bmatrix} 0.6 & 0.3 \\ 0.4 & 0.7 \end{bmatrix}$ and states S, T.

23. Show that the kth power of a Markov matrix A is a Markov matrix for all positive integers k.

24. In the context of Problem 22, compute the probability distribution $\begin{bmatrix} 0.6 & 0.3 \\ 0.4 & 0.7 \end{bmatrix}^3 \begin{bmatrix} 0.5 \\ 0.5 \end{bmatrix}$ predicted for the twelfth year following a year when the population in states S and T were equal. Then compute the distance from this to the stable probability distribution.

25. Suppose that the row spaces of two $n \times n$ matrices A and B are the same. Without using the theorems of this section, show the following.

(a) $B = CA$ for some matrix C. (***Hint:*** This is sketched in a proof in this section.)

(b) If column A_k of A can be written as $A_k = r_1 A_1 + \cdots + r_n A_n$, then column B_k of B can be written as $B_k = r_1 B_1 + \cdots + r_n B_n$. (***Hint:*** Use the fact that $B = CA$.)

26. Show that the row space of a matrix A contains the row space of a matrix B if and only if $B = CA$ for some matrix C.

27. If the row space of a matrix A contains the row space of a matrix B, show that Rank $B \leq$ Rank A. (***Hint:*** First show that $B = CA$ and, therefore, $B' = C'A'$ for some C and C', where A' and B' are reduced echelon forms for A and B.)

28. Show that the column space of a matrix A contains the column space of a matrix B if and only if $B = AD$ for some matrix D.

29. Show that if $B = AD$, then Rank $B \leq$ Rank A and Rank $B \leq$ Rank D.

30. For any $m \times n$ matrix A and $n \times m$ matrix B, show that if $AB = I$, then $c(A) = F^m$, $r(B) = F_m$, $n(B) = 0$, and $m \leq n$.

31. If A is an $m \times n$ matrix of rank m, then the matrix obtained from A by discarding the nonpivot columns is invertible.

32. If A and B are $m \times n$ matrices of rank m and if $B = CA$, show that C is invertible.

3.7 THE LDU DECOMPOSITION

We now confront the problem of computing solutions $\mathbf{x}$ to equations $A\mathbf{x} = \mathbf{p}$ *efficiently*. Assume that A is stored in *memory* (which could be an array in computer memory or, more simply, the collection of entries of a matrix A written on the chalkboard, where we can erase and change some or all of the entries during the computation). Given vectors $\mathbf{p}$, one at a time, we want to find the corresponding solutions $\mathbf{x}$ to $A\mathbf{x} = \mathbf{p}$.

Thus far, our method for solving $A\mathbf{x} = \mathbf{p}$ has been to row-reduce the matrix $A|\mathbf{p}$ to $U|\mathbf{p}'$, where U is an echelon matrix, and then solve the equivalent system $U\mathbf{x} = \mathbf{p}'$ by back-substitution. For an $n \times n$ matrix A and column vector $\mathbf{p}$, if we stop the reduction as soon as U is an echelon matrix, the reduction requires at most $n(n+1)(2n+1)/6 \approx n^3/3$ multiplications or division operations (Problem 16). The back-substitution is then very fast and requires only at most $n(n-1)/2 \approx n^2/2$ operations (Problem 17). So, the total number of such operations needed to solve for $\mathbf{x}$ is at most $n(n+1)(2n+1)/6 + n(n-1)/2 \approx n^3/3$.

This is quite good if we want to solve $A\mathbf{x} = \mathbf{p}$ for only a single $\mathbf{p}$. What should we do, however, if we want to solve $A\mathbf{x} = \mathbf{p}$ repeatedly for a large number of $\mathbf{p}$'s?

Fortunately, while finding the first solution we can save information useful for later solutions in the form of a factorization of A. After reducing $A \mid \mathbf{p}$ to $U \mid \mathbf{p}' = E_d \cdots E_1 A \mid E_d \cdots E_1 \mathbf{p}$ with U echelon, solving $A\mathbf{x} = \mathbf{p}$ is equivalent to solving $U\mathbf{x} = \mathbf{p}'$, where $\mathbf{p}' = E_d \cdots E_1 \mathbf{p}$. Since $E_d \cdots E_1 A = U$, we get the factorization $A = E_1^{-1} \cdots E_d^{-1} U$ of A. Since each of the E's is a row interchange I_{ij} $(i \neq j)$, a lower triangular matrix $A_{ij}(-c_{ij})$ to subtract c_{ij} times row j from row i $(i > j)$, or a diagonal matrix $M_i(1/d_i)$ to divide row i by d_i, the factors E_k^{-1} of A are of the form I_{ji} $(i \neq j)$ to interchange rows j and i, $A_{ij}(c_{ij})$ to add c_{ij} times row j to row i $(i > j)$, or $M_i(d_i)$ to multiply row i by d_i in reverse order.

When A is invertible and no row interchanges are needed, this factorization is easy to describe, doing first the A's column by column and then the M's. Taking $c_{ij} = 0$ when no row subtraction is needed and $d_i = 1$ when no row division is needed, we get the following theorem.

Theorem 3.31. *LDU Factorization of an Invertible Matrix A.*
$A = LDU$, where U is an echelon matrix and

$$\begin{aligned} L &= A_{21}(c_{21}) \cdots A_{n1}(c_{n1}) \cdots A_{nn-1}(c_{nn-1}) && (L \text{ is lower triangular}), \\ D &= M_1(d_1) \cdots M_n(d_n) = \operatorname{Diag}(d_1, \ldots, d_n) && (D \text{ is diagonal}), \\ U &= D^{-1}L^{-1}A. \end{aligned}$$

Since the $A_{ij}(c_{ij})$ are lower triangular with 1s on the diagonal, so is L. In fact, its (i, j)-entry is c_{ij} for $i > j$, since it is obtained from the identity matrix by applying the factors of L in reverse order, adding c_{nn-1} times row $n-1$ to row $n, \ldots,$ and, finally, c_{21} times row 2 to row 1:

$$I \to A_{nn-1}(c_{nn-1})I = \begin{bmatrix} 1 & \cdots & 0 & 0 \\ \vdots & \ddots & \vdots & \vdots \\ 0 & \cdots & 1 & 0 \\ 0 & \cdots & c_{nn-1} & 1 \end{bmatrix}$$

$$\to \cdots \to L = A_{21}(c_{21}) \cdots A_{nn-1}(c_{nn-1})I = \begin{bmatrix} 1 & \cdots & 0 & 0 \\ c_{21} & \ddots & & \\ \vdots & & 1 & 0 \\ c_{n1} & \cdots & c_{nn-1} & 1 \end{bmatrix}$$

Since $\mathbf{p}' = E_d \cdots E_1\mathbf{p}$, $\mathbf{p} = E_1^{-1} \cdots E_d^{-1}\mathbf{p}' = LD\mathbf{p}'$. So, our method of solving $A\mathbf{x} = \mathbf{p}$ becomes that of solving $U\mathbf{x} = \mathbf{p}'$, where $\mathbf{p}' = D^{-1}L^{-1}\mathbf{p}$. We can view this as solving $A\mathbf{x} = LDU\mathbf{x} = \mathbf{p}$ as for $\mathbf{x}$ as follows:

Theorem 3.32. *Solving* $A\mathbf{x} = \mathbf{p}$ *Using the Factorization* $A = LDU$.
When an invertible matrix A is factored as $A = LDU$, then to solve $A\mathbf{x} = \mathbf{p}$ is equivalent to doing the following:

1. Solve $L\mathbf{z} = \mathbf{p}$ for $\mathbf{z}$ (*forward elimination*).
2. Solve $D\mathbf{y} = \mathbf{z}$ for $\mathbf{y}$ (*stationary division*).
3. Solve $U\mathbf{x} = \mathbf{y}$ for $\mathbf{x}$ (*back-substitution*).

Proof. The factors L, D, and U are invertible, so each step is possible. The result is $A\mathbf{x} = LDU\mathbf{x} = LD\mathbf{y} = L\mathbf{z} = \mathbf{p}$. So, $A\mathbf{x} = \mathbf{p}$. There is only one possible solution $\mathbf{x}$, since A is invertible, so we have the complete solution. ■

EXAMPLES

1. For $\begin{bmatrix} 2 & 2 \\ 2 & 5 \end{bmatrix} = \begin{bmatrix} 1 & 0 \\ 1 & 1 \end{bmatrix}\begin{bmatrix} 2 & 0 \\ 0 & 3 \end{bmatrix}\begin{bmatrix} 1 & 1 \\ 0 & 1 \end{bmatrix}$, the corresponding factorization of the linear transformation $R(\mathbf{x}) = \begin{bmatrix} 2 & 2 \\ 2 & 5 \end{bmatrix}\mathbf{x}$ is the road map for solving $\begin{bmatrix} 2 & 2 \\ 2 & 5 \end{bmatrix}\mathbf{x} = \begin{bmatrix} 6 \\ 12 \end{bmatrix}$ in steps. Just find the inverse images under the three factors:

a. Solve $\begin{bmatrix} 1 & 0 \\ 1 & 1 \end{bmatrix}\mathbf{z} = \begin{bmatrix} 6 \\ 12 \end{bmatrix}$ for $\mathbf{z} = \begin{bmatrix} 6 \\ 6 \end{bmatrix}$.

b. Solve $\begin{bmatrix} 2 & 0 \\ 0 & 3 \end{bmatrix}\mathbf{y} = \begin{bmatrix} 6 \\ 6 \end{bmatrix}$ for $\mathbf{y} = \begin{bmatrix} 3 \\ 2 \end{bmatrix}$.

c. Solve $\begin{bmatrix} 1 & 1 \\ 0 & 1 \end{bmatrix}\mathbf{x} = \begin{bmatrix} 3 \\ 2 \end{bmatrix}$ for $\mathbf{x} = \begin{bmatrix} 1 \\ 2 \end{bmatrix}$.

Then

$$\begin{bmatrix} 2 & 2 \\ 2 & 5 \end{bmatrix}\begin{bmatrix} 1 \\ 2 \end{bmatrix} = \begin{bmatrix} 1 & 0 \\ 1 & 1 \end{bmatrix}\begin{bmatrix} 2 & 0 \\ 0 & 3 \end{bmatrix}\begin{bmatrix} 1 & 1 \\ 0 & 1 \end{bmatrix}\begin{bmatrix} 1 \\ 2 \end{bmatrix} = \begin{bmatrix} 1 & 0 \\ 1 & 1 \end{bmatrix}\begin{bmatrix} 2 & 0 \\ 0 & 3 \end{bmatrix}\begin{bmatrix} 3 \\ 2 \end{bmatrix}$$
$$= \begin{bmatrix} 1 & 0 \\ 1 & 1 \end{bmatrix}\begin{bmatrix} 6 \\ 6 \end{bmatrix} = \begin{bmatrix} 6 \\ 12 \end{bmatrix}.$$

2. We now illustrate how to get the factorization $A = LDU$. Note that we use boldface for the pivots and we adjust row multiples only at the

very end of the reduction:

$$\begin{bmatrix} 2 & 4 & 8 \\ 6 & 15 & 33 \\ 4 & 14 & 2 \end{bmatrix} \to A_{31}(-\tfrac{4}{2})A_{21}(-\tfrac{6}{2}) \begin{bmatrix} 2 & 4 & 8 \\ 6 & 15 & 33 \\ 4 & 14 & 2 \end{bmatrix} = \begin{bmatrix} \mathbf{2} & 4 & 8 \\ 0 & 3 & 9 \\ 0 & 6 & -14 \end{bmatrix}$$

$$\to A_{32}(-\tfrac{6}{3}) \begin{bmatrix} \mathbf{2} & 4 & 8 \\ 0 & 3 & 9 \\ 0 & 6 & -14 \end{bmatrix} = \begin{bmatrix} \mathbf{2} & 4 & 8 \\ 0 & \mathbf{3} & 9 \\ 0 & 0 & -\mathbf{32} \end{bmatrix}$$

$$\to M_3(\tfrac{1}{-32})M_2(\tfrac{1}{3})M_1(\tfrac{1}{2}) \begin{bmatrix} \mathbf{2} & 4 & 8 \\ 0 & \mathbf{3} & 9 \\ 0 & 0 & -\mathbf{32} \end{bmatrix} = \begin{bmatrix} 1 & 2 & 4 \\ 0 & 1 & 3 \\ 0 & 0 & 1 \end{bmatrix} = U.$$

Since

$$U = M_3(\tfrac{1}{-32})M_2(\tfrac{1}{3})M_1(\tfrac{1}{2})A_{32}(-\tfrac{6}{3})A_{31}(-\tfrac{4}{2})A_{21}(-\tfrac{6}{2}) \begin{bmatrix} 2 & 4 & 8 \\ 6 & 15 & 33 \\ 4 & 14 & 2 \end{bmatrix},$$

we have

$$\begin{bmatrix} 2 & 4 & 8 \\ 6 & 15 & 33 \\ 4 & 14 & 2 \end{bmatrix} = A_{21}(3)A_{31}(2)A_{32}(2)M_1(2)M_2(3)M_3(-32)U = LDU,$$

where

$$U = \begin{bmatrix} 1 & 2 & 4 \\ 0 & 1 & 3 \\ 0 & 0 & 1 \end{bmatrix},$$

$$L = A_{21}(3)A_{31}(2)A_{32}(2) = \begin{bmatrix} 1 & 0 & 0 \\ 3 & 1 & 0 \\ 2 & 2 & 1 \end{bmatrix},$$

$$D = M_1(2)M_2(3)M_3(-32) = \begin{bmatrix} \mathbf{2} & 0 & 0 \\ 0 & \mathbf{3} & 0 \\ 0 & 0 & -\mathbf{32} \end{bmatrix}.$$

The LDU reduction

Fortunately, it takes only $n(n+1)(2n+1)/6 - n \approx n^3/3$ operations to perform the factorization $A = LDU$ just described. And, given any such factorization with D invertible, *we can solve* $A\mathbf{x} = \mathbf{p}$ *for* $\mathbf{x}$ *for any given* $\mathbf{p}$ *as* *often as we like, each time using at most n^2 multiplication or division operations:*

1. To solve $L\mathbf{z} = \mathbf{p}$ for $\mathbf{z}$ requires at most $n(n-1)/2$ operations.
2. To solve $D\mathbf{y} = \mathbf{z}$ for $\mathbf{y}$ then requires at most n operations.
3. Finally, to solve $U\mathbf{x} = \mathbf{y}$ for $\mathbf{x}$ then requires at most $n(n-1)/2$ operations.

It would be hard to ask for more, since even to multiply out $A\mathbf{x}$ takes n^2 multiplication operations!

We can get the factors L, D, and U by a simple but very important variation of row reduction, a process called ***LDU* reduction**. This is done in n stages, where stage i is concerned with computing row i and column i of L, D, and U from the last $n - i + 1$ rows and columns of A and with preparing the last $n - i$ rows and columns of A for the next stage. Since the first i rows and columns of A are not needed for later computations, we can put the computed entries of the first i rows and columns of L, D, and U in the memory that had held the first i rows and columns of A. They all fit nicely there, because we do not have to store the usual 0s and 1s of L, D, and U. We use the diagonal for D, the upper portion for U, and the lower portion for L. The ith stage is given below. It is based on the entries for the last $n - i + 1$ rows and columns of A supplied at the end of the prior stage $i - 1$. Double square matrix brackets $[\![\quad]\!]$ are used instead of $\left[\quad\right]$ to indicate that the entries are stored in memory, later to be separated into triangular and diagonal matrices.

Stage i of the Process of LDU Reduction.

1. The (i, i)-entry of D is a_{ii}, *which we write in boldface in position* (i, i). (The boldface diagonal separates the stored parts of L from those of U.)
2. The (r, i)-entry of L is a_{ri}/a_{ii} for $r > i$, which we write in position (r, i).
3. The (i, s)-entry of U is a_{is}/a_{ii} for $s > i$.
4. The (r, s)-entry of A is changed from a_{rs} to $a_{rs} - (a_{ri}/a_{ii})a_{is}$ for all $r, s > i$.

The number of multiplication or division operations needed for this reduction is $n^2 - 1$ for stage 1, since each entry except the (1, 1)-entry requires one such operation for its computation. We then also need $(n-1)^2 - 1$ for stage $2, \ldots, 1^2 - 1$ for stage $n - 1$, and 0 for stage n, for a total of $n(n+1)(2n+1)/6 - n \approx n^3/3$ operations. (Prove!)

EXAMPLES

1. Letting

$$A = \begin{bmatrix} 2 & 4 & 8 \\ 6 & 15 & 33 \\ 4 & 14 & 2 \end{bmatrix},$$

we again want to factor A as $A = LDU$, this time using the LDU reduction. This is done in $n = 3$ stages, where $\rightarrow$ represents the progression that takes place in stage i for $i = 1, 2, 3$:

$$\begin{bmatrix} 2 & 4 & 8 \\ 6 & 15 & 33 \\ 4 & 14 & 2 \end{bmatrix} \rightarrow \begin{bmatrix} \mathbf{2} & 2 & 4 \\ 3 & \multicolumn{2}{|c|}{\begin{matrix} 15-12 & 33-24 \\ 14-\ 8 & 2-16 \end{matrix}} \\ 2 & & \end{bmatrix} = \begin{bmatrix} \mathbf{2} & 2 & 4 \\ 3 & \multicolumn{2}{|c|}{\begin{matrix} 3 & 9 \\ 6 & -14 \end{matrix}} \\ 2 & & \end{bmatrix}$$

$$\rightarrow \begin{bmatrix} \mathbf{2} & 2 & 4 \\ 3 & \mathbf{3} & 3 \\ 2 & 2 & \boxed{-32} \end{bmatrix} \rightarrow \begin{bmatrix} \mathbf{2} & 2 & 4 \\ 3 & \mathbf{3} & 3 \\ 2 & 2 & \mathbf{-32} \end{bmatrix}.$$

At the end of stage 3, L, D, and U are fitted nicely inside the area of memory that had held A as

$$\begin{bmatrix} & & U \\ & D & \\ L & & \end{bmatrix} = \begin{bmatrix} \mathbf{2} & 2 & 4 \\ 3 & \mathbf{3} & 3 \\ 2 & 2 & \mathbf{-32} \end{bmatrix}.$$

Extracting L, D, and U from memory, we get the factorization $A = LDU$ as

$$\begin{bmatrix} 2 & 4 & 8 \\ 6 & 15 & 33 \\ 4 & 14 & 2 \end{bmatrix} = \begin{bmatrix} 1 & 0 & 0 \\ 3 & 1 & 0 \\ 2 & 2 & 1 \end{bmatrix} \begin{bmatrix} 2 & 0 & 0 \\ 0 & 3 & 0 \\ 0 & 0 & -32 \end{bmatrix} \begin{bmatrix} 1 & 2 & 4 \\ 0 & 1 & 3 \\ 0 & 0 & 1 \end{bmatrix}.$$

(Check!) To solve $A\mathbf{x} = \mathbf{p}$ for $\mathbf{x}$, solve $LDU\mathbf{x} = \mathbf{p}$ for $\mathbf{x}$, that is, solve $L\mathbf{z} = \mathbf{p}$ for $\mathbf{z}$; then solve $D\mathbf{y} = \mathbf{z}$ for $\mathbf{y}$ and $U\mathbf{x} = \mathbf{y}$ for $\mathbf{x}$. The $\mathbf{x}$ we get satisfies $A\mathbf{x} = LDU\mathbf{x} = LD\mathbf{y} = L\mathbf{z} = \mathbf{p}$, as desired. The number of multiplication or division operations used is at most $n^2 = 9$ for each $\mathbf{p}$.

2. Since a_{rs} is changed to $a_{rs} - \dfrac{a_{ri}a_{is}}{a_{ii}}$ and a_{sr} to $a_{sr} - \dfrac{a_{si}a_{ir}}{a_{ii}}$, if A is symmetric before it is changed by the ith stage of the LDU reduction process, it is symmetric after the change. (Verify!) So, an LDU factorization for a symmetric matrix A is of the form $A = LDL^T$. (Explain!) For example, the LDU factorization for $A = \begin{bmatrix} 1 & 1 \\ 1 & 3 \end{bmatrix}$ is $\begin{bmatrix} 1 & 1 \\ 1 & 3 \end{bmatrix} = \begin{bmatrix} 1 & 0 \\ 1 & 1 \end{bmatrix} \begin{bmatrix} 1 & 0 \\ 0 & 2 \end{bmatrix} \begin{bmatrix} 1 & 1 \\ 0 & 1 \end{bmatrix}$.

LDU reduction for rectangular matrices

In general, when an $m \times n$ matrix A of rank r can be row-reduced to an echelon matrix J without using any interchanges, we can get by with using only multiplications by elementary matrices $A_{ip(j)}(-a)$ for $j = 1, \ldots, r$ and, for each j, $i = j + 1, \ldots, r$; and then by $M_1(d_1), \ldots, M_r(d_r)$. Here, $p(1), \ldots, p(r)$ give the positions of the pivot columns of A. Letting L be the first r columns of the product of the $A_{ip(j)}(a)$'s in the order just given, D be the first r rows and columns of the product of the M's, and U be the first r rows of J, we get $A = LDU$, as before. It is easy to get L, D, U by performing the corresponding LDU reduction, in which we move from one stage to the next by going to the next row and next *pivot column*. The LDU reduction ends at stage r with memory

$$\begin{bmatrix} D & U \\ L & \boxed{*} \end{bmatrix}$$

occupied by L, D, U, and an unused residue (which is 0, if we bother to compute it). To read L, D, and U out of this memory, it is necessary that the numbers $p(1), \ldots, p(r)$ giving the positions of the pivot columns be recorded somehow during the LDU reduction. We record them here simply by writing the pivots in boldface. Then we get L, D, and U from memory as follows:

1. L is $m \times r$ with (j, j)-entry 1 for all j. The (i, j)-entry of L for $i > j$ is located in position $(i, p(j))$. All other entries are 0.
2. D is $r \times r$ with (j, j)-entry located in position $(j, p(j))$ for all j.
3. U is $r \times n$ with $(j, p(j))$-entry 1 for all j. The (i, j)-entry of U for $i < j$ is located in position $(i, p(j))$. All other entries are 0.

EXAMPLE

Letting

$$A = \begin{bmatrix} 1 & 1 & 2 & 3 & 4 \\ 2 & 2 & 3 & 4 & 5 \\ 3 & 3 & 4 & 5 & 6 \end{bmatrix},$$

we want to factor A as $A = LDU$:

$$\begin{bmatrix} 1 & 1 & 2 & 3 & 4 \\ 2 & 2 & 3 & 4 & 5 \\ 3 & 3 & 4 & 5 & 6 \end{bmatrix} \to \begin{bmatrix} \mathbf{1} & 1 & 2 & 3 & 4 \\ 2 & \boxed{0} & -1 & -2 & -3 \\ 3 & 0 & -2 & -4 & -6 \end{bmatrix}$$

$$\to \begin{bmatrix} \mathbf{1} & 1 & 2 & 3 & 4 \\ 2 & 0 & \mathbf{-1} & 2 & 3 \\ 3 & 0 & 2 & \boxed{* \quad *} \end{bmatrix}$$

At the end of stage $r = 2$, L, D, and U are fitted nicely inside the area of memory that had held A, as

$$\begin{bmatrix} D & U \\ L & \boxed{* \qquad *} \end{bmatrix} = \begin{bmatrix} \mathbf{1} & 1 & 2 & 3 & 4 \\ 2 & 0 & \mathbf{-1} & 2 & 3 \\ 3 & 0 & 2 & \boxed{*} & \boxed{*} \end{bmatrix}.$$

The factorization $A = LDU$ is, therefore,

$$\begin{bmatrix} 1 & 1 & 2 & 3 & 4 \\ 2 & 2 & 3 & 4 & 5 \\ 3 & 3 & 4 & 5 & 6 \end{bmatrix} = \begin{bmatrix} 1 & 0 \\ 2 & 1 \\ 3 & 2 \end{bmatrix} \begin{bmatrix} 1 & 0 \\ 0 & -1 \end{bmatrix} \begin{bmatrix} 1 & 1 & 2 & 3 & 4 \\ 0 & 0 & 1 & 2 & 3 \end{bmatrix}.$$

(Check!)

If A has such a factorization $A = LDU$, we call it the ***LDU* decomposition** (or ***LDU* factorization**) of A. Fortunately, the L, D, and U are then unique, as we prove in the next theorem.

Theorem 3.33. *Uniqueness of the LDU Decomposition.*
Let A be an $m \times n$ matrix of rank r and suppose that $A = LDU = L'D'U'$, where L and L' are lower triangular $m \times r$ matrices with 1s on the diagonal, D and D' are diagonal $r \times r$ matrices, and U and U' are echelon $r \times n$ matrices. Then $L = L'$, $D = D'$, and $U = U'$.

Proof. We first prove this when A is invertible. Since $A = LDU = L'D'U'$ and A is invertible, all the factors are invertible, and we have $L^{-1}L'D'D^{-1} = UU'^{-1}$. The left-hand side is lower triangular with diagonal occupied by the diagonal part of $D'D^{-1}$, and the right-hand side is upper triangular with diagonal occupied by the diagonal part of I. So, $D'D^{-1} = I$, $L^{-1}L' = I$ and $UU'^{-1} = I$.

In the general case, we use the fact that the pivot columns of U and U' are in the same positions, because U and U' are row equivalent. (Both are row equivalent to A.) Letting V and V' be the matrices obtained from U and U' by discarding the nonpivot columns and letting M and M' be the matrices obtained from L and L' by discarding the last $m - r$ rows, the equation $LDU = L'D'U'$ implies that $MDV = M'D'V'$. By the invertible case done in the first part of the proof, $M = M'$, $D = D'$, and $V = V'$. But this then implies that $U = U'$, since U and U' are row equivalent matrices having equal pivot columns. (Explain!) To show that $L = L'$, let R and R' be the ith rows of L and L'. Then $RDV = R'DV$ and, canceling the invertible DV, $R = R'$. So, $L = L'$. ■

The upper left-hand corner matrices

Letting A_i denote the $i \times i$ matrix located in the first i rows and columns of an invertible matrix A, the first i stages of the LDU reduction of A, when no interchanges are needed, give the LDU decomposition $A_i = L_i D_i U_i$, the L_i, D_i, and U_i being stored in memory in the first i rows and columns. This simple fact is destined to have important consequences.

EXAMPLE

After two stages,

$$A = \begin{bmatrix} 2 & 4 & 8 \\ 6 & 15 & 33 \\ 4 & 14 & 2 \end{bmatrix} \to A = \begin{bmatrix} \mathbf{2} & 2 & 4 \\ 3 & 3 & 9 \\ 2 & 6 & -14 \end{bmatrix} \to A = \begin{bmatrix} \mathbf{2} & 2 & 4 \\ 3 & \mathbf{3} & 3 \\ 2 & 2 & \boxed{-32} \end{bmatrix}$$

of the LDU reduction for

$$A = \begin{bmatrix} 2 & 4 & 8 \\ 6 & 15 & 33 \\ 4 & 14 & 2 \end{bmatrix},$$

we have reduced $A_2 = \begin{bmatrix} 2 & 4 \\ 6 & 15 \end{bmatrix}$ to $A_2 = \begin{bmatrix} \mathbf{2} & 2 \\ 3 & \mathbf{3} \end{bmatrix}$, giving

$$\begin{bmatrix} 2 & 4 \\ 6 & 15 \end{bmatrix} = A_2 = L_2 D_2 U_2 = \begin{bmatrix} 1 & 0 \\ 3 & 1 \end{bmatrix} \begin{bmatrix} 2 & 0 \\ 0 & 3 \end{bmatrix} \begin{bmatrix} 1 & 2 \\ 0 & 1 \end{bmatrix}.$$

The PLDU reduction

We can refine the LDU reduction to a ***PLDU* reduction** for use together with row interchanges. In the $PLDU$ reduction, interchanges can be carried out as often as you like. They are absorbed into the matrix P obtained from I by carrying out the same interchanges on its columns, thereby forming a record of the net affect of the interchanges. This matrix P is a permutation matrix in the sense of the following definition.

Definition. *Permutation Matrix.*
A **permutation matrix** is a matrix P obtained from I by rearranging (*permuting*) the columns of the identity matrix.

The $PLDU$ reduction gives us a factorization $A = PLDU$ called the ***PLDU* decomposition**.

Theorem 3.34. *The PLDU Decomposition.*
Any $m \times n$ matrix A can be factored as $A = PLDU$, where

1. P is a permutation matrix;
2. L is an $m \times r$ matrix with (i, j)-entry 0 for $i < j$ and 1 for $i = j$;
3. D is an $r \times r$ matrix with (i, j)-entry 1 for $i = j$ and 0 otherwise;
4. U is an $r \times n$ echelon matrix.

To prove this theorem, we simply describe the important $PLDU$ reduction which gives it. This shows how to get P. Then we can get the factorization $P^TA = LDU$ as before. Multiplying by P then gives us the $PLDU$ decomposition $A = PP^TA = PLDU$. (Show that $P^T = P^{-1}$ for any permutation matrix P.)

Given an $m \times n$ matrix A, we proceed as before with the LDU reduction, except that, to prepare to take interchanges into account, we number the rows of A. Then, when an interchange takes place, instead of interchanging the locations of the entries of A in the two rows, we interchange the two row numbers. The matrix P is then the $m \times m$ matrix whose jth row is e_i (ith row of I) if row number j is in position i.

EXAMPLE

Letting

$$B = \begin{bmatrix} 0 & 0 & 2 \\ 2 & 4 & 8 \\ 6 & 15 & 33 \end{bmatrix},$$

we want first to factor B as $B = PLDU$ and then to use P, L, D, and U to give a fast method for solving $A\mathbf{x} = \mathbf{p}$ for $\mathbf{x}$ given any $\mathbf{p}$.

First, our LDU reduction (with interchanges) is

$$\begin{bmatrix} 0 & 0 & 2 \\ 2 & 4 & 8 \\ 6 & 15 & 33 \end{bmatrix} = \begin{matrix}\mathbf{1}\\ \mathbf{2}\\ \mathbf{3}\end{matrix}\begin{bmatrix} 0 & 0 & 2 \\ 2 & 4 & 8 \\ 6 & 15 & 33 \end{bmatrix} \to \begin{matrix}\mathbf{2}\\ \mathbf{1}\\ \mathbf{3}\end{matrix}\begin{bmatrix} 0 & 0 & 2 \\ 2 & 4 & 8 \\ 6 & 15 & 33 \end{bmatrix} \to \begin{matrix}\mathbf{2}\\ \mathbf{1}\\ \mathbf{3}\end{matrix}\left[\begin{array}{c|c} 0 & \boxed{0 \quad 2} \\ \mathbf{2} & 2 \quad 4 \\ 3 & \boxed{3 \quad 9} \end{array}\right]$$

$$\to \begin{matrix}\mathbf{3}\\ \mathbf{1}\\ \mathbf{2}\end{matrix}\left[\begin{array}{c|c} 0 & \boxed{0 \quad 2} \\ \mathbf{2} & 2 \quad 4 \\ 3 & \boxed{3 \quad 9} \end{array}\right] \to \begin{matrix}\mathbf{3}\\ \mathbf{1}\\ \mathbf{2}\end{matrix}\begin{bmatrix} 0 & 0 & \boxed{2} \\ \mathbf{2} & 2 & 4 \\ 3 & \mathbf{3} & 3 \end{bmatrix} \to \begin{matrix}\mathbf{3}\\ \mathbf{1}\\ \mathbf{2}\end{matrix}\begin{bmatrix} 0 & 0 & \mathbf{2} \\ \mathbf{2} & 2 & 4 \\ 3 & \mathbf{3} & 3 \end{bmatrix}.$$

The columns of the matrix P are $\mathbf{e}_2$, $\mathbf{e}_3$, and $\mathbf{e}_1$, since row 1 is in position 2, row 2 is in position 3, and row 3 is in position 1. Its 1s are arranged in the same manner as are the pivots. Reading L, D, and U from memory, taking the numbering of the rows into account, we get the factorization $B = PLDU$ as

$$\begin{bmatrix} 0 & 0 & 2 \\ 2 & 4 & 8 \\ 6 & 15 & 33 \end{bmatrix} = \begin{bmatrix} 0 & 0 & 1 \\ 1 & 0 & 0 \\ 0 & 1 & 0 \end{bmatrix}\begin{bmatrix} 1 & 0 & 0 \\ 3 & 1 & 0 \\ 0 & 0 & 1 \end{bmatrix}\begin{bmatrix} \mathbf{2} & 0 & 0 \\ 0 & \mathbf{3} & 0 \\ 0 & 0 & \mathbf{2} \end{bmatrix}\begin{bmatrix} 1 & 2 & 4 \\ 0 & 1 & 3 \\ 0 & 0 & 1 \end{bmatrix}.$$

(Check!)

Now, to solve $A\mathbf{x} = \mathbf{p}$ for $\mathbf{x}$, solve $PLDU\mathbf{x} = \mathbf{p}$ for $\mathbf{x}$—that is, solve $P\mathbf{p}' = \mathbf{p}$ for $\mathbf{p}'$, $L\mathbf{z} = \mathbf{p}'$ for $\mathbf{z}$, $D\mathbf{y} = \mathbf{z}$ for $\mathbf{y}$, and $U\mathbf{x} = \mathbf{y}$ for $\mathbf{x}$. The only change from the earlier example is that we now must first solve for $\mathbf{p}'$. If

$$\mathbf{p} = \begin{bmatrix} p_1 \\ p_2 \\ p_3 \end{bmatrix}, \quad \text{then} \quad P\begin{bmatrix} p_2 \\ p_3 \\ p_1 \end{bmatrix} = \begin{bmatrix} 0 & 0 & 1 \\ 1 & 0 & 0 \\ 0 & 1 & 0 \end{bmatrix}\begin{bmatrix} p_2 \\ p_3 \\ p_1 \end{bmatrix} = \begin{bmatrix} p_1 \\ p_2 \\ p_3 \end{bmatrix}.$$

So, our solution $\mathbf{p}'$ is just $\mathbf{p}$ rearranged with its ith entry in the jth position if $\mathbf{e}_i$ is in column j of P. Note that no multiplications or divisions, except by 1s, are needed, so that the number of multiplications or divisions used is still at most $n^2 = 9$.

In the example, we've taken row interchanges into account by renumbering. By this device, we avoid carrying along the permutation matrix as excess baggage. Nothing is really lost, since we recover it in the end anyway. To validate what transpires algebraically, we can absorb the row interchanges as column interchanges in a permutation matrix destined to evolve into P. The example could be recast, using interchange matrices instead of row labels, as

$$B = I\begin{bmatrix} 0 & 0 & 2 \\ 2 & 4 & 8 \\ 6 & 15 & 33 \end{bmatrix} = (II_{12})I_{12}\left[\!\!\begin{bmatrix} 0 & 0 & 2 \\ 2 & 4 & 8 \\ 6 & 15 & 33 \end{bmatrix}\!\!\right] = (II_{12})\left[\!\!\begin{bmatrix} \mathbf{2} & 2 & 4 \\ 0 & \boxed{\begin{matrix} 0 & 2 \end{matrix}} \\ 3 & \boxed{\begin{matrix} 3 & 9 \end{matrix}} \end{bmatrix}\!\!\right]$$

$$= (II_{12}I_{23})I_{23}\left[\!\!\begin{bmatrix} \mathbf{2} & 2 & 4 \\ 0 & \boxed{\begin{matrix} 0 & 2 \end{matrix}} \\ 3 & \boxed{\begin{matrix} 3 & 9 \end{matrix}} \end{bmatrix}\!\!\right] = (II_{12}I_{23})\left[\!\!\begin{bmatrix} \mathbf{2} & 2 & 4 \\ 0 & \mathbf{3} & 3 \\ 3 & 0 & \mathbf{2} \end{bmatrix}\!\!\right]$$

$$= P\begin{bmatrix} 1 & 0 & 0 \\ 3 & 1 & 0 \\ 0 & 0 & 1 \end{bmatrix}\begin{bmatrix} \mathbf{2} & 0 & 0 \\ 0 & \mathbf{3} & 0 \\ 0 & 0 & \mathbf{2} \end{bmatrix}\begin{bmatrix} 1 & 2 & 4 \\ 0 & 1 & 3 \\ 0 & 0 & 1 \end{bmatrix}$$

where $P = II_{12}I_{23} = \begin{bmatrix} 0 & 0 & 1 \\ 1 & 0 & 0 \\ 0 & 1 & 0 \end{bmatrix}$.

Numerical stability

Not only can we use the $PLDU$ reduction with any $m \times n$ matrix A, but we can also perform the reduction in a very *numerically stable* (computationally accurate) manner. We look through each pivot column $j = p(i)$ for the most desirable (e.g., largest in absolute value) candidate for the pivot to use for that column and then interchange rows to put it in row i. (Remember that Theorem 3.26 shows that there is no freedom of choice for the pivot *column*. Using interchanges, however, there is plenty of freedom of choice for the *row* that gives the pivot entry itself.)

PROBLEMS

NUMERICAL PROBLEMS

1. When it exists, find an LDU decomposition for A when A is

(a) $\begin{bmatrix} 1 & 2 & 3 \\ 2 & 3 & 4 \\ 5 & 6 & 7 \end{bmatrix}$; **(b)** $\begin{bmatrix} 1 & 0 & 0 \\ 2 & 2 & 2 \\ 3 & 4 & 7 \end{bmatrix}$.

2. Find a $PLDU$ decomposition $A = PLDU$ for the A in Problem 1(a), based on a $PLDU$ reduction using interchanges to maximize the absolute value of the pivots.

3. For each of the A's in Problem 1, solve the equation

$$A\mathbf{x} = \begin{bmatrix} 12 \\ 17 \\ 32 \end{bmatrix}$$

for $\mathbf{x}$ using an LDU or $PLDU$ decomposition of A.

4. Find an LDU decomposition for each of the following **Cartan matrices**.

(a) $A = \begin{bmatrix} 2 & -1 \\ -1 & 2 \end{bmatrix}$ **(b)** $B = \begin{bmatrix} 2 & -1 & 0 \\ -1 & 2 & -1 \\ 0 & -2 & 2 \end{bmatrix}$

(c) $C = \begin{bmatrix} 2 & -1 & 0 \\ -1 & 2 & -2 \\ 0 & -1 & 2 \end{bmatrix}$ **(d)** $D = \begin{bmatrix} 2 & -1 & 0 & 0 \\ -1 & 2 & -1 & -1 \\ 0 & -1 & 2 & 0 \\ 0 & -1 & 0 & 2 \end{bmatrix}$

(e) $E = \begin{bmatrix} 2 & -1 & 0 & 0 & 0 & 0 \\ -1 & 2 & -1 & 0 & 0 & 0 \\ 0 & -1 & 2 & -1 & 0 & -1 \\ 0 & 0 & -1 & 2 & -1 & 0 \\ 0 & 0 & 0 & -1 & 2 & 0 \\ 0 & 0 & -1 & 0 & 0 & 2 \end{bmatrix}$

(f) $F = \begin{bmatrix} 2 & -1 & 0 & 0 \\ -1 & 2 & -2 & 0 \\ 0 & -1 & 2 & -1 \\ 0 & 0 & -1 & 2 \end{bmatrix}$ **(g)** $G = \begin{bmatrix} 2 & -1 \\ -3 & 2 \end{bmatrix}$

5. In Problem 4, verify that the LDU decomposition for A is the upper left corner of each of B, C, D, E, F after completion of the second stage of the LDU decomposition for these matrices.

6. Show that the only factorization of

$$A = \begin{bmatrix} 1 & 0 & 0 \\ 2 & 1 & 0 \\ 3 & 4 & 1 \end{bmatrix}$$

is $A = LDU$, where L and U are lower and upper triangular matrices with 1s on the diagonal and D is diagonal is the factorization $A = AII$ (the case $A = L$, $D = U = I$).

7. Perform an LDU reduction of $A = \begin{bmatrix} 1 & 0 \\ 100 & 1 \end{bmatrix}$ using interchanges to maximize the absolute values of the pivots, and give the corresponding factorization $A = PLDU$.

8. Express the following matrices as products of elementary matrices.

(a) $\begin{bmatrix} 1 & 0 & 0 \\ 2 & 1 & 0 \\ 3 & 4 & 1 \end{bmatrix}$ **(b)** $\begin{bmatrix} 1 & 2 & 3 \\ 0 & 1 & 4 \\ 0 & 0 & 1 \end{bmatrix}$ **(c)** $\begin{bmatrix} 3 & 0 & 0 \\ 0 & 9 & 0 \\ 0 & 0 & 4 \end{bmatrix}$

(d) $\begin{bmatrix} 1 & 0 & 0 \\ a & 1 & 0 \\ b & c & 1 \end{bmatrix}$ **(e)** $\begin{bmatrix} d & 0 & 0 \\ 0 & e & 0 \\ 0 & 0 & f \end{bmatrix}$ **(f)** $\begin{bmatrix} 1 & g & h \\ 0 & 1 & i \\ 0 & 0 & 1 \end{bmatrix}$

9. Show that $\begin{bmatrix} 2 & -1 \\ -3 & 2 \end{bmatrix}$ has two different $PLDU$ decompositions.

10. Given the memory

$$\begin{matrix} \mathbf{2} \\ \mathbf{1} \\ \mathbf{3} \end{matrix} \begin{bmatrix} 1 & \mathbf{2} & 4 \\ \mathbf{3} & 1 & 3 \\ 3 & 3 & \mathbf{1} \end{bmatrix}$$

resulting from LDU reduction of some matrix A, find A and express it as a product $A = PLDU$.

11. Given the memory

$$\begin{matrix} \mathbf{2} \\ \mathbf{1} \\ \mathbf{3} \end{matrix} \begin{bmatrix} 1 & \mathbf{2} & 1 \\ \mathbf{1} & 2 & 2 \\ 3 & 1 & \mathbf{2} \end{bmatrix}$$

for A, solve $A\mathbf{x} = \mathbf{e}_1$.

THEORETICAL PROBLEMS

12. Show that P is a permutation matrix if and only if P can be obtained from the identity I by permuting its *rows*.

13. Show that the product of two permutation matrices of degree n is a permutation matrix.

14. Show that $P^T = P^{-1}$ for any permutation matrix P.

15. If Rank A is the number of rows of A and A has the $PLDU$ factorization $A = PLDU$, show that PLD is invertible.

16. For an $n \times n$ matrix A, show that reduction of $A \mid \mathbf{p}$ to $A' \mid \mathbf{p}$, where A' is echelon, requires at most $n(n+1)(2n+1)/6$ multiplications or divisions. (***Hint:*** For row 1, n operations are needed to get leading coefficient 1. For each of the $n-1$ rows below it, n operations are needed to get 0 in column 1. This gives n^2 operations. Working with one fewer row and column, the next row gives $(n-1)^2$ and so forth.)

17. After reduction of the $A \mid \mathbf{p}$ in the preceding problem, show that back-substitution requires at most $n(n-1)/2$ multiplications. (***Hint:*** We need $0, 1, \ldots, n-1$ multiplications for entries $1, \ldots, n$.)

18. Show that if $A = LDU$ where L and U are lower and upper $n \times n$ matrices with 1s on the diagonal and D is an invertible diagonal matrix, then $A\mathbf{x} = \mathbf{p}$ can be solved using at most n^2 multiplications or divisions using the entries of L, D, and U.

19. Show that if a given matrix A can be written in the form $A = UDL$, where U and L are upper and lower triangular with 1s on the diagonal and D is diagonal, the equation $UDL\mathbf{x} = \mathbf{p}$ can be solved in at most n^2 steps, where n is the degree of A.

20. Let P be a permutation matrix of degree n. Show that the numbers $1, \ldots, n$ can be arranged in an order $p_1, \ldots, p_n$ such that

$$P^T \mathrm{Diag}(d_1, \ldots, d_n) P = \mathrm{Diag}(d_{p_1}, \ldots, d_{p_n})$$

for all choices of d's.

21. Show that any invertible matrix A has a $PLDU$ decomposition $A = PLDU$ such that the (r, s)-entry of L is 0 when $p_r < p_s$. (See Problem 20.) (***Hint:*** When $A = LDU$, the permutation is I and $p = r$ for all r, so $A = ILDU$ is the desired decomposition. When A has no factorization $A = LDU$, construct the $PLDU$ decomposition by using interchanges only when needed to replace a 0 by a nonzero pivot.)

22. Show that if A and A' are row equivalent matrices and each pivot column of A equals the corresponding pivot column of A', then $A = A'$.

3.8 POSITIVE DEFINITE MATRICES

Of all real matrices, symmetric matrices are those most frequently used in real-world applications. When we discussed quadratic forms in Section 2.7, we expressed them in the form $[x \quad y]\begin{bmatrix} a & b \\ b & d \end{bmatrix}\begin{bmatrix} x \\ y \end{bmatrix}$ and used the spectral theorem for $\begin{bmatrix} a & b \\ b & d \end{bmatrix}$ to find the normal form. This is done in Chapter 7.

There, the emphasis is on positive definite quadratic forms, which are of great importance for the theory of minimization and for many other things as well.

Here, we can prepare the way by introducing positive definite matrices and quadratic forms and exploring some of their basic properties.

EXAMPLE

For a function f from $\mathbb{R}^3$ to $\mathbb{R}$ having continuous third order partial derivatives, the **Hessian** of f at **p** is

$$\begin{bmatrix} x_1 \\ x_2 \\ x_3 \end{bmatrix}^T \begin{bmatrix} f_{11} & f_{12} & f_{13} \\ f_{21} & f_{22} & f_{23} \\ f_{31} & f_{32} & f_{33} \end{bmatrix} \begin{bmatrix} x_1 \\ x_2 \\ x_3 \end{bmatrix} = f_{11}x_1^2 + f_{22}x_2^2 + f_{33}x_3^2 + 2f_{12}x_1x_2 + 2f_{13}x_1x_3 + 2f_{23}x_2x_3,$$

where $f_{ij} = \dfrac{\partial^2 f}{\partial x_i \partial x_j}(\mathbf{p})$. This is a quadratic form. At a critical point, f has a relative minimum at **p** if the Hessian is positive definite in the sense defined below.

We now turn to the formal definitions for quadratic forms and positive definite forms and matrices.

Definition. *Quadratic Forms.*

A **real quadratic form** is a function $f(\mathbf{v}) = \mathbf{v}^T A \mathbf{v}$ ($\mathbf{v} \in \mathbb{R}^n$), where A is a real symmetric matrix of degree n.

Definition. *Positive and Negative Definite Matrices and Quadratic Forms.*

Let A be a real symmetric matrix and $f(\mathbf{v}) = \mathbf{v}^T A \mathbf{v}$ ($\mathbf{v} \in \mathbb{R}^n$) be the corresponding quadratic form. If $f(\mathbf{v}) > 0$ for all nonzero $\mathbf{v}$, A and f are said to be **positive definite**. If $f(\mathbf{v}) < 0$ for all nonzero $\mathbf{v}$, A and f are said to be **negative definite**.

Using the LDU reduction, we determine criteria for when a matrix A is positive definite. For a positive definite matrix, we will find that we get an LDU factorization $A = LDL^T$ (no interchanges are needed) and all the pivots are positive. So, the process is numerically stable and twice as fast. (We get U as L^T without doing any work!)

To get underway, however, note the following.

1. If A is positive definite, then so is B^TAB for every invertible real matrix B of the same degree. If $\mathbf{v}$ is a nonzero real vector, then so is $B\mathbf{v}$,

and we have $\mathbf{v}^T B^T A B \mathbf{v} = (B\mathbf{v})^T A (B\mathbf{v}) > 0$. Conversely, if $B^T A B$ is positive definite, where B is invertible and real, then $A = (B^{-1})^T (B^T A B) B^{-1}$ is positive definite.

2. The matrix $\mathrm{Diag}(d_1, \ldots, d_n)$ where the d's are positive real numbers, is positive definite. So, $B^T \mathrm{Diag}(d_1, \ldots, d_n) B$ is positive definite for all invertible real matrices B of degree n.
3. In particular, I is positive definite. So, $B^T B$ is positive definite for all invertible real matrices B by (1).
4. Let A be positive definite. Then each diagonal entry a_{ss} is positive, since $a_{ss} = e_s^T A e_s$. (Prove!)
5. Let A be symmetric and suppose that a_{11} is positive. Then we can use a_{11} as the pivot to get the **first stage** A of the LDU reduction (the part of the LDU reduction carried out using the first pivot). Since A is symmetric, this is of the form $L'A'L'^T$ with A' symmetric:

$$A = \begin{bmatrix} \mathbf{a}_{11} & c_2 \ldots c_n \\ c_2 & \\ \vdots & \boxed{B} \\ c_n & \end{bmatrix} \qquad \text{where } c_2 = \frac{a_{21}}{a_{11}}, \ldots, c_n = \frac{a_{n1}}{a_{11}},$$

$$\begin{bmatrix} a_{11} & a_{21} \ldots a_{n1} \\ a_{21} & a_{22} \quad a_{n2} \\ \vdots & \vdots \quad\quad \vdots \\ a_{n1} & a_{n2} \ldots a_{nn} \end{bmatrix} = \begin{bmatrix} 1 & 0 \ldots 0 \\ c_2 & \\ \vdots & \boxed{I} \\ c_n & \end{bmatrix} \begin{bmatrix} a_{11} & 0 \ldots 0 \\ 0 & \\ \vdots & \boxed{B} \\ 0 & \end{bmatrix} \begin{bmatrix} 1 & c_2 \ldots c_n \\ 0 & \\ \vdots & \boxed{I} \\ 0 & \end{bmatrix} = L'A'L'^T.$$

(Verify by multiplying out!) By (1), A is positive definite if and only if A' is positive definite. If

$$A' = \begin{bmatrix} a_{11} & 0 \ldots 0 \\ 0 & \\ \vdots & \boxed{B} \\ 0 & \end{bmatrix}$$

is positive definite, then

$$\begin{bmatrix} 0 \\ v_2 \\ \vdots \\ v_n \end{bmatrix}^T \begin{bmatrix} a_{11} & 0 \ldots 0 \\ 0 & \\ \vdots & \boxed{B} \\ 0 & \end{bmatrix} \begin{bmatrix} 0 \\ v_2 \\ \vdots \\ v_n \end{bmatrix}$$

is positive for all nonzero real vectors

$$\begin{bmatrix} 0 \\ v_2 \\ \vdots \\ v_n \end{bmatrix}.$$

But then $\mathbf{w}^T B \mathbf{w}$ is positive for all nonzero $\mathbf{w} \in \mathbb{R}^{n-1}$. (Explain!) Since A' is symmetric, so is B. So, B is positive definite. Conversely, if B is positive definite, then

$$\begin{bmatrix} v_1 \\ v_2 \\ \vdots \\ v_n \end{bmatrix}^T A' \begin{bmatrix} v_1 \\ v_2 \\ \vdots \\ v_n \end{bmatrix} = a_{11}(v_1)^2 + \begin{bmatrix} v_2 \\ \vdots \\ v_n \end{bmatrix}^T B \begin{bmatrix} v_2 \\ \vdots \\ v_n \end{bmatrix} > 0 \qquad \text{for all nonzero} \begin{bmatrix} v_1 \\ v_2 \\ \vdots \\ v_n \end{bmatrix},$$

since a_{11} is positive. So, A' is positive definite. It follows that A is positive definite if and only if B is positive definite.

If the upper-left-hand entry b_{11} of B is positive, we can go on to get the second stage of the LDU reduction for A by performing the first stage of the LDU reduction for B using b_{11} as pivot. The *prior row and column are left undisturbed.* Repeating this for successive stages for as long as the next upper-left-hand entry is positive, we either complete the LDU reduction for A using only positive entries, or we encounter a negative or zero upper-left-hand entry, in which case we conclude that A is not positive definite.

EXAMPLES

1. The matrix $A = \begin{bmatrix} 1 & 1 \\ 1 & 0 \end{bmatrix}$ is not positive definite, because a_{22} is 0. (Find a nonzero real $\mathbf{v}$ such that $\mathbf{v}^T A \mathbf{v}$ is not positive.)

2. The matrix $A = \begin{bmatrix} 2 & 2 \\ 2 & 1 \end{bmatrix}$ is not positive definite, since its form at the end of the first stage of the LDU reduction is $\begin{bmatrix} \mathbf{2} & 1 \\ 1 & \boxed{1-2} \end{bmatrix}$ and the 1×1 matrix $B = [-1]$ is not positive definite. (Find a nonzero real $\mathbf{v}$ such that $\mathbf{v}^T A \mathbf{v}$ is not positive!)

3. For

$$A = \begin{bmatrix} 2 & 6 & 4 \\ 6 & 19 & 14 \\ 4 & 14 & 15 \end{bmatrix},$$

the first stage of the LDU reduction gives us

$$A = \left[\!\begin{bmatrix} \mathbf{2} & 3 & 2 \\ 3 & \boxed{19-18} & \boxed{14-12} \\ 2 & \boxed{14-12} & \boxed{15-\ 8} \end{bmatrix}\!\right] = \left[\!\begin{bmatrix} \mathbf{2} & 3 & 2 \\ 3 & \boxed{1} & \boxed{2} \\ 2 & \boxed{2} & \boxed{7} \end{bmatrix}\!\right]$$

$$= \begin{bmatrix} 1 & 0 & 0 \\ 3 & \boxed{1} & \boxed{0} \\ 2 & \boxed{0} & \boxed{1} \end{bmatrix} \begin{bmatrix} 2 & 0 & 0 \\ 0 & \boxed{1} & \boxed{2} \\ 0 & \boxed{2} & \boxed{7} \end{bmatrix} \begin{bmatrix} 1 & 3 & 2 \\ 0 & \boxed{1} & \boxed{0} \\ 0 & \boxed{0} & \boxed{1} \end{bmatrix}.$$

(Verify by multiplying out the right-hand side.) So, A is positive definite if and only if $B = \begin{bmatrix} 1 & 2 \\ 2 & 7 \end{bmatrix}$ is positive definite. Since B reduces to

$$B = \begin{bmatrix} \mathbf{1} & 2 \\ 2 & \mathbf{3} \end{bmatrix} = \begin{bmatrix} 1 & 0 \\ 2 & 1 \end{bmatrix} \begin{bmatrix} 1 & 0 \\ 0 & 3 \end{bmatrix} \begin{bmatrix} 1 & 2 \\ 0 & 1 \end{bmatrix}$$ (verify), B is positive definite because $\begin{bmatrix} 1 & 0 \\ 0 & 3 \end{bmatrix}$ is.

The symmetric LDU decomposition $A = LDL^T$ for A positive definite

What we observed in (5) proves Theorem 3.35.

Theorem 3.35. *Pivot Criteria for A to Be Positive Definite.*
Let A be symmetric. Then A is positive definite if and only if the LDU reduction without interchanges leads to a factorization $A = LDL^T$, where L is a lower triangular matrix with 1s on the diagonal and D is a diagonal matrix with positive entries on the diagonal.

When the LDU decomposition takes on the symmetric form $A = LDL^T$, it is called the **symmetric** $\boldsymbol{LDU}$ **decomposition** of A. Theorem 3.35 assures that every positive definite symmetric matrix has a symmetric LDU decomposition. Then, since every positive definite matrix is invertible (prove), its LDU decomposition is unique by Theorem 3.33.

Theorem 3.36. *Equivalent Conditions for A to Be Positive Definite.*
The following conditions on a real invertible matrix are equivalent:

1. A is positive definite.
2. B^TAB is positive definite, B being any invertible real matrix.
3. $A = LDL^T$, where L is lower triangular with 1s on the diagonal and D is a real diagonal matrix with positive entries.
4. At every stage of the LDU reduction, the new upper-left-hand entry (the next candidate for a pivot) is positive.
5. $A = S^TS$ for some invertible matrix S.

Proof. We have already proved that (1)–(4) are equivalent, and we observed also that (5) implies (1). We now prove that (3) implies (5), which completes our equivalences. Given that $A = LDL^T$, we let E be the *positive square root* of D, which is the diagonal matrix whose diagonal entries are the positive square roots of the diagonal entries of D. Then $D = EE$, and we have $A = LEEL^T = S^TS$, where $S = EL^T$. ■

PROBLEMS

NUMERICAL PROBLEMS

1. Determine which of the following matrices are positive definite.

(a) $\begin{bmatrix} 1 & 1 \\ 1 & 0 \end{bmatrix}$ **(b)** $\begin{bmatrix} 2 & 2 \\ 2 & d \end{bmatrix}$ **(c)** $\begin{bmatrix} 2 & 3 \\ 3 & 4 \end{bmatrix}$

(d) $\begin{bmatrix} 1 & 5 \\ 5 & 2 \end{bmatrix}$ **(e)** $\begin{bmatrix} 1 & 3 & 5 \\ 3 & 2 & 7 \\ 5 & 7 & 8 \end{bmatrix}$ **(f)** $\begin{bmatrix} 1 & 2 & 3 \\ 2 & 5 & 2 \\ 3 & 2 & 9 \end{bmatrix}$

(g) $\begin{bmatrix} 1 & 1 & 1 \\ 1 & 3 & 3 \\ 1 & 3 & 9 \end{bmatrix}$ **(h)** $\begin{bmatrix} 1 & 1 & 1 & 1 \\ 1 & 2 & 2 & 2 \\ 1 & 2 & 4 & 4 \\ 1 & 2 & 4 & 8 \end{bmatrix}$

2. Find the symmetric LDU decomposition for those of the matrices in Problem 1 that are positive definite.

3. Find an LDU decomposition for A when A is

(a) $\begin{bmatrix} 1 \\ 2 \\ 2 \\ 2 \end{bmatrix} [1 \quad 2 \quad 2 \quad 2]$; **(b)** $\begin{bmatrix} 2 & -1 & 0 & 0 & 0 & 0 \\ -1 & 2 & -1 & 0 & 0 & 0 \\ 0 & -1 & 2 & -1 & 0 & 0 \\ 0 & 0 & -1 & 2 & -1 & 0 \\ 0 & 0 & 0 & -1 & 2 & -1 \\ 0 & 0 & 0 & 0 & -1 & 2 \end{bmatrix}$.

Hard

4. Let A be a positive definite 3×3 matrix whose pivots are 2, 3, and 4. Show that the surface $\{\mathbf{v} \in \mathbb{R}^3 \mid \mathbf{v}^T A \mathbf{v} = 1\}$ is the image

$$\left\{ M \begin{bmatrix} x \\ y \\ z \end{bmatrix} \middle| \; 2x^2 + 3y^2 + 4z^2 = 1 \right\}$$

of an ellipsoid under a linear transformation whose matrix M is lower triangular with 1s on the diagonal.

THEORETICAL PROBLEMS

5. Show that if a symmetric matrix A is positive definite, then A is invertible.

6. Show that $\begin{bmatrix} a & b \\ b & d \end{bmatrix}$ is positive definite if and only if a and $\begin{vmatrix} a & b \\ b & d \end{vmatrix}$ are positive.

7. Show, for $a > 0$, that the LDU decomposition of $\begin{bmatrix} a & b \\ b & d \end{bmatrix}$ is

$$\begin{bmatrix} a & b \\ b & d \end{bmatrix} = \begin{bmatrix} \mathbf{a} & b/a \\ b/a & \mathbf{d} - \mathbf{b}^2/\mathbf{a} \end{bmatrix} = \begin{bmatrix} 1 & 0 \\ b/a & 1 \end{bmatrix} \begin{bmatrix} a & 0 \\ 0 & d - b^2/a \end{bmatrix} \begin{bmatrix} 1 & b/a \\ 0 & 1 \end{bmatrix}.$$

8. Using the equation in Problem 7, explain how one might come to express the quadratic equation $ax^2 + 2bxy + dy^2 = 1$ in the form

$$a(x + (b/a)y)^2 + (d - b^2/a)y^2 = 1.$$

9. Using Problems 7 and 8, show that $ax^2 + 2bxy + dy^2 = 1$ is never a parabola (image under a rigid motion of a parabola $y = cx^2$ with $c > 0$) for any values of a, b, d.

Hard

10. Let

$$A = \begin{bmatrix} a & b & c \\ b & d & e \\ c & e & f \end{bmatrix}$$

be invertible and suppose that a and $\begin{vmatrix} a & b \\ b & d \end{vmatrix}$ are both positive. Show that A has an LDU decomposition with pivots $a > 0$, $d' > 0$, and $f' \neq 0$. Use this to show that the two surfaces $\{\mathbf{v} \in \mathbb{R}^3 \mid \mathbf{v}^T A \mathbf{v} = \pm 1\}$ are the images

$$\left\{ M \begin{bmatrix} x \\ y \\ z \end{bmatrix} \,\middle|\, ax^2 + d'y^2 + f'z^2 = \pm 1 \right\}$$

of an ellipsoid and empty set ($a, d', f' > 0$) or hyperboloids of one sheet and two sheets ($a, d' > 0$, $f' < 0$) under a linear transformation whose matrix M is lower triangular with 1s on the diagonal (Figure 3.18).

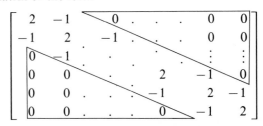

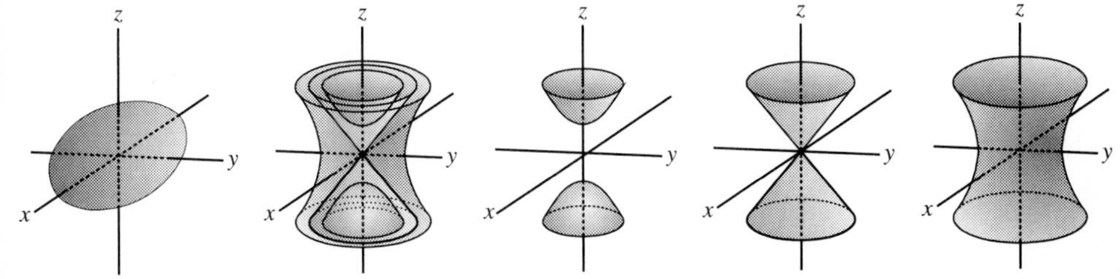

Figure 3.18 The ellipsoid, cone, and hyperboloids $ax^2 + d'y^2 + f'z^2 = g$ about the z-axis.

11. An $n \times n$ matrix of the form

$$\begin{bmatrix} 2 & -1 & 0 & \cdot & \cdot & \cdot & 0 & 0 \\ -1 & 2 & -1 & \cdot & \cdot & \cdot & 0 & 0 \\ 0 & -1 & \cdot & \cdot & \cdot & \cdot & \vdots & \vdots \\ 0 & 0 & \cdot & \cdot & \cdot & 2 & -1 & 0 \\ 0 & 0 & \cdot & \cdot & \cdot & -1 & 2 & -1 \\ 0 & 0 & \cdot & \cdot & \cdot & 0 & -1 & 2 \end{bmatrix}$$

is called a **Cartan matrix** of type A_n. Show that it is positive definite for all n, and give its LDU decomposition.

12. A quadratic form $f(\mathbf{v}) = \mathbf{v}^T A \mathbf{v}$ (A real symmetric) is **nondegenerate** if for every nonzero real vector $\mathbf{v}$, $f(\mathbf{v} + \mathbf{w}) - f(\mathbf{v} - \mathbf{w})$ is nonzero for some nonzero real vector $\mathbf{w}$. Show that if A is a 2×2 matrix, $\mathbf{v}^T A \mathbf{v}$ is nondegenerate if and only if $|A|$ is nonzero.

13. Show that $\mathbf{v}^T A \mathbf{v}$ is nondegenerate if and only if A is invertible.

Very Hard

14. Using the results of Problem 7, show that the equation

$$ax_1^2 + bx_1x_2 + dx_2^2 + ex_1 + fx_2 + g = 0,$$

where $\begin{vmatrix} a & b/2 \\ b/2 & d \end{vmatrix}$ is nonzero, is the general equation for the ellipse when $a > 0$ and $\begin{vmatrix} a & b/2 \\ b/2 & d \end{vmatrix} > 0$ and that otherwise it is the general equation for the hyperbola. (***Hint:*** Compute $f(\mathbf{x} - \mathbf{u}) = h$ to get the linear and constant terms. By Section 2.8, ellipses and hyperbolas are the only possibilities. (Why?) Now use the fact that ellipses are bounded and hyperbolas are not.)

15. An $n \times n$ matrix of the form $\begin{bmatrix} A_n & & 0 & \\ & & -1 & -1 \\ & -1 & 2 & 0 \\ 0 & -1 & 0 & 2 \end{bmatrix}$ is called a *Cartan matrix* of type B_{n+2}. Show that it is positive definite for all n, and give its LDU decomposition.

16. If A is symmetric, then $A = PLDL^TP^T$, where P is a permutation matrix, L is lower triangular with 1s on the diagonal, and D is a symmetric matrix of the form $D = \begin{bmatrix} D_k & 0 \\ 0 & \begin{matrix} 0 & \ddots & * \\ * & & 0 \end{matrix} \end{bmatrix}$, D_k being an invertible diagonal matrix of degree k for some k.

SUGGESTED READING

Ben Noble and James W. Daniel, *Applied Linear Algebra*, Prentice Hall, Englewood Cliffs, N. J., 1977. [The main goal of the book is to present the fundamental concepts of linear algebra that can be applied as well as presenting applications for illustrative and motivational purposes.]

Gilbert Strang, *Linear Algebra and Its Applications*, Harcourt Brace Jovanovich, San Diego, 1988. [This book covers an impressive amount of linear algebra and applications, including many rather sophisticated topics.]

CHAPTER 4

VECTOR SPACES AND LINEAR TRANSFORMATIONS

In this chapter, what in Chapters 2 and 3 is explicit and visible becomes more abstract and symbolic. The reason for this is quite simple. As we worked out the linear algebra of F^n, our language developed accordingly. Now we can use this same language to talk about other things.

The linear transformations of F^n are now to be generalized to linear transformations of **vector spaces over F**, whose elements can be added and multiplied by scalars in a manner which, *by decree*, conforms to certain properties. Although F^n is one example of a vector space over F, there are many others. So, all of what we say about vector spaces holds equally well for F^n and the other examples.

On one hand, this is a classic example of the idea of abstracting to the general from the concrete by developing a general theory applicable to any concrete instance. On the other hand, we see in Section 4.8 that F^n is the perfect model of a vector space V of dimension n over F. Not only do the theorems about V apply to the concrete instance F^n; but the following **metatheorem** (theorem about theorems) applies.

Metatheorem. *Transfer of Theorems from F^n to V.*

Any linear property of a vector space V of dimension n over F holds in the model F^n and conversely.

EXAMPLE

To prove that an onto linear transformation of V is invertible, it suffices, by the metatheorem, to observe that this is true when $V = F^n$, by Theorem 3.21.

As we now pass from F^n to an n-dimensional vector space over F, the spotlight moves from the coordinates of the vectors in F^n to the properties of the algebraic operations in V. Although you may be frustrated at first, when the vectors in this chapter have no entries and the computations are symbolic in nature, you soon will find that the computations are simpler and more to the point. By chapter's end, you will have seen some of the awesome power of the algebraic theory of vector spaces. For more, look at material from the Suggested Reading list at the end of the chapter.

4.1 VECTOR SPACES

Cartesian n-space F^n is a set of points with a special element, denoted $\mathbf{0}$, having operations of addition and scalar multiplication conforming to certain properties. We now go from the specific to the general in the following definition.

Definition. *Vector Space.*

A **vector space** is a set V of points with a special element denoted $\mathbf{0}$ having operations $\mathbf{v} + \mathbf{w} \in V$ and $s\mathbf{v} \in V$ for $s \in F$, $\mathbf{v}, \mathbf{w} \in V$, called **addition** and **scalar multiplication**, which satisfy the following properties, where $\mathbf{u}, \mathbf{v}, \mathbf{w}$ denote elements of V and s, t denote scalars from F.

1. $(\mathbf{u} + \mathbf{v}) + \mathbf{w} = \mathbf{u} + (\mathbf{v} + \mathbf{w})$.
2. $\mathbf{v} + \mathbf{0} = \mathbf{v}$ and $\mathbf{v} + \mathbf{w} = \mathbf{w} + \mathbf{v}$.
3. $\mathbf{u} + \mathbf{w} = \mathbf{v}$ has a unique solution $\mathbf{w}$, denoted by $\mathbf{w} = \mathbf{v} - \mathbf{u}$.
4. $t(\mathbf{v} + \mathbf{w}) = t\mathbf{v} + t\mathbf{w}$.
5. $(s + t)\mathbf{v} = s\mathbf{v} + t\mathbf{v}$ and $(st)\mathbf{v} = s(t(\mathbf{v}))$.
6. $0\mathbf{v} = \mathbf{0}$ and $1\mathbf{v} = \mathbf{v}$.

EXAMPLES

A few examples follow.

1. A set $\{\mathbf{0}\}$ consisting of a single element $\mathbf{0}$, called **zero**, together with the operations $\mathbf{0} + \mathbf{0} = \mathbf{0}$ and $a\mathbf{0} = \mathbf{0}$ for all $a \in F$ is a vector space over F, called the **zero vector space**.

2. Any subspace of F^n (column n-space over F) or F_n (row n-space over F) is a vector space over F. For instance, the intersection V of

$$\left\{\begin{bmatrix} a \\ b \\ c \end{bmatrix} \middle| \, a + 3b + 2c = 0 \right\} \quad \text{and} \quad F\begin{bmatrix} 1 \\ 2 \\ 3 \end{bmatrix} + F\begin{bmatrix} 2 \\ 5 \\ 8 \end{bmatrix}$$

is a subspace of F^3.

3. Any subspace of $\mathbb{C}^n$ is a vector space over $\mathbb{R}$. For instance, the one-dimensional subspace

$$\mathbb{C}\begin{bmatrix} 1 \\ 3 \\ 3 \end{bmatrix} = \mathbb{R}\begin{bmatrix} 1 \\ 3 \\ 3 \end{bmatrix} + \mathbb{R}\mathbf{i}\begin{bmatrix} 1 \\ 3 \\ 3 \end{bmatrix}$$

of $\mathbb{C}^3$ is a vector space over $\mathbb{R}$.

4. Any vector space over $\mathbb{C}$ is a vector space over $\mathbb{R}$. (Vectors are added in the same way and scalar multiplication is the same, but the latter is used only when the scalars are real.)

5. The set Functions(X, V) of all functions from X to V is a vector space over F if X is a nonempty set, V is a vector space over F, and $f + g$, af are defined as follows for functions f and g from X to V and $a \in F$:

$$(f + g)(\mathbf{x}) = f(\mathbf{x}) + g(\mathbf{x}) \qquad \text{for all } \mathbf{x} \in X;$$

$$(af)(\mathbf{x}) = af(\mathbf{x}) \qquad \text{for all } \mathbf{x} \in X.$$

Two specific instances of this are

a. Functions(X, F^n) (the case where $V = F^n$);
b. Functions(X, F) (the case where $V = F^1 = F$).

6. The set $F[z]$ of polynomials over F in the variable z is a vector space over F. The operations of addition and scalar multiplication are as defined in (5), since $F[z] \subseteq$ Functions(F, F) (see Figure 4.1).

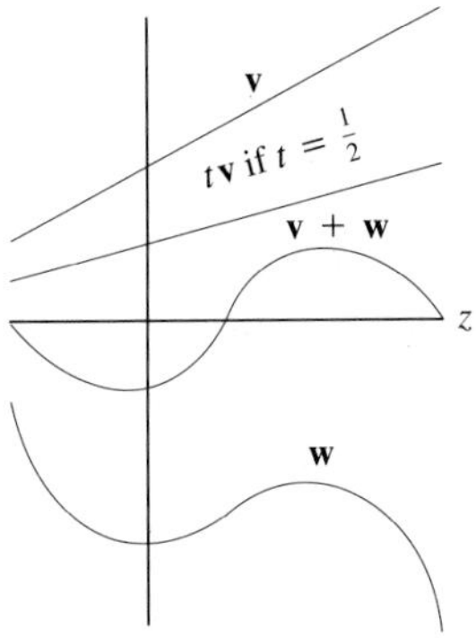

Figure 4.1 Graph of $\mathbf{v} + \mathbf{w}$ and $t\mathbf{v}$ in $\mathbb{R}[z]$ when $\mathbf{v} = rz + s$ and $\mathbf{w} = az^3 + bz^2 + cz + d$.

7. The set $F[z]_n$ of polynomials over F of degree at most n in the variable z.

8. The set Diff($\mathbb{R}$, $\mathbb{R}$) of differentiable functions from $\mathbb{R}$ to $\mathbb{R}$, with the operations defined in (5).

9. The set $M_{m\times n}F$ of $m \times n$ matrices over F, with operations already defined.

10. The set $M_nF = M_{n\times n}F$ of $n \times n$ matrices over F.

11. The set $L(F^n, F^m)$ of linear transformations from F^n to F^m.

Before going on, we pause to observe some simple consequences of the vector space properties.

1. As in F^n, the associative law for sums (Property 1) enables us to drop parentheses in sums.
2. As in F^n, we define $-\mathbf{v} = \mathbf{0} - \mathbf{v}$, so that $-\mathbf{v}$ is the unique solution $\mathbf{w}$ to the equation $\mathbf{v} + \mathbf{w} = \mathbf{0}$.
3. If $a, b \in F$ with a nonzero and if $\mathbf{v} \in V$, then $(1/a)(b\mathbf{v}) = ((1/a)b)\mathbf{v} = (b/a)\mathbf{v}$ and, if $a = b$, $(1/a)(a\mathbf{v}) = (a/a)\mathbf{v} = 1\mathbf{v} = \mathbf{v}$. (See (5) and (6).) This gives us the new properties

$$\left(\frac{1}{a}\right)(b\mathbf{v}) = \left(\frac{b}{a}\right)\mathbf{v}, \qquad \left(\frac{1}{a}\right)(a\mathbf{v}) = \mathbf{v} \qquad (a, b \in F,\ a \text{ nonzero},\ \mathbf{v} \in V).$$

It follows that if $a\mathbf{v} = a\mathbf{v}'$ with a nonzero, then $\mathbf{v} = \mathbf{v}'$. (Prove!) For this reason, we say that if $a\mathbf{v} = a\mathbf{v}'$ with a nonzero, *we can get* $\mathbf{v} = \mathbf{v}'$ *by cancellation by* a.
4. We also have $-\mathbf{v} = (-1)\mathbf{v}$, since both are solutions $\mathbf{w}$ to $\mathbf{v} + \mathbf{w} = \mathbf{0}$ and there is only one such solution, by condition (3).

$$\mathbf{v} + (-\mathbf{v}) = \mathbf{v} + (\mathbf{0} - \mathbf{v}) = \mathbf{0} \qquad \text{(Cite properties used!)}$$

$$\begin{aligned}\mathbf{v} + (-1)\mathbf{v} &= 1\mathbf{v} + (-1)\mathbf{v} \\ &= (1 + (-1))\mathbf{v} = 0\mathbf{v} = \mathbf{0} \qquad \text{(Cite properties used!)}\end{aligned}$$

5. $-(-\mathbf{v}) = \mathbf{v}$, $-(a\mathbf{v}) = (-a)\mathbf{v}$, and $-(\mathbf{u} - \mathbf{v}) = \mathbf{v} - \mathbf{u}$. (Prove!)

EXAMPLE

Given elements $\mathbf{v}$, $\mathbf{w}$ in a vector space V over F and given $a \in F$, we can simplify the equation $(5a(\mathbf{v} + \mathbf{w}) + (7a\mathbf{w} - a\mathbf{v})) = -(-2a\mathbf{v} + 2a\mathbf{w})$ to $2a\mathbf{v} = -10a\mathbf{w}$. (Verify!) If $a = 0$, this reduces to $\mathbf{0} = \mathbf{0}$. Otherwise, it reduces to $2\mathbf{v} = -10\mathbf{w}$, or $\mathbf{v} = -5\mathbf{w}$.

PROBLEMS

NUMERICAL PROBLEMS

1. Verify that the following are, in fact, examples of vector spaces over F.

(a) Functions(X, F^2) **(b)** $F[z]_1$

(c) $F[z]_2$ **(d)** $M_{2\times 3}F$

2. Simplify the following expressions in a vector space, citing the properties used. Here, a, b, and t are scalars and $\mathbf{u}$, $\mathbf{v}$, and $\mathbf{w}$ are vectors.

(a) $-(3\mathbf{w} - (-2)\mathbf{v})$ **(b)** $-(2\mathbf{v} - 3\mathbf{w}) + 2\mathbf{w}$

(c) $(3 + 4)(a\mathbf{v} + \mathbf{w} - \mathbf{u}) - (\mathbf{v} - \mathbf{w})$ **(d)** $t(3 - a)(b\mathbf{v} + \mathbf{u}) - 4(\mathbf{v} + \mathbf{u})$

(e) $(2\mathbf{v} + 3\mathbf{w} - \mathbf{v}) + (\mathbf{u} - 3\mathbf{w}) - 4\mathbf{w}$ **(f)** $(3 + a)((t + 4)\mathbf{v} - (3 - a)\mathbf{w})$

3. Determine each of the expressions in Problem 2, parts (a) and (b), when

$$\mathbf{u} = \begin{bmatrix} q \\ 2 \\ 0 \end{bmatrix}, \qquad \mathbf{v} = \begin{bmatrix} q \\ 3 \\ 1 \end{bmatrix}, \qquad \mathbf{w} = \begin{bmatrix} q \\ f \\ 2 \end{bmatrix},$$

using the simplified expression you found.

THEORETICAL PROBLEMS

4. If $a\mathbf{v}$ and $b\mathbf{v}$ are equal and nonzero, show that $a = b$.

5. Prove that $-(\mathbf{v} - \mathbf{u}) = \mathbf{u} - \mathbf{v}$ in a vector space.

6. Show that the set Functions(X, V) with addition and scalar multiplication introduced in Example 5 is a vector space over F for any nonempty set X and vector space V over F.

7. Show that $F[z]$ is a vector space over F.

8. Is the set of polynomials $f(z)$ for which $f(0) = 0$ a vector space?

9. Is the set of polynomials $f(z)$ for which $f(0) + 3f'(0) + 4f''(0) = 0$ a vector space?

10. Is the set of polynomials $f(z)$ for which $f(0) = 1$ a vector space?

11. Show that Diff$(\mathbb{R}, \mathbb{R})$ is a vector space over $\mathbb{R}$.

12. Show that the set Nondiff$(\mathbb{R}, \mathbb{R})$ of nondifferentiable functions from $\mathbb{R}$ to itself is not a vector space.

4.2 LINEAR TRANSFORMATIONS. ISOMORPHISMS

A vector space over F, by itself, is no more interesting than is F^n by itself. Taking $n = 2$, life in the plane is much more interesting when we introduce linear transformations of $\mathbb{R}^2$, determine the rigid motions, and find the principal axis of a quadratic form. Similarly, life in a vector space becomes more interesting when we make the following definition.

Definition. *Linear Transformation.*

A function R from a vector space V over F to a vector space W over F is a **linear transformation** if it satisfies the **linearity properties**

1. $R(\mathbf{v} + \mathbf{w}) = R(\mathbf{v}) + R(\mathbf{w})$ for all $\mathbf{v}, \mathbf{w} \in V$;
2. $R(t\mathbf{v}) = tR(\mathbf{v})$ for all $t \in F$, $\mathbf{v} \in V$.

The set of linear transformations from V to W is denoted by $L(V, W)$.

Our definition is taken from Theorem 3.3, which characterizes the linear transformations from F^n to F^m by these properties, so we are justified in using a similar term.

EXAMPLES

1. All the examples of linear transformations from F^n to F^m qualify as examples here.

2. For any vector spaces V and W over F, the *zero function*, denoted by 0, which maps every vector $\mathbf{v}$ of V to $\mathbf{0}$ is a linear transformation from V to W.

3. The identity function I, which maps the vectors $\mathbf{v}$ of a vector space V over F to $I(\mathbf{v}) = \mathbf{v}$, is a linear transformation from V to V called the *identity*.

4. The mapping t_L $(t \in F)$ from a vector space V to itself defined by $t_L(\mathbf{v}) = t\mathbf{v}$ for $\mathbf{v} \in V$ is a linear transformation. It is called *scalar multiplication by t*. Note that $0_L = 0$.

5. The function D from the vector space $\mathbb{R}[z]$ of polynomials to itself which maps $f(z) = a_0 + a_1 z + \cdots + a_n z^n$ to its *derivative* $D(f(z)) = f'(z) = a_1 + 2a_2 z + \cdots + na_n z^{n-1}$ is a linear transformation of $\mathbb{R}[z]$, as is the function E which maps $f(z) = a_0 + a_1 z + \cdots + a_n z^n$ to the *antiderivative* $E(f(z)) = a_0 z + (a_1/2)z^2 + \cdots + (a_n/n)z^{n+1}$. Note that the composite of D and E is $DE = I$, whereas the composite of E and D is J, where J is the *projection* $J(f(z)) = a_1 z + \cdots + a_n z^n$ of the polynomial $f(z)$ onto the part of it that vanishes at $\mathbf{0}$. The projection J is also a linear transformation.

6. The mapping $m(R)$ from $L(F^n, F^m)$ to $M_{m \times n}F$ which sends a linear transformation R to its matrix A is a linear transformation from $L(F^n, F^m)$ to $M_{m \times n}F$.

7. The mapping from F to $L(F^n, F^n)$ sending t to the scalar multiplication t_L by t defined in (4) is a linear transformation.

8. The mapping Diag from F_n to $M_n F$ mapping $[a \ \ldots \ b]$ to $\operatorname{Diag}(a, \ldots, b)$ is a linear transformation.

The product of two linear transformations

Given vector spaces U, V, W over F and linear transformations R from V to W and S from U to V, we can form the product (composite) function RS from U to W. It is a linear transformation, as we now show.

Theorem 4.1. *Products of Linear Transformations.*
Let R be a linear transformation from V to W and S be a linear transformation from U to V. Then the product function RS from U to W is a linear transformation.

Proof. We simply crank out the linearity properties, first through S and then through R.

1. $$(RS)(\mathbf{v} + \mathbf{w}) = R(S(\mathbf{v} + \mathbf{w})) = R(S(\mathbf{v}) + S(\mathbf{w})) = R(S(\mathbf{v})) + R(S(\mathbf{w})) = (RS)(\mathbf{v}) + (RS)(\mathbf{w})$$
   for all $\mathbf{v}, \mathbf{w} \in V$.
2. $(RS)(t\mathbf{v}) = R(S(t\mathbf{v})) = R(tS(\mathbf{v})) = tR(S(\mathbf{v})) = t(RS)(\mathbf{v})$
   for all $t \in F$, $\mathbf{v} \in V$. ■

EXAMPLE

We've seen examples of this for linear transformations of n spaces F^n, all of which serve to illustrate this theorem. Another example is the product $DE = J$ in (5) of the last example.

Invertible linear transformations

What we showed for invertibility of linear transformations of n spaces F^n is true in this more general setting.

Theorem 4.2. *The Inverse of a Linear Transformation Is a Linear Transformation.*
If a linear transformation from a vector space V over F to a vector space W over F is an invertible function, then its inverse is a linear transformation from W to V.

Proof. The proof is identical to that of the corollary to Theorem 3.3. ■

EXAMPLE

The mapping $m(R)$ from $L(F^n, F^m)$ to $M_{m \times n}F$, which maps R to its matrix A, is a linear transformation. Since $m(R)$ is an invertible function, its inverse, which maps $A \in M_{m \times n}F$ to the linear transformation $R(\mathbf{x}) = A\mathbf{x}$, is a linear transformation from $M_{m \times n}F$ to $L(F^n, F^m)$.

Of course, the theorem has the following consequence.

Corollary. A linear transformation R from a vector space V over F to itself is invertible if and only if there is a linear transformation S from V to itself such that $RS = SR = I$.

EXAMPLES

1. For any $n \times n$ matrix A, the linear transformation $R(\mathbf{x}) = A\mathbf{x}$ is invertible if and only if A is invertible. For example, $R(\mathbf{x}) = \begin{bmatrix} 1 & 2 \\ 3 & 5 \end{bmatrix}\mathbf{x}$ is invertible.
2. The mapping R from the vector space $V = \{a + bz \mid a, b \in F\}$ of polynomials of degree at most 1 to itself defined by $R(a+bz) = (a+2b) + (3a+5b)z$ is an invertible linear transformation. (Compare with the preceding example.)
3. If D is differentiation and E is antidifferentiation of $\mathbb{R}[z]$, although $DE = I$, neither D nor E is invertible. (Prove!) However, the function D is onto. This shows that the corollaries to Theorems 4.21 and 4.22 for linear transformations of F^n have no counterparts for linear transformations of the vector space $F[z]$. The difference between the two situations is that F^n is finite-dimensional (Section 4.5), whereas $F[z]$ is not.

Isomorphic vector spaces

To compare two vector spaces V and W over F, we often use a linear transformation R from V to W. When R is invertible, it deserves a special name.

Definition. *Isomorphism.*

An **isomorphism** from V to W is an invertible linear transformation from V to W. If there exists an isomorphism from V to W, we say that V and W are **isomorphic**. (See Figure 4.2.)

EXAMPLES

The following pairs of vector spaces are isomorphic by the given linear transformation. This can be verified, in each case, by proving that the given linear transformation is an invertible function. (Do so!)

1. The vector spaces $V = \text{Functions}(\{j \mid 1 \le j \le n\}, F)$ and F^n are isomorphic by the mapping that sends function $f \in V$ to the vector $\mathbf{x} \in F^n$ whose jth entry is $\mathbf{x}_j = f(j)$ for $1 \le j \le n$.
2. The vector spaces $V = \text{Functions}(\{i, j) \mid 1 \le i \le m,\ 1 \le j \le n\}, F)$ and $M_{m \times n}F$ are isomorphic by the mapping which sends a function $f \in V$ to the matrix A whose (i, j)-entry is $a_{ij} = f(i, j)$ for $1 \le i \le m$, $1 \le j \le n$.
3. The vector spaces $V = \text{Functions}(\{j \mid 1 \le j \le n\}, F^m)$ and $L(F^n, F^m)$ are isomorphic by the mapping α which sends a function $f \in V$ to the linear transformation R which maps $\mathbf{e}_j$ to $f(j)$ for $1 \le j \le n$.

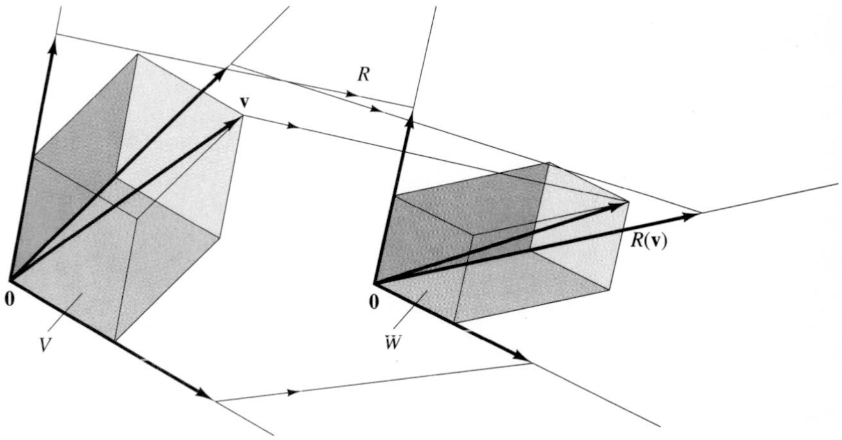

Figure 4.2 Isomorphic vector spaces V and W under R. Length and angle play no roles here.

4. The vector spaces $L(F^n, F^m)$ and $M_{m\times n}F$ are isomorphic, since the linear transformation $m(R)$ is an isomorphism from $L(F^n, F^m)$ and $M_{m\times n}F$. (See Theorem 3.11.) This fact was exploited to prove Theorem 3.12, wherein the properties of matrices corresponding to those of linear transformations were given.

5. The vector spaces F^n and F_n are isomorphic by the mapping taking each vector to its transpose.

6. The vector spaces F^n and F^m are isomorphic if and only if $m = n$. This is the corollary to Theorem 3.4.

Algebraic operations on linear transformations

Linear transformations from a vector space V to a vector space W can be combined algebraically just as they were when $V = F^n$ and $W = F^m$. Fortunately for vector spaces, coordinates are not needed for introducing the operations.

Definition. *Sums, Differences, and Scalar Products.*

For two linear transformations R and S from V to W, the sum $R + S$, difference $R - S$ and scalar product tR $(t \in F)$ are the mappings given by

1. $(R + S)(\mathbf{v}) = R(\mathbf{v}) + S(\mathbf{v})\ (\mathbf{v} \in V)$;
2. $(R - S)(\mathbf{v}) = R(\mathbf{v}) - S(\mathbf{v})\ (\mathbf{v} \in V)$;
3. $(tR)(\mathbf{v}) = t(R(\mathbf{v}))\ (\mathbf{v} \in V)$.

When $V = F^n$ and $W = F^m$, our new definition for these operations is equivalent to the old definition of Section 3.2. (Check!) Furthermore, $R + S$,

$R - S$, and tR ($t \in F$) are linear transformations, as we now verify. The $\mathbf{v}$, $\mathbf{w}$ are from V and a is from F.

1.
$$(R + S)(\mathbf{v} + \mathbf{w}) = R(\mathbf{v} + \mathbf{w}) + S(\mathbf{v} + \mathbf{w}) = R(\mathbf{v}) + R(\mathbf{w}) + S(\mathbf{v}) + S(\mathbf{w})$$
$$= R(\mathbf{v}) + S(\mathbf{v}) + R(\mathbf{w}) + S(\mathbf{w}) = (R + S)(\mathbf{v}) + (R + S)(\mathbf{w})$$
$$(R + S)(a\mathbf{v}) = R(a\mathbf{v}) + S(a\mathbf{v}) = aR(\mathbf{v}) + aS(\mathbf{v})$$
$$= a(R(\mathbf{v}) + S(\mathbf{v})) = a((R + S)(v)).$$

2.
$$(tR)(\mathbf{v} + \mathbf{w}) = t(R(\mathbf{v} + \mathbf{w})) = t(R(\mathbf{v}) + R(\mathbf{w}))$$
$$= tR(\mathbf{v}) + tR(\mathbf{w}) = (tR)(\mathbf{v}) + (tR)(\mathbf{w})$$
$$(tR)(a\mathbf{v}) = t(R(a\mathbf{v})) = t(aR(\mathbf{v}))$$
$$= (ta)R(\mathbf{v}) = a(tR(\mathbf{v})) = a(tR)(\mathbf{v}).$$

3. $R - S = R + (-1)S$, since $(R - S)(\mathbf{v}) = R(\mathbf{v}) - S(\mathbf{v}) = R(\mathbf{v}) + (-1)S(\mathbf{v})$ for all $\mathbf{v} \in V$. Since $R + (-1)S$ is a linear transformation by (1) and (2), so is $R - S$.

The vector space of linear transformations from V to W

With respect to the operations of addition and scalar multiplication just introduced, the set $L(V, W)$ of linear transformations from a vector space V over F to a vector space W over F is itself a vector space, as we now prove.

Theorem 4.3. *The Vector Space of Linear Transformation.* $L(V, W)$ is a vector space.

Proof. The zero function 0 from V to W is a linear transformation such that $R + 0 = R$ for $R \in L(V, W)$. The vector space properties are easily verified by computing both sides of the equation for each property and showing them to be equal. For properties (2), (3), and (4), this is how it goes:

2. $(R + 0)(\mathbf{v}) = R(\mathbf{v}) + 0(\mathbf{v}) = R(\mathbf{v})$ for all $\mathbf{v} \in V$, so $R + 0 = R$; $(R + S)(\mathbf{v}) = R(\mathbf{v}) + S(\mathbf{v}) = S(\mathbf{v}) + R(\mathbf{v}) = (S + R)(\mathbf{v})$ for all $\mathbf{v} \in V$, so $R + S = S + R$.
3. $R + T = S$ has a unique solution T, namely, $T = S - R$. (Verify!)
4. $t(R + S)(\mathbf{v}) = t(R(\mathbf{v}) + S(\mathbf{v})) = tR(\mathbf{v}) + tS(\mathbf{v}) = (tR)(\mathbf{v}) + (tS)(\mathbf{v}) = (tR + tS)(\mathbf{v})$ for all $\mathbf{v} \in V$, so $t(R + S) = tR + tS$.

The remaining properties are proved in much the same way. ■

Other properties of linear transformations

In addition to the vector space properties for the set $L(V, W)$ of linear transformations from a vector space V to a vector space W over F, we have the following properties involving products.

Theorem 4.4. *Properties of Products.*
Products of linear transformations satisfy the following properties, where U, V, W, and X are vector spaces over F, 0_{VW} denotes the 0 linear transformation from V to W, and I_V denotes the identity linear transformation from V to V.

1. $RI_V = I_W R = R$ for $R \in L(V, W)$.
2. $R0_{VV} = 0_{WW}R = 0_{VW}$ for $R \in L(V, W)$.
3. $(RS)T = R(ST)$ for $R \in L(W, X)$, $S \in L(V, W)$, $T \in L(U, V)$.
4. $(R + S)T = RT + ST$ for $R, S \in L(V, W)$, $T \in L(U, V)$.
5. $T(R + S) = TR + TS$ for $T \in L(V, W)$, $R, S \in L(U, V)$.
6. $a(RS) = (aR)S = R(aS)$ for $R \in L(W, X)$, $S \in L(V, W)$.

Proof. The first three properties are just the identity and associativity properties of functions, which we already know, and the zero properties, which are obvious. We now prove (4) and (6), skipping (5), which follows closely the proof of (4):

4. $((R + S)T)(\mathbf{v}) = (R + S)(T(\mathbf{v})) = R(T(\mathbf{v})) + S(T(\mathbf{v})) = (RT)(\mathbf{v}) + (ST)(\mathbf{v}) = (RT + ST)(\mathbf{v})$ for all $\mathbf{v}$, so that $(R + S)T = RT + ST$.
6. $(a(RS))(\mathbf{v}) = a((RS)(\mathbf{v})) = a(R(S(\mathbf{v}))) = (aR)(S(\mathbf{v})) = ((aR)S)(\mathbf{v})$ for all $\mathbf{v}$, so that $a(RS) = (aR)S$. Since $a(R(S(\mathbf{v}))) = R(aS(\mathbf{v})) = (R(aS))(\mathbf{v})$ for all $\mathbf{v}$, we also have $a(RS) = R(aS)$. ■

PROBLEMS

NUMERICAL PROBLEMS

1. Determine whether R is a linear transformation from V to W in each of the following cases.
   (a) $R(f) = f'$ (the derivative of f with respect to z for $f \in V$), where V and W are both equal to $F[z]$.
   (b) $R(f) = f^2$, where V and W are both equal to $F[z]$.
   (c) $R(f) = f + 2$, where V and W are both equal to $F[z]$.
   (d) $R(f) = f(3)$, where V and W are both equal to $F[z]$.

2. In each of the following cases, determine whether there is an isomorphism from V to W and, if so, determine all such isomorphisms.
   (a) $V = \left\{ \begin{bmatrix} a \\ b \\ c \end{bmatrix} \middle| \, a + 2c = 0 \right\}, W = \left\{ \begin{bmatrix} a \\ b \\ c \end{bmatrix} \middle| \, 2a + 2c = 0 \right\}$
   (b) $V = F\begin{bmatrix} 5 \\ 1 \\ 4 \end{bmatrix} + F\begin{bmatrix} 6 \\ 2 \\ 3 \end{bmatrix}, W = F\begin{bmatrix} 3 \\ 2 \\ 6 \end{bmatrix} + F\begin{bmatrix} 4 \\ 1 \\ 5 \end{bmatrix}$

(c) V is the intersection of

$$\left\{\begin{bmatrix} a \\ b \\ c \end{bmatrix} \middle| \; a + 2c = 0\right\} \quad \text{and} \quad F\begin{bmatrix} 5 \\ 1 \\ 4 \end{bmatrix} + F\begin{bmatrix} 6 \\ 2 \\ 3 \end{bmatrix};$$

W is the intersection of

$$\left\{\begin{bmatrix} a \\ b \\ c \end{bmatrix} \middle| \; 2a + 2c = 0\right\} \quad \text{and} \quad F\begin{bmatrix} 3 \\ 2 \\ 6 \end{bmatrix} + F\begin{bmatrix} 4 \\ 1 \\ 5 \end{bmatrix}.$$

3. Show that there is an invertible linear transformation from F^3 to the vector space of polynomials $f(z)$ of degree at most 2 which maps $\mathbf{e}_i$ to $(z - 4)^{i-1}$ for $i = 1, 2, 3$.

4. Show that every subspace of F^2 is isomorphic to one of the vector spaces $\{\mathbf{0}\}$, F, F^2.

5. Show that $F\mathbf{e}_1 + \cdots + F\mathbf{e}_{n-1}$ is isomorphic to the hyperplane $nx_1 + (n-1)x_2 + \cdots + 1x_n = 0$ in F^n.

Hard

6. Show that the set of simultaneous solutions to two equations

$$a_1x_1 + a_2x_2 + \cdots + a_nx_n = 0, \qquad b_1x_1 + b_2x_2 + \cdots + b_nx_n = 0$$

is a subspace of F^n isomorphic to F^{n-2} or F^{n-1} or F^n.

THEORETICAL PROBLEMS

7. For $V = F^n$ and $W = F^m$, show that the definition of addition and scalar multiplication of linear transformations from V to W is equivalent to definition of Section 3.2.

8. Let V be a vector space over F. For $t \in F$, show that the scalar multiplication t_L from V to itself is a linear transformation.

9. Let V be a vector space over F. For $\mathbf{v} \in V$, show that the mapping $\mathbf{v}_R$ from F to V defined by $\mathbf{v}_R(t) = t\mathbf{v}$ for $t \in F$ is a linear transformation whose image is $F\mathbf{v}$.

10. Verify that $R + T = S$ has unique solution T, namely, $T = S - R$.

11. Show that the mapping from the vector space $V = \{a + bz \mid a, b \in F\}$ of polynomials of degree at most 1 to itself which sends $a + bz$ to $(a + 2b) + (3a + 5b)z$ is an invertible linear transformation. Describe its inverse.

12. If D is the differentiation and E is the antidifferentiation of $\mathbb{R}[z]$ introduced in a previous example, show that neither D nor E is invertible.

13. Describe all of the isomorphisms from $F[z]_1$ to F^2.

Hard

14. Show that $F[z]_n$ is isomorphic to F^{n+1}.

15. Find an invertible function from the set of isomorphisms from $F[z]_2$ to F^3 to the set of invertible 3×3 matrices over F.

16. Find an isomorphism from $L(F[z]_2, F^5)$ to $M_{5 \times 3}F$.

17. Suppose that α is an isomorphism from F^n to a vector space V over F, and let W be a vector space over F. Show, for any elements $\mathbf{w}_1, \ldots, \mathbf{w}_n$ of W, that there is one and only one linear transformation R from V to W such that $R(\alpha(\mathbf{e}_j)) = \mathbf{w}_j$ for $1 \leq j \leq n$.

4.3 SUBSPACES. THE SPAN OF A SET OF VECTORS

We see how a vector space V over F is built by looking at its subspaces, which we now introduce within the confines of the language of vector spaces.

Definition. *Subspace of a Vector Space.*
A **subspace** of a vector space U over F is a subset V of U containing $\mathbf{0}$ such that if $\mathbf{v}, \mathbf{w} \in V$, then $\mathbf{v} + \mathbf{w}, a\mathbf{v} \in V$ for all $a \in F$.

As for F^m, we see for any vector space U over F that the following are true.

1. A subspace V of U is, like U itself, a set of vectors with operations of addition, subtraction, and scalar multiplication. The subtraction operation comes to us by way of addition and scalar multiplication as $\mathbf{w} - \mathbf{v} = \mathbf{w} + (-1)\mathbf{v}$.
2. The subspace V inherits from U all the properties in the definition of vector space. So, a subspace V of a vector space U over F is itself a vector space over F.
3. U is a subspace of itself.
4. $\{\mathbf{0}\}$ is a subspace of U called the **zero subspace**.
5. For any vector $\mathbf{v} \in U$, $F\mathbf{v} = \{a\mathbf{v} \mid a \in F\}$ is a subspace called the **span** of $\mathbf{v}$.
6. If V and W are subspaces of U, then $V + W = \{\mathbf{v} + \mathbf{w} \mid \mathbf{v} \in V, \mathbf{w} \in W\}$ is a subspace of U called the **sum** of V and W. The proof follows the one for F^n.
7. For any two vectors $\mathbf{v}$ and $\mathbf{w}$, $F\mathbf{v} + F\mathbf{w} = \{a\mathbf{v} + b\mathbf{w} \mid a, b \in F\}$ is a subspace, by (6). It is called the *span* of $\mathbf{v}$ and $\mathbf{w}$.
8. For any n vectors $\mathbf{v}_1, \ldots, \mathbf{v}_n$, the sum

$$F\mathbf{v}_1 + \cdots + F\mathbf{v}_n = \{a_1\mathbf{v}_1 + \cdots + a_n\mathbf{v}_n \mid a_1, \ldots, a_n \in F\}$$

is a subspace, by repeated application of (6). It is called *span* of $\mathbf{v}_1, \ldots, \mathbf{v}_n$.

The element

$$a_1\mathbf{v}_1 + \cdots + a_n\mathbf{v}_n$$

is called a *linear combination* of $\mathbf{v}_1, \ldots, \mathbf{v}_n$.

9. For any two subspaces V and W of U, the intersection $V \cap W$ is a subspace of U. The proof, again, is the same as it was for F^n.

10. Similarly, the intersection of any collection of subspaces of U is a subspace of U.

If V is the span of a set of vectors, it is convenient to say that V is spanned by them. To keep our language crisp and unambiguous, we formalize this convention as a definition.

Definition. *Vector Space Spanned by Given Vectors.*
A vector space V over F is **spanned** by $\mathbf{v}_1, \ldots, \mathbf{v}_n$ if $V = F\mathbf{v}_1 + \cdots + F\mathbf{v}_n$.

EXAMPLES

Of course, since our definition of subspace agrees with the earlier definition in the case of F^m, all the subspaces of F^m from Chapters 3 and 4, notably lines, planes, intersections of hyperplanes, and column spaces, are examples. We now concentrate on examples of subspaces of other vector spaces.

1. For any nonzero vector $\mathbf{v}$, the *line* through $\mathbf{v}$ and $\mathbf{0}$ is the subspace $F\mathbf{v}$ of U.

2. A *plane* through $\mathbf{0}$ is a subspace of the form $F\mathbf{v} + F\mathbf{w}$, where $\mathbf{v}$ is nonzero and $\mathbf{w}$ is not in the line $F\mathbf{v}$. Note that

   a. $F(a\mathbf{v} + b\mathbf{w})$ is a line in the plane $F\mathbf{v} + F\mathbf{w}$ if either a or b is nonzero;
   b. Two lines $F(a\mathbf{v} + b\mathbf{w})$ and $F(c\mathbf{v} + d\mathbf{w})$ in the plane $F\mathbf{v} + F\mathbf{w}$ are equal provided that the lines $F\begin{bmatrix} a \\ b \end{bmatrix}$ and $F\begin{bmatrix} c \\ d \end{bmatrix}$ in F^2 are equal. (Prove!) See Figure 4.3.

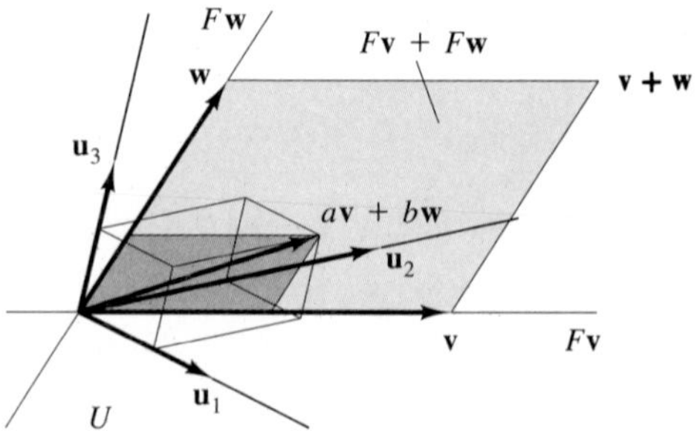

Figure 4.3 The lines $F\mathbf{v}$ and $F\mathbf{w}$ and plane $F\mathbf{v} + F\mathbf{w}$ in $U = F\mathbf{u}_1 + F\mathbf{u}_2 + F\mathbf{u}_3$.

3. Suppose that $U = F\mathbf{u}_1 + F\mathbf{u}_2 + F\mathbf{u}_3$, where $F\mathbf{u}_1 + F\mathbf{u}_2$ is a plane not containing $\mathbf{u}_3$. Then any plane $F\mathbf{v} + F\mathbf{w}$ is the set of vectors $x_1\mathbf{u}_1 + x_2\mathbf{u}_2 + x_3\mathbf{u}_3$ such that $ax_1 + bx_2 + cx_3 = 0$ for some $a, b, c \in F$. For $U = F^3$, this is just Theorem 3.6. To prove it here, simply take the linear transformation α from F^3 to U defined by

$$\alpha\begin{bmatrix} r \\ s \\ t \end{bmatrix} = r\mathbf{u}_1 + s\mathbf{u}_2 + t\mathbf{u}_3.$$

This α is an isomorphism from F^3 to U mapping $\mathbf{e}_j$ to $\mathbf{u}_j$ for $j = 1, 2, 3$. (Prove!) We let $\mathbf{v}'$, $\mathbf{w}'$ denote the elements of F^3 such that $\alpha(\mathbf{v}') = \mathbf{v}$ and $\alpha(\mathbf{w}') = \mathbf{w}$. Then α maps the plane $F\mathbf{v}' + F\mathbf{w}'$ onto the plane $F\mathbf{v} + F\mathbf{w}$. But we know that any plane $F\mathbf{v}' + F\mathbf{w}'$ in F^3 is the set of vectors $x_1\mathbf{e}_1 + x_2\mathbf{e}_2 + x_3\mathbf{e}_3$ such that $ax_1 + bx_2 + cx_3 = 0$ for some $a, b, c \in F$. Applying α, it follows that the plane $F\mathbf{v} + F\mathbf{w}$ in U is the set of vectors

$$\begin{aligned}\alpha(x_1\mathbf{e}_1 + x_2\mathbf{e}_2 + x_3\mathbf{e}_3) &= x_1\alpha(\mathbf{e}_1) + x_2\alpha(\mathbf{e}_2) + x_3\alpha(\mathbf{e}_3) \\ &= x_1\mathbf{u}_1 + x_2\mathbf{u}_2 + x_3\mathbf{u}_3\end{aligned}$$

such that $ax_1 + bx_2 + cx_3 = 0$ for some $a, b, c \in F$ (Figure 4.4).

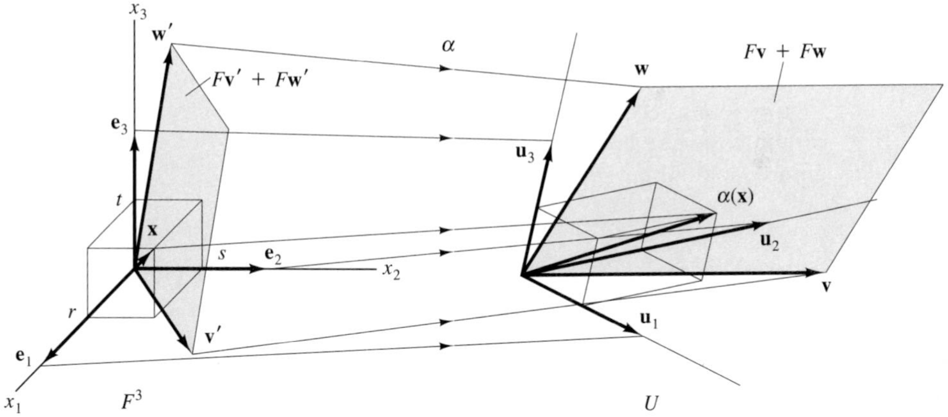

Figure 4.4 The isomorphism α from F^3 to U. The plane $F\mathbf{v}' + F\mathbf{w}' = \alpha^{-1}(F\mathbf{v} + F\mathbf{w})$.

The kernel and image of a linear transformation

Given a linear transformation R from a vector space V over F to a vector space W over F, we get the subspaces

$$\text{Kernel } R = \{\mathbf{v} \in V \mid R(\mathbf{v}) = \mathbf{0}\},$$

$$\text{Image } R = \{R(\mathbf{v}) \mid \mathbf{v} \in V\},$$

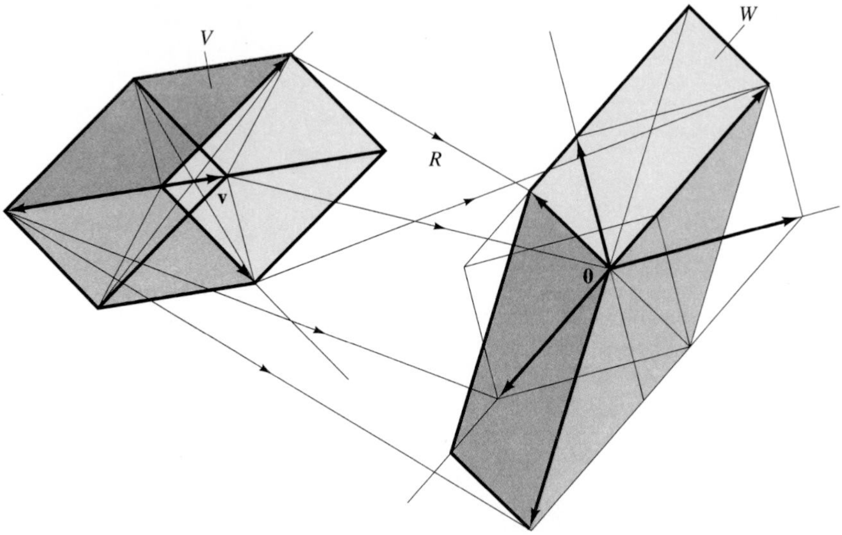

Figure 4.5 The kernel $F\mathbf{v}$ and image of a linear transformation R from V to W. (Compare with Figure 3.16.) The entire line $F\mathbf{v}$ through $\mathbf{v}$ is mapped to $\mathbf{0}$ by R. The image of V is a plane.

called the **kernel** and **image** of R. For $V = F^n$ and $W = F^m$, these are just the nullspace and column space of the matrix A of R, which we studied in Chapter 3. In Section 4.8, we show how to apply the results of Chapter 3 to compute the kernel and image of any linear transformation R from a finite-dimensional vector space V to W (Figure 4.5).

EXAMPLES

1. When R is a nonzero linear transformation from a vector space V over F to $F^1 = F$, its kernel is called a **hyperplane** through $\mathbf{0}$. In the case $V = F^n$, the matrix of R is a $1 \times n$ matrix $A = [a_1 \quad \dots \quad a_n]$ and the kernel of R is the nullspace of A, which is also the set of

$$\begin{bmatrix} x_1 \\ \vdots \\ x_n \end{bmatrix}$$

such that $a_1x_1 + \cdots + a_nx_n = 0$. When $F = \mathbb{R}$, A^T is the *normal* to this hyperplane.

2. When R is a nonzero linear transformation from $F = F^1$ to a vector space V over F, its image is the line through $\mathbf{0}$ and $\mathbf{v} = R(1)$. In the case

$V = F^n$, the matrix of R is an $n \times 1$ matrix

$$A = \begin{bmatrix} a_1 \\ \vdots \\ a_n \end{bmatrix}$$

and the image of R is the column space of A, that is, the line

$$F\begin{bmatrix} a_1 \\ \vdots \\ a_n \end{bmatrix}$$

through $\begin{bmatrix} a_1 \\ \vdots \\ a_n \end{bmatrix}$ and $\mathbf{0}$.

Just as for linear transformations of F^n, we have the following two theorems. The proofs are the same as before.

Theorem 4.5. *Linear Transformations Whose Kernels Are* $\mathbf{0}$.
A linear transformation R from a vector space V over F to a vector space W over F is 1-1 if and only if Kernel $R = \{\mathbf{0}\}$.

Theorem 4.6. *Invertible Linear Transformations.*
A linear transformation R from a vector space V over F to a vector space W over F is invertible if and only if Kernel $R = \{\mathbf{0}\}$ and Image $R = W$.

Preservation of span

When subspaces V and W of a vector space U are expressed as spans

$$V = F\mathbf{v}_1 + \cdots + F\mathbf{v}_n$$
$$W = F\mathbf{w}_1 + \cdots + F\mathbf{w}_m$$

of vectors of U, there is a useful criteria for inclusion and equality of V and W.

Theorem 4.7. *Conditions for Inclusion and Equality of Spans.*
For vectors $\mathbf{v}_i$, $\mathbf{w}_j$ in a vector space U over F, we have

1. $F\mathbf{v}_1 + \cdots + F\mathbf{v}_n \subseteq F\mathbf{w}_1 + \cdots + F\mathbf{w}_m$ if $\mathbf{v}_1, \ldots, \mathbf{v}_n \in F\mathbf{w}_1 + \cdots + F\mathbf{w}_m$;
2. $F\mathbf{v}_1 + \cdots + F\mathbf{v}_n = F\mathbf{w}_1 + \cdots + F\mathbf{w}_m$ if $\mathbf{v}_1, \ldots, \mathbf{v}_n \in F\mathbf{w}_1 + \cdots + F\mathbf{w}_m$ and $\mathbf{w}_1, \ldots, \mathbf{w}_m \in F\mathbf{v}_1 + \cdots + F\mathbf{v}_n$.

Proof. Suppose first that $\mathbf{v}_1, \ldots, \mathbf{v}_n \in F\mathbf{w}_1 + \cdots + F\mathbf{w}_m$. Since

$$F\mathbf{w}_1 + \cdots + F\mathbf{w}_m$$

is a subspace, any linear combination $a_1\mathbf{v}_1 + \cdots + a_n\mathbf{v}_n$ is also in

$$F\mathbf{w}_1 + \cdots + F\mathbf{w}_m.$$

This proves (1). Since $V \subseteq W$ and $W \subseteq V$ implies $W = V$, (2) follows from (1). ■

EXAMPLE

To prove that $F(\mathbf{u} - \mathbf{v}) + F(\mathbf{v} - \mathbf{w}) = F(2\mathbf{u} - \mathbf{v} - \mathbf{w}) + F(3\mathbf{u} - 5\mathbf{v} + 2\mathbf{w})$, simply verify that $\mathbf{u} - \mathbf{v}$ and $\mathbf{v} - \mathbf{w}$ are in $F(2\mathbf{u} - \mathbf{v} - \mathbf{w}) + F(3\mathbf{u} - 5\mathbf{v} + 2\mathbf{w})$ and that $2\mathbf{u} - \mathbf{v} - \mathbf{w}$ and $3\mathbf{u} - 5\mathbf{v} + 2\mathbf{w}$ are in $F(\mathbf{u} - \mathbf{v}) + F(\mathbf{v} - \mathbf{w})$. (Verify!)

The preceding theorem shows that the inclusion or equality of two spans $F\mathbf{v}_1 + \cdots + F\mathbf{v}_n$, $F\mathbf{w}_1 + \cdots + F\mathbf{w}_m$ is not disturbed if we apply any of the following operations to either of the sets $\{\mathbf{v}_1, \ldots, \mathbf{v}_n\}$, $\{\mathbf{w}_1, \ldots, \mathbf{w}_m\}$.

Elementary Operations on Sets of Vectors.

1. Add a times the jth vector to the ith vector, where $i \neq j$.
2. Multiply the jth vector by a nonzero scalar a.
3. Interchange vectors i and j, where $i \neq j$.

EXAMPLES

1. For the set of rows of a matrix, the elementary operations on vectors are just the elementary row operations.

2. When the set of vectors is the set of column vectors of a matrix B, called the **edges** of B, then the elementary operations are elementary column operations, called **edge shears**, **edge expansions**, and **edge interchanges**. These operations can be achieved by multiplying B on the right by the corresponding elementary matrix (see Figure 4.6):

a. $BA_{ji}(a)$ is B after it undergoes a shear on edge i in the direction of edge j—that is, a times its jth edge is added to its ith edge.
b. $BM_j(a)$ is B after it undergoes expansion by a of its jth edge, that is, its jth edge is multiplied by a. ("Expansion" as used here conforms with its casual meaning only in the special case where a is a real number greater than 1.)
c. BI_{ij} is B after interchanging edges i and j.

3. To find a simple form for the plane $F(3\mathbf{v} + 4\mathbf{w}) + F(2\mathbf{v} + 3\mathbf{w})$, we observe that

$$\begin{aligned} F(3\mathbf{v} + 4\mathbf{w}) + F(2\mathbf{v} + 3\mathbf{w}) &\to F(1\mathbf{v} + 1\mathbf{w}) + F(2\mathbf{v} + 3\mathbf{w}) \\ &\to F(1\mathbf{v} + 1\mathbf{w}) + F(0\mathbf{v} + 1\mathbf{w}) \\ &\to F(1\mathbf{v} + 0\mathbf{w}) + F(0\mathbf{v} + 1\mathbf{w}) = F\mathbf{v} + F\mathbf{w}. \end{aligned}$$

(Verify!)

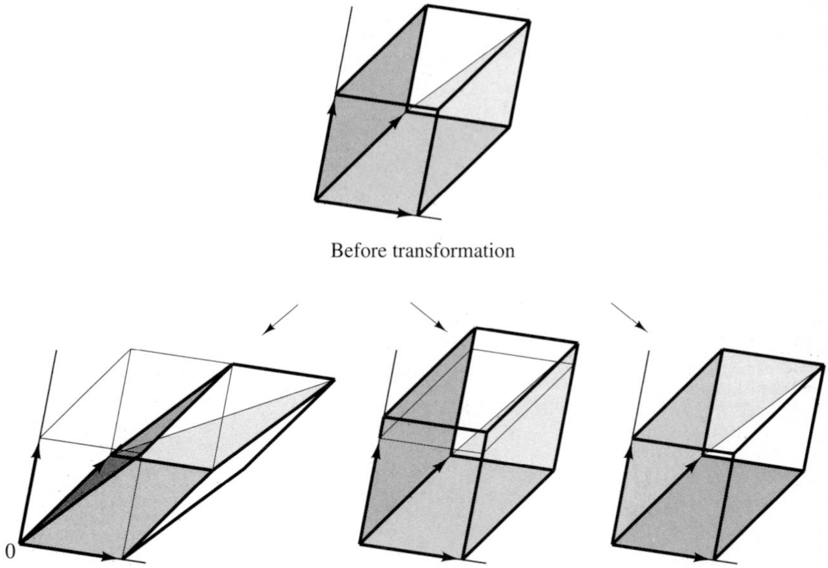

(a) Edge shear (b) Edge expansion (c) Edge interchange

Figure 4.6 The effect on B of (a) a shear, (b) an expansion, and (c) an interchange of edges.

PROBLEMS

NUMERICAL PROBLEMS

1. Let U be a vector space over F and $\mathbf{u}, \mathbf{v}, \mathbf{w} \in U$.

(a) Is the set V of vectors $\mathbf{u} + r\mathbf{v} + s\mathbf{w}$ $(r, s \in F)$ always a subspace?

(b) Is the set V of vectors $(3s + 2r)\mathbf{u} + (s - r)\mathbf{v} + t\mathbf{w}$ $(r, s, t \in F)$ always a subspace?

2. Prove that $F(\mathbf{u} - \mathbf{v}) + F(\mathbf{v} - \mathbf{w}) = F(2\mathbf{u} - \mathbf{v} - \mathbf{w}) + F(3\mathbf{u} - 5\mathbf{v} + 2\mathbf{w})$ using elementary operations on sets of vectors.

3. Apply the result in Problem 2 to the following cases.

(a) $\mathbf{u} = \begin{bmatrix} 1 \\ 4 \end{bmatrix}, \mathbf{v} = \begin{bmatrix} 2 \\ 1 \end{bmatrix}, \mathbf{w} = \begin{bmatrix} 9 \\ 4 \end{bmatrix}$ **(b)** $\mathbf{u} = \begin{bmatrix} 2 \\ 3 \\ 5 \end{bmatrix}, \mathbf{v} = \begin{bmatrix} 5 \\ 5 \\ 1 \end{bmatrix}, \mathbf{w} = \begin{bmatrix} 4 \\ 2 \\ 3 \end{bmatrix}$

(c) $\mathbf{u} = \begin{bmatrix} 2 \\ 4 \\ 1 \end{bmatrix}, \mathbf{v} = \begin{bmatrix} 4 \\ 1 \\ 2 \end{bmatrix}, \mathbf{w} = \begin{bmatrix} 2 \\ 7 \\ 5 \end{bmatrix}$

4. Let $U = F\mathbf{u}_1 + F\mathbf{u}_2 + F\mathbf{u}_3$, where $F\mathbf{u}_1 + F\mathbf{u}_2$ is a plane not containing $\mathbf{u}_3$. Are the two planes $F\mathbf{v} + F\mathbf{w}$ and $F\mathbf{v}' + F\mathbf{w}'$ equal

(a) If $\mathbf{v} = 2\mathbf{u}_1 + 3\mathbf{u}_2 + 4\mathbf{u}_3$, $\mathbf{w} = 1\mathbf{u}_1 + 2\mathbf{u}_2 + 3\mathbf{u}_3$, $\mathbf{v}' = 2\mathbf{u}_1 + 3\mathbf{u}_2 + 4\mathbf{u}_3$ and $\mathbf{w}' = 1\mathbf{u}_1 + 1\mathbf{u}_2 + 1\mathbf{u}_3$?

(b) If $\mathbf{v} = 2\mathbf{u}_1 + 3\mathbf{u}_2 + 4\mathbf{u}_3$, $\mathbf{w} = 1\mathbf{u}_1 + 1\mathbf{u}_2 + 2\mathbf{u}_3$, $\mathbf{v}' = 3\mathbf{u}_1 + 3\mathbf{u}_2 + 4\mathbf{u}_3$ and $\mathbf{w}' = 1\mathbf{u}_1 + 1\mathbf{u}_2 + 1\mathbf{u}_3$?

Hard

5. Let $U = F\mathbf{u}_1 + F\mathbf{u}_2 + F\mathbf{u}_3$, where $F\mathbf{u}_1 + F\mathbf{u}_2$ is a plane not containing $\mathbf{u}_3$.

(a) Show that the linear transformation α from F^3 to U defined by

$$\alpha\begin{bmatrix} r \\ s \\ t \end{bmatrix} = r\mathbf{u}_1 + s\mathbf{u}_2 + t\mathbf{u}_3$$

is an isomorphism from F^3 to U mapping $\mathbf{e}_j$ to $\mathbf{u}_j$ for $j = 1, 2, 3$.

(b) For each of the following planes, find a corresponding plane in F^3 that maps onto it under α.

(i) $F(\mathbf{u}_1 + a\mathbf{u}_3) + F(\mathbf{u}_2 + b\mathbf{u}_3)$

(ii) $F(\mathbf{u}_1 + c\mathbf{u}_2) + F\mathbf{u}_1$

(iii) $F\mathbf{u}_1 + F\mathbf{u}_2$

(iv) $F(3\mathbf{u}_1 + 3\mathbf{u}_2 + 4\mathbf{u}_3) + F(1\mathbf{u}_1 + 3\mathbf{u}_2 + 4\mathbf{u}_3)$

(v) $F(-2\mathbf{u}_1 + 1\mathbf{u}_2 + 5\mathbf{u}_3) + F(1\mathbf{u}_1 - 3\mathbf{u}_2 - 5\mathbf{u}_3)$

(vi) $F(\mathbf{u}_1 + \mathbf{u}_2 + \mathbf{u}_3) + F(2\mathbf{u}_1 - 3\mathbf{u}_2 - 8\mathbf{u}_3)$

(c) Find the equation of each of the planes listed in (b).

THEORETICAL PROBLEMS

6. Show that $F\mathbf{v} + F\mathbf{w} = F\mathbf{v} + F(\mathbf{w} + a\mathbf{v})$ for any $a \in F$.

7. Show that two lines $F(a\mathbf{v} + b\mathbf{w})$ and $F(c\mathbf{v} + d\mathbf{w})$ in a plane $F\mathbf{v} + F\mathbf{w}$ are equal provided that the lines $F\begin{bmatrix} a \\ b \end{bmatrix}$ and $F\begin{bmatrix} c \\ d \end{bmatrix}$ in F^2 are equal.

8. The intersection of any collection of subspaces of F^n is a subspace.

9. Show that for any vector spaces V and W over F, $L(V, W)$ is a subspace of the vector space Functions(V, W) introduced as an example in Section 4.2.

Hard

10. Given a $k \times n$ matrix V and $k \times m$ matrix W, show that the column space $c(V)$ of V is contained in $c(W)$ if and only if there is an $m \times n$ matrix X such that $V = WX$.

11. Show that the subspaces $F1 + F(z - 1) + \cdots + F(z - n)^n$ and $F1 + F(z - n) + \cdots + F(z - 1)^n$ of $F[z]$ are equal.

4.4 LINEAR INDEPENDENCE. BASIS OF A VECTOR SPACE

The condition that $\mathbf{v}$ be in the span of vectors $\mathbf{v}_1, \ldots, \mathbf{v}_n$ of a vector space U over F is a condition of dependence of a certain kind. Specifically, we say that a vector $\mathbf{v}$ *depends linearly* on a set of vectors $\mathbf{v}_1, \ldots, \mathbf{v}_n$ if it can be expressed as a linear combination $\mathbf{v} = a_1\mathbf{v}_1 + \cdots + a_n\mathbf{v}_n$ (Figure 4.7).

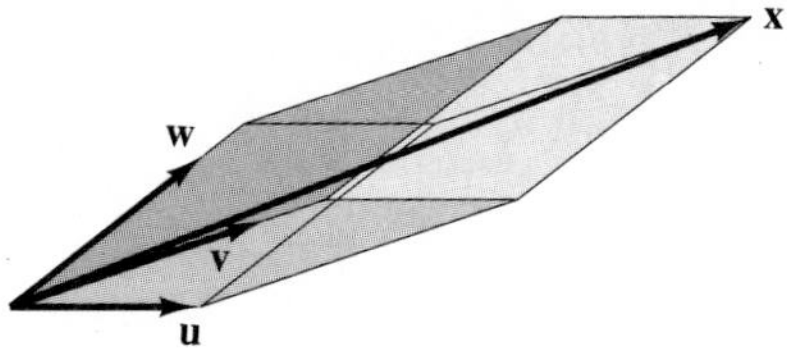

Figure 4.7 Linear dependence of **x** on **u**, **v**, **w**.

EXAMPLES

1. **0** depends linearly on any nonempty set of vectors.
2. For nonzero vectors **v** and **w**, **w** depends linearly on **v** and **v** on **w** if and only if $F\mathbf{v} = F\mathbf{w}$. (Prove!)
3. If $F\mathbf{v} + F\mathbf{w}$ is a plane in F^3, then **v** does not depend linearly on **w** and **w** does not depend linearly on **v**. (Prove!)
4. In F^3, $\mathbf{e}_1$ does not depend linearly on $\mathbf{e}_2$ and $\mathbf{e}_3$, $\mathbf{e}_2$ does not depend linearly on $\mathbf{e}_1$ and $\mathbf{e}_3$, and $\mathbf{e}_3$ does not depend linearly on $\mathbf{e}_1$ and $\mathbf{e}_2$.
5. In F^n and for $1 \le j \le n$, $\mathbf{e}_j$ does not depend linearly on $\mathbf{e}_1, \ldots, \mathbf{e}_{j-1}, \mathbf{e}_{j+1}, \ldots, \mathbf{e}_n$. (Prove!)

It seems from these examples that the negation of linear dependence is the more dominant concept. So, we now turn our terminology around.

Definition. *Linearly Independent Set of Vectors.*
A set of vectors $\mathbf{v}_1, \ldots, \mathbf{v}_n$ is **linearly independent** if the vectors are nonzero and, for $1 \le j \le n$, $\mathbf{v}_j$ cannot be expressed as a linear combination of the other vectors $\mathbf{v}_1, \ldots, \mathbf{v}_{j-1}, \mathbf{v}_{j+1}, \ldots, \mathbf{v}_n$. A set of vectors is **linearly dependent** if it is not linearly independent (Figure 4.8).

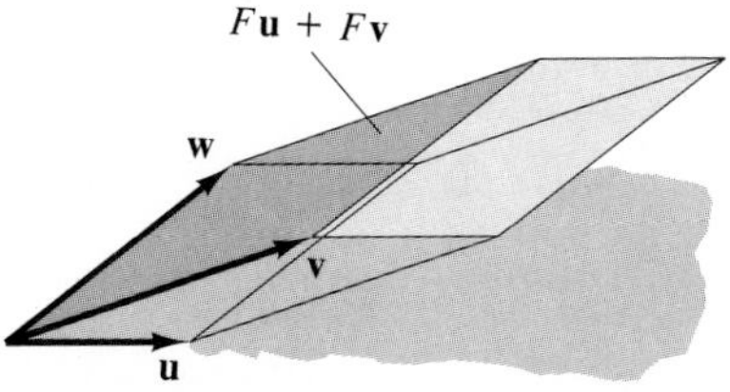

Figure 4.8 Linear independence of vectors **u**, **v**, and **w** occurs when $F\mathbf{u} + F\mathbf{v}$ is a plane not containing **w**.

Criteria for linear independence

Fortunately, this somewhat clumsy notion of linear independence is equivalent to a more convenient condition.

Theorem 4.8. *Condition for Linear Independence of a Given Set of Vectors.* A set of vectors $\mathbf{v}_1, \ldots, \mathbf{v}_n$ in a vector space U over F is linearly independent if and only if each linear combination $a_1\mathbf{v}_1 + \cdots + a_n\mathbf{v}_n$ $(a_1, \ldots, a_n \in F)$ is $\mathbf{0}$ only if $a_1 = \cdots = a_n = 0$.

Proof. Suppose first that the set of vectors $\mathbf{v}_1, \ldots, \mathbf{v}_n$ is linearly independent. If a linear combination $a_1\mathbf{v}_1 + \cdots + a_n\mathbf{v}_n$ $(a_1, \ldots, a_n \in F)$ is $\mathbf{0}$, the coefficient a_1 is zero, for otherwise we could divide by a_1. Since $\mathbf{v}_1$ is nonzero, we have $n > 1$, and we can solve for $\mathbf{v}_1$ as a linear combination of $\mathbf{v}_2, \ldots, \mathbf{v}_n$, which, by our supposition, is not possible. Similarly, all the other coefficients a_j are zero. This proves one direction of the theorem. For the other, suppose that a linear combination $a_1\mathbf{v}_1 + \cdots + a_n\mathbf{v}_n$ $(a_1, \ldots, a_n \in F)$ can be $\mathbf{0}$ only if $a_1 = \cdots = a_n = 0$. Then $\mathbf{v}_1$ is not a linear combination of $\mathbf{v}_2, \ldots, \mathbf{v}_n$. Otherwise, we could express it as $\mathbf{v}_1 = a_2\mathbf{v}_2 + \cdots + a_n\mathbf{v}_n$, so that $(-1)\mathbf{v}_1 + a_2\mathbf{v}_2 + \cdots + a_n\mathbf{v}_n = \mathbf{0}$, contrary to our supposition. By a similar argument, no $\mathbf{v}_j$ is a linear combination of the others. Since the $\mathbf{v}$'s are nonzero (explain), it follows that $\mathbf{v}_1, \ldots, \mathbf{v}_n$ is an independent set of vectors. ∎

A linear combination, some of whose coefficients are nonzero, is called a **nontrivial** linear combination. So, we can say that a set of vectors is linearly independent if and only if no nontrivial linear combination of them is $\mathbf{0}$. For instance, the vectors

$$\begin{bmatrix} 1 \\ 3 \\ 5 \end{bmatrix}, \quad \begin{bmatrix} 4 \\ 5 \\ 6 \end{bmatrix}, \quad \begin{bmatrix} 3 \\ 6 \\ 9 \end{bmatrix}$$

are linearly dependent because the nontrivial linear combination

$$\begin{bmatrix} 1 \\ 3 \\ 5 \end{bmatrix} - \begin{bmatrix} 4 \\ 5 \\ 6 \end{bmatrix} + \begin{bmatrix} 3 \\ 2 \\ 1 \end{bmatrix}$$

is $\mathbf{0}$ (Figure 4.9).

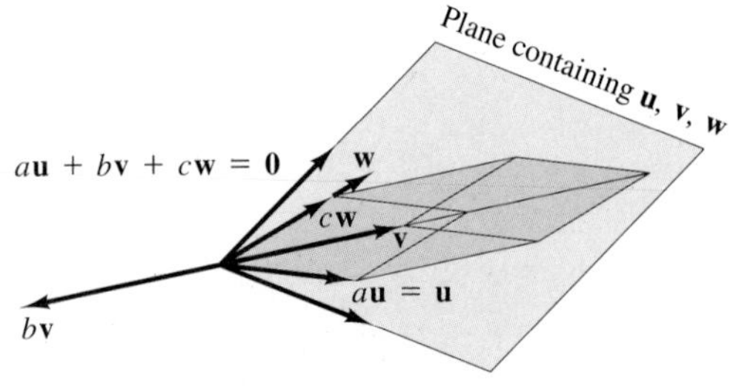

Figure 4.9 A nontrivial linear combination $a\mathbf{u} + b\mathbf{v} + c\mathbf{w} = \mathbf{0}$ exists only when $\mathbf{u}, \mathbf{v}, \mathbf{w}$ lie in some plane.

EXAMPLES

1. Any set of vectors containing $\mathbf{0}$ is linearly dependent. (Verify!)

2. The set $\mathbf{e}_1, \ldots, \mathbf{e}_n$ of standard unit vectors in F^n is linearly independent, since $a_1\mathbf{e}_1 + \cdots + a_n\mathbf{e}_n = 0$ implies that

$$\begin{bmatrix} a_1 \\ \vdots \\ a_m \end{bmatrix} = \mathbf{0}.$$

3. The columns of an $m \times n$ reduced echelon matrix are linearly independent if and only if the rank is n. The reason for this is that

a. The pivot columns are linearly independent since they are standard unit vectors;

b. The other columns are in the span of the pivot columns, so there is no other column if and only if the columns are linearly independent. (Explain!)

4. If matrices A and B are row equivalent, then the columns of A are linearly independent if and only if the columns of B are linearly independent. (Prove!)

5. The columns of an $m \times n$ matrix A are linearly independent if and only if the rank of A equals n. The reason for this is that the columns of A are linearly independent if and only if those of the row equivalent reduced echelon matrix A' are linearly independent, by (4), and we have already proved this for A' in (3).

6. The columns of

$$\begin{bmatrix} 1 & 3 & 5 & 7 \\ 1 & 2 & 3 & 4 \\ 7 & 5 & 3 & 1 \end{bmatrix}$$

are linearly dependent by (5), since its rank is less than 4.

Preservation of linear independence

In the last section we used the following elementary operations on sets of vectors to change vectors without changing their span.

1. Add a times the jth vector to the ith vector, where $i \neq j$.
2. Multiply the jth vector by a nonzero scalar a.
3. Interchange vectors i and j, where $i \neq j$.

When it is unclear whether a set of vectors is linearly independent, we can change to another set without disturbing the independence or dependence.

Theorem 4.9. *Preservation of Independence under Elementary Operations.* The linear independence or dependence of a set of vectors $\{\mathbf{v}_1, \ldots, \mathbf{v}_n\}$ is not disturbed if we apply any of the elementary operations on sets of vectors to it.

Proof. If the set is changed by an operation of type (2) or (3), it is obvious that the linear independence or dependence does not change. Now consider the set $\{\mathbf{v}_1 + a\mathbf{v}_j, \ldots, \mathbf{v}_n\}$, where $j > 1$. If $\{\mathbf{v}_1, \ldots, \mathbf{v}_n\}$ is linearly independent and $a_1(\mathbf{v}_1 + a\mathbf{v}_j) + \cdots + a_n\mathbf{v}_n = \mathbf{0}$, then $a_i = 0$ for $i \neq j$ and $a_1 a + a_j = 0$. Since $a_1 = 0$, this implies that $a_j = 0$ as well. A similar argument works for a_i instead of a_1. This proves one direction of the theorem. For the other direction, suppose that $\{\mathbf{v}_1 + a\mathbf{v}_j, \ldots, \mathbf{v}_n\}$ is linearly independent, where $j > 1$. Adding $-a$ times $\mathbf{v}_j$ to $\mathbf{v}_1 + a\mathbf{v}_j$, we know from the part of the theorem already proved that the resulting set, which is $\{\mathbf{v}_1, \ldots, \mathbf{v}_n\}$, is linearly independent. Again, a similar argument works for $\mathbf{v}_i$ instead of $\mathbf{v}_1$. This proves the other direction. ■

We use $\rightarrow$, $\rightarrow\rightarrow$, etc. to denote transition from a set to another by one or more elementary operations.

EXAMPLES

1. If matrices A and B are column equivalent, then the columns of A are linearly independent if and only if the columns of B are linearly independent.
2. Suppose that $\mathbf{u}$, $\mathbf{v}$, and $\mathbf{w}$ are linearly independent and let $\mathbf{x} = 2\mathbf{v} + \mathbf{w} - \mathbf{u}$, $\mathbf{y} = \mathbf{v} + \mathbf{w} - \mathbf{u}$, and $\mathbf{z} = \mathbf{v} - \mathbf{u}$. Using seven elementary operations, we get

$$\begin{aligned}\{\mathbf{x}, \mathbf{y}, \mathbf{z}\} &= \{2\mathbf{v} + \mathbf{w} - \mathbf{u}, \mathbf{v} + \mathbf{w} - \mathbf{u}, \mathbf{v} - \mathbf{w}\} \rightarrow \{\mathbf{v}, \mathbf{v} + \mathbf{w} - \mathbf{u}, \mathbf{v} - \mathbf{w}\} \\ &\rightarrow\rightarrow \{\mathbf{v}, \mathbf{w} - \mathbf{u}, -\mathbf{w}\} \rightarrow \{\mathbf{v}, -\mathbf{u}, -\mathbf{w}\} \rightarrow\rightarrow\rightarrow \{\mathbf{u}, \mathbf{v}, \mathbf{w}\}.\end{aligned}$$

The resulting set is linearly independent, so $\{\mathbf{x}, \mathbf{y}, \mathbf{z}\}$ is too.

Criteria for an isomorphism

The concept of linear independence enables us to express when a subspace $F\mathbf{v}_1 + \cdots + F\mathbf{v}_n$ is isomorphic to F^n.

Theorem 4.10. *Isomorphisms from F^n to a Vector Space.* Let $V = F\mathbf{v}_1 + \cdots + F\mathbf{v}_n$ be a subspace of a vector space U. Consider the linear transformation

$$R\begin{bmatrix} a_1 \\ \vdots \\ a_n \end{bmatrix} = a_1\mathbf{v}_1 + \cdots + a_n\mathbf{v}_n$$

from F^n to V. Then R is an isomorphism if and only if the vectors $\mathbf{v}_1, \ldots, \mathbf{v}_n$ are linearly independent.

Proof. Since R is onto, its suffices to show that R is 1-1 if and only if $\mathbf{v}_1, \ldots, \mathbf{v}_n$ are linearly independent. Suppose first that $\mathbf{v}_1, \ldots, \mathbf{v}_n$ are linearly independent. By Theorem 4.5, to show that R is 1-1, it suffices to show that Kernel $R = \{\mathbf{0}\}$. So, we let $a_1\mathbf{e}_1 + \cdots + a_n\mathbf{e}_n$ be in the kernel of R. Then $\mathbf{0} = R(a_1\mathbf{e}_1 + \cdots + a_n\mathbf{e}_n) = a_1\mathbf{v}_1 + \cdots + a_n\mathbf{v}_n$. So, since $\mathbf{v}_1, \ldots, \mathbf{v}_n$ are linearly independent, the a_j are 0. But then $a_1\mathbf{e}_1 + \cdots + a_n\mathbf{e}_n = \mathbf{0}$, so the kernel of R is $\{\mathbf{0}\}$. This proves one direction. For the converse, assume that R is 1-1. If a linear combination $a_1\mathbf{v}_1 + \cdots + a_n\mathbf{v}_n$ is $\mathbf{0}$, then we have $\mathbf{0} = a_1\mathbf{v}_1 + \cdots + a_n\mathbf{v}_n = R(a_1\mathbf{e}_1 + \cdots + a_n\mathbf{e}_n)$ and $a_1\mathbf{e}_1 + \cdots + a_n\mathbf{e}_n$ is in the kernel of R. Since R is 1-1, its kernel is $\{\mathbf{0}\}$. So, we have $a_1\mathbf{e}_1 + \cdots + a_n\mathbf{e}_n = \mathbf{0}$ and the a_j are all 0. This shows that the $\mathbf{v}_1, \ldots, \mathbf{v}_n$ are linearly independent. ∎

EXAMPLE

Suppose that $\mathbf{u}$, $\mathbf{v}$, and $\mathbf{w}$ are linearly independent elements of a vector space V over F. Then there is an isomorphism

$$R\begin{bmatrix} a \\ b \\ c \end{bmatrix} = a\mathbf{u} + b\mathbf{v} + c\mathbf{w}$$

from F^3 to $F\mathbf{u} + F\mathbf{v} + F\mathbf{w}$. Since $\{\mathbf{x}, \mathbf{y}, \mathbf{z}\} = \{2\mathbf{v} + \mathbf{w} - \mathbf{u}, \mathbf{v} + \mathbf{w} - \mathbf{u}, \mathbf{v} - \mathbf{w}\}$ is also a linearly independent set, there is also an isomorphism

$$S\begin{bmatrix} a \\ b \\ c \end{bmatrix} = a\mathbf{x} + b\mathbf{y} + c\mathbf{z}$$

from F^3 to $F\mathbf{x} + F\mathbf{y} + F\mathbf{z}$. But then there is an isomorphism SR^{-1} from $F\mathbf{u} + F\mathbf{v} + F\mathbf{w}$ to $F\mathbf{x} + F\mathbf{y} + F\mathbf{z}$ mapping $\mathbf{u}$ to $\mathbf{x}$, $\mathbf{v}$ to $\mathbf{y}$, and $\mathbf{w}$ to $\mathbf{z}$. (Note, by the way, that $F\mathbf{u} + F\mathbf{v} + F\mathbf{w} = F\mathbf{x} + F\mathbf{y} + F\mathbf{z}$.)

A useful and instructive consequence of this theorem is the following.

Corollary. Suppose that $\mathbf{v}_1, \ldots, \mathbf{v}_n$ are linearly independent elements of a vector space U over F. Then $a_1\mathbf{v}_1 + \cdots + a_n\mathbf{v}_n = b_1\mathbf{v}_1 + \cdots + b_n\mathbf{v}_n$ (where the a's and b's come from F) only if $a_1 = b_1, \ldots, a_n = b_n$.

Proof. The linear transformation

$$R\begin{bmatrix} a_1 \\ \vdots \\ a_n \end{bmatrix} = a_1\mathbf{v}_1 + \cdots + a_n\mathbf{v}_n$$

from F^n to $F\mathbf{v}_1 + \cdots + F\mathbf{v}_n$ is an isomorphism, since the vectors $\mathbf{v}_1, \ldots, \mathbf{v}_n$ are linearly independent. Since

$$a_1\mathbf{v}_1 + \cdots + a_n\mathbf{v}_n = b_1\mathbf{v}_1 + \cdots + b_n\mathbf{v}_n$$

translates to

$$R\begin{bmatrix} a_1 \\ \vdots \\ a_n \end{bmatrix} = R\begin{bmatrix} b_1 \\ \vdots \\ b_n \end{bmatrix}$$

and R is 1-1, it follows that

$$\begin{bmatrix} a_1 \\ \vdots \\ a_n \end{bmatrix} = \begin{bmatrix} b_1 \\ \vdots \\ b_n \end{bmatrix}.$$

So, $a_j = b_j$ for all j. ■

Basis of a vector space

When F^n and $V = F\mathbf{v}_1 + \cdots + F\mathbf{v}_n$ are isomorphic by an isomorphism $R(a_1\mathbf{e}_1 + \cdots + a_n\mathbf{e}_n) = a_1\mathbf{v}_1 + \cdots + a_n\mathbf{v}_n$, R can be used to translate problems about V into problems about F^n. So, we give a special name to the set of vectors $\mathbf{v}_1, \ldots, \mathbf{v}_n$.

Definition. *Basis for a Vector Space.*
Let V be a vector space over F. Then a **basis** for V is a set of linearly independent vectors $\mathbf{v}_1, \ldots, \mathbf{v}_n$ such that $V = F\mathbf{v}_1 + \cdots + F\mathbf{v}_n$. For $\mathbf{v} = a_1\mathbf{v}_1 + \cdots + a_n\mathbf{v}_n$, a_r is the rth *coordinate of* $\mathbf{v}$ *with respect to the basis* $\mathbf{v}_1, \ldots, \mathbf{v}_n$.

In terms of bases, Theorem 4.10 becomes the following (see Figure 4.10).

Theorem 4.11. *Isomorphism Condition for a Basis of a Vector Space.*
For any vector space V, $\mathbf{v}_1, \ldots, \mathbf{v}_n$ is a basis for V if and only if the linear transformation $R(a_1\mathbf{e}_1 + \cdots + a_n\mathbf{e}_n) = a_1\mathbf{v}_1 + \cdots + a_n\mathbf{v}_n$ is an isomorphism from F^n to V.

EXAMPLES

1. The set of standard unit vectors $\mathbf{e}_j$ of F^n is a basis for F^n. (Prove!)
2. The set of standard unit matrices E_{ij} of $M_{m \times n}F$ is a basis for $M_{m \times n}F$. (Prove!) Recall, here, that E_{ij} is the matrix with (i, j)-entry 1 and all other entries 0.
3. The set of columns of an $n \times n$ matrix A over F is a basis for F^n if and only if A is invertible. (Prove this by taking $V = F^n$ in the theorem and considering the linear transformation $R(\mathbf{x}) = A\mathbf{x}$.)
4. If R is an isomorphism from F^n to a vector space V over F, then every basis of V can be expressed as the set of images under R of the columns of an invertible $n \times n$ matrix over F. (Prove!)

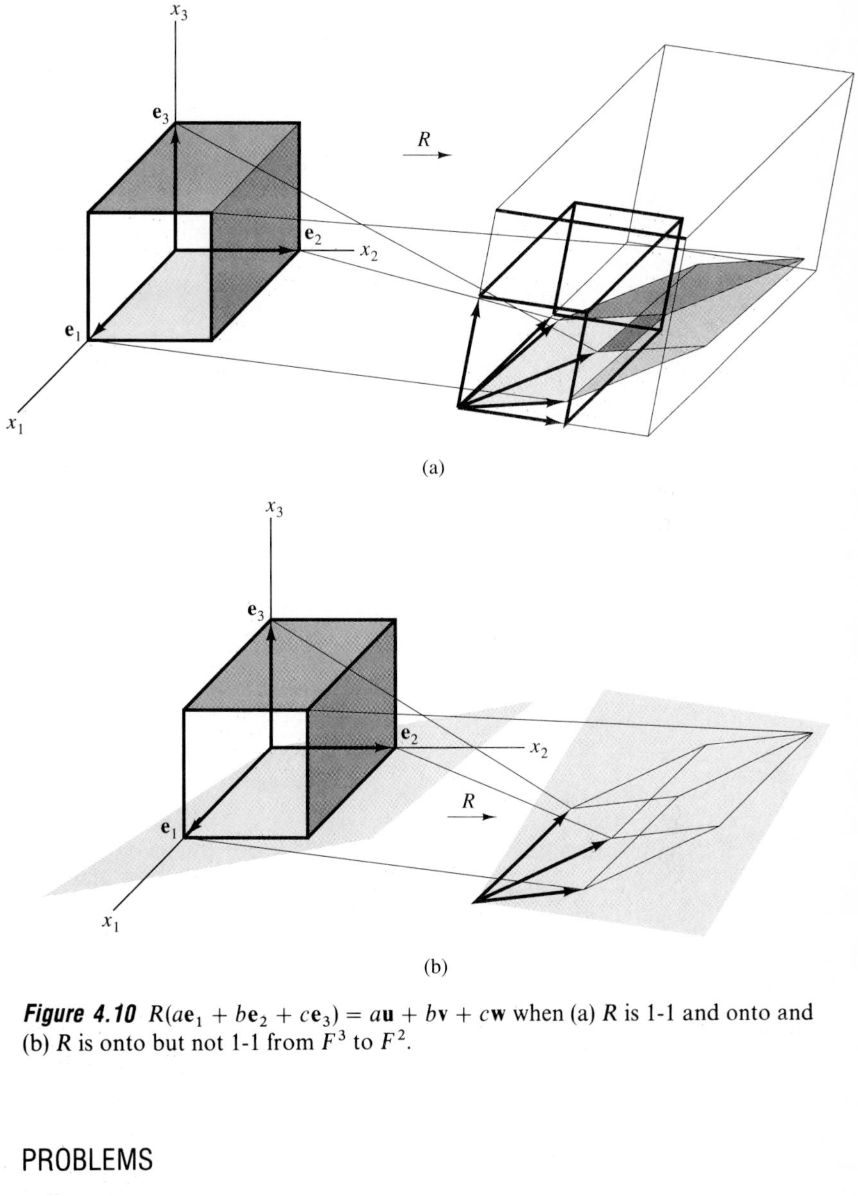

Figure 4.10 $R(a\mathbf{e}_1 + b\mathbf{e}_2 + c\mathbf{e}_3) = a\mathbf{u} + b\mathbf{v} + c\mathbf{w}$ when (a) R is 1-1 and onto and (b) R is onto but not 1-1 from F^3 to F^2.

PROBLEMS

NUMERICAL PROBLEMS

1. For each of the following sets of vectors, determine whether the first vector is linearly dependent on the remaining vectors.

(a) $\begin{bmatrix} 1 \\ 3 \\ 5 \end{bmatrix}, \begin{bmatrix} 1 \\ 4 \\ 5 \end{bmatrix}, \begin{bmatrix} 1 \\ 5 \\ 5 \end{bmatrix}$ **(b)** $\begin{bmatrix} 1 \\ 3 \\ 5 \end{bmatrix}, \begin{bmatrix} 2 \\ 4 \\ 5 \end{bmatrix}, \begin{bmatrix} 3 \\ 5 \\ 5 \end{bmatrix}$

(c) $\begin{bmatrix}1\\3\\5\end{bmatrix}, \begin{bmatrix}2\\4\\6\end{bmatrix}, \begin{bmatrix}3\\5\\7\end{bmatrix}$ (d) $\begin{bmatrix}1\\3\\5\end{bmatrix}, \begin{bmatrix}2\\4\\6\end{bmatrix}, \begin{bmatrix}3\\5\\8\end{bmatrix}$

2. For each of the sets of vectors in Problem 1, either show that the set is linearly independent or find a nontrivial linear combination which is $\mathbf{0}$.
3. For each of the sets of vectors in Problem 1, show that the set is linearly independent exactly in those cases where the kernel of the linear transformation $R(\mathbf{x}) = A\mathbf{x}$ is $\{\mathbf{0}\}$, A being the matrix whose columns are the given vectors.
4. Determine whether the rows of the following matrices are linearly independent.

(a) $\begin{bmatrix}2 & 1 & 2\\1 & 4 & 1\\5 & 5 & 2\end{bmatrix}$ (b) $\begin{bmatrix}2 & 1 & 3\\2 & 3 & 1\\6 & 5 & 7\end{bmatrix}$ (c) $\begin{bmatrix}2 & 8 & 2\\1 & 4 & 1\\1 & 10 & 4\end{bmatrix}$

5. Determine whether the columns of the matrices in Problem 4 are linearly independent.
6. Suppose that $\mathbf{u}$, $\mathbf{v}$, and $\mathbf{w}$ are linearly independent and let $\mathbf{x} = 3\mathbf{v} + 2\mathbf{w} - 3\mathbf{u}$, $\mathbf{y} = 3\mathbf{v} + 3\mathbf{w} + \mathbf{u}$, $\mathbf{z} = \mathbf{v} - \mathbf{w}$. Using elementary operations, determine whether the set $\{\mathbf{x}, \mathbf{y}, \mathbf{z}\}$ is linearly independent.
7. Redo Problem 6 by using the isomorphism

$$R(a\mathbf{u} + b\mathbf{v} + c\mathbf{w}) = \begin{bmatrix}a\\b\\c\end{bmatrix}$$

to translate the problem to one of linear independence of columns of a matrix. Then solve that problem using elementary row and or column operations.

THEORETICAL PROBLEMS

8. Show that any set of vectors including $\mathbf{0}$ is linearly dependent.
9. For nonzero vectors $\mathbf{v}$ and $\mathbf{w}$ in a vector space V over F, show that $\mathbf{w}$ depends linearly on $\mathbf{v}$ and $\mathbf{v}$ on $\mathbf{w}$ if and only if $F\mathbf{v} = F\mathbf{w}$.
10. If $F\mathbf{v} + F\mathbf{w}$ is a plane in F^3, show that $\mathbf{v}$ does not depend linearly on $\mathbf{w}$ and $\mathbf{w}$ does not depend linearly on $\mathbf{v}$.
11. In F^3, show that $\mathbf{e}_1$ does not depend linearly on $\mathbf{e}_2$ and $\mathbf{e}_3$, $\mathbf{e}_2$ does not depend linearly on $\mathbf{e}_1$ and $\mathbf{e}_3$, and $\mathbf{e}_3$ does not depend linearly on $\mathbf{e}_1$ and $\mathbf{e}_2$.
12. In F^n and for $1 \le j \le n$, show that $\mathbf{e}_j$ does not depend linearly on $\mathbf{e}_1, \ldots, \mathbf{e}_{j-1}, \mathbf{e}_{j+1}, \ldots, \mathbf{e}_n$.
13. If matrices A and B are row equivalent, show that the columns of A are linearly independent if and only if the columns of B are linearly independent.
14. Show that the set of standard unit vectors e_j of F^n is a basis for F^n.

15. Show that the set of standard unit matrices E_{ij} of $M_{m\times n}F$ is a basis for $M_{m\times n}F$.

Hard

16. If $\mathbf{v}_1, \ldots, \mathbf{v}_n$ is a basis for a vector space V and $\mathbf{w}_1, \ldots, \mathbf{w}_n$ are elements of a vector space W over the same field, show that there is one and only one linear transformation R from V to W which maps $\mathbf{v}_j$ to $\mathbf{w}_j$ for all j.

17. In Problem 16, show that R is an isomorphism if and only if $\mathbf{w}_1, \ldots, \mathbf{w}_n$ is a basis for W.

18. Letting $\mathbf{w}_1, \ldots, \mathbf{w}_n$ be linearly independent elements of F^m, show that the linear transformation $T(\mathbf{x}) = [\mathbf{w}_1 \ \ldots \ \mathbf{w}_n]\mathbf{x}$ from F^n to F^m is 1-1.

19. For any matrix A, show that the columns of A are linearly independent if and only if the kernel of the linear transformation $R(\mathbf{x}) = A\mathbf{x}$ is $\{\mathbf{0}\}$, A being the matrix whose columns are the given vectors.

20. Show that the set of columns of an $n \times n$ matrix A over F is a basis for F^n if and only if A is invertible. (***Hint:*** Prove this by considering the linear transformation $R(\mathbf{x}) = A\mathbf{x}$.)

21. For a square matrix A, show that its rows are linearly independent if and only if its columns are linearly independent.

22. If the sums of the entries of each column of a square matrix A are all 0, show that the columns of A are linearly dependent.

23. If the sums of the entries of each column of a square matrix A are all equal to d, show that $A\mathbf{v} = d\mathbf{v}$ for some nonzero vector $\mathbf{v}$.

24. If R is an isomorphism from F^n to a vector space V over F, show that every basis of V can be expressed as the set of images under R of the columns of an invertible $n \times n$ matrix over F.

25. Give an argument showing that applying an elementary operation to vectors $\mathbf{u}$, $\mathbf{v}$, and $\mathbf{w}$ not in any plane through $\mathbf{0}$ results in vectors $\mathbf{u}'$, $\mathbf{v}'$, and $\mathbf{w}'$ not in any plane through $\mathbf{0}$.

26. Following Figure 4.6(a), draw a figure illustrating the LDU factorization $A = LDU$ of $A = \begin{bmatrix} a & b \\ b & c \end{bmatrix}$ $(a \neq 0)$ by finding a shear $V = \begin{bmatrix} 1 & e \\ 0 & 1 \end{bmatrix}$ such that $AV = LD$ and setting $U = \begin{bmatrix} 1 & -e \\ 0 & 1 \end{bmatrix}$.

4.5 DIMENSION OF A VECTOR SPACE

The time has come to unveil a principal new actor in the subject of linear algebra, the concept of *dimension*. Informally, we say that F^n has dimension n since the general element

$$\begin{bmatrix} a_1 \\ \vdots \\ a_n \end{bmatrix} \in F^n$$

can be selected with n degrees of freedom, one for each coordinate. If a vector space V is isomorphic to F^n, we will define its dimensions to be n. First, however, we rule out the possibility of ambiguity arising from the existence of another isomorphism from V to F^m with m different from n.

Theorem 4.12. *Uniqueness of n such that a Given V Is Isomorphic to F^n.* If a vector space V is isomorphic to F^m and F^n, then $m = n$.

Proof. Let R be an isomorphism from V to F^m and S an isomorphism from V to F^n. Then $T = RS^{-1}$ is an isomorphism from F^n to F^m. But then $m = n$ by the corollary to Theorem 3.4. ■

This having been done, we formally define dimension.

Definition. *Dimension of a Vector Space.* If a vector space V over F is isomorphic to F^n, we say that its **dimension** is n and denote it Dim $V = n$. A vector space over F is **finite-dimensional** if it is of dimension n for some positive integer n.

From this follow many facts.

1. F^n is n-dimensional.
2. A vector space V has a basis of n elements if and only if it is of dimension n.
3. Given a basis $\mathbf{v}_1, \ldots, \mathbf{v}_n$ for V, the isomorphism $R(a_1\mathbf{v}_1 + \cdots + a_n\mathbf{v}_n) = a_1\mathbf{e}_1 + \cdots + a_n\mathbf{e}_n$ from V to F^n is called the **coordinate isomorphism** corresponding to the basis $\mathbf{v}_1, \ldots, \mathbf{v}_n$, and $R(\mathbf{v})$ is called the **vector of coordinates** of $\mathbf{v}$ for $\mathbf{v} \in V$.
4. Any isomorphism from V to F^n is the coordinate isomorphism corresponding to some basis for V, namely, the basis
$$\mathbf{v}_1 = R^{-1}(\mathbf{e}_1), \ldots, \mathbf{v}_n = R^{-1}(\mathbf{e}_n).$$
5. $F[z]$ is of dimension $n + 1$, since $1, z, \ldots, z^{n+1}$ is a basis.
6. $M_{m \times n}F$ is of dimension mn, since the set of unit matrices E_{ij} is a basis for $M_{m \times n}F$.
7. A basis for the column space $c(A)$ of a matrix A is the set of pivot columns of A (Theorem 3.27). So, its dimension is the rank of A.
8. Since the ranks of A and A^T are the same, by the corollary to Theorem 3.27, the dimension of the row space $r(A)$ of a matrix A is the rank of A.
9. Functions(X, F) is n-dimensional, where n is the number of elements of X. If X is infinite, Functions(X, F) is **infinite-dimensional** (not finite-dimensional). (Verify!)

EXAMPLE

$\mathbb{R}[z]_3$ has basis $1, z, z^2, z^3$, Functions($\{1, 2, 3, 4\}, \mathbb{R}$) has dimension 4, and both are isomorphic to $\mathbb{R}^4$. (Verify!) For any basis f_1, f_2, f_3, f_4 of Functions($\{1, 2, 3, 4\}, \mathbb{R}$), there is an isomorphism from $\mathbb{R}[z]_3$ to Functions($\{1, 2, 3, 4\}, \mathbb{R}$) which maps 1 to f_1, z to f_2, z^2 to f_3, and z^3 to f_4. (Explain!)

We state (2) as a corollary for future reference.

Corollary. Any basis of an n-dimensional vector space has n elements.

The bases of F^n

Since each basis of an n-dimensional vector space has n elements, we can easily determine the bases of F^n.

Theorem 4.13. *The Bases of F^n as the Invertible $n \times n$ Matrices.* A set of vectors is a basis of F^n if and only if it is the set of column vectors of an invertible $n \times n$ matrix.

Proof. By the corollary to Theorem 4.12, a basis for F^n is a set $\mathbf{v}_1, \ldots, \mathbf{v}_n$ of n linearly independent elements of F^n which span F^n. By Theorem 4.11, given such a set $\mathbf{v}_1, \ldots, \mathbf{v}_n$, the linear transformation

$$R\begin{bmatrix} a_1 \\ \vdots \\ a_n \end{bmatrix} = a_1\mathbf{v}_1 + \cdots + a_n\mathbf{v}_n$$

is an isomorphism from F^n to itself. But then the matrix $A = [\mathbf{v}_1 \ \ \ldots \ \ \mathbf{v}_n]$ of R is an invertible matrix. Conversely, if $A = [\mathbf{v}_1 \ \ \ldots \ \ \mathbf{v}_n]$ is an invertible matrix, then $\mathbf{v}_1, \ldots, \mathbf{v}_n$ span the column space of A, which is F^n, and they are linearly independent, since the nullspace of A is $\{\mathbf{0}\}$. ■

Knowing the bases for F^n, we can now describe the bases for a vector space of dimension n, as the following example shows for $n = 2$.

EXAMPLE

To determine all bases for a two-dimensional vector space V, we start with an isomorphism R from F^2 to V and let $R(\mathbf{e}_1) = \mathbf{v}_1$ and $R(\mathbf{e}_2) = \mathbf{v}_2$. For any basis $\mathbf{u}_1, \mathbf{u}_2$ for F^2, $[\mathbf{u}_1 \ \ \mathbf{u}_2]$ is an invertible matrix $\begin{bmatrix} a & b \\ c & d \end{bmatrix}$, $\mathbf{u}_1 = \begin{bmatrix} a \\ c \end{bmatrix} = a\mathbf{e}_1 + c\mathbf{e}_2$, and $\mathbf{u}_2 = \begin{bmatrix} b \\ d \end{bmatrix} = b\mathbf{e}_1 + d\mathbf{e}_2$. We can use R to transfer this basis to the basis $R(\mathbf{u}_1) = aR(\mathbf{e}_1) + cR(\mathbf{e}_2) = a\mathbf{v}_1 + c\mathbf{v}_2$, $R(\mathbf{u}_2) = bR(\mathbf{e}_1) + dR(\mathbf{e}_2) = b\mathbf{v}_1 + d\mathbf{v}_2$ for V. It follows that the bases

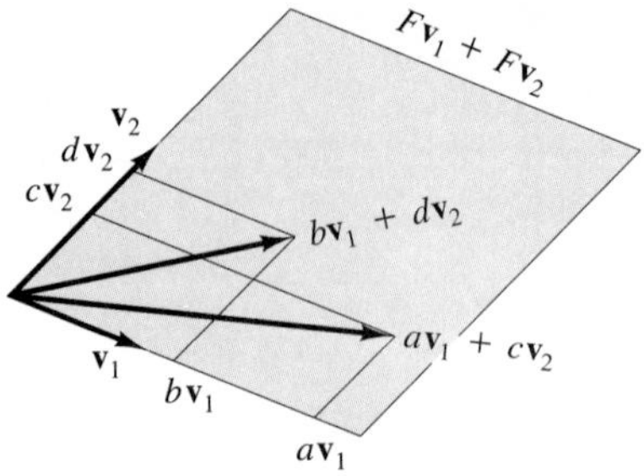

Figure 4.11 A basis for a two-dimensional vector space $F\mathbf{v}_1 + F\mathbf{v}_2$ is a pair $a\mathbf{v}_1 + c\mathbf{v}_2, b\mathbf{v}_1 + d\mathbf{v}_2$ of two nonparallel nonzero vectors.

for V are the $a\mathbf{v}_1 + c\mathbf{v}_2$, $b\mathbf{v}_1 + d\mathbf{v}_2$, where $\begin{bmatrix} a & b \\ c & d \end{bmatrix}$ is an invertible matrix. These are just the sets of two nonparallel vectors. (Explain!) See Figure 4.11.

The dimension of a subspace

It is important to know how a linearly independent set of vectors of an n-dimensional vector space V relates to V. The following theorem clarifies this relationship and also determines how the dimension of a subspace of V relates to that of V itself.

Theorem 4.14. *Subspaces of an n-Dimensional Vector Space.*
Let V be an n-dimensional vector space over F.

1. If $\mathbf{w}_1, \ldots, \mathbf{w}_m$ is a linearly independent set of elements of V, then $m \leq n$.
2. If W is a subspace of V and $\mathbf{w}_1, \ldots, \mathbf{w}_r$ is a linearly independent set in W, then W is of dimension m for some m with $n \geq m \geq r$ and W has a basis $\mathbf{w}_1, \ldots, \mathbf{w}_m$ extending the given linearly independent set.
3. If W is a subspace of V of dimension n, then $W = V$.

Proof. We first prove (1). For this, let $\mathbf{v}_1, \ldots, \mathbf{v}_n$ be a basis for V and let $R(a_1\mathbf{v}_1 + \cdots + a_n\mathbf{v}_n) = a_1\mathbf{e}_1 + \cdots + a_n\mathbf{e}_n$ be the corresponding isomorphism from V to F^n. Letting $\mathbf{w}_1, \ldots, \mathbf{w}_m$ be linearly independent elements of V, the corresponding elements $R(\mathbf{w}_1), \ldots, R(\mathbf{w}_m)$ of F^n are linearly independent, and the linear transformation

$$T(\mathbf{x}) = [R(\mathbf{w}_1) \quad \ldots \quad R(\mathbf{w}_m)]\mathbf{x}$$

from F^m to F^n is 1-1. (Prove!) By Theorem 3.4, it follows that $m \leq n$. This proves (1).

For (2), take a linear independent set $\mathbf{w}_1, \ldots, \mathbf{w}_r, \mathbf{w}_{r+1}, \ldots, \mathbf{w}_m$ of elements of W. Then $m \leq n$ by (1). Continuing, taking m as great as possible, we still have $m \leq n$, for the same reason. If $\mathbf{w} \in V$ and $\mathbf{w}$ is not a linear combination of $\mathbf{w}_1, \ldots, \mathbf{w}_m$, then $\mathbf{w}_1, \ldots, \mathbf{w}_m, \mathbf{w}$ is linearly independent. Otherwise, we would have a nontrivial linear combination

$$a_1\mathbf{w}_1 + \cdots + a_m\mathbf{w}_m + a\mathbf{w} = 0,$$

where a is 0 (since $\mathbf{w}$ is not a linear combination of the $\mathbf{w}_s$), which contradicts the linear independence of the $\mathbf{w}_s$. But then $\mathbf{w}$ is not in W, since we cannot further increase the size of our linearly independent set of m elements of W. It follows that each element of W is a linear combination of $\mathbf{w}_1, \ldots, \mathbf{w}_m$, so that $\mathbf{w}_1, \ldots, \mathbf{w}_m$ is a basis for W. So, the dimension of W *is* m.

For (3), let $\mathbf{w}_1, \ldots, \mathbf{w}_n$ be a basis for W. If it is not also a basis for V, then we can find some $\mathbf{w} \in V$ which is not a linear combination of it, as in the proof of (2). But then $\mathbf{w}_1, \ldots, \mathbf{w}_m, \mathbf{w}$ is linearly independent. From this, it follows by (1) that $n + 1 \leq n$, which is not possible. So, we can find no such $\mathbf{w}$. But then $\mathbf{w}_1, \ldots, \mathbf{w}_n$ is a basis for V, so that $V = W$. ■

EXAMPLE

Let V be a three-dimensional subspace. Then the dimensions of the nonzero subspaces of V can only be 3, 2 and 1. So, the nonzero subspaces of V are V, $F\mathbf{v} + F\mathbf{w}$, where neither $\mathbf{v}$ nor $\mathbf{w}$ is a multiple of the other, and $F\mathbf{v}$, where $\mathbf{v}$ is nonzero.

Corollary. If V is an n-dimensional vector space over F and $\mathbf{v}_1, \ldots, \mathbf{v}_r$ is a linearly independent set in V, then $r \leq n$ and it can be extended to a basis $\mathbf{v}_1, \ldots, \mathbf{v}_n$ of V.

Proof. Take $W = V$ and $\{\mathbf{w}_1, \ldots, \mathbf{w}_r\} = \{\mathbf{v}_1, \ldots, \mathbf{v}_r\}$ in the preceding theorem. ■

EXAMPLE

$$\mathbf{v}_1 = \begin{bmatrix} 1 \\ 2 \\ 3 \end{bmatrix}, \qquad \mathbf{v}_2 = \begin{bmatrix} 1 \\ 3 \\ 3 \end{bmatrix}$$

is a linearly independent set in F^3. At least one of $\mathbf{e}_1, \mathbf{e}_2, \mathbf{e}_3$ is not in $F\mathbf{v}_1 + F\mathbf{v}_2$. (In fact, none of them is.) In particular, $\mathbf{e}_1$ is not, so we can take $\mathbf{v}_3 = \mathbf{e}_1$. Then $\mathbf{v}_1, \mathbf{v}_2, \mathbf{v}_3$ is a basis for F^3. (Verify!)

The dimensions of the kernel and image of a linear transformation

We showed that the nullity plus rank of an $m \times n$ matrix A is n. So, Dim Kernel T + Dim Image $T = n$ for the linear transformation $T(\mathbf{x}) = A\mathbf{x}$ from F^n to F^m. We now give the dimension formula in general.

Theorem 4.15. *Sum of Kernel and Image Dimensions.*
Let T be a linear transformation from a finite-dimensional vector space V to a vector space W. Then

$$\text{Dim Kernel } T + \text{Dim Image } T = \text{Dim } V.$$

Proof. Extend a basis $\mathbf{v}_1, \ldots, \mathbf{v}_s$ for Kernel T to a basis

$$\mathbf{v}_1, \ldots, \mathbf{v}_s, \mathbf{v}_{s+1}, \ldots, \mathbf{v}_{s+r}$$

for V. Then Image T is spanned by $T(\mathbf{v}_{s+1}), \ldots, T(\mathbf{v}_{s+r})$, since the $\mathbf{v}$'s in the kernel get mapped to $\mathbf{0}$ by T. If $c_{s+1}T(\mathbf{v}_{s+1}) + \cdots + c_{s+r}T(\mathbf{v}_{s+r}) = \mathbf{0}$, then $T(c_{s+1}\mathbf{v}_{s+1} + \cdots + c_{s+r}\mathbf{v}_{s+r}) = \mathbf{0}$ and $c_{s+1}\mathbf{v}_{s+1} + \cdots + c_{s+r}\mathbf{v}_{s+r}$ is in Kernel T. But then $c_{s+1} = \cdots = c_{s+r} = \mathbf{0}$. This establishes that the vectors $T(\mathbf{v}_{s+1}), \ldots, T(\mathbf{v}_{s+r})$ are linearly independent and so form a basis for Image T. But then Dim $V = s + r =$ Dim Kernel T + Dim Image T. ■

EXAMPLES

1. Let T be the linear transformation $T(f(z)) = f'(z)$ (differentiation with respect to z) of $\mathbb{R}[z]_n$ (vector space of real polynomials of degree at most n). Then the kernel of T is one-dimensional and $\mathbb{R}[z]_n$ is $(n + 1)$-dimensional. (Verify!) So, our dimension formula is $1 +$ Dim Image $T = n + 1$. This jibes with the fact that the image of T is the set of polynomials of degree at most $n - 1$, which is n-dimensional. (Verify!)

2. Let S be the linear transformation $S(f(z)) = f(0)$ (evaluation at 0) of $\mathbb{R}[z]_n$. The image of S is one-dimensional and $\mathbb{R}[z]_n$ is $(n + 1)$-dimensional. So, our dimension formula is Dim Kernel $S + 1 = n + 1$. Thus, Kernel S is n-dimensional. (Find a basis for Kernel S.)

The dimension of the intersection of two subspaces

An important example of how the dimension formula for the kernel and image is used is the following formula.

Theorem 4.16. *Dimension Formula for the Sum and Intersection of Two Subspaces.*
Let U and V be finite-dimensional subspaces of a vector space W over F. Then Dim $(U + V) =$ Dim U + Dim V − Dim $(U \cap V)$.

Proof. Let $\mathbf{u}_1, \ldots, \mathbf{u}_r$ and $\mathbf{v}_1, \ldots, \mathbf{v}_s$ be bases for U and V, and let T be the linear transformation

$$T(\mathbf{x}) = x_1\mathbf{u}_1 + \cdots + x_r\mathbf{u}_r + x_{r+1}\mathbf{v}_1 + \cdots + x_s\mathbf{v}_s$$

from F^{r+s} to W. Then Kernel $T = U \cap V$ and Image $T = U + V$. (Explain!) So, we have

$$\text{Dim } U + \text{Dim } V = \text{Dim } F^{r+s} = \text{Dim Kernel } T + \text{Dim Image } T,$$

$$\text{Dim } U + \text{Dim } V = \text{Dim } (U \cap V) + \text{Dim } (U + V). \qquad \blacksquare$$

EXAMPLES

1. In the two preceding examples, Kernel S and Image T are two *different* n-dimensional subspaces of an $(n + 1)$-dimensional space. So, their sum is $(n + 1)$-dimensional, and the dimension d of their intersection satisfies the dimension formula $n + n - d = n + 1$—that is, $d = n - 1$. This agrees with the fact that the intersection is the set of real polynomials of degree n and constant term 0. (Verify!)

2. To show in F^n that the dimension of the intersection of a subspace V and a hyperplane W through $\mathbf{0}$ not containing it is Dim $V - 1$, note that $V + W = F^n$, so that $n = \text{Dim } V + \text{Dim } W - \text{Dim } V \cap W$; that is, $n = \text{Dim } V + n - 1 - \text{Dim } V \cap W$ and $\text{Dim } V \cap W = \text{Dim } V - 1$. An intersection $V \cap W$ is called a **cross section** of V by the hyperplane W. Of course, it contains the cross sections of any objects in V (Figure 4.12).

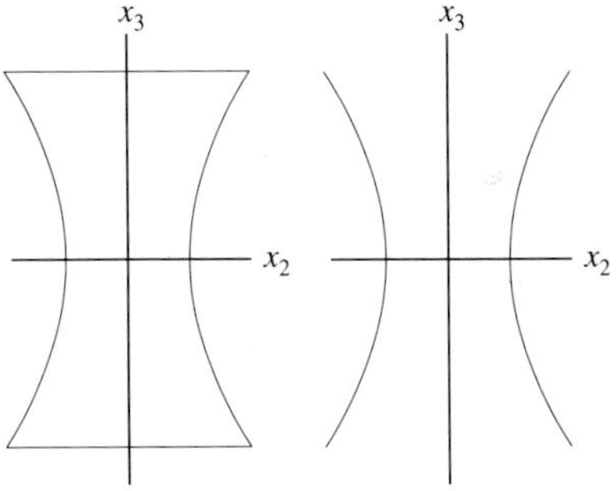

Figure 4.12 Cross section of the hyperboloid and the plane $x_1 = 0$.

PROBLEMS

NUMERICAL PROBLEMS

1. Find the dimensions of the spans of the following sets of vectors, which you analyzed for linear independence in the last section.

(a) $\begin{bmatrix}1\\3\\5\end{bmatrix}, \begin{bmatrix}1\\4\\5\end{bmatrix}, \begin{bmatrix}1\\5\\5\end{bmatrix}$ **(b)** $\begin{bmatrix}1\\3\\5\end{bmatrix}, \begin{bmatrix}2\\4\\5\end{bmatrix}, \begin{bmatrix}3\\5\\5\end{bmatrix}$

(c) $\begin{bmatrix}1\\3\\5\end{bmatrix}, \begin{bmatrix}2\\4\\6\end{bmatrix}, \begin{bmatrix}3\\5\\7\end{bmatrix}$ **(d)** $\begin{bmatrix}1\\3\\5\end{bmatrix}, \begin{bmatrix}2\\4\\6\end{bmatrix}, \begin{bmatrix}3\\5\\8\end{bmatrix}$

2. Determine the dimensions of the columns spaces of the following matrices, which you analyzed for row and column independence in the last section.

(a) $\begin{bmatrix}2 & 1 & 2\\1 & 4 & 1\\5 & 5 & 2\end{bmatrix}$ **(b)** $\begin{bmatrix}2 & 1 & 3\\2 & 3 & 1\\6 & 5 & 7\end{bmatrix}$ **(c)** $\begin{bmatrix}2 & 8 & 2\\1 & 4 & 1\\1 & 10 & 4\end{bmatrix}$

3. Find the dimension of the column space of the $n \times n$ matrix $A = [\mathbf{e}_2 \;\; \dots \;\; \mathbf{e}_n \;\; \mathbf{e}_1] - I$.

4. Find a basis for the column space of

$$\begin{bmatrix}2 & 8 & 2\\5 & 6 & 7\\3 & 5 & 4\\2 & 1 & 3\end{bmatrix}$$

and extend it to a basis for F^4.

5. Find the dimension of the intersection of the column spaces of the matrices

$$\begin{bmatrix}1 & 2 & 3\\2 & 3 & 4\\3 & 4 & 5\end{bmatrix}, \quad \begin{bmatrix}5 & 4 & 3\\4 & 3 & 2\\3 & 2 & 1\end{bmatrix}.$$

Hard

6. Find the dimension of the column space of the $n \times n$ matrix $A = [a_1\mathbf{e}_2 \;\; \dots \;\; a_{n-1}\mathbf{e}_n \;\; a_n\mathbf{e}_1] - \text{Diag}(a_1, \dots, a_n)$ when all the a_j are nonzero.

7. Find the dimension of the column space of the $n \times n$ matrix $A = [a_1\mathbf{e}_2 \;\; \dots \;\; a_{n-1}\mathbf{e}_n \;\; a_n\mathbf{e}_1] - \text{Diag}(a_1, \dots, a_n)$ when $a_1 = 0$ and all the other a_j are nonzero.

8. Is the set of polynomials of the form $(n - j + 1)z^j + jz^{j-1}$ $(j = 0, 1, \dots, n)$ a basis for $\mathbb{C}[z]_n$? Prove your answer.

9. Give an isomorphism from $\mathbb{R}[z]_3$ to $\mathbb{R}^4$.

10. Give an isomorphism from $\mathbb{R}[z]_3$ to Functions($\{1, 2, 3, 4\}$, $\mathbb{R}$).

11. Give a basis $\mathbf{f}_1, \mathbf{f}_2, \mathbf{f}_3, \mathbf{f}_4$ of Functions($\{1, 2, 3, 4\}$, $\mathbb{R}$).

THEORETICAL PROBLEMS

12. Show that the dimension of the column space $c(A)$ of a matrix A is d, where the largest invertible square submatrix of A (matrix obtained from A by deleting 0 or more rows and or columns) is a $d \times d$ matrix.

13. Show that the dimensions of the column spaces of a matrix A and its transpose are equal.

14. Show that the dimension of the intersection of a subspace V of F^n of dimension m and two hyperplanes is m, $m - 1$, or $m - 2$.

15. If A is an $n \times n$ matrix and $c(A) + c(A^T) = F^n$, show that the rank of A is the average of n and the dimension of $c(A) \cap c(A^T)$.

16. Show that if $\mathbf{v}_1, \mathbf{v}_2$ is a basis for V, then the following conditions are equivalent:

(i) $a\mathbf{v}_1 + c\mathbf{v}_2, b\mathbf{v}_1 + d\mathbf{v}_2$ is a basis for V.

(ii) $\begin{bmatrix} a & b \\ c & d \end{bmatrix}$ is an invertible matrix.

(iii) Neither of $a\mathbf{v}_1 + c\mathbf{v}_2$, $b\mathbf{v}_1 + d\mathbf{v}_2$ is a multiple of the other.

17. Let S be the linear transformation $S(f(z)) = f(\mathbf{0})$ (evaluation at $\mathbf{0}$) of $\mathbb{R}[z]_n$. Find a basis for Kernel S.

18. Let T be the linear transformation $T(f(z)) = f'(z)$ of $\mathbb{R}[z]_n$. Find a basis for Image T.

19. Find a basis for the intersection of the subspaces Kernel S and Image T which you found in the preceding two problems.

Hard

20. Find a formula for the dimension of the sum of three finite-dimensional subspaces U, V, and W of a vector space over F which generalizes the formula given in Theorem 4.16.

4.6 THE MATRIX OF A LINEAR TRANSFORMATION

Given a linear transformation T from a vector space V over F to a vector space W over F, it often must be represented by a matrix of scalars. For instance, this must be done before numerical methods can be used. This is done using coordinate isomorphisms for V and W.

Suppose that V and W have the bases $\mathbf{v}_1, \ldots, \mathbf{v}_n$ and $\mathbf{w}_1, \ldots, \mathbf{w}_m$, and let R and S be the corresponding coordinate isomorphisms

$$R(a_1\mathbf{v}_1 + \cdots + a_n\mathbf{v}_n) = a_1\mathbf{e}_1 + \cdots + a_n\mathbf{e}_n \text{ (the } \mathbf{e}\text{'s being in } F^n\text{)},$$

$$S(a_1\mathbf{w}_1 + \cdots + a_m\mathbf{w}_m) = a_1\mathbf{e}_1 + \cdots + a_m\mathbf{e}_m \text{ (the } \mathbf{e}\text{'s being in } F^m\text{)}.$$

From these, we get the transformation STR^{-1} from F^n to F^m which maps the vector of coordinates $R(\mathbf{v})$ of $\mathbf{v}$ to the vector of coordinates $S(T(\mathbf{v}))$ of $T(\mathbf{v})$.

The diagram

$$\begin{array}{ccc} \mathbf{v} \in V & \xrightarrow[T]{\qquad\qquad} & W \ni T(\mathbf{v}) \\ \Big\downarrow R & & S \Big\downarrow \\ R(\mathbf{v}) \in F^n & \xrightarrow{STR^{-1}} & F^m \ni STR^{-1}(R(\mathbf{v})) = S(T(\mathbf{v})) \end{array}$$

portrays how the coordinate isomorphisms R and S lead from the linear transformation T from V to W to the corresponding linear transformation STR^{-1} from F^n to F^m (Figure 4.13). We use its matrix $m(STR^{-1})$ to represent T, as follows.

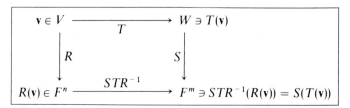

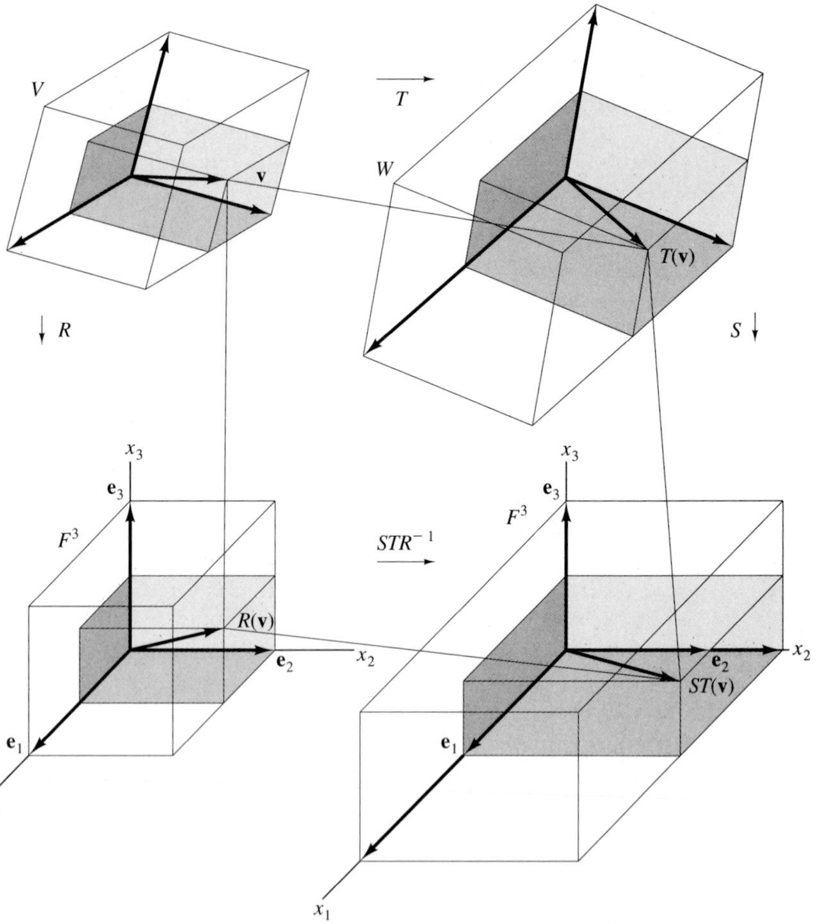

Figure 4.13 Transferring the transformation T from V to W to the transformation STR^{-1} from F^3 to F^3 using R and S.

Definition.   *Matrix of a Linear Transformation with Respect to Coordinates R and S.*

The matrix of the linear transformation T from V to W *with respect to the coordinate isomorphisms R and S* is the matrix $m(STR^{-1})$. It is denoted by $m_{R,S}(T) = m(STR^{-1})$.

The mapping T and corresponding matrix $m_{R,S}(T)$ are intertwined by T and the coordinate isomorphisms R and S in the equations

$$m_{R,S}(T)R(\mathbf{v}) = ST(\mathbf{v}) \quad \Big| \quad m_{R,S}(T)\mathbf{x} = STR^{-1}(\mathbf{x})$$

just as they are intertwined in the corresponding diagrams:

$$
\begin{array}{c}
V \xrightarrow{\quad T \quad} W \\
\ \ \downarrow R \qquad\qquad \downarrow S \\
F^{n} \xrightarrow[\ m_{R,S}(T)\ ]{} F^{m}
\end{array}
\qquad\qquad
F^{n} \xrightarrow[\ m_{R,S}(T)\ ]{\ STR^{-1}\ } F^{m}
$$

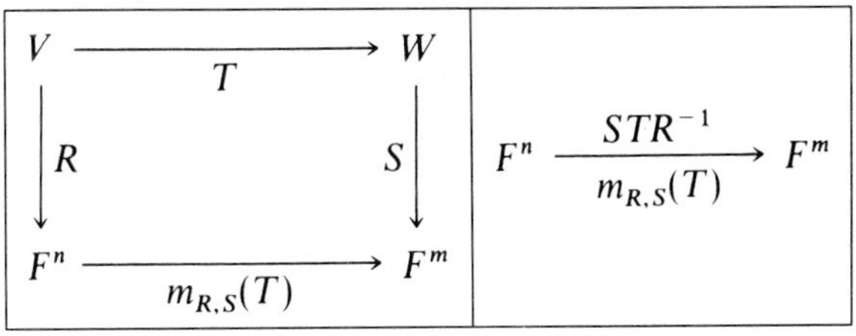

The matrix of *T* in terms of the bases

Since $m_{R,S}(T)$ can be expressed solely in terms of T and the bases $\mathbf{v}_1, \ldots, \mathbf{v}_n$ and $\mathbf{w}_1, \ldots, \mathbf{w}_m$ for V and W, it is also called the *matrix of T with respect to the bases* $\mathbf{v}_1, \ldots, \mathbf{v}_n$ *and* $\mathbf{w}_1, \ldots, \mathbf{w}_m$ *for V and W*. To see what its entries are, denote $m_{R,S}(T) = m(STR^{-1})$ by

$$
C = \begin{bmatrix} c_{11} & \cdots & c_{1n} \\ \vdots & & \vdots \\ c_{m1} & \cdots & c_{mn} \end{bmatrix}.
$$

Then $STR^{-1}(\mathbf{e}_s) = C\mathbf{e}_s = c_{1s}\mathbf{e}_1 + \cdots + c_{ms}\mathbf{e}_m$, so

$$STR^{-1}(\mathbf{e}_s) = c_{1s}\mathbf{e}_1 + \cdots + c_{ms}\mathbf{e}_m$$

gives the effect of $S^{-1}TR$ on the e's. Multiplying by S^{-1}, this becomes $TR^{-1}(\mathbf{e}_s) = c_{1s}S^{-1}(\mathbf{e}_1) + \cdots + c_{ms}S^{-1}(\mathbf{e}_m)$, which, using $R^{-1}(\mathbf{e}_s) = \mathbf{v}_s$ and $S^{-1}(\mathbf{e}_r) = \mathbf{w}_r$, becomes

$$T(\mathbf{v}_s) = c_{1s}\mathbf{w}_1 + \cdots + c_{ms}\mathbf{w}_m$$

This gives us the entries of the matrix C of T.

Theorem 4.17. *The Entries of the Matrix of a Linear Transformation as Coefficients.*

The matrix of the linear transformation T from V to W with respect to the bases $\mathbf{v}_1, \ldots, \mathbf{v}_n$ and $\mathbf{w}_1, \ldots, \mathbf{w}_m$ for V and W is the $m \times n$ matrix C of entries c_{rs} such that:

$$\begin{aligned} T(\mathbf{v}_1) &= c_{11}\mathbf{w}_1 + \cdots + c_{m1}\mathbf{w}_m, \\ &\vdots \\ T(\mathbf{v}_n) &= c_{1n}\mathbf{w}_1 + \cdots + c_{mn}\mathbf{w}_m. \end{aligned}$$

By the theorem, to find the matrix C of T with respect to the $\mathbf{v}$'s and $\mathbf{w}$'s amounts to computing the $T(\mathbf{v})$'s in terms of the $\mathbf{w}$'s and taking C to be the transpose of the resulting matrix of coefficients.

EXAMPLE

To find the matrix C of the linear transformation

$$T(a\mathbf{v}_1 + b\mathbf{v}_2 + c\mathbf{v}_3) = (3a + 2c)\mathbf{w}_1 + (2b - c)\mathbf{w}_2$$

with respect to the bases $\mathbf{v}_1, \mathbf{v}_2, \mathbf{v}_3$ and $\mathbf{w}_1, \mathbf{w}_2$, compute

$$\begin{aligned} T(\mathbf{v}_1) &= 3\mathbf{w}_1 + 0\mathbf{w}_2, \\ T(\mathbf{v}_2) &= 0\mathbf{w}_1 + 2\mathbf{w}_2, \\ T(\mathbf{v}_3) &= 2\mathbf{w}_1 - 1\mathbf{w}_2. \end{aligned}$$

Then C is the transpose of the resulting matrix of coefficients, which is $C = \begin{bmatrix} 3 & 0 & 2 \\ 0 & 2 & -1 \end{bmatrix}$. To check this amounts to checking whether multiplication by C has the effect on $a\mathbf{e}_1 + b\mathbf{e}_2 + c\mathbf{e}_3$ in F^3 that corresponds to the effect of T on $a\mathbf{v}_1 + b\mathbf{v}_2 + c\mathbf{v}_3$. The effect of C is

$$\begin{bmatrix} 3 & 0 & 2 \\ 0 & 2 & -1 \end{bmatrix} \begin{bmatrix} a \\ b \\ c \end{bmatrix} = \begin{bmatrix} 3a + 0b + 2c \\ 0a + 2b - c \end{bmatrix}$$

$$C(a\mathbf{e}_1 + b\mathbf{e}_2 + c\mathbf{e}_3) = (3a + 2c)\mathbf{e}_1 + (2b - c)\mathbf{e}_2$$

Since the effect of T is

$$T(a\mathbf{v}_1 + b\mathbf{v}_2 + c\mathbf{v}_3) = (3a + 2c)\mathbf{w}_1 + (2b - c)\mathbf{w}_2,$$

we conclude that it does.

The matrix of a linear transformation from V to itself

When $V = W$ and the two bases are both $\mathbf{v}_1, \ldots, \mathbf{v}_n$, we take the corresponding coordinate isomorphism

$$R(a_1\mathbf{v}_1 + \cdots + a_n\mathbf{v}_n) = a_1\mathbf{e}_1 + \cdots + a_n\mathbf{e}_n$$

and adopt the following simplified terminology.

Definition. *Matrix of a Linear Transformation from V to Itself.* The *matrix* of the linear transformation T from V to itself *with respect to the coordinate isomorphism* R is the matrix $m(RTR^{-1})$. It is denoted by $m_R(T) = m(RTR^{-1})$.

Given the coordinate isomorphism R corresponding to a basis $\mathbf{v}_1, \ldots, \mathbf{v}_n$ for a vector space V over F, the linear transformation of F^n corresponding to $T \in L(V, V)$ takes $\mathbf{x}$ to $m_R(T)\mathbf{x} = \mathbf{y}$, where $\mathbf{x} = R(\mathbf{v})$ and $\mathbf{y} = RT(\mathbf{v})$, and we have

$m_R(T)R(\mathbf{v}) = RT(\mathbf{v})$	$m_R(T)\mathbf{x} = RTR^{-1}(\mathbf{x})$

Since $m_R(T)$ can be expressed solely in terms of T and the basis $\mathbf{v}_1, \ldots, \mathbf{v}_n$, it is also called the *matrix* of T *with respect to the basis* $\mathbf{v}_1, \ldots, \mathbf{v}_n$. Theorem 4.17 now becomes the following.

Theorem 4.18. *The Matrix of a Linear Transformation from V to Itself.* The matrix of the linear transformation T from V to itself with respect to the basis $\mathbf{v}_1, \ldots, \mathbf{v}_n$ is the $n \times n$ matrix C such that $T(\mathbf{v}_s) = c_{1s}\mathbf{v}_1 + \cdots + c_{ns}\mathbf{v}_n$ for $1 \le s \le n$.

EXAMPLE

To find the matrix C of the linear transformation $T(a\mathbf{v}_1 + b\mathbf{v}_2 + c\mathbf{v}_3) = (3a + 2c)\mathbf{v}_1 + (2b - c)\mathbf{v}_2 + b\mathbf{v}_3$ with respect to the basis $\mathbf{v}_1, \mathbf{v}_2, \mathbf{v}_3$, compute

$$T(\mathbf{v}_1) = 3\mathbf{v}_1 + 0\mathbf{v}_2 + 0\mathbf{v}_3$$

$$T(\mathbf{v}_2) = 0\mathbf{v}_1 + 2\mathbf{v}_2 + 1\mathbf{v}_3$$

$$T(\mathbf{v}_3) = 2\mathbf{v}_1 - 1\mathbf{v}_2 + 0\mathbf{v}_3$$

and let C be the transpose of the resulting matrix of coefficients, which is

$$C = \begin{bmatrix} 3 & 0 & 2 \\ 0 & 2 & -1 \\ 0 & 1 & 0 \end{bmatrix}.$$

Checking, as in the previous example, we find that multiplication by C has the effect

$$\begin{bmatrix} 3 & 0 & 2 \\ 0 & 2 & -1 \\ 0 & 1 & 0 \end{bmatrix} \begin{bmatrix} a \\ b \\ c \end{bmatrix} = \begin{bmatrix} 3a + 0b + 2c \\ 0a + 2b - c \\ 0a + 1b + 0c \end{bmatrix}$$

$$C(a\mathbf{e}_1 + b\mathbf{e}_2 + c\mathbf{e}_3) = (3a + 2c)\mathbf{e}_1 + (2b - c)\mathbf{e}_2 + b\mathbf{e}_3$$

corresponding to applying T to $a\mathbf{v}_1 + b\mathbf{v}_2 + c\mathbf{v}_3$ in V.

The isomorphism $m_{R,S}(T)$

Given isomorphisms R, S from vector spaces V and W over F to F^n and F^m, it should come as no big surprise that the assignment $m_{R,S}(T) = m(STR^{-1})$ of matrices to $T \in L(V, W)$ given here should have properties like those of the assignment $m(S)$ of matrices to $S \in L(F^n, F^n)$ given in Chapter 3. To transfer the properties, we simply crank them through the formula $m_{R,S}(T) = m(STR^{-1})$. The result is this.

Theorem 4.19. *Isomorphism from $L(V, W)$ to $M_{m\times n}F$.*
The mapping $m_{R,S}$ from the vector space $L(V, W)$ to the vector space $M_{m\times n}F$ is an isomorphism.

Proof. We first show that $m_{R,S}$ is a linear transformation:

1. $m_{R,S}(T + T') = m(S(T + T')R^{-1}) = m(STR^{-1}) + m(ST'R^{-1}) = m_{R,S}(T) + m_{R,S}(T')$, since $S(T + T')R^{-1} = STR^{-1} + ST'R^{-1}$. (Prove!)
2. $m_{R,S}(aT) = m(S(aT)R^{-1}) = m(aSTR^{-1}) = am(STR^{-1}) = am_{R,S}(T)$, since $S(aT)R^{-1} = aSTR^{-1}$. (Prove!)

To show that the linear transformation $m_{R,S}$ is invertible, we show that it is 1-1 and onto as follows. Suppose that $m_{R,S}(T) = 0$. Then $0 = m_{R,S}(T) = m(STR^{-1})$. Since m is 1-1, this implies that $STR^{-1} = 0$. But then $T = 0$ as well. This shows that the kernel of $m_{R,S}$ is $\{0\}$, so $m_{R,S}$ is 1-1. To show that $m_{R,S}$ is onto, take any $C \in M_{m\times n}F$ and let T be the linear transformation

$$T(\mathbf{v}) = S^{-1}(CR(\mathbf{v})).$$

Letting $\mathbf{x} = R(\mathbf{v})$ be the element of F^n corresponding to $\mathbf{v}$, we have $\mathbf{v} = R^{-1}(\mathbf{x})$ and $TR^{-1}(\mathbf{x}) = S^{-1}(C\mathbf{x})$, that is,

$$STR^{-1}(\mathbf{x}) = C\mathbf{x}.$$

But then $m_R(T) = m(STR^{-1}) = C$. ∎

When we have an isomorphism R from a vector space V over F to F^n, we can take $W = V$ and $S = R$ in the preceding theorem to get the first part of the following theorem.

Theorem 4.20. *Isomorphism from $L(V, V)$ to M_nF.*
The mapping m_R from the vector space $L(V, V)$ to the vector space M_nF is an isomorphism such that $m_R(TT') = m_R(T)m_R(T')$ for $T, T' \in L(V, V)$. If $T \in L(V, V)$ is invertible, then $m_R(T)$ is invertible and $m_R(T^{-1}) = m_R(T)^{-1}$.

Proof. That m_R is an isomorphism follows from Theorem 4.19. To see that $m_R(TT') = m_R(T)m_R(T')$ for $T, T' \in L(V, V)$, observe that

$$\begin{aligned} m_R(TT') &= m(R(TT')R^{-1}) = m((RTR^{-1})(RT'R^{-1})) \\ &= m(RTR^{-1})m(RT'R^{-1}) = m_R(T)m_R(T'), \end{aligned}$$

since $R(TT')R^{-1} = (RTR^{-1})(RT'R^{-1})$. (Prove!)

When T is invertible, it follows that

$$I = m_R(I) = m_R(TT^{-1}) = m_R(T)m_R(T^{-1})$$
$$I = m_R(I) = m_R(T^{-1}T) = m_R(T^{-1})m_R(T),$$

which implies that $m_R(T)$ is invertible and $m_R(T^{-1}) = m_R(T)^{-1}$. ■

Often, m_R is given by specifying that $m_R(T)$ is the matrix of T with respect to a given basis, as in the following example of Theorem 4.20.

EXAMPLE

Let $V = F^2$, $T(\mathbf{x}) = \begin{bmatrix} 4 & 2 \\ 2 & 4 \end{bmatrix}\mathbf{x}$, and $m_R(T)$ be the matrix of T with respect to the basis $\begin{bmatrix} 1 \\ -1 \end{bmatrix}, \begin{bmatrix} 1 \\ 1 \end{bmatrix}$. Since

$$T\begin{bmatrix} 1 \\ -1 \end{bmatrix} = \begin{bmatrix} 4 & 2 \\ 2 & 4 \end{bmatrix}\begin{bmatrix} 1 \\ -1 \end{bmatrix} = \begin{bmatrix} 2 \\ -2 \end{bmatrix} = 2\begin{bmatrix} 1 \\ -1 \end{bmatrix} + 0\begin{bmatrix} 1 \\ 1 \end{bmatrix},$$

$$T\begin{bmatrix} 1 \\ 1 \end{bmatrix} = \begin{bmatrix} 4 & 2 \\ 2 & 4 \end{bmatrix}\begin{bmatrix} 1 \\ 1 \end{bmatrix} = \begin{bmatrix} 6 \\ 6 \end{bmatrix} = 0\begin{bmatrix} 1 \\ -1 \end{bmatrix} + 6\begin{bmatrix} 1 \\ 1 \end{bmatrix},$$

we have $m_R(T) = \begin{bmatrix} 2 & 0 \\ 0 & 6 \end{bmatrix}$. Since m_R is an isomorphism,

$$m_R(T^{53}) = \begin{bmatrix} 2^{53} & 0 \\ 0 & 6^{53} \end{bmatrix}.$$

(Explain!)

PROBLEMS

NUMERICAL PROBLEMS

1. Find the matrix of $T(\mathbf{x}) = \begin{bmatrix} 2 & 4 \\ 2 & 6 \end{bmatrix}\mathbf{x}$ with respect to the following bases for F^2.

(a) $\begin{bmatrix} 1 \\ -1 \end{bmatrix}, \begin{bmatrix} 1 \\ 1 \end{bmatrix}$ **(b)** $\begin{bmatrix} 1 \\ 1 \end{bmatrix}, \begin{bmatrix} 1 \\ -1 \end{bmatrix}$

(c) $\begin{bmatrix} 1 \\ 0 \end{bmatrix}, \begin{bmatrix} 3 \\ 1 \end{bmatrix}$ **(d)** $\begin{bmatrix} 3 \\ 1 \end{bmatrix}, \begin{bmatrix} 1 \\ 0 \end{bmatrix}$

2. Find the matrix of $T(\mathbf{x}) = \begin{bmatrix} a & b \\ c & d \end{bmatrix}\mathbf{x}$ with respect to the basis $\begin{bmatrix} 1 \\ 0 \end{bmatrix}$, $\begin{bmatrix} 3 \\ 1 \end{bmatrix}$.

3. Let $\begin{bmatrix} a & b \\ c & d \end{bmatrix}$ be the matrix of T with respect to a basis $\mathbf{v}$, $\mathbf{w}$ of a vector space V. Find the matrix of T with respect to the following new bases.
   (a) $\mathbf{v}, \mathbf{w} + t\mathbf{v}$
   (b) $\mathbf{w} + t\mathbf{v}, \mathbf{v}$
   (c) $t\mathbf{v}, \mathbf{w}$ (t nonzero)
   (d) $\mathbf{v}, t\mathbf{w}$ (t nonzero)
   (e) $s\mathbf{v}, t\mathbf{w}$ (s, t nonzero)
   (f) $\mathbf{w}, \mathbf{v}$

4. The matrix m_R of $T(\mathbf{x}) = \begin{bmatrix} 4 & 2 \\ 2 & 4 \end{bmatrix}\mathbf{x}$ with respect to the basis $\begin{bmatrix} 1 \\ -1 \end{bmatrix}$, $\begin{bmatrix} 1 \\ 1 \end{bmatrix}$ is $\begin{bmatrix} 2 & 0 \\ 0 & 6 \end{bmatrix}$, by our last example. Using the fact that m_R is an isomorphism, show that $m_R(T^k) = \begin{bmatrix} 2^k & 0 \\ 0 & 6^k \end{bmatrix}$.

THEORETICAL PROBLEMS

5. Show that $S(T + T')R^{-1} = STR^{-1} + ST'R^{-1}$.
6. Show that $S(aT)R^{-1} = aSTR^{-1}$.
7. Show that $R(TT')R^{-1} = (RTR^{-1})(RT'R^{-1})$.

Hard

8. In Section 2.7, it was shown that for any real symmetric matrix A, there is a basis $\mathbf{u}_1$, $\mathbf{u}_2$ of vectors for $\mathbb{R}^2$ such that $A\mathbf{u}_1 = d_1\mathbf{u}_1$, $A\mathbf{u}_2 = d_2\mathbf{u}_2$ (d_1, d_2 real). Suppose now that V is a real vector space of dimension 2 and T is a linear transformation of V. Let $\mathbf{v}_1$, $\mathbf{v}_2$ be a basis for V and let A denote the matrix of T with respect to this basis. Assuming that A is symmetric, show the following.
   (a) There is a basis $\mathbf{u}_1$, $\mathbf{u}_2$ for V such that $T(\mathbf{u}_1) = d_1\mathbf{u}_1$, $T(\mathbf{u}_2) = d_2\mathbf{u}_2$.
   (b) For any such basis, the matrix of T^k is $m_R(T^k) = \begin{bmatrix} d_1^k & 0 \\ 0 & d_2^k \end{bmatrix}$.

9. Apply the results in Problem 8 to find a basis $\mathbf{u}_1$, $\mathbf{u}_2$ for $V = \mathbb{R}[z]_1$ such that $T(\mathbf{u}_1) = d_1\mathbf{u}_1$, $T(\mathbf{u}_2) = d_2\mathbf{u}_2$, where T is the linear transformation $T(r + sz) = -2s - 2rz$.

4.7 CHANGE OF BASIS. SIMILAR MATRICES

In the last section, we introduced the matrix $m_{R,S}(T)$ of a linear transformation T from V to W with respect to given bases for V and W. When V and W are F^n and F^m, we can compare this matrix to $m(T)$.

Theorem 4.21. *The Matrix of T with Respect to Given Bases of F^n and F^m.* Let $\mathbf{v}_1, \ldots, \mathbf{v}_n$ and $\mathbf{w}_1, \ldots, \mathbf{w}_m$ be bases for F^n and F^m. Let A and B be the corresponding invertible matrices $A = [\mathbf{v}_1 \ \ \ldots \ \ \mathbf{v}_n]$ and $B = [\mathbf{w}_1 \ \ \ldots \ \ \mathbf{w}_m]$.

1. The coordinate isomorphisms R, S corresponding to the bases A and B are $R(\mathbf{x}) = A^{-1}\mathbf{x}$ and $S(\mathbf{y}) = B^{-1}\mathbf{y}$.
2. The matrix of any linear transformation T of F^n with respect to these bases is $m_{R,S}(T) = B^{-1}m(T)A$.

Proof. $R(\mathbf{x}) = A^{-1}\mathbf{x}$, since

$$A^{-1}(a_1\mathbf{v}_1 + \cdots + a_n\mathbf{v}_n) = A^{-1}A(a_1\mathbf{e}_1 + \cdots + a_n\mathbf{e}_n) = a_1\mathbf{e}_1 + \cdots + a_n\mathbf{e}_n.$$

Similarly, $S(\mathbf{y}) = B^{-1}\mathbf{y}$, which proves (1). So, the matrix of T with respect to $\mathbf{v}_1, \ldots, \mathbf{v}_n$ is

$$m_{R,S}(T) = m(STR^{-1}) = m(S)m(T)m(R)^{-1} = B^{-1}m(T)A. \qquad \blacksquare$$

Corollary. Let $\mathbf{v}_1, \ldots, \mathbf{v}_n$ be a basis for F^n and let A be the corresponding invertible matrix $A = [\mathbf{v}_1 \ \ \ldots \ \ \mathbf{v}_n]$. Then the coordinate isomorphism R corresponding to the basis A is $R(\mathbf{x}) = A^{-1}\mathbf{x}$ and the matrix of any linear transformation T of F^n with respect to the basis A is $m_R(T) = A^{-1}m(T)A$.

Corresponding to the equations

$m_{R,S}(T) = B^{-1}m(T)A$	$m_R(T) = A^{-1}m(T)A$

of Theorem 4.21 and its corollary are the following diagrams intertwining A and B:

$$\begin{array}{ccc} F^n & \xrightarrow{\ m_{R,S}(T)\ } & F^m \\ \downarrow A & & \downarrow B \\ F^n & \xrightarrow[\ T\ ]{} & F^m \end{array} \qquad \begin{array}{ccc} F^n & \xrightarrow{\ m_R(T)\ } & F^n \\ \downarrow A & & \downarrow A \\ F^n & \xrightarrow[\ T\ ]{} & F^n \end{array}$$

EXAMPLES

1. To compute the matrix $m_R(T)$ of the linear transformation $T\begin{bmatrix} x_1 \\ x_2 \end{bmatrix} = \begin{bmatrix} tx_1 + 3x_1 \\ 0x_2 + 4x_2 \end{bmatrix}$ with respect to the basis $\mathbf{v}_1 = \begin{bmatrix} 5 \\ 0 \end{bmatrix}$, $\mathbf{v}_2 = \begin{bmatrix} 3 \\ 2 \end{bmatrix}$, we let

$A = \begin{bmatrix} 5 & 3 \\ 0 & 2 \end{bmatrix}$ and compute $A^{-1} = \begin{bmatrix} 1/5 & -3/10 \\ 0 & 1/2 \end{bmatrix}$. Then

$$m_R(T) = A^{-1}m(T)A = \begin{bmatrix} 1/5 & -3/10 \\ 0 & 1/2 \end{bmatrix} \begin{bmatrix} t & 3 \\ 0 & 4 \end{bmatrix} \begin{bmatrix} 5 & 3 \\ 0 & 2 \end{bmatrix}$$
$$= \begin{bmatrix} t & (3t-6)/5 \\ 0 & 4 \end{bmatrix}.$$

When $t = 2$, for instance, the matrix of

$$T\begin{bmatrix} x_1 \\ x_2 \end{bmatrix} = \begin{bmatrix} 2x_1 + 3x_1 \\ 0x_2 + 4x_2 \end{bmatrix} \quad \text{is} \quad m_R(T) = \begin{bmatrix} 2 & 0 \\ 0 & 4 \end{bmatrix}.$$

2. The spectral theorem which we used for the theory of quadratic functions in Section 2.8 states that for any symmetric matrix $\begin{bmatrix} a & b \\ b & d \end{bmatrix}$, there exists a basis $\mathbf{v}$, $\mathbf{w}$ for $\mathbb{R}^2$ such that $\begin{bmatrix} a & b \\ b & d \end{bmatrix}\mathbf{v} = a'\mathbf{v}$, $\begin{bmatrix} a & b \\ b & d \end{bmatrix}\mathbf{w} = d'\mathbf{w}$ for some $a', d' \in \mathbb{R}$. The matrix $m_R(T)$ of $T(\mathbf{x}) = \begin{bmatrix} a & b \\ b & d \end{bmatrix}\mathbf{x}$ is then $\begin{bmatrix} a' & 0 \\ 0 & d' \end{bmatrix}$. (Explain!) The equation $m_R(T) = [\mathbf{v} \quad \mathbf{w}]^{-1}m(T)[\mathbf{v} \quad \mathbf{w}]$ of our theorem is then

$$\begin{bmatrix} a' & 0 \\ 0 & d' \end{bmatrix} = [\mathbf{v} \quad \mathbf{w}]^{-1}\begin{bmatrix} a & b \\ b & d \end{bmatrix}[\mathbf{v} \quad \mathbf{w}],$$

which is easy to verify directly. (Do so!)

Similarity

For a given $n \times n$ matrix C, the matrix of the linear transformation $T(\mathbf{x}) = C\mathbf{x}$ with respect to the basis consisting of the columns of an invertible matrix A is $A^{-1}CA$ (corollary to Theorem 4.21). For this reason, B can be the matrix of $T(\mathbf{x}) = C\mathbf{x}$ if and only if B is similar to C in the following sense.

Definition. *Similar Matrices.*
A matrix $B \in M_nF$ is **similar** (or **similar over** F) to a matrix $C \in M_nF$ if $C = A^{-1}CA$ for some invertible matrix $A \in M_nF$.

Theorem 4.22. *The Equivalence Relation Properties.*
The relation "B is similar to C" on $B, C \in M_nF$ satisfies the following equivalence relation properties.

1. C is similar to C.
2. If B is similar to C, then C is similar to B.
3. If B is similar to C and C is similar to D, then B is similar to D.

Proof. Simply note that:

1. $C = I^{-1}CI$;
2. If $B = A^{-1}CA$, then $C = (A^{-1})^{-1}BA^{-1}$;
3. If $B = A^{-1}CA$ and $C = A'^{-1}DA'$, then

$$B = A^{-1}A'^{-1}DA'A = (A'A)^{-1}DA'A. \quad \blacksquare$$

EXAMPLE

The matrices $\begin{bmatrix} 1 & 0 \\ 0 & 2 \end{bmatrix}$ and $\begin{bmatrix} 1 & -1 \\ 0 & 2 \end{bmatrix}$ are similar, since the second is the matrix of the linear transformation $T(\mathbf{x}) = \begin{bmatrix} 1 & 0 \\ 0 & 2 \end{bmatrix}\mathbf{x}$ with respect to the basis $\begin{bmatrix} 1 \\ 0 \end{bmatrix}, \begin{bmatrix} 1 \\ 1 \end{bmatrix}$. (Verify!)

Change of basis

One of the most powerful tools in linear algebra is to change from one basis to another with respect to which the matrix of a given linear transformation is particularly nice and easy to use. To use this method, it is necessary to solve the following problem.

The Change-of-Basis Problem.
Given a basis $\mathbf{v}_1, \ldots, \mathbf{v}_n$ for a vector space V over F and given an invertible linear transformation S of V affecting a **change of basis** from the $\mathbf{v}_j$ to the $\mathbf{w}_j = S(\mathbf{v}_j)$, how is the matrix of $T \in L(V, V)$ with respect to the $\mathbf{v}$'s related to the matrix of T with respect to the $\mathbf{w}$'s?

When $V = F^n$, $S(\mathbf{x}) = A\mathbf{x}$, and the basis $\mathbf{v}_j$ is the standard basis $I = [\mathbf{e}_1 \;\; \cdots \;\; \mathbf{e}_n]$, the solution to this problem is given in the corollary to Theorem 4.21.

Solution When the Basis I Is Changed to the Basis A.
The matrix of T with respect to the standard basis is $m(T)$ and the matrix of T with respect to the basis A is $A^{-1}m(T)A$.

EXAMPLE

The matrix of $S(\mathbf{x}) = \begin{bmatrix} 1 & -1 \\ 0 & 2 \end{bmatrix}\mathbf{x}$ with respect to the standard basis is $\begin{bmatrix} 1 & -1 \\ 0 & 2 \end{bmatrix}$, and the matrix of S with respect to the basis $\begin{bmatrix} 1 & -1 \\ 0 & 1 \end{bmatrix}$ is

$$\begin{bmatrix} 1 & 1 \\ 0 & 1 \end{bmatrix}\begin{bmatrix} 1 & -1 \\ 0 & 2 \end{bmatrix}\begin{bmatrix} 1 & -1 \\ 0 & 1 \end{bmatrix} = \begin{bmatrix} 1 & 0 \\ 0 & 2 \end{bmatrix}.$$

To solve the change-of-basis problem in general, let R be the coordinate isomorphism corresponding to the given basis $\mathbf{v}_1, \ldots, \mathbf{v}_n$ for the vector space

V over F, so that $R(\mathbf{v}_j) = \mathbf{e}_j$ for all j. Then RS^{-1} is the coordinate isomorphism corresponding to the basis $\mathbf{w}_1, \ldots, \mathbf{w}_n$, since $RS^{-1}(\mathbf{w}_j) = R(\mathbf{v}_j) = \mathbf{e}_j$ for all j. So, the matrix of T with respect to $\mathbf{w}_1, \ldots, \mathbf{w}_n$ is

$$m_{RS^{-1}}(T) = m(RS^{-1}TSR^{-1}) = m_R(S^{-1}TS) = m_R(S)^{-1}m_R(T)m_R(S).$$

This determines the matrix of T with respect to the new basis as follows.

Theorem 4.23. *The Matrix of T with Respect to a Changed Basis.* Given a basis $\mathbf{v}_1, \ldots, \mathbf{v}_n$ for a vector space V over F and an invertible linear transformation S of V, the matrix of $T \in L(V, V)$ with respect to the new basis $\mathbf{w}_j = S(\mathbf{v}_j)$ is $A^{-1}CA$, where C and A are the matrices of T and S with respect to $\mathbf{v}_1, \ldots, \mathbf{v}_n$.

EXAMPLE

Suppose that we are given a basis

$$\mathbf{v} = \begin{bmatrix} 2 \\ 3 \\ 5 \\ \pi \end{bmatrix}, \qquad \mathbf{w} = \begin{bmatrix} -\pi^2 \\ 3+i \\ 5 \\ \pi \end{bmatrix}$$

for a subspace V of $\mathbb{C}^4$ and an invertible linear transformation $S(a\mathbf{v} + b\mathbf{w}) = (a + 3b)\mathbf{v} + (0 + b)\mathbf{w}$. (Verify invertibility!) Then we can find the matrix of any linear transformation $T(a\mathbf{v} + b\mathbf{w}) = (ra + sb)\mathbf{v} + (ta + ub)\mathbf{w}$ (r, s, t, u being the scalars defining T) with respect to the new basis

$$S(\mathbf{v}) = \mathbf{v} = \begin{bmatrix} 2 \\ 3 \\ 5 \\ \pi \end{bmatrix}, \qquad S(\mathbf{w}) = 3\mathbf{v} + \mathbf{w} = 3\begin{bmatrix} 2 \\ 3 \\ 5 \\ \pi \end{bmatrix} + \begin{bmatrix} -\pi^2 \\ 3+i \\ 5 \\ \pi \end{bmatrix}$$

in terms of the matrices of S and T with respect to the basis $\mathbf{v}, \mathbf{w}$. Since these matrices are $\begin{bmatrix} 1 & 3 \\ 0 & 1 \end{bmatrix}$ and $\begin{bmatrix} r & s \\ t & u \end{bmatrix}$, the matrix of T with respect to the new basis is

$$\begin{bmatrix} 1 & 3 \\ 0 & 1 \end{bmatrix}^{-1} \begin{bmatrix} r & s \\ t & u \end{bmatrix} \begin{bmatrix} 1 & 3 \\ 0 & 1 \end{bmatrix} = \begin{bmatrix} 1 & -3 \\ 0 & 1 \end{bmatrix} \begin{bmatrix} r & s \\ t & u \end{bmatrix} \begin{bmatrix} 1 & 3 \\ 0 & 1 \end{bmatrix}.$$

PROBLEMS

NUMERICAL PROBLEMS

1. Let $\begin{bmatrix} a & b \\ c & d \end{bmatrix}$ be the matrix of T with respect to a basis $\mathbf{v}, \mathbf{w}$ of a vector space V. Find A such that the matrix of T with respect to the given

basis is $A^{-1}\begin{bmatrix} a & b \\ c & d \end{bmatrix}A$ for each of the new bases listed next. Compare the matrix found here with the matrix found in Problem 3, Section 4.6, in each case.

(a) $\mathbf{v}, \mathbf{w} + t\mathbf{v}$ **(b)** $\mathbf{w} + t\mathbf{v}, \mathbf{v}$

(c) $t\mathbf{v}, \mathbf{w}$ (t nonzero) **(d)** $\mathbf{v}, t\mathbf{w}$ (t nonzero)

(e) $s\mathbf{v}, t\mathbf{w}$ (s, t nonzero) **(f)** $\mathbf{w}, \mathbf{v}$

2. Describe the matrix of

$$T(\mathbf{x}) = \begin{bmatrix} 3 & 2 & 1 \\ 3 & 3 & 2 \\ 3 & 3 & 3 \end{bmatrix}\mathbf{x}$$

with respect to each of the following bases, using the matrix of the change of basis.

(a) $\begin{bmatrix} 1 \\ 0 \\ 0 \end{bmatrix}, \begin{bmatrix} 2 \\ 1 \\ 0 \end{bmatrix}, \begin{bmatrix} 0 \\ 3 \\ 1 \end{bmatrix}$ **(b)** $\begin{bmatrix} 1 \\ 2 \\ 0 \end{bmatrix}, \begin{bmatrix} 0 \\ 1 \\ 3 \end{bmatrix}, \begin{bmatrix} 0 \\ 0 \\ 1 \end{bmatrix}$ **(c)** $\begin{bmatrix} 0 \\ 0 \\ 1 \end{bmatrix}, \begin{bmatrix} 1 \\ 0 \\ 0 \end{bmatrix}, \begin{bmatrix} 0 \\ 1 \\ 0 \end{bmatrix}$

3. If the matrix of $T(\mathbf{x})$ with respect to the basis $\begin{bmatrix} 1 & 3 \\ 0 & 1 \end{bmatrix}$ is $\begin{bmatrix} 4 & 3 \\ 1 & 1 \end{bmatrix}$, what is its matrix with respect to the basis I (standard basis)?

4. If the matrix of $T(\mathbf{x})$ with respect to the basis $\begin{bmatrix} 1 & 3 \\ 0 & 1 \end{bmatrix}$ is $\begin{bmatrix} 4 & 3 \\ 1 & 1 \end{bmatrix}$, what is its matrix with respect to the basis $\begin{bmatrix} 1 & 0 \\ 3 & 1 \end{bmatrix}$?

THEORETICAL PROBLEMS

5. Given $T \in L(V, V)$, whose matrix with respect to a basis $\mathbf{v}_1, \ldots, \mathbf{v}_n$ for V is C, show that its matrix D with respect to a basis $\mathbf{w}_1, \ldots, \mathbf{w}_n$ is:

(a) $D = A_{ij}(-a)CA_{ij}(a)$ if $\{\mathbf{w}_1, \ldots, \mathbf{w}_n\}$ is obtained from $\mathbf{v}_1, \ldots, \mathbf{v}_n$ by adding a times $\mathbf{v}_i$ to $\mathbf{v}_j$;

(b) $D = M_j(1/a)CM_j(a)$ if $\{\mathbf{w}_1, \ldots, \mathbf{w}_n\}$ is obtained from $\mathbf{v}_1, \ldots, \mathbf{v}_n$ by multiplying a times $\mathbf{v}_j$;

(c) $D = I_{ij}CI_{ij}$ if $\{\mathbf{w}_1, \ldots, \mathbf{w}_n\}$ is obtained from $\mathbf{v}_1, \ldots, \mathbf{v}_n$ by interchanging $\mathbf{v}_i$ times $\mathbf{v}_j$;

(d) $D = E_d^{-1} \cdots E_1^{-1}CE_1 \cdots E_d$ if $\{\mathbf{w}_1, \ldots, \mathbf{w}_n\}$ is obtained from $\mathbf{v}_1, \ldots, \mathbf{v}_n$ by d elementary operations. What are the matrices E_j?

Hard

6. We say that a matrix B is **equivalent** to a matrix C if $B = A'CA$ for some invertible matrices A and A'.

(a) Show that the relation "B is equivalent to C" on $B, C \in M_nF$ satisfies the following equivalence relation properties:

(i) C is equivalent to C.

(ii) If B is equivalent to C, then C is equivalent to B.

(iii) If B is equivalent to C and C is equivalent to D, then B is equivalent to D.

(b) Show that B is equivalent to a unique matrix of the form

$$\begin{bmatrix} I_r & \square \\ \square & \square \end{bmatrix},$$

where I_r is the $r \times r$ identity matrix surrounded in B by blocks of 0s. This matrix is the normal form of B. (See Theorem 3.28.)

(c) Show that B and C are equivalent in the defined sense if and only if C can be obtained from B by a sequence of elementary row and column operations.

4.8 COMPUTATIONAL METHODS

A natural strategy for performing computations encountered when using vector spaces and linear transformations to solve specific problems is to translate the problem into the corresponding problem for the spaces F^n and matrices. Before discussing specific methods, we address the general question of translating problems from one form to another.

Transfer of linear properties using the isomorphism $m_{R,S}$

In this chapter, we often used isomorphisms from a vector space V to F^n to prove certain properties of V from corresponding properties of F^n. We now look at the process for doing this.

Given vector spaces V and W over F of dimensions n and m, we take bases $\mathbf{v}_1, \ldots, \mathbf{v}_n$ and $\mathbf{w}_1, \ldots, \mathbf{w}_m$ for V and W and get the corresponding coordinate isomorphisms $R(a_1\mathbf{v}_1 + \cdots + a_n\mathbf{v}_n) = a_1\mathbf{e}_1 + \cdots + a_n\mathbf{e}_n$ and $S(a_1\mathbf{w}_1 + \cdots + a_m\mathbf{w}_m) = a_1\mathbf{e}_1 + \cdots + a_m\mathbf{e}_m$. For $T \in L(V, W)$, R, S, and T are interrelated as portrayed in the following diagram, where $m_{R,S}(T) = m(STR^{-1})$.

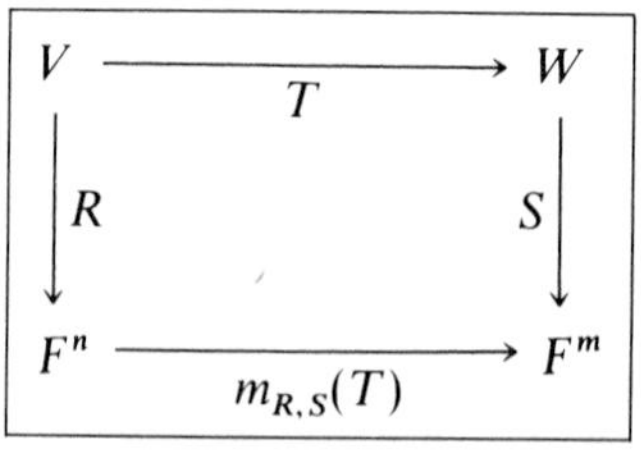

Properties involving some or all of V, W, and linear transformations from V to W correspond to properties involving some or all of F^n, F^m, and $m \times n$ matrices. The correspondence comes from the coordinate isomorphisms R and S, together with the isomorphism α from $L(V, W)$ to $M_{m \times n}F$ mapping $T \in L(V, V)$ to $m_{R,S}(T)$. Because the isomorphisms R, S, and T are invertible mappings preserving addition and scalar multiplication, the following metatheorem can be proved for certain linear properties.

Metatheorem. *Transfer of Linear Properties Using the Isomorphism $m_{R,S}$.* Linear properties proved in the context of F^n, F^m, and $L(F^n, F^m)$ also hold in the context of V, W, and $L(V, W)$.

This metatheorem is a kind of headline for the methodological theme of this chapter, that of using coordinate isomorphisms R and S and corresponding isomorphism $m_{R,S}$. Informally, *linear properties are those properties which, by their very nature, can be transferred using the isomorphism $m_{R,S}$*. Among such properties are all the theorems on linear transformations in this chapter.

We now give an example to illustrate when the metatheorem applies and why it is true. Variations of the method used in this example can be used to carry over the theorems of Chapter 3 from the context of $L(F^n, F^m)$ to the context of $L(V, W)$. Suppose that we want to settle a certain conjecture (a statement suspected—but not known—to be a theorem) about $T \in L(V, V)$. The conjecture is that any onto linear transformation T from an n-dimensional vector space V over F to itself is invertible. This is a reasonable conjecture, since we proved it in Theorem 3.21 for the special case when $V = F^n$.

Taking an isomorphism R from V to F^n, we get the corresponding linear transformation RTR^{-1} of F^n. Since T is onto, so is RTR^{-1}. (Prove!) Since RTR^{-1} is an onto linear transformation of F^n, it is invertible by Theorem 3.21. From this, it follows that T is also invertible. This proves the conjecture for $T \in L(V, V)$, which we state for future reference.

Theorem 4.24 *A Condition for Invertibility of a Linear Transformation.* A linear transformation of a finite-dimensional vector space is invertible if it is onto.

Computational problems and their solutions

We now state and solve three specific computational problems concerning a given linear transformation T from V to W, where V and W are vector spaces over F with bases $\mathbf{v}_1, \ldots, \mathbf{v}_n$ and $\mathbf{w}_1, \ldots, \mathbf{w}_m$.

Three Computational Problems Concerning a Linear Transformation T.

1. Find Kernel T.
2. Find Image T.
3. Find all solutions $\mathbf{v}$ to $T\mathbf{v} = \mathbf{w}$ for $\mathbf{w} \in$ Image T.

We assume that the linear transformation T is given to us in the form

$$T(\mathbf{v}_1) = c_{11}\mathbf{w}_1 + \cdots + c_{m1}\mathbf{w}_m$$
$$\vdots$$
$$T(\mathbf{v}_n) = c_{1n}\mathbf{w}_1 + \cdots + c_{mn}\mathbf{w}_m$$

Then, by Theorem 4.17, the $m \times n$ matrix C is the matrix $m_{R,S}(T)$ of T with respect to the coordinate isomorphisms $R(a_1\mathbf{v}_1 + \cdots + a_n\mathbf{v}_n) = a_1\mathbf{e}_1 + \cdots + a_n\mathbf{e}_n$ and $S(a_1\mathbf{w}_1 + \cdots + a_m\mathbf{w}_m) = a_1\mathbf{e}_1 + \cdots + a_m\mathbf{e}_m$ from V to F^n and from W to F^m. For this reason, C is related to T by the equation $C(R(\mathbf{v})) = ST(\mathbf{v})$. The coordinate isomorphisms R and S are invertible. Applying R, S, and their inverses does not involve any computations as long as all vectors in V and W are expressed in terms of their coordinates in the bases $\mathbf{v}_j$, $\mathbf{w}_i$. Keeping this in mind, note that equation $C(R(\mathbf{v})) = ST(\mathbf{v})$ implies the following:

1. $T(\mathbf{v}) = \mathbf{0}$ if and only if $C(R(\mathbf{v})) = \mathbf{0}$. It follows that $T(\mathbf{v})$ is $\mathbf{0}$ if and only if $\mathbf{v} = R^{-1}(\mathbf{x})$ with $C\mathbf{x} = \mathbf{0}$. So,

$$\boxed{\text{Kernel } T = \{R^{-1}(\mathbf{x}) \mid \mathbf{x} \in \text{nullspace } C\}.}$$

   This gives the means to compute Kernel T, since we know how to find a basis for the nullspace of C in terms of back-substitution equations corresponding to the nonpivot columns of an echelon matrix row equivalent to C.

2. $T(\mathbf{v}) = \mathbf{w}$ if and only if $C(R(\mathbf{v})) = S(\mathbf{w})$. It follows that $T(\mathbf{v}) = \mathbf{w}$ if and only if $\mathbf{w} = S^{-1}(\mathbf{y})$ with $\mathbf{y}$ in the column space $c(C)$ of C. So,

$$\boxed{\text{Image } T = \{S^{-1}(y) \mid y \in c(C)\}.}$$

   This gives us the means to compute Image T, since we can get $c(C)$:
   (a) We know that a basis for $c(C)$ is the set of its pivot columns.
   (b) We could also get $c(C)$ as the span of the transposes of the rows of any echelon matrix row equivalent to C^T. (Prove!)

3. Suppose that $\mathbf{v}$ is a solution to $T(\mathbf{v}) = \mathbf{w}$; then $\mathbf{v}' \in V$ is a solution to $T(\mathbf{v}) = \mathbf{w}$ if and only if $t(\mathbf{v} - \mathbf{v}') = \mathbf{w} - \mathbf{w} = \mathbf{0}$—that is, $\mathbf{v} - \mathbf{v}' \in$ Kernel T. So, the set of all solutions to $T(\mathbf{v}) = \mathbf{w}$ is

$$\mathbf{v} + \text{Kernel } T = \{\mathbf{v} + \mathbf{u} \mid \mathbf{u} \in \text{Kernel } T\}$$

   where $\mathbf{v}$ is one solution. Since we know what Kernel T is, by (1), it remains to see how to find $\mathbf{v}$, assuming $\mathbf{w} \in$ Image T.

By the equation $C(R(\mathbf{v})) = ST(\mathbf{v})$,

$$\boxed{\mathbf{w} = T(\mathbf{v}) \quad \text{if and only if} \quad C(R(\mathbf{v})) = S(\mathbf{w}).}$$

Therefore,

$$\boxed{\mathbf{w} \in \text{Image } T \quad \text{if and only if} \quad S(\mathbf{w}) \text{ is in } c(C).}$$

Assuming that $S(\mathbf{w}) \in c(C)$, there is a solution $\mathbf{x}$ to $C\mathbf{x} = S(\mathbf{w})$, which we can find by the LDU reduction of C, or by Gaussian elimination. Take $\mathbf{v}$ to be the corresponding $R^{-1}(\mathbf{x})$. Once this is done the set of solutions is

$$\boxed{\mathbf{v} + \text{Kernel } T = \{\mathbf{v} + \mathbf{u} \mid \mathbf{u} \in \text{Kernel } T\}}$$

where Kernel T can be determined in (1) of the preceding list.

PROBLEMS

NUMERICAL PROBLEMS

1. Suppose that it has been verified for 3×3 matrices A and B that if $AB = BA$, then $(A + B)^2 = A^2 + 2AB + B^2$. Use the method in the preceding example to transfer this to the corresponding property for linear transformations S, T of a three-dimensional vector space: If $ST = TS$, then $(S + T)^2 = S^2 + 2ST + T^2$.

2. Find the kernel and image of the linear transformation $T(a + bz + cz^2) = (a + 2b + 3c) + (2a + 3b + 4c)z + (3a + 4b + 5c)z^2$ of $\mathbb{R}[z]_2$.

3. For each of the following polynomials $f(z)$, determine whether it is in the image of T (from Problem 2); if so, determine all polynomials $g(z)$ such that $T(g(z)) = f(z)$.

(a) $f(z) = 1 - z^2$ **(b)** $f(z) = 6 + 7z + 8z^2$

(c) $f(z) = 1 + 1z + 1z^2$

4. Problem 3 can be solved by setting up and solving a matrix equation of the form $A\mathbf{x} = b$ in each of the three cases. What are these three equations?

THEORETICAL PROBLEMS

5. Show that the column space $c(C)$ of a matrix C is the span of the transposes of the nonzero rows of any echelon matrix row equivalent to C^T.

6. Given an isomorphism R from a vector space V to a vector space W and linear transformations $S, T \in L(V, V)$:

(a) Show that T is onto if and only if RTR^{-1} is onto.

(b) Show that T is 1-1 if and only if RTR^{-1} is 1-1.

(c) Show that T is invertible if and only if RTR^{-1} is invertible.

(d) Show that $ST = TS$ if and only if $RSR^{-1}RTR^{-1} = RTR^{-1}RSR^{-1}$.

(e) Show that $S(\mathbf{u}) = T(\mathbf{v})$ if and only if $(RSR^{-1})R(\mathbf{u}) = (RTR^{-1})R(\mathbf{v})$.

SUGGESTED READING

David J. Winter and I. N. Herstein, *Matrix Theory and Linear Algebra.* Macmillan, New York, 1988. [Abstract linear algebra, including finite- and infinite-dimensional abstract vector spaces and their linear transformations, Jordan canonical forms, and their applications to solving differential equations.]

PART 3

THE LINEAR ALGEBRA AND GEOMETRY OF n-SPACE

CHAPTER 5

THE ALGEBRA OF $n \times n$ MATRICES

5.1 INTRODUCTION

The vector space $M_{m \times n}F$ of $m \times n$ matrices is particularly interesting when $m = n$, in which case it is denoted by M_nF. In addition to its vector space operations, M_nF has the product operation $AA' \in M_nF$ $(A, A' \in M_nF)$, which completes a nice list of algebraic operations.

Definition. *The Algebra of $n \times n$ Matrices over F.*
The vector space M_nF together with its product operation is called the **algebra of $n \times n$ matrices.**

We also have a product $A\mathbf{x} \in F^n$ $(A \in M_nF, \mathbf{x} \in F^n)$ between matrices and vectors. We say that A **acts** on F^n, the *action* being that any $\mathbf{x} \in F^n$ is sent by A to $A\mathbf{x}$. In other words, even though A is just a matrix, *it acts on vectors,* by way of the matrix vector product, *just as does the linear transformation* $R(\mathbf{x}) = A\mathbf{x}$ (Figure 5.1).

Theorem 5.1 summarizes some basic results of Chapter 3 on the algebra M_nF and the action of its elements on F^n.

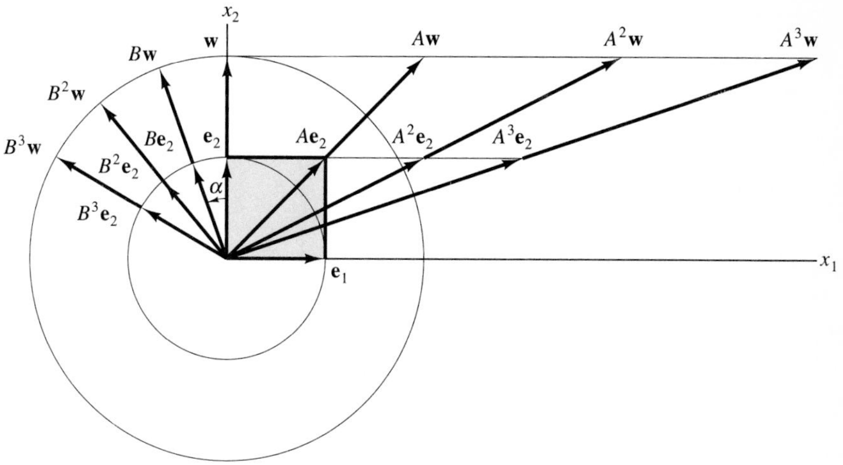

Figure 5.1 Successive action of $A = \begin{bmatrix} 1 & 1 \\ 0 & 1 \end{bmatrix}$ and $B = \begin{bmatrix} \cos\alpha & -\sin\alpha \\ \sin\alpha & \cos\alpha \end{bmatrix}$ on $\mathbb{R}^2$.

Theorem 5.1. *The Algebra of $n \times n$ Matrices and Its Action on F^n.* M_nF and F^n are vector spaces over F with product operations $AA' \in M_nF$, $A\mathbf{x} \in F^n$ ($A, A' \in M_nF$, $\mathbf{x} \in F^n$). The following properties are satisfied:

1. In M_nF, $0A = A0 = 0$ and $IA = AI = A$ for all $A \in M_nF$, where 0 and I are the zero and identity elements of M_nF.
2. $(AA')A'' = A(A'A'')$ for all $A, A', A'' \in M_nF$.
3. $(A + A')A'' = AA'' + A'A''$ and $A(A' + A'') = AA' + AA''$ for all A, $A', A'' \in M_nF$.
4. $a(AA') = (aA)A' = A(aA')$ for all $A, A' \in M_nF$ and $a \in F$.
5. $A(\mathbf{x} + \mathbf{x}') = A(\mathbf{x}) + A(\mathbf{x}')$ and $A(a\mathbf{x}) = aA(\mathbf{x})$ for all $A \in M_nF$, $\mathbf{x}$, $\mathbf{x}' \in F^n$, and $a \in F$.
6. $(A + A')(\mathbf{x}) = A(\mathbf{x}) + A'(\mathbf{x})$ and $(aA)(\mathbf{x}) = a(A(\mathbf{x}))$ for all $A, A' \in M_nF$, $\mathbf{x} \in F^n$, and $a \in F$.
7. $(AA')(\mathbf{x}) = A(A'(\mathbf{x}))$ for all $A, A' \in M_nF$ and $\mathbf{x} \in F^n$.

To further summarize, the vector space M_nF is of dimension n^2 and has the basis consisting of the standard unit matrices E_{rs} with $1 \leq r, s \leq n$. Any matrix $A \in M_nF$ can be written as $A = a_{11}E_{11} + \cdots + a_{rs}E_{rs} + \cdots + a_{nn}E_{nn}$, where a_{rs} denotes its (r, s)-entry. The E's multiply by the formulas $E_{rs}E_{st} = E_{rt}$ and $E_{rs}E_{s't} = 0$ ($1 \leq r, s, s', t \leq n$, $s \neq s'$). (Verify!) The vector space F^n is of dimension n and has the basis consisting of the standard unit vectors $\mathbf{e}_s$ with $1 \leq s \leq n$. Any vector $\mathbf{x} \in F^n$ can be written as $\mathbf{x} = x_1\mathbf{e}_1 + \cdots + x_n\mathbf{e}_n$, where x_s denotes its sth entry. The products of E's with $\mathbf{e}$'s are given by the formulas $E_{rs}\mathbf{e}_s = \mathbf{e}_s$, $E_{rs}\mathbf{e}_{s'} = 0$ ($1 \leq r, s, s' \leq n$, $s \neq s'$).

EXAMPLES

1. The product $\begin{bmatrix} 1 & a \\ 0 & 1 \end{bmatrix}\begin{bmatrix} 1 & b \\ 0 & 1 \end{bmatrix} = \begin{bmatrix} 1 & a+b \\ 0 & 1 \end{bmatrix}$ can be expressed and computed as

$$(E_{11} + aE_{12} + E_{22})(E_{11} + bE_{12} + E_{22}) = (E_{11} + (a + b)E_{12} + E_{22}).$$

(Verify!)

2. The product $\begin{bmatrix} 1 & a \\ 0 & 1 \end{bmatrix}\begin{bmatrix} b \\ c \end{bmatrix} = \begin{bmatrix} b+ac \\ c \end{bmatrix}$ can be expressed and computed as

$$(E_{11} + aE_{12} + E_{22})(b\mathbf{e}_1 + c\mathbf{e}_2) = ((b + ac)\mathbf{e}_1 + c\mathbf{e}_2).$$

(Verify!)

When V is a vector space over F with basis $\mathbf{v}_1, \ldots, \mathbf{v}_n$, V is isomorphic to F^n by the isomorphism

$$R(a_1\mathbf{v}_1 + \cdots + a_n\mathbf{v}_n) = a_1\mathbf{e}_1 + \cdots + a_n\mathbf{e}_n.$$

The vector space $L(V, V)$ of linear transformations of V is then isomorphic to M_nF by the isomorphism m_R, where $m_R(T)R(\mathbf{v}) = R(T(\mathbf{v}))$ for all $\mathbf{v} \in V$ (Section 4.6).

Corresponding to the matrix product AA' in M_nF is the product $TT' \in L(V, V)$ (the composite of $T, T' \in L(V, V)$). Under the isomorphism m_R, the product TT' becomes the product AA' of the matrices $A = m_R(T)$, $A' = m_R(T')$. This is expressed by the equation $m_R(TT') = m_R(T)m_R(T')$ and the following diagram:

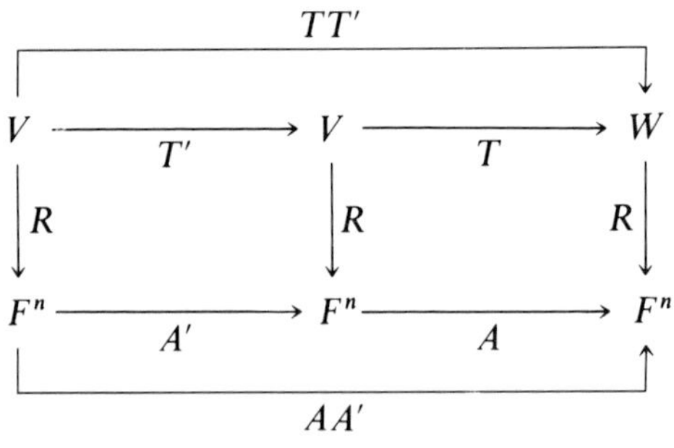

Definition. *The Algebra of Linear Transformations of V.*
$L(V, V)$ together with the product TT' is called the **algebra of linear transformations of V**.

The following theorem summarizes those results of Chapter 4 which say for linear transformations what Theorem 5.1 says for matrices.

Theorem 5.2. *The Algebra of Linear Transformations and Its Action on V.*
$L(V, V)$ and V are vector spaces over F with operations $TT' \in L(V, V)$,

$T(\mathbf{x}) \in V$ $(T, T' \in L(V, V), \mathbf{x} \in V)$. The following properties are satisfied:

1. In $L(V, V)$, $0T = T0 = 0$ and $IT = TI = T$ for all $T \in M_nF$, where 0 and I are the zero and identity elements of $L(V, V)$.
2. $(TT')T'' = T(T'T'')$ for all $T, T', T'' \in L(V, V)$.
3. $(T + T')T'' = TT'' + T'T''$ and $T(T' + T'') = TT' + TT''$ for all $T, T', T'' \in L(V, V)$.
4. $a(TT') = (aT)T' = T(aT')$ for all $T, T' \in L(V, V)$, $a \in F$.
5. $T(\mathbf{x} + \mathbf{x}') = T(\mathbf{x}) + T(\mathbf{x}')$ and $T(a\mathbf{x}) = aT(\mathbf{x})$ for all $T \in L(V, V)$, $\mathbf{x}$, $\mathbf{x}' \in V$, and $a \in F$.
6. $(T + T')(\mathbf{x}) = T(\mathbf{x}) + T'(\mathbf{x})$ and $(aT)(\mathbf{x}) = a(T(\mathbf{x}))$ for all T, $T' \in L(V, V)$, $\mathbf{x} \in V$, and $a \in F$.
7. $(TT')(\mathbf{x}) = (T(T'(\mathbf{x}))$ for all $T, T' \in L(V, V)$ and $\mathbf{x} \in V$.

The results in Theorem 5.2 can also be proved directly from those in Theorem 5.1 using the isomorphism m_R and the methods of Section 4.8.

PROBLEMS

NUMERICAL PROBLEMS

1. Perform the following multiplications.
   (a) $E_{13}E_{32}$ **(b)** $E_{12}E_{32}$ **(c)** $E_{13}E_{31}E_{12}$
   (d) $E_{21}E_{13}\mathbf{e}_2$ **(e)** $E_{22}E_{23}\mathbf{e}_3$
2. Perform the following multiplications.
   (a) $(aE_{13} + 3E_{32})(2\mathbf{e}_1 + 5\mathbf{e}_2)$
   (b) $(aE_{12} + dE_{43})(2\mathbf{e}_1 + 5\mathbf{e}_2 + 6\mathbf{e}_3)$
   (c) $E_{13}E_{31}E_{12}\mathbf{e}_2$
3. Compute $(aE_{11} + bE_{12} + cE_{21} + dE_{22})(aE_{11} + bE_{12} + cE_{21} + dE_{22})$.
4. Interpret the product in Problem 3 as that of two 2×2 matrices.
5. Interpret the product in Problem 3 as that of two 3×3 matrices.
6. Express and perform the following multiplications in terms of the E's.
   (a) $\begin{bmatrix} 2 & 0 \\ 0 & 1 \end{bmatrix}\begin{bmatrix} a & b \\ 0 & 1 \end{bmatrix}$ **(b)** $\begin{bmatrix} 1 & b \\ 0 & 1 \end{bmatrix}\begin{bmatrix} 2 & 0 \\ 0 & 1 \end{bmatrix}$ **(c)** $\begin{bmatrix} 1 & b \\ 0 & 1 \end{bmatrix}\begin{bmatrix} 1 & 0 \\ c & 1 \end{bmatrix}$

THEORETICAL PROBLEMS

7. Verify the formulas $E_{rs}E_{st} = E_{rt}$ and $E_{rs}E_{s't} = 0$ $(1 \leq r, s, s', t \leq n, s \neq s')$ for multiplication of standard unit matrices.
8. Using the formulas in Problem 7, simplify the expression

$$(a_{11}E_{11} + \cdots + a_{rs}E_{rs} + \cdots + a_{nn}E_{nn})(b_{11}E_{11} + \cdots + b_{st}E_{st} + \cdots + b_{nn}E_{nn})$$

   for
   (a) $n = 2$; **(b)** Any n.

9. Verify the following parts of Theorem 5.1, using Theorem 5.2, the isomorphism m_R, and the methods of Section 4.8.
   (a) Parts (2) and (3)
   (b) Part (4)
   (c) Part (7)

5.2 DETERMINANTS

For the Cartesian plane $\mathbb{R}^2$, we showed that

$$T(\mathbf{x}) = \begin{bmatrix} a & b \\ c & d \end{bmatrix} \mathbf{x}$$

maps the unit square

$$\left\{ \begin{bmatrix} r \\ s \end{bmatrix} \middle| 0 \le r, s \le 1 \right\}$$

to a parallelogram of area equal to the 2×2 determinant $\begin{vmatrix} a & b \\ c & d \end{vmatrix} = ad - bc$. Note that this area is negative if T interchanges the orders of the edges, as in the case of $T(\mathbf{x}) = \begin{bmatrix} a & b \\ c & d \end{bmatrix} \mathbf{x}$ when the determinant is -2 (Figure 5.2).

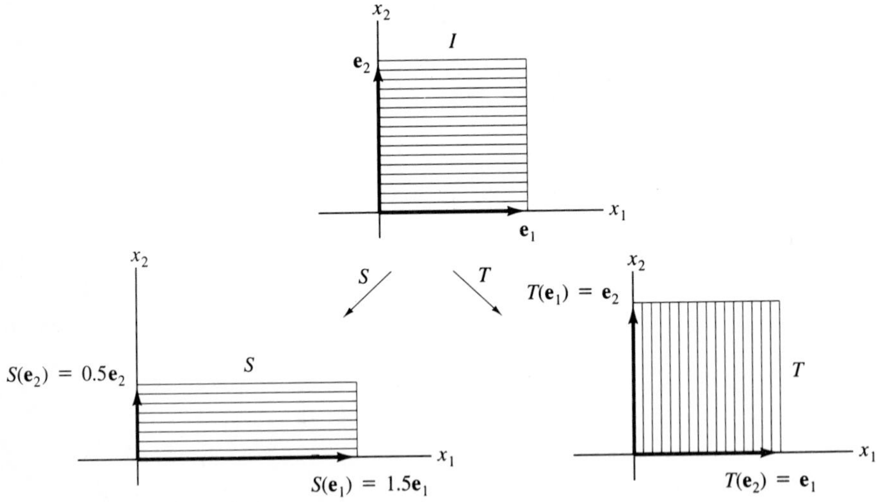

Figure 5.2 The unit square is mapped to positive and negative areas by the transformations $S(\mathbf{x}) = \begin{bmatrix} 1.5 & 0 \\ 0 & 0.5 \end{bmatrix}$ and $T(\mathbf{x}) = \begin{bmatrix} 0 & 1 \\ 1 & 0 \end{bmatrix}$.

We see in the next section that

$$T(\mathbf{x}) = \begin{bmatrix} a & b & c \\ d & e & f \\ g & h & i \end{bmatrix} \mathbf{x}$$

maps the unit cube

$$\left\{ \begin{bmatrix} r \\ s \\ t \end{bmatrix} \middle| \; 0 \le r, s, t \le 1 \right\}$$

to a parallelepiped of volume equal to the 3 × 3 determinant

$$|T| = \begin{vmatrix} a & b & c \\ d & e & f \\ g & h & i \end{vmatrix} = a \begin{vmatrix} e & f \\ h & i \end{vmatrix} - b \begin{vmatrix} d & f \\ g & i \end{vmatrix} + c \begin{vmatrix} d & e \\ g & h \end{vmatrix}.$$

(See Figure 5.3.)

In general, the definition of determinant is based on the notion of the (r, s) **minor submatrix** A_{rs}, the matrix obtained from A by removing its

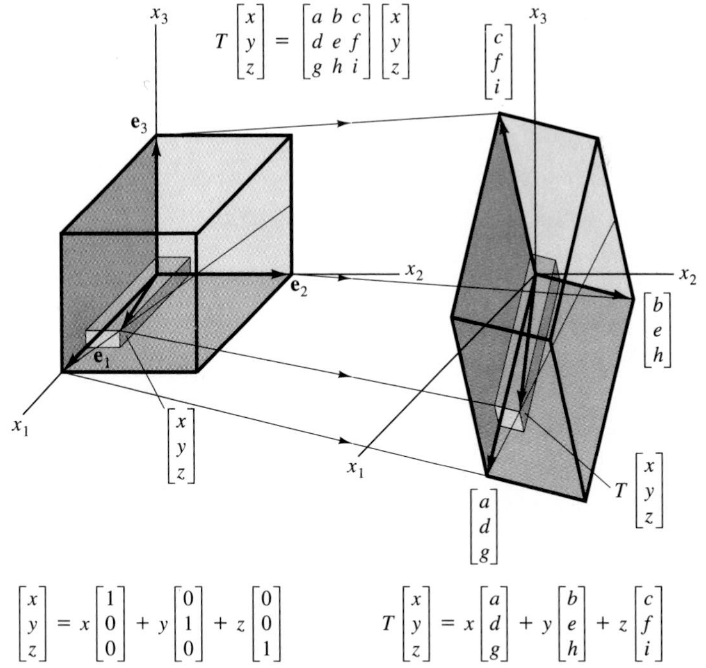

Figure 5.3 Portrayal of the volume in $\mathbb{R}^3$ of the image of the unit cube under T.

rth row and sth column. For example, the (2, 3) minor submatrix of

$$A = \begin{bmatrix} a & b & c & d \\ e & f & g & h \\ i & j & k & l \\ m & n & o & p \end{bmatrix} \quad \text{is} \quad A_{23} = \begin{bmatrix} a & b & \boxed{c} & d \\ \boxed{e} & \boxed{f} & \boxed{g} & \boxed{h} \\ i & j & \boxed{k} & l \\ m & n & \boxed{o} & p \end{bmatrix} = \begin{bmatrix} a & b & d \\ i & j & l \\ m & n & p \end{bmatrix}.$$

The determinant of a linear transformation or an $n \times n$ matrix A will be defined in terms of the $(n-1) \times (n-1)$ determinants $|A_{rs}|$. We call $|A_{rs}|$ the (r, s) minor of A. Given this terminology, we can define the determinant by *first-row* expansion as follows.

Definition. *Definition of the Determinant of a Transformation T or Matrix A.* The **determinant** of $T(\mathbf{x}) = A\mathbf{x}$ (or of the matrix A) is

$$|T| = |A| = a_{11}|A_{11}| + \cdots + (-1)^{s+1}a_{1s}|A_{1s}| + \cdots + (-1)^{n+1}a_{1n}|A_{1n}|.$$

Since the signs alternate, the determinant of A is often abbreviated

$$|A| = +a_{11}|A_{11}| - \cdots \pm a_{1n}|A_{1n}|.$$

In the next section it is shown that the determinant is also given by corresponding formulas for expansion along *any* row or column. The sign of the coefficient a_{rs} in the formula is then just the $+$ or $-$ sign located in row r and column s of the corresponding **sign matrix**. For $n = 2, 3$, the sign matrices are

$$\begin{bmatrix} + & - \\ - & + \end{bmatrix}, \quad \begin{bmatrix} + & - & + \\ - & + & - \\ + & - & + \end{bmatrix}.$$

So, for $n = 3$, the expansions of the determinant along the second row and third columns are

$$|A| = -a_{21}|A_{21}| + a_{22}|A_{22}| - a_{23}|A_{23}|,$$
$$|A| = +a_{13}|A_{13}| + a_{23}|A_{23}| - a_{33}|A_{33}|.$$

EXAMPLES

1. The determinant

$$|A| = \begin{vmatrix} 1 & 0 & 2 \\ 3 & 0 & 1 \\ 5 & 4 & 6 \end{vmatrix}$$

can be computed as follows:

a. By the $\begin{bmatrix} \boxed{+ \quad - \quad +} \\ - \quad + \quad - \\ + \quad - \quad + \end{bmatrix}$ expansion as

$$+1\begin{vmatrix} 0 & 1 \\ 4 & 6 \end{vmatrix} - 0\begin{vmatrix} 3 & 1 \\ 5 & 6 \end{vmatrix} + 2\begin{vmatrix} 3 & 0 \\ 5 & 4 \end{vmatrix} = 20;$$

b. By the $\begin{bmatrix} + & \boxed{-} & + \\ - & \boxed{+} & - \\ + & \boxed{-} & + \end{bmatrix}$ expansion as

$$-0\begin{vmatrix} 3 & 1 \\ 5 & 6 \end{vmatrix} + 0\begin{vmatrix} 1 & 2 \\ 5 & 6 \end{vmatrix} - 4\begin{vmatrix} 1 & 2 \\ 3 & 1 \end{vmatrix} = 20.$$

2. If

$$T(\mathbf{x}) = A\mathbf{x} = \begin{bmatrix} a & b & c & d \\ e & f & g & h \\ i & j & k & l \\ m & n & o & p \end{bmatrix}\mathbf{x},$$

then the determinant formula is

$$|T| = |A| = +a|A_{11}| - b|A_{12}| + c|A_{13}| - d|A_{14}|.$$

So, computing the determinant reduces to computing its minors $|A_{1s}|$. To compute the minor $|A_{12}|$, for instance, delete row 1 and column 2 of A and compute the 3×3 determinant

$$|A_{12}| = \begin{vmatrix} \boxed{a} & \boxed{b} & \boxed{c \quad d} \\ e & \boxed{f} & g & h \\ i & \boxed{j} & k & l \\ m & \boxed{n} & o & p \end{vmatrix}$$

$$= \begin{vmatrix} e & g & h \\ i & k & l \\ m & o & p \end{vmatrix}.$$

3. $\begin{vmatrix} a & 0 & 0 & 0 \\ e & f & g & h \\ i & j & k & l \\ m & n & o & p \end{vmatrix}$ expands as

$$+a\begin{vmatrix} a & 0 & 0 & 0 \\ e & f & g & h \\ i & j & k & l \\ m & n & o & p \end{vmatrix} - 0\begin{vmatrix} a & 0 & 0 & 0 \\ e & f & g & h \\ i & j & k & l \\ m & n & o & p \end{vmatrix} + 0\begin{vmatrix} a & 0 & 0 & 0 \\ e & f & g & h \\ i & j & k & l \\ m & n & o & p \end{vmatrix} - 0\begin{vmatrix} a & 0 & 0 & 0 \\ e & f & g & h \\ i & j & k & l \\ m & n & o & p \end{vmatrix}$$

$$= +a\left(f\begin{vmatrix} f & g & h \\ j & k & l \\ n & o & p \end{vmatrix} - g\begin{vmatrix} f & g & h \\ j & k & l \\ n & o & p \end{vmatrix} + h\begin{vmatrix} f & g & h \\ j & k & l \\ n & o & p \end{vmatrix}\right)$$

$$= +a(f(kp - lo) - g(jp - ln) + h(jo - kn)).$$

Computation of the determinant

The first-row expansion used to define $|A|$ enables us to develop the theory of determinants and efficient methods for computing them. For this, it is essential. However, it is hopelessly inefficient computationally. A computer would take years, using the method recursively, to compute determinants which it can find routinely in a matter of seconds by other methods.

The number of multiplication operations required to compute $|A|$ for an $n \times n$ matrix A, using the first-row expansion recursively, is $n!$. (Explain!) Yet, we need only $n(n+1)(2n+1)/6 - n$ (multiplication and division) operations to get the factorization $A = LDU$ (Section 3.7). From this factorization, it takes a mere n multiplications to get the determinant, as we see in the next section (Corollary to Theorem 5.12). So, only $n(n+1)(2n+1)/6 \approx n^3/3$ operations are needed to compute the determinant of A by way of the LDU factorization. From this, we see that computing the determinant recursively by its first-row expansion takes about $n!/(n^3/3) \approx 3(n-3)!$ times as long as does computation based on the LDU decomposition—a staggering difference even for 15×15 matrices!

EXAMPLE

If it takes a microcomputer 1 second to compute the determinant of a 13×13 matrix A using the LDU factorization, it takes the same computer $3((13-3)!) = 3(10!)$ seconds $= 126$ days to compute it recursively by its first-row expansion. (Verify!)

In contrast to the horrors of calculating determinants for large *dense* matrices (those with few zero entries), computation of the determinant is virtually instantaneous for diagonal and upper or lower triangular matrices.

Theorem 5.3. *The Determinant of a Triangular Matrix.*
Suppose that $A \in M_nF$ is either upper or lower triangular. Then $|A|$ is the product $a_{11} \cdots a_{nn}$ of its diagonal elements.

Proof. Suppose first that A is a lower triangular $n \times n$ matrix. Then $A = a_{11}|A_{11}|$, where A_{11} is an $(n-1) \times (n-1)$ lower triangular matrix. So, to get $|A|$, we remove the first row and column of A and multiply the determinant of the remaining minor submatrix by the entry that was in the upper-left-hand corner. Applying this same method to $|A_{11}|$ and to the subsequent lower triangular determinants encountered, we see that $|A| = a_{11} \cdots a_{nn}$. For instance,

$$\begin{vmatrix} a & 0 & 0 & 0 \\ e & f & 0 & 0 \\ i & j & k & 0 \\ m & n & o & p \end{vmatrix} = a\begin{vmatrix} f & 0 & 0 \\ j & k & 0 \\ n & o & p \end{vmatrix} = af\begin{vmatrix} k & 0 \\ n & p \end{vmatrix} = afkp.$$

Suppose next that A is an upper triangular $n \times n$ matrix. Then

$$|A| = a_{11}|A_{11}| + \cdots + (-1)^{s+1}a_{1s}|A_{1s}| + \cdots + (-1)^{n+1}a_{1n}|A_{1n}|$$

where $A_{11}, \ldots, A_{1n}$ are upper triangular matrices. We claim that $|A|$ is the product $a_{11} \cdots a_{nn}$ of its diagonal entries. We can easily see why, assuming it for the smaller upper triangular matrices $A_{11}, \ldots, A_{1n}$. Just observe that one of the diagonal entries is 0 for each of $A_{12}, \ldots, A_{1n}$, so that $|A_{12}|, \ldots, |A_{1n}|$ are all 0. This means that the preceding formula for $|A|$ reduces to

$$|A| = a_{11}|A_{11}|.$$

Since $|A_{11}|$ is the product $a_{22} \cdots a_{nn}$ of its diagonal entries, we get

$$|A| = a_{11}a_{22} \cdots a_{nn}$$

as claimed. For instance,

$$\begin{vmatrix} a & b & c & d \\ 0 & f & g & h \\ 0 & 0 & k & l \\ 0 & 0 & 0 & p \end{vmatrix} = a\begin{vmatrix} f & g & h \\ 0 & k & l \\ 0 & 0 & p \end{vmatrix} = af\begin{vmatrix} k & l \\ 0 & p \end{vmatrix} = afkp,$$

since

$$b\begin{vmatrix} 0 & g & h \\ 0 & k & l \\ 0 & 0 & p \end{vmatrix}, \quad c\begin{vmatrix} 0 & f & h \\ 0 & 0 & l \\ 0 & 0 & p \end{vmatrix}, \quad d\begin{vmatrix} 0 & f & h \\ 0 & 0 & k \\ 0 & 0 & 0 \end{vmatrix}$$

are all 0. ■

EXAMPLES

1. Let $A = LDU$, where U is upper triangular, L is lower triangular, U and L have only 1s on the main diagonal, and D is diagonal with

$d_1 \cdots d_n$ on the main diagonal. Then $|L| = |U| = 1$ and $|D| = d_1 \cdots d_n$. This is used in the next section to show that $|A| = d_1 \cdots d_n$ (Corollary to Theorem 5.12).

2. If $A = \begin{bmatrix} B & 0 \\ * & D \end{bmatrix}$, where B and D are square matrices, $*$ represents a block of entries below B, and 0 represents a block of 0s above D, we say that A is **lower block triangular**. The determinant of such an A is the product of the determinants of B and D. For instance, the determinant of

$$\begin{bmatrix} B & 0 \\ C & D \end{bmatrix} = \begin{bmatrix} a\,b & 0\,0 \\ c\,d & 0\,0 \\ e\,f & i\,j \\ g\,h & k\,l \end{bmatrix} \quad \text{is} \quad \begin{vmatrix} B & 0 \\ C & D \end{vmatrix} = \begin{vmatrix} a\,b & 0\,0 \\ c\,d & 0\,0 \\ e\,f & i\,j \\ g\,h & k\,l \end{vmatrix} = \begin{vmatrix} a & b \\ c & d \end{vmatrix} \begin{vmatrix} i & j \\ k & l \end{vmatrix}.$$

This is a block version of the preceding theorem. It can be proved for $n \times n$ matrices in much the same way, but using the block version for $(n-1) \times (n-1)$ matrices. $\left(\text{Do so for } A \text{ of the form } \begin{bmatrix} B & 0 \\ C & D \end{bmatrix}.\right)$

3. Using (2), the determinant of a square matrix

$$A = \begin{bmatrix} A_1 & & 0 \\ & \ddots & \\ * & & A_n \end{bmatrix}$$

with square blocks A_r on the diagonal and 0s above them is $|A_1| \cdots |A_n|$. (Explain!)

4. If, in (3), each of the A_r is either upper or lower triangular, then the determinant of A is the product of its diagonal elements. For instance, the determinant of

$$\begin{bmatrix} a\,0 & 0\,0 \\ c\,d & 0\,0 \\ e\,g & i\,j \\ g\,h & 0\,l \end{bmatrix}$$

is *adil*.

Determinant as a signed volume

The ***n*-cube** in $\mathbb{R}^n$ is the set

$$I_n = \left\{ \begin{bmatrix} x_1 \\ \vdots \\ x_n \end{bmatrix} \middle| \, 0 \le x_r \le 1 \right\},$$

and its **edges** are the standard unit vectors $\mathbf{e}_1, \ldots, \mathbf{e}_n$. So,

$$I_n = \{x_1\mathbf{e}_n + \cdots + x_n\mathbf{e}_n \mid 0 \le x_r \le 1\},$$

and its image under the linear transformation $T(\mathbf{x}) = A\mathbf{x}$ is the **parallelepiped** $\{x_1A_1 + \cdots + x_nA_n \mid 0 \le x_r \le 1\}$ with **edge vectors** A_s, where $A_s = A\mathbf{e}_s$ is column s of A (Figure 5.4).

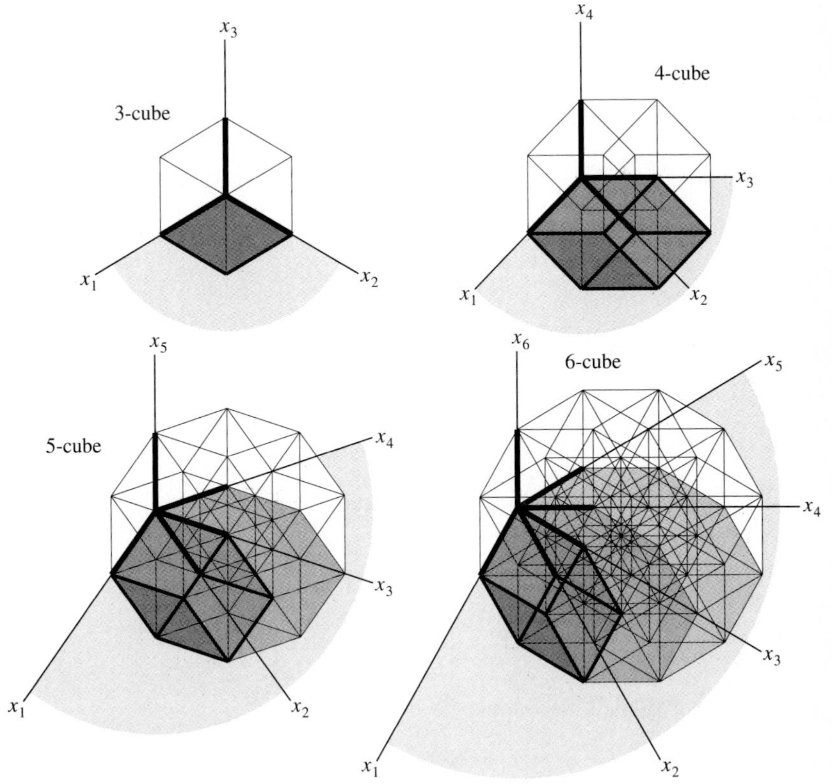

Figure 5.4 Isometric drawings of four n-cubes ($n = 3, 4, 5, 6$).

We build an **orientation** into any such parallelepiped by numbering its edges. So, this oriented parallelepiped corresponds to the matrix A whose jth column is the jth edge of the parallelogram.

We define the **signed volume** of a parallelepiped as the determinant $|A|$ of the corresponding matrix A.

EXAMPLES

1. The signed volume of the n-cube

$$I_n = \left\{ \begin{bmatrix} x_1 \\ \vdots \\ x_n \end{bmatrix} \middle| \, 0 \le x_r \le 1 \right\}$$

is the determinant of the identity transformation $T(\mathbf{x}) = I\mathbf{x} = \mathbf{x}$, which is $|T| = |I| = 1$. (Verify!)

2. $A_{13}(d) = \begin{bmatrix} 1 & 0 & d \\ 0 & 1 & 0 \\ 0 & 0 & 1 \end{bmatrix}$ represents

$$\left\{ a\begin{bmatrix} 1 \\ 0 \\ 0 \end{bmatrix} + b\begin{bmatrix} 0 \\ 1 \\ 0 \end{bmatrix} + c\begin{bmatrix} d \\ 0 \\ 1 \end{bmatrix} \middle| \, 0 \le a, b, c \le 1 \right\},$$

which has edges

$$\begin{bmatrix} 1 \\ 0 \\ 0 \end{bmatrix}, \quad \begin{bmatrix} 0 \\ 1 \\ 0 \end{bmatrix}, \quad \begin{bmatrix} d \\ 0 \\ 1 \end{bmatrix}$$

and signed volume $|A_{13}(d)| = 1$. (Verify!)

3. $M_2(k) = \begin{bmatrix} 1 & 0 & 0 \\ 0 & k & 0 \\ 0 & 0 & 1 \end{bmatrix}$ represents

$$\left\{ a\begin{bmatrix} 1 \\ 0 \\ 0 \end{bmatrix} + b\begin{bmatrix} 0 \\ k \\ 0 \end{bmatrix} + c\begin{bmatrix} 0 \\ 0 \\ 1 \end{bmatrix} \middle| \, 0 \le a, b, c \le 1 \right\},$$

which has edges

$$\begin{bmatrix} 1 \\ 0 \\ 0 \end{bmatrix}, \quad \begin{bmatrix} 0 \\ k \\ 0 \end{bmatrix}, \quad \begin{bmatrix} 0 \\ 0 \\ 1 \end{bmatrix}$$

and signed volume $|M_2(k)| = k$. (Verify!)

4. $I_{13} = \begin{bmatrix} 0 & 0 & 1 \\ 0 & 1 & 0 \\ 1 & 0 & 0 \end{bmatrix}$ represents

$$\left\{ a\begin{bmatrix} 0 \\ 0 \\ 1 \end{bmatrix} + b\begin{bmatrix} 0 \\ 1 \\ 0 \end{bmatrix} + c\begin{bmatrix} 1 \\ 0 \\ 0 \end{bmatrix} \middle| \, 0 \le a, b, c \le 1 \right\},$$

which has edges

$$\begin{bmatrix} 0 \\ 0 \\ 1 \end{bmatrix}, \quad \begin{bmatrix} 0 \\ 1 \\ 0 \end{bmatrix}, \quad \begin{bmatrix} 1 \\ 0 \\ 0 \end{bmatrix}$$

and signed volume $|I_{13}| = -1$. (Verify!)

Determinants of elementary matrices

Multiplying a matrix A on the right by an elementary matrix produces distinct results:

1. Multiplying A on the right-hand side by $A_{rs}(a)$ produces a **one-edge shear** of A as a parallelepiped; that is, it adds a times edge r of A to edge s of A and leaves the other edges of A alone. (Verify!)
2. Multiplying A on the right by $M_s(a)$ produces a **one-edge expansion** of A; that is, it multiplies edge s of A by a and leaves the other edges of A alone. (Verify!)
3. Finally, multiplying A on the right by I_{rs} interchanges edges r and s. (Verify!)

The following theorem shows that these **elementary edge operations** have the following effects on the signed volume of I:

1. The signed volume of the n cube I in $\mathbb{R}^n$ after undergoing a one-edge shear $I \to IA_{rs}(a)$ (add a times edge r to edge s) is still 1.
2. The signed volume of I is multiplied by a when it undergoes a one-edge expansion $I \to IM_s(a)$ (multiply edge s by a).
3. The sign of the signed volume of I changes when two edges of I are interchanged.

(See Figure 5.5.)

Theorem 5.4. *Determinants of the Elementary Matrices.*
The determinants of the elementary matrices over F are

1. $|E| = 1$ if $E = A_{rs}(a) \quad (r \neq s)$;
2. $|E| = a$ if $E = M_r(a)$;
3. $|E| = -1$ if $E = I_{rs} \quad (r \neq s)$.

Proof. For (1) and (2), use the fact that the determinant of an upper or lower triangular matrix is the product of its diagonal elements. For (3), the determinant $|I_{rs}|$ is -1, which is easily verified. (Do so!) ■

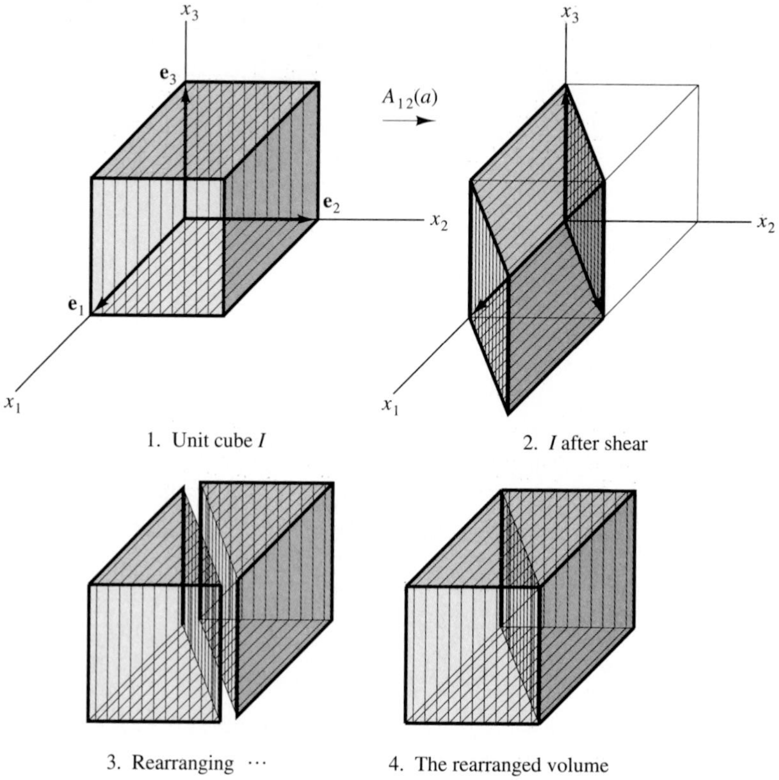

Figure 5.5 The volume of I before and after a one-edge shear is the same.

We show in Section 5.3 that the elementary edge operations have the same effect on the signed volume of any parallelepiped A as on that of I.

PROBLEMS

NUMERICAL PROBLEMS

1. Write out the sign matrix for $n = 4$.

2. Express the (1, 1), (1, 2), (1, 3) minors of

$$\begin{bmatrix} 2 & 4 & 6 \\ 3 & 4 & 5 \\ 4 & 6 & 8 \end{bmatrix}$$

in terms of 2×2 determinants.

3. Compute the determinants of the following matrices.

(a) $A = \begin{bmatrix} 1 & 1 & 1 \\ 0 & 3 & 5 \\ 1 & 0 & 0 \end{bmatrix}$ **(b)** $B = \begin{bmatrix} 1 & 0 & 1 \\ 0 & 5 & 3 \\ 1 & 0 & 0 \end{bmatrix}$

(c) $C = \begin{bmatrix} 0 & 1 & 0 \\ 0 & 2 & 7 \\ 1 & 0 & 0 \end{bmatrix}$ **(d)** $D = \begin{bmatrix} 1 & 2 & 3 & 4 \\ 2 & 0 & 0 & 0 \\ 3 & 0 & 5 & 6 \\ 0 & 2 & 0 & 0 \end{bmatrix}$

(e) $E = \begin{bmatrix} a & 0 & 0 \\ 0 & 1 & 0 \\ 0 & 0 & 3 \end{bmatrix}$.

4. Compute the determinants of the following block matrices, the blocks A, B, C, D, being those in Problem 3.

(a) $\begin{bmatrix} B & * & 0 \\ 0 & A & 0 \\ * & * & B \end{bmatrix}$ (9×9 matrix)

(b) $\begin{bmatrix} A & 0 & 0 \\ * & B & * \\ * & 0 & A \end{bmatrix}$ (9×9 matrix)

(c) $\begin{bmatrix} A & 0 & 0 \\ * & B & * \\ 0 & 0 & D \end{bmatrix}$ (10×10 matrix)

5. Suppose that it takes a microcomputer 1 second to compute the determinant of a 13×13 matrix A using the LDU factorization.

(a) Verify that it takes the same computer 3(10!) seconds = 126 days to compute a 13×13 matrix recursively from its definition.

(b) How many seconds does it take the same computer to compute the determinant of a 15×15 determinant using the LDU factorization?

(c) How many years does it take the same computer to compute the determinant for a 15×15 determinant recursively by first-row expansion? How many centuries for a 16×16 determinant?

6. Compute the determinants

$$\begin{vmatrix} 2 & 1 \\ 1 & 2 \end{vmatrix}, \quad \begin{vmatrix} 2 & 1 & 0 \\ 1 & 2 & 1 \\ 0 & 1 & 2 \end{vmatrix}, \quad \begin{vmatrix} 2 & 1 & 0 & 0 \\ 1 & 2 & 1 & 0 \\ 0 & 1 & 2 & 1 \\ 0 & 0 & 1 & 2 \end{vmatrix}$$

directly from the definition of determinant.

7. The

$$\begin{bmatrix} + & \boxed{-} & + \\ - & \boxed{+} & - \\ + & \boxed{-} & + \end{bmatrix}$$

expansion of $|A|$ is $-3\begin{vmatrix} 7 & 3 \\ 5 & 6 \end{vmatrix} + 4\begin{vmatrix} 3 & 8 \\ 5 & 6 \end{vmatrix} - 5\begin{vmatrix} 3 & 8 \\ 7 & 3 \end{vmatrix}$. What is A?

THEORETICAL PROBLEMS

8. Show that $|AE| = |A||E|$ if A and E are 2×2 matrices and E is elementary.
9. For $n = 2$, prove that if $A = LDU$ (L, U triangular with 1s on the diagonal), then $|A| = |D|$.
10. For $n = 2$, prove by direct computation that $|AB| = |A||B|$ for A, $B \in M_nF$.
11. Prove that $|I_{rs}| = -1$:
    (a) For $n = 3$; (b) For $n = 4$; (c) For any n.

5.3 PROPERTIES OF DETERMINANTS

Column properties

The image of the n-cube I_n under the linear transformation $T(\mathbf{x}) = A\mathbf{x}$ is represented by A, whereby its edges are represented by the columns of A and its signed volume is $|A|$. If the sth column of A is the sum $\mathbf{v} + \mathbf{w}$ of the sth columns $\mathbf{v}$ and $\mathbf{w}$ of matrices B and C whose $n - 1$ other columns are identical to those of A, we represent A by $A_{\mathbf{v}+\mathbf{w}}$, B by $A_{\mathbf{v}}$, and C by $A_{\mathbf{w}}$.

EXAMPLE

For $s = 2$, $A_{\mathbf{v}} = \begin{bmatrix} 1 & 2 & 3 \\ 5 & 3 & 3 \\ 1 & 4 & 4 \end{bmatrix}$ and $A_{\mathbf{w}} = \begin{bmatrix} 1 & 0 & 3 \\ 5 & 2 & 3 \\ 1 & 5 & 4 \end{bmatrix}$, then

$$A_{\mathbf{v}+\mathbf{w}} = \begin{bmatrix} 1 & 2+0 & 3 \\ 5 & 3+2 & 3 \\ 1 & 4+5 & 4 \end{bmatrix}.$$

Our first theorem says that the signed volume $|A_{\mathbf{v}+\mathbf{w}}|$ is the sum of the signed volumes $|A_{\mathbf{v}}|$ and $|A_{\mathbf{w}}|$ (Figure 5.6).

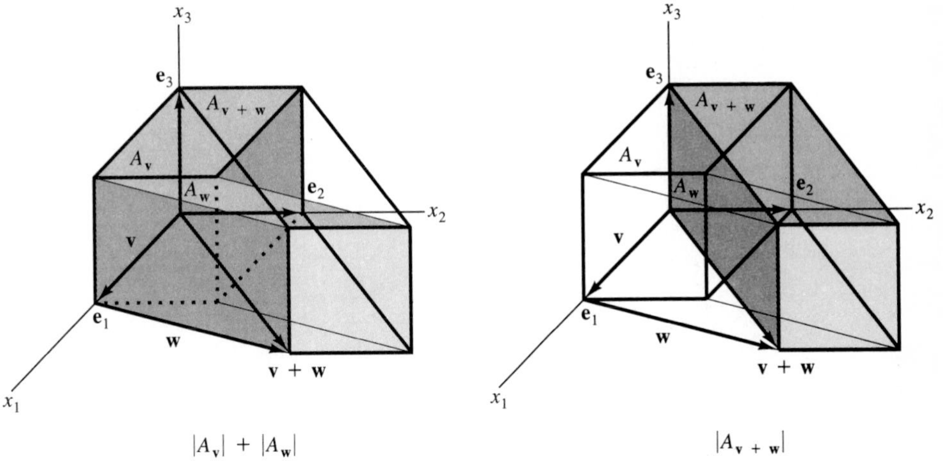

Figure 5.6 The signed volume of A_{v+w} is the sum of that of A_v and A_w.

Theorem 5.5. *Additivity of the Determinant in a Given Column.*
Let A, B, and C be $n \times n$ matrices over F. Suppose that column s of A is the sum of the column s of B and column s of C, but all the remaining $n-1$ columns of A, B, and C are the same. Then $|A| = |B| + |C|$.

Proof. The proof for $n = 2$ is left to the reader, and we turn to the proof for $n = 3$. For $n > 3$, the proof goes the same way, and we omit the details.

We'll assume $s = 1$, although the same argument works for any s. Then

$$\begin{vmatrix} a+a' & b & c \\ d+d' & e & f \\ g+g' & h & i \end{vmatrix} = (a+a')\begin{vmatrix} e & f \\ h & i \end{vmatrix} - b\begin{vmatrix} d+d' & f \\ g+g' & i \end{vmatrix} + c\begin{vmatrix} d+d' & e \\ g+g' & h \end{vmatrix}$$

$$= a\begin{vmatrix} e & f \\ h & i \end{vmatrix} - b\begin{vmatrix} d & f \\ g & i \end{vmatrix} + c\begin{vmatrix} d & e \\ g & h \end{vmatrix}$$

$$+ a'\begin{vmatrix} e & f \\ h & i \end{vmatrix} - b\begin{vmatrix} d' & f \\ g' & i \end{vmatrix} + c\begin{vmatrix} d' & e \\ g' & h \end{vmatrix}$$

$$= \begin{vmatrix} a & b & c \\ d & e & f \\ g & h & i \end{vmatrix} + \begin{vmatrix} a' & b & c \\ d' & e & f \\ g' & h & i \end{vmatrix} = |B| + |C|.$$

Note that we actually use the property for $n = 2$ to split up the determinants $\begin{vmatrix} d+d' & f \\ g+g' & i \end{vmatrix}$ and $\begin{vmatrix} d+d' & e \\ g+g' & h \end{vmatrix}$. ■

EXAMPLE

To compute the determinant

$$\begin{vmatrix} a & b & c \\ d & e & f \\ 0 & h & i \end{vmatrix},$$

write it as

$$\begin{vmatrix} a & b & c \\ d & e & f \\ 0 & h & i \end{vmatrix} = \begin{vmatrix} a & b & c \\ 0 & e & f \\ 0 & h & i \end{vmatrix} + \begin{vmatrix} 0 & b & c \\ d & e & f \\ 0 & h & i \end{vmatrix}$$

$$= a\begin{vmatrix} e & f \\ h & i \end{vmatrix} - bdi + cdh.$$

(Explain!)

Theorem 5.6. *Column Properties of the Determinant.*
The determinant $|A|$ has the following properties.

1. $|A|$ is unchanged if a multiple of one column is added to another.
2. $|A|$ is multiplied by t if one column is replaced by t times itself.
3. $|A|$ is multiplied by -1 if two columns of A are interchanged.
4. $|A|$ is 0 if A has two equal columns.

Proof. We leave the proof of this theorem for $n = 2$ to the reader and prove it for $n = 3$. The proof goes the same way for $n > 3$, and we again omit the details.

For Property 3, assume first that the columns to be interchanged are adjacent. We may as well assume that the first two columns are to be interchanged, since the proof goes the same way for any two adjacent columns. When we expand the matrices before and after interchange of the two adjacent columns, the signs of the terms corresponding to these two columns change:

$$\begin{vmatrix} a & b & c \\ d & e & f \\ g & h & i \end{vmatrix} = a\begin{vmatrix} e & f \\ h & i \end{vmatrix} - b\begin{vmatrix} d & f \\ g & i \end{vmatrix} + c\begin{vmatrix} d & e \\ g & h \end{vmatrix},$$

$$\begin{vmatrix} b & a & c \\ e & d & f \\ h & g & i \end{vmatrix} = b\begin{vmatrix} d & f \\ g & i \end{vmatrix} - a\begin{vmatrix} e & f \\ h & i \end{vmatrix} + c\begin{vmatrix} e & d \\ h & g \end{vmatrix}.$$

For the terms corresponding to the other columns, each one is obtained by interchanging two adjacent columns in the $(n-1) \times (n-1)$ determinant part of that term. Since we are able to assume the theorem for $n - 1$, these terms also change signs. So, the net effect of the interchange of adjacent columns is to change the sign of the determinant. What happens when the columns are not adjacent? If we perform the adjacent interchanges needed to interchange the given columns r and s, leaving the other columns unchanged, we need an odd number, $2(s - r) - 1$, of interchanges. (Verify!) For example, to interchange columns 2 and 5, we perform the $5 = 2(5 - 2) - 1$ interchanges

$$1234567 \to 1324567 \to 1342567 \to 1345267 \to 1354267 \to 1534267$$

needed. So, there are an odd number of corresponding sign changes, resulting in a single net sign change.

Given (3), we easily get (4). Interchanging the two equal columns certainly has no effect on $|A|$. By (3), on the other hand, such an interchange results in $|A|$ being multiplied by a factor of -1. So, $|A| = -|A|$, which implies that $|A|$ must be 0.

Next we prove (2), assuming that column 1 is to be multiplied by t. The proof goes the same way for the other columns.

$$\begin{aligned}\begin{vmatrix} ta & b & c \\ td & e & f \\ tg & h & i \end{vmatrix} &= ta\begin{vmatrix} e & f \\ h & i \end{vmatrix} - b\begin{vmatrix} td & f \\ tg & i \end{vmatrix} + c\begin{vmatrix} td & e \\ tg & h \end{vmatrix} \\ &= ta\begin{vmatrix} e & f \\ h & i \end{vmatrix} - bt\begin{vmatrix} d & f \\ g & i \end{vmatrix} + ct\begin{vmatrix} d & e \\ g & h \end{vmatrix} \\ &= t\left(a\begin{vmatrix} e & f \\ h & i \end{vmatrix} - b\begin{vmatrix} b & c \\ h & i \end{vmatrix} + c\begin{vmatrix} b & c \\ e & f \end{vmatrix}\right) \\ &= t\begin{vmatrix} a & b & c \\ d & e & f \\ g & h & i \end{vmatrix} = t|A|.\end{aligned}$$

Finally, we prove (1). For this, we'll assume that t times column 3 is added to column 1. The proof goes the same way for any other two columns. We get

$$\begin{vmatrix} a+tc & b & c \\ d+tf & e & f \\ g+ti & h & i \end{vmatrix} = (a + tc)\begin{vmatrix} e & f \\ h & i \end{vmatrix} - b\begin{vmatrix} d+tf & f \\ g+ti & i \end{vmatrix} + c\begin{vmatrix} d+tf & e \\ g+ti & h \end{vmatrix}.$$

By Theorem 5.5 and Parts (2), (3), (4) of Theorem 5.6, we have

$$\begin{vmatrix} d+tf & f \\ g+ti & i \end{vmatrix} = \begin{vmatrix} d & f \\ g & i \end{vmatrix} + t\begin{vmatrix} f & f \\ i & i \end{vmatrix} = \begin{vmatrix} d & f \\ g & i \end{vmatrix} + 0,$$

$$\begin{vmatrix} d+tf & e \\ g+ti & h \end{vmatrix} = \begin{vmatrix} d & e \\ g & h \end{vmatrix} + t\begin{vmatrix} f & e \\ i & h \end{vmatrix} = \begin{vmatrix} d & e \\ g & h \end{vmatrix} - t\begin{vmatrix} e & f \\ h & i \end{vmatrix}.$$

Substituting these expressions and simplifying results in

$$\begin{vmatrix} a+tc & b & c \\ d+tf & e & f \\ g+ti & h & i \end{vmatrix} = a\begin{vmatrix} e & f \\ h & i \end{vmatrix} - b\begin{vmatrix} d & f \\ g & i \end{vmatrix} + c\begin{vmatrix} d & e \\ g & h \end{vmatrix} = |A|. \quad \blacksquare$$

EXAMPLES

1. $\begin{vmatrix} a & b \\ 0 & d \end{vmatrix} = ad$ and $\begin{vmatrix} a+3b & b \\ 3d & d \end{vmatrix} = ad + 3bd - 3bd = ad$
2. $\begin{vmatrix} a & bt \\ 0 & dt \end{vmatrix} = adt$ and $t\begin{vmatrix} a & b \\ 0 & d \end{vmatrix} = tad$
3. $\begin{vmatrix} b & a \\ d & 0 \end{vmatrix} = 0b - ad = -ad$

The effect of column reduction

Theorem 5.6 enables us to monitor accumulating changes in the determinant as A undergoes a column reduction

$$A \to AE_1 \to \cdots \to AE_1 \cdots E_d.$$

Theorem 5.7. *Determinants and Products by Elementary Matrices.* $|AE_1 \cdots E_d| = |A||E_1| \cdots |E_d|$ for any matrix A and elementary matrices $E_1, \ldots, E_d$.

Proof. We first prove that $|AE| = |A||E|$ for any elementary matrix E. There are three cases.

1. Let $E = A_{rs}(t)$ $(r \neq s)$. Then AE is the matrix obtained from A by adding t times column r to column s, so that AE and A have the same determinant, by Theorem 5.6. Since $|E| = 1$, by Theorem 5.4, we have $|AE| = |A| = |A||E|$.
2. Let $E = M_r(t)$. Then AE is the matrix obtained from A by multiplying column r by t. We then have $|AE| = t|A|$ by Theorem 5.6. Since $|E| = t$, by Theorem 5.4, $|AE| = t|A| = |A||E|$.
3. Finally, for $E = I_{rs}$ $(r \neq s)$, AE is obtained from A by interchanging columns r and s. So, $|AE| = -|A|$, by Theorem 5.6. Since $|E| = -1$ by Theorem 5.4, we again have $|AE| = |A||E|$.

Since $|AE| = |A||E|$ for any elementary matrix and any A, we can apply the equation repeatedly to get

$$\begin{aligned} |AE_1 \cdots E_{d-1}E_d| &= |AE_1 \cdots E_{d-1}||E_d| \\ &\ \vdots \\ &= |AE_1| \cdots |E_{d-1}||E_d| \\ &= |A||E_1| \cdots |E_{d-1}||E_d|. \quad \blacksquare \end{aligned}$$

Theorem 5.7 unleashes the latent potential of the determinant function. The powerful consequences of it, which we collect here, are indispensable tools for the remainder of the book.

The determinant of the transpose

An invertible matrix A can be written as a product $A = E_1 \cdots E_d$ of elementary matrices, by Theorem 3.24. Taking transposes, $A^T = E_d^T \cdots E_1^T$. Since E_s is an elementary matrix, $|E_s^T| = |E_s|$. (Prove!) It follows from Theorem 5.7 that

$$|A^T| = |E_d^T| \cdots |E_1^T| = |E_1| \cdots |E_d| = |A|,$$

which proves the following theorem, illustrated in Figure 5.7.

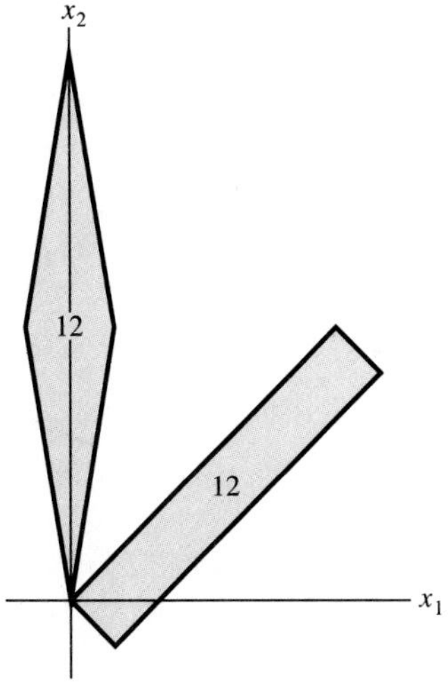

Figure 5.7 The transposed determinants $\begin{vmatrix} 1 & 6 \\ -1 & 6 \end{vmatrix}$ and $\begin{vmatrix} 1 & -1 \\ 6 & 6 \end{vmatrix}$ both equal 12.

Theorem 5.8. *The Determinant of an Invertible Matrix.*
If A is invertible, then $|A|$ is nonzero and $|A| = |A^T|$.

As different as A and A^T can be, they share many properties. We know from Section 3.6 that they have the same rank. Theorem 5.8 shows that they have the same determinant when A is invertible, and Theorem 5.11 shows the same even when A is not invertible. Further shared properties of A and A^T are discussed in the next chapter.

Row properties

The transpose operation enables us to transfer our column properties to row properties.

Corollary. The determinant $|A|$ has the following properties:

1. $|A|$ is unchanged if a multiple of one row is added to another.
2. $|A|$ is multiplied by t if one row is replaced by t times itself.
3. $|A|$ is multiplied by -1 if two rows of A are interchanged.
4. $|A|$ is 0 if A has two equal rows.

Proof. For (3), note that if two rows of A are interchanged to get B, then two columns of A^T are interchanged to get B^T. By Theorems 5.7 and 5.8, it follows that $|B| = |B^T| = -|A^T| = -|A|$. The other properties are proved the same way. ■

Any row or column becomes the first row after appropriate row and column interchanges and the transpose are performed.

EXAMPLE

The second column of $\begin{bmatrix} a & b \\ c & d \end{bmatrix}$ becomes the first row upon transposing to $\begin{bmatrix} a & c \\ b & d \end{bmatrix}$ and interchanging rows to $\begin{bmatrix} b & d \\ a & c \end{bmatrix}$.

Taking sign changes into account along the way, we get the following.

Theorem 5.9. *Row and Column Expansions of the Determinant.* The determinant of A is given by the equations

$$|A| = (-1)^{r+1}a_{r1}|A_{r1}| + \cdots + (-1)^{r+s}a_{rs}|A_{rs}| + \cdots + (-1)^{r+n}a_{rn}|A_{rn}|,$$
$$|A| = (-1)^{1+s}a_{1s}|A_{1s}| + \cdots + (-1)^{r+s}a_{rs}|A_{rs}| + \cdots + (-1)^{n+s}a_{ns}|A_{ns}|,$$

for any row r and column s.

EXAMPLES

1. The column 3 expansion of

$$\begin{vmatrix} 2 & 1 & 3 \\ 3 & 1 & 2 \\ 2 & 1 & 0 \end{vmatrix} \quad \text{is} \quad 3\begin{vmatrix} 3 & 0 \\ 2 & 1 \end{vmatrix} - 2\begin{vmatrix} 2 & 1 \\ 2 & 1 \end{vmatrix} + 0 = 3.$$

2. The row 2 expansion of

$$\begin{vmatrix} 2 & 1 & 3 \\ 3 & 0 & 2 \\ 2 & 1 & 0 \end{vmatrix} \quad \text{is} \quad -3\begin{vmatrix} 1 & 3 \\ 1 & 0 \end{vmatrix} + 0 - 2\begin{vmatrix} 2 & 1 \\ 2 & 1 \end{vmatrix} = 3.$$

When A is not invertible, neither is its transpose A^T. (Explain!) So, A^T is row equivalent to an echelon matrix whose last row is $\mathbf{0}$. (Explain!) It follows that A is column equivalent to a matrix B whose last column is $\mathbf{0}$, and we have $AE_1 \cdots E_d = B$, where the E's are the elementary matrices used to get a column reduction of A to B. Since B has a zero column, its determinant is zero, by Property 2 of Theorem 5.6. (Explain!) But then $|A||E_1| \cdots |E_d| = |B| = 0$. Since the $|E_s|$'s are nonzero, it follows that $|A|$ is 0. The converse is also true, by Theorem 5.8, so we have proved the following theorem.

Theorem 5.10. *The Determinant and Invertibility of A.*
A is invertible if and only if $|A|$ is nonzero.

By Theorem 5.10, the determinants of A and A^T are both 0 when A is not invertible. By Theorem 5.8, this gives us the following.

Theorem 5.11. *The Determinant of the Transpose.*
The determinants of A and A^T are always equal.

The product formula

Since factoring a matrix A as product of simpler factors is so easy and so useful, it would be very convenient to have a formula relating the determinant of A to that of its factors. Fortunately, the relationship is simple and has far-reaching consequences. It is given in the following theorem and illustrated in Figure 5.8.

Theorem 5.12. *The Product Formula.*
For $A, B \in M_{n \times n}F$, $|AB| = |A||B|$.

Proof. Suppose first that A or B is not invertible. Then AB is not invertible, by Theorem 3.22. In this case, $|AB| = 0 = |A||B|$ by Theorem 5.10.

Suppose next that A and B are invertible. Then AB is invertible. Factoring A and B as products $A = E_1 \cdots E_d$ and $B = E_{d+1} \cdots E_e$ of elementary matrices, we have

$$|AB| = |E_1 \cdots E_d E_{d+1} \cdots E_e| = |E_1| \cdots |E_d||E_{d+1}| \cdots |E_e|$$

$$|A||B| = |E_1 \cdots E_d||E_{d+1} \cdots E_e| = |E_1| \cdots |E_d||E_{d+1}| \cdots |E_e|$$

by Theorem 5.7, and $|AB| = |A||B|$. ■

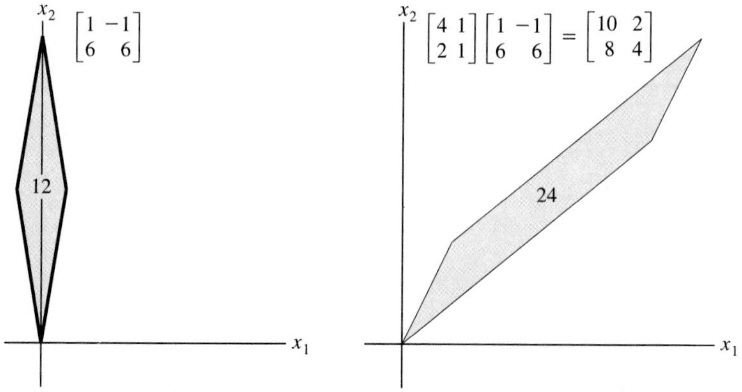

Figure 5.8 By the product formula, upon multiplying B by A, $|B|$ changes to $|AB| = |A||B|$.

EXAMPLE

The determinant of $\begin{bmatrix}1 & 2\\3 & 1\end{bmatrix}\begin{bmatrix}1 & 3\\2 & 1\end{bmatrix}$ is $\begin{vmatrix}1 & 2\\3 & 1\end{vmatrix}^2 = 25$, by Theorems 5.11 and 5.12.

The product formula for the determinant gives us the following corollary.

Corollary. If A is invertible, then $|A^{-1}| = |A|^{-1}$.

Proof. $1 = |I| = |AA^{-1}| = |A||A^{-1}|$. ■

EXAMPLE

The determinant of $\begin{bmatrix}12\\31\end{bmatrix}^{-1}$ is $\frac{1}{6}$.

Computation of the determinant

One of the big, albeit simple, successes of the product formula is the following corollary, which provides a very efficient method for computing the determinant of a matrix (see Section 5.2).

Corollary. *The Determinant of a Matrix with LDU Factorization.*
If $A = LDU$, where $D = \text{Diag}(d_1 \cdots d_n)$ and L and U are lower and upper triangular with 1s on the diagonal, then $|A| = d_1 \cdots d_n$.

Proof. By the product formula, we have $|A| = |L||D||U|$. So, by Theorem 5.3, $|L| = 1$, $|D| = d_1 \cdots d_n$, $|U| = 1$, and $|A| = d_1 \cdots d_n$. ■

When an invertible matrix A does not factor as $A = LDU$, it does factor as $A = PLDU$, where $|P| = (-1)^k$, k being the number of row interchanges taken to form P from I (Section 3.7 and Theorem 5.3). So, the most general formula for the determinant of A is

$$|A| = (-1)^k d_1 \cdots d_n$$

where the d's are the pivots in the $PLDU$ reduction and k is the number of row interchanges used to get them.

EXAMPLES

1. Since

$$\begin{bmatrix} 4 & 4 \\ 4 & 7 \end{bmatrix} = \begin{bmatrix} 1 & 0 \\ 1 & 1 \end{bmatrix} \begin{bmatrix} 4 & 0 \\ 0 & 3 \end{bmatrix} \begin{bmatrix} 1 & 1 \\ 0 & 1 \end{bmatrix},$$

its determinant is $4 \cdot 3 = 12$. No P is needed since the matrix is positive definite.

2. Since $\begin{bmatrix} 0 & 4 \\ 4 & 8 \end{bmatrix} = \begin{bmatrix} 0 & 1 \\ 1 & 0 \end{bmatrix} \begin{bmatrix} 4 & 8 \\ 0 & 4 \end{bmatrix} = \begin{bmatrix} 0 & 1 \\ 1 & 0 \end{bmatrix} \begin{bmatrix} 1 & 0 \\ 0 & 1 \end{bmatrix} \begin{bmatrix} 4 & 0 \\ 0 & 4 \end{bmatrix} \begin{bmatrix} 1 & 2 \\ 0 & 1 \end{bmatrix}$ is the $PLDU$ decomposition of $\begin{bmatrix} 0 & 4 \\ 4 & 8 \end{bmatrix}$ and $k = 1$ row interchange was needed, the determinant is $(-1)^1 4 \cdot 4 = -16$.

The determinant of a linear transformation

Theorem 5.13. If A and B are similar, then $|A| = |B|$.

Proof. Since A and B are similar, there is an invertible matrix C such that $B = CAC^{-1}$. But then $|B| = |CAC^{-1}| = |C||A||C|^{-1} = |A|$. ■

Given a finite-dimensional vector space V over F and linear transformation $T \in L(V, V)$, we have seen that the matrix of T with respect to one basis is similar to the matrix of T with respect to another basis. Since similar matrices have the same determinant, the following definition is justified.

Definition. *The Determinant of a Linear Transformation of V.*
For any finite-dimensional vector space V over F, the **determinant** of a linear transformation $T \in L(V, V)$ is the determinant of its matrix with respect to some basis of V.

EXAMPLE

Let V be the hyperplane $x_1 + x_2 - 2x_3 = 0$ and suppose that $T \in L(V, V)$ is defined as

$$T\begin{bmatrix} a \\ b \\ c \end{bmatrix} = \begin{bmatrix} b \\ a \\ c \end{bmatrix} \quad \text{for} \quad \begin{bmatrix} a \\ b \\ c \end{bmatrix} \in V.$$

Note that $\begin{bmatrix} b \\ a \\ c \end{bmatrix} \in V$ if $\begin{bmatrix} a \\ b \\ c \end{bmatrix} \in V$. (Explain!) Let $\mathbf{v}$, $\mathbf{w}$ be the basis

$$\begin{bmatrix} 1 \\ 2 \\ -3 \end{bmatrix}, \quad \begin{bmatrix} 1 \\ 0 \\ -1 \end{bmatrix}$$

of V. (We chose this basis not since it was the best to use, but as a typical basis to illustrate the phenomena.) The matrix of T is the transpose of the coefficient matrix for the equations

$$T\begin{bmatrix} 1 \\ 2 \\ -3 \end{bmatrix} = \begin{bmatrix} 0 \\ 1 \\ -3 \end{bmatrix} = \tfrac{1}{2}\begin{bmatrix} 1 \\ 2 \\ -3 \end{bmatrix} + \tfrac{3}{2}\begin{bmatrix} 1 \\ 0 \\ -1 \end{bmatrix},$$

$$T\begin{bmatrix} 1 \\ 0 \\ -1 \end{bmatrix} = \begin{bmatrix} 0 \\ 1 \\ -1 \end{bmatrix} = \tfrac{1}{2}\begin{bmatrix} 1 \\ 2 \\ -3 \end{bmatrix} - \tfrac{1}{2}\begin{bmatrix} 1 \\ 0 \\ -1 \end{bmatrix}.$$

So, the matrix of T is $\begin{bmatrix} 1/2 & 1/2 \\ 3/2 & -1/2 \end{bmatrix}$ and the determinant of T is $-\frac{1}{4} - \frac{3}{4} = -1$.

By the isomorphism R from a vector space V over F to F^n, theorems on determinants of matrices go over to theorems on determinants of linear transformations. We now restate Theorem 5.10 as an example.

The Determinant and Invertibility of T.
If V is an n-dimensional vector space and $T \in L(V, V)$, T is invertible if and only if $|T|$ is nonzero.

PROBLEMS

NUMERICAL PROBLEMS

1. Compute the determinants of the following matrices by any method.

(a) $\begin{bmatrix} 1 & 2 & 1 \\ 2 & 3 & 1 \\ 0 & 1 & 2 \end{bmatrix}$ (b) $\begin{bmatrix} 1 & 2 & 2 & 1 \\ 2 & 1 & 4 & 4 \\ 3 & 0 & 0 & 0 \\ 5 & 1 & 0 & 1 \end{bmatrix}$ (c) $\begin{bmatrix} 2 & 0 & 0 & 3 \\ 0 & 1 & 0 & 4 \\ 3 & 5 & 16 & 2 \\ 5 & 1 & 0 & 1 \end{bmatrix}$

2. Compute the determinants of the following products of matrices.

(a) $\begin{bmatrix} 1 & 2 & 1 \\ 2 & 3 & 1 \\ 0 & 1 & 2 \end{bmatrix}\begin{bmatrix} 1 & 2 & 0 \\ 2 & 3 & 1 \\ 1 & 1 & 2 \end{bmatrix}$ (b) $\begin{bmatrix} 1 & 2 & 2 & 1 \\ 2 & 1 & 4 & 4 \\ 3 & 0 & 0 & 0 \\ 5 & 1 & 0 & 1 \end{bmatrix}\begin{bmatrix} 2 & 0 & 0 & 3 \\ 0 & 1 & 0 & 4 \\ 3 & 5 & 16 & 2 \\ 5 & 1 & 0 & 1 \end{bmatrix}$

3. Compute $|T|$ if:

(a) $T(\mathbf{x}) = \begin{bmatrix} 2x_1 + 2x_2 + 0x_3 \\ 1x_1 + 2x_2 + 1x_3 \\ 0x_1 + 1x_2 + 2x_3 \end{bmatrix}$; (b) $T(\mathbf{x}) = \begin{bmatrix} 2x_1 + 3x_2 + 4x_3 \\ 5x_1 + 6x_2 + 7x_3 \\ 0x_1 + 0x_2 + 1x_3 \end{bmatrix}$;

(c) $T(\mathbf{x}) = \begin{bmatrix} 2x_1 + 1x_2 + 0x_3 \\ 2x_1 + 4x_2 + 2x_3 \\ 0x_1 + 1x_2 + 2x_3 \end{bmatrix}$.

4. Find the determinant of the Cartan matrix

$$C = \begin{bmatrix} 2 & -1 & 0 \\ -1 & 2 & -2 \\ 0 & -1 & 2 \end{bmatrix}$$

by way of the LDU factorization. (See Problem 4, Section 3.7.)

5. Find the determinant of the Cartan matrix

$$A_3 = \begin{bmatrix} 2 & -1 & 0 \\ -1 & 2 & -1 \\ 0 & -1 & 2 \end{bmatrix}$$

by way of the LDL^T factorization. (See Problem 11, Section 3.8.)

THEORETICAL PROBLEMS

6. Let $A \in M_n F$. If $\mathbf{v}A = \mathbf{0}$ for some nonzero row vector $\mathbf{v}$, show that $A\mathbf{w} = \mathbf{0}$ for some nonzero vector $\mathbf{w}$.

7. Show that if we perform the adjacent interchanges needed to interchange the given columns r and s, leaving the other columns unchanged, we need an odd number, $2(s - r) - 1$, of interchanges. (Assume $r < s$.)

8. Explain why $|A|$ is a linear function of the jth column of A, all entries in the other columns being held fixed.

9. If

$$A = \begin{bmatrix} A_1 & & * \\ & \ddots & \\ 0 & & A_n \end{bmatrix}$$

with square blocks A_r on the diagonal and 0s above them, show that the determinant is $|A_1| \cdots |A_n|$. (***Hint:*** Use the corresponding result for the transpose of A.)

10. Let A be invertible. Then, after some permutation of the columns of A, all entries on the main diagonal are nonzero.

11. Let A be invertible. Then, after some permutation of the columns of A, all principal minors are nonzero. Here, the ***r*th principal minor** of A is the determinant $|A_r|$ of the $r \times r$ matrix in the first r rows and columns of A.

5.4 VOLUME

We introduced the *signed volume* of the oriented parallelepiped represented by A as the determinant $|A|$. Now, we define its (absolute) **volume** to be the absolute value $||A||$ of $|A|$. Letting $f(A)$ denote the volume of A, we have the following (see Figure 5.9).

1. $f(A)$ is nonnegative and $f(A) = 0$ if any column of A is 0;
2. $f(A) = f(A')$ if A' is obtained from A by a one-edge shear (add a times edge r to edge s) or interchange of two columns;
3. $f(A) = |d_1 \cdots d_n|$ if its edges are $d_1\mathbf{e}_1, \ldots, d_n\mathbf{e}_n$.

The following theorem shows that this is the only such function, which gives assurance that we have the right definition for volume.

Theorem 5.14. *Volume of a Parallelepiped.*

Suppose that a function $g(A)$ of $n \times n$ matrices A satisfies the following conditions for all A.

1. $g(A)$ is nonnegative and $g(0) = 0$ if any column of A is 0.
2. $g(A) = g(A')$ if A' is obtained from A by a one-edge shear or interchange of two columns.
3. $g(A) = |d_1 \cdots d_n|$ if $A = \mathrm{Diag}(d_1, \ldots, d_n)$.

Then $g(A)$ is the absolute value of $|A|$ for all A.

Proof. Using only the elementary matrices $A_{ij}(t)$ and I_{ij}, we can column-reduce A to a matrix A', which is either diagonal or has a zero

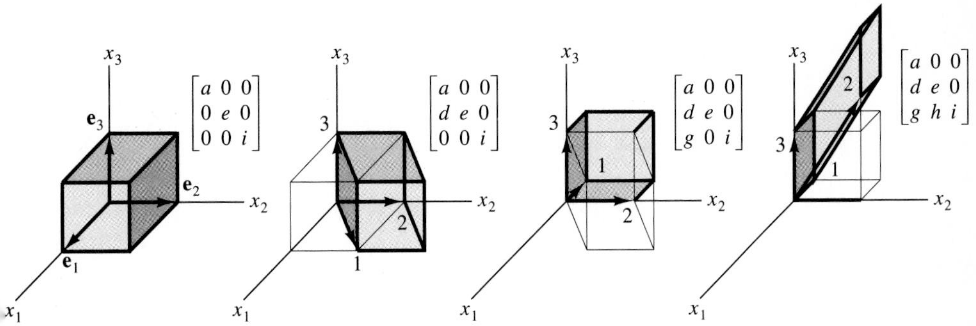

(a)

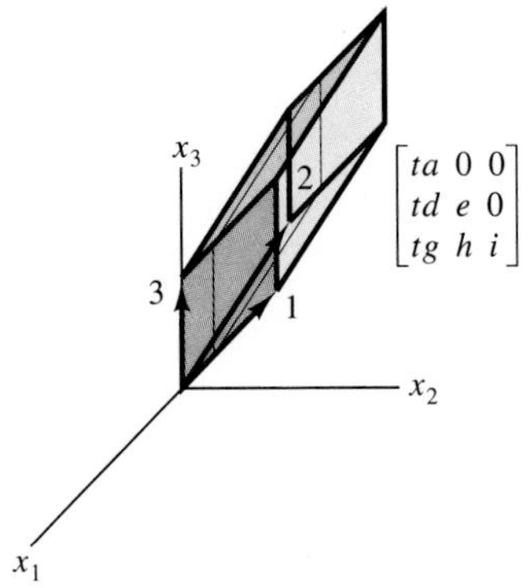

(b)

Figure 5.9 (a) The volume of

$$\begin{bmatrix} a & 0 & 0 \\ 0 & e & 0 \\ 0 & 0 & i \end{bmatrix} \text{ equals that of } \begin{bmatrix} a & 0 & 0 \\ d & e & 0 \\ 0 & 0 & i \end{bmatrix}, \quad \begin{bmatrix} a & 0 & 0 \\ d & e & 0 \\ g & 0 & i \end{bmatrix}, \quad \begin{bmatrix} a & 0 & 0 \\ d & e & 0 \\ g & h & i \end{bmatrix},$$

obtained in succession by one-edge shears

$$\begin{bmatrix} a \\ 0 \\ 0 \end{bmatrix} \to \begin{bmatrix} a \\ d \\ 0 \end{bmatrix}, \quad \begin{bmatrix} a \\ d \\ 0 \end{bmatrix} \to \begin{bmatrix} a \\ d \\ g \end{bmatrix}, \quad \begin{bmatrix} 0 \\ e \\ 0 \end{bmatrix} \to \begin{bmatrix} 0 \\ e \\ h \end{bmatrix}.$$

(b) The volume of $\begin{bmatrix} ta & 0 & 0 \\ td & e & 0 \\ tg & h & i \end{bmatrix}$, resulting from $\begin{bmatrix} a & 0 & 0 \\ d & e & 0 \\ g & h & i \end{bmatrix}$

by edge expansion.

column. (Explain!) Since multiplication of A on the right by $A_{ij}(t)$ is a one-edge shear of A and by I_{ij} is an interchange of columns, $f(A) = f(A')$ and $g(A) = g(A')$. But $f(A') = g(A') = 0$ if A' has a zero column and $f(A') = g(A') = |d_1 \cdots d_n|$ if $A' = \text{Diag}(d_1, \ldots, d_n)$. So, $g(A) = f(A)$ is the absolute value of the determinant of A. ■

The product formula $|AB| = |A||B|$ gives the **expansion** (or *expansion/contraction*) **factor** $|A| = |T|$ for the change from the signed volume of the parallelepiped B to that of its image AB under the linear transformation $T(\mathbf{x}) = A\mathbf{x}$ (Figure 5.8).

Since n-space is filled by a *grid* of unit n-cubes, an invertible linear transformation T maps any geometric shape (set of points in n-space) in this grid to a geometric shape in an image grid of congruent parallelepipeds (Figure 5.10). By refining the grid, the volume of the shape is **inner approximated** by the total volume of the *enclosed* grid elements. Similarly, the volume is **outer approximated** by the total volume of the *enclosing* grid elements. Upon taking finer grids, the outer approximations decrease and the inner approximations increase. (Explain!) Passing to the limit as the size of the grid element goes to 0, the outer approximations converge to the **outer volume** and the inner approximations converge to the **inner volume**, where the inner volume is less or equal to the outer volume. (Explain!) For nice shapes such as circles, ellipses, ellipsoids, and squares (including the enclosed points), the outer and inner volume are both equal to what we then call the *volume* of the shape. Of course, when $n = 2$, this volume is called the *area* of the shape.

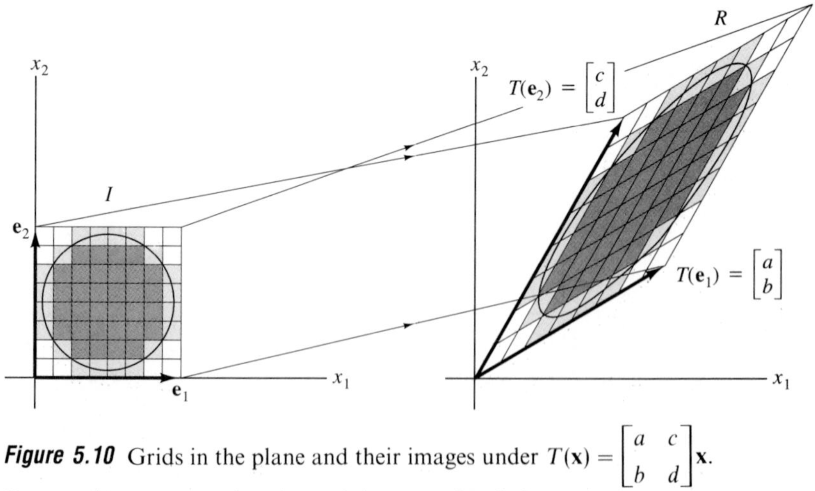

Figure 5.10 Grids in the plane and their images under $T(\mathbf{x}) = \begin{bmatrix} a & c \\ b & d \end{bmatrix}\mathbf{x}$. Inner and outer approximations of the area of a circle and its image under T.

Definition. *Volume of a Shape in* $\mathbb{R}^n$.
When the inner volume and outer volume of a shape in $\mathbb{R}^n$ are equal, they are the **volume** of the shape, and the shape is said to be **measurable**.

It can be shown using Theorem 5.14 that *a parallelepiped A is measurable and its volume $g(A)$ as just defined is the absolute value of* $|A|$. Using this, the following theorem can be proved along the lines of Problems 4–7.

Theorem 5.15. *Volume of the Image of a Shape under a Linear Transformation.* Let $T(\mathbf{x}) = A\mathbf{x}$ be a linear transformation of $\mathbb{R}^n$. If S is a measurable shape of volume $\text{Vol}(S)$, then its image AS under T is a measurable shape of volume $\text{Vol}(AS) = ||A|| \text{ Vol}(S)$.

PROBLEMS

NUMERICAL PROBLEMS

1. Use the formula for the area of a circle $x^2 + y^2 = r^2$ and the product formula for determinants to compute the area of the ellipse

$$\left\{ \begin{bmatrix} 1 & 2 \\ 3 & 8 \end{bmatrix} \begin{bmatrix} x \\ y \end{bmatrix} \middle| x^2 + y^2 = 5^2 \right\}.$$

THEORETICAL PROBLEMS

2. Use the formula for the area of a circle $x^2 + y^2 = 1$ and the product formula for determinants to derive a formula for the area of the ellipse

$$\frac{x^2}{r^2} + \frac{y^2}{s^2} = 1.$$

3. Use the formula for the volume of a sphere $x^2 + y^2 + z^2 = 1$ and the product formula for determinants to derive a formula for the volume of the ellipsoid

$$\frac{x^2}{r^2} + \frac{y^2}{s^2} + \frac{z^2}{t^2} = 1.$$

Hard

4. A function from $\mathbb{R}^n$ to $\mathbb{R}^m$ is *continuous* if its coordinate functions f_i from $\mathbb{R}^n$ to $\mathbb{R}$ are continuous; that is, for any $\varepsilon > 0$ and any $\mathbf{x} \in \mathbb{R}^n$, there exists $\delta > 0$ such that $|f_i(\mathbf{y}) - f_i(\mathbf{x})| < \varepsilon$ if $|y_j - x_j| < \delta$ for all j.

(a) Show that any linear function from $\mathbb{R}^n$ to $\mathbb{R}$ is continuous.

(b) Show that any linear transformation from $\mathbb{R}^n$ to $\mathbb{R}^m$ is continuous.

5. Consider three grids of side lengths $1/a$, $1/b$, $1/ab$ less than 1. Show that

(a) The outer volumes for a shape when the lengths of the grid's sides are $1/a$ and $1/b$ are greater than or equal to the outer volume when it is $1/ab$;

(b) The inner volumes for a shape when the lengths of the grid's sides are $1/a$ and $1/b$ are less than or equal to the inner volume when it is $1/ab$;

(c) For each of the three grids, the outer volume for a shape is greater than or equal to its inner volume.

6. Any outer volume for a shape is greater than or equal to any inner volume.

7. Show that if a shape S in $\mathbb{R}^n$ is measurable and if T is a linear transformation from $\mathbb{R}^n$ to $\mathbb{R}^m$, then its image $T(S)$ is a measurable shape in $\mathbb{R}^m$. Also, show that if a shape S in $\mathbb{R}^n$ is measurable and if T is a linear transformation from $\mathbb{R}^n$ to $\mathbb{R}^m$, then the volume of its image $T(S)$ is $||T||$ times the volume of S. (***Hint:*** Use the product formula to prove this when the shape is a finite union of grid elements. Then use this as a tool for the general case.)

8. Prove the formula

$$a = \frac{1}{2!}\begin{vmatrix} x_1 & y_1 & 1 \\ x_2 & y_2 & 1 \\ x_3 & y_3 & 1 \end{vmatrix}$$

of Lagrange for the signed area a of a triangle and relate it to Figure 5.11.

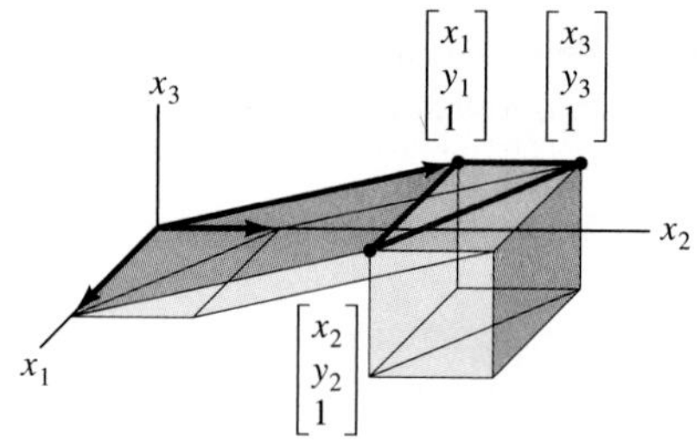

Figure 5.11 The formula of Lagrange for the area of a given triangle.

9. Prove the formula

$$v = \frac{1}{3!}\begin{vmatrix} x_1 & y_1 & z_1 & 1 \\ x_2 & y_2 & z_2 & 1 \\ x_3 & y_3 & z_3 & 1 \\ x_4 & y_4 & z_4 & 1 \end{vmatrix}$$

of Lagrange for the signed volume v of a tetrahedron and relate it to Figure 5.12.

10. Prove that tetrahedrons (1) and (2) of Figure 5.12 have equal volume.

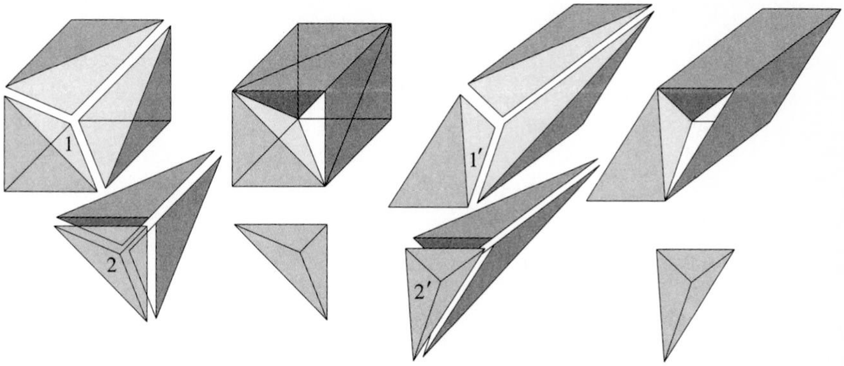

Figure 5.12 A decomposition of a parallelepiped into six tetrahedrons of equal volume corresponding to a similar decomposition of the unit cube.

11. Using Problem 10, explain why tetrahedrons (1′) and (2′) of Figure 5.12 have equal volume.

5.5 SURFACES

Now that we have the determinant function, we can put it to use to study surfaces in $\mathbb{R}^n$ and corresponding equations. Here, a **surface** in $\mathbb{R}^n$ (*curve* when $n = 2$) is defined to be the **locus of points** $\{\mathbf{x} \in \mathbb{R}^n \mid f(\mathbf{x}) = p\}$ of the equation $f(\mathbf{x}) = p$, where f is a function from $\mathbb{R}^n$ to $\mathbb{R}$ and p is an element of $\mathbb{R}$. Its **corresponding equation** is $f(\mathbf{x}) = p$.

EXAMPLES

1. The general equation of the circle is $a(x^2 + y^2) + ex + fy + g = 0$. (Prove!)

2. The equation $ax^2 + dy^2 + g = 0$ $(ad > 0)$ is the general equation for an ellipse whose axes are the coordinate axis.

3. If f is a nonzero linear function from $\mathbb{R}^n$ to $\mathbb{R}$, the surface $f(\mathbf{x}) = 0$ is a hyperplane H through $\mathbf{0}$. Writing f as $f(\mathbf{x}) = A\mathbf{x}$, where A is a nonzero $n \times 1$ matrix, H is the nullspace of A. Since A has rank 1, the dimension of H is $n - 1$.

4. If f is a nonzero linear function from $\mathbb{R}^n$ to $\mathbb{R}$ and if $\mathbf{u} \in \mathbb{R}^n$ and $p \in \mathbb{R}$, the surface $f(\mathbf{x}) = p$ and $f(\mathbf{x} - \mathbf{u}) = 0$ are hyperplanes. Note that the hyperplane $f(\mathbf{x} - \mathbf{u}) = 0$ passes through $\mathbf{u}$. By the linearity of f, the hyperplanes of $f(\mathbf{x} - \mathbf{u}) = 0$ and $f(\mathbf{x}) = f(\mathbf{u})$ are the same.

Determinant equations

To use the determinant to compute a specific surface, write the general equation of the surface, followed by the specific equations for points on the surface. Then, if possible, solve this system of equations to determine a single specific equation for the desired curve or surface. A few examples for $n = 1, 2, 3$ should suffice to illustrate the method, which is useful for $n > 3$ as well.

EXAMPLES

1. Let's first look at how it goes for the line in $\mathbb{R}^2$. The problem is to find the formula for the line passing through two different points $\begin{bmatrix} p \\ q \end{bmatrix}, \begin{bmatrix} r \\ s \end{bmatrix}$. We write the general equation for the line and then write equations we get from it by substituting in the coordinates p, q, r, s of the two given points:

$$ax + by + c = 0$$

$$ap + bq + c = 0$$

$$ar + bs + c = 0$$

For such a system to have a nonzero solution

$$\begin{bmatrix} a \\ b \\ c \end{bmatrix},$$

the determinant

$$\begin{vmatrix} x & y & 1 \\ p & q & 1 \\ r & s & 1 \end{vmatrix}$$

must be 0. (Explain!) Setting it to 0 and expanding along the first row, we get the desired equation $(q - s)x + (r - p)y + ps - qr = 0$. Replacing x and y by p and q or by r and s must give 0, since the determinant then has two equal rows in both cases. For instance, when p, q, r, and s are 1, 2, 3, and 4, the equation is

$$\begin{vmatrix} x & y & 1 \\ 1 & 2 & 1 \\ 3 & 4 & 1 \end{vmatrix} = 0,$$

that is, $-2x + 2y = 2$. (Verify!)

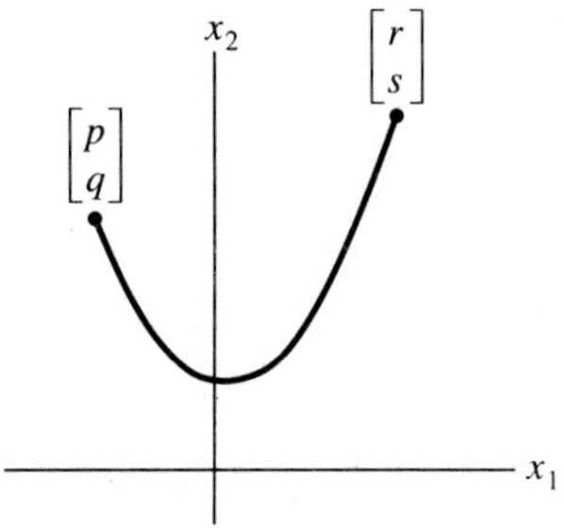

Figure 5.13 The parabola $ax^2 + by + c = 0$ through $\begin{bmatrix} p \\ q \end{bmatrix}$ and $\begin{bmatrix} r \\ s \end{bmatrix}$.

2. For curves of the form $ax^2 + by + c = 0$ passing through points $\begin{bmatrix} p \\ q \end{bmatrix}$ and $\begin{bmatrix} r \\ s \end{bmatrix}$ (see Figure 5.13), the equation is

$$0 = \begin{vmatrix} x^2 & y & 1 \\ p^2 & q & 1 \\ r^2 & s & 1 \end{vmatrix} = (q - s)x^2 + (r^2 - p^2)y + p^2 s - r^2 q.$$

For instance, the parabola through $\begin{bmatrix} 1 \\ 2 \end{bmatrix}$ and $\begin{bmatrix} 2 \\ 3 \end{bmatrix}$ is $(2-3)x^2 + (4-1)y + 1 \cdot 3s - 4 \cdot 2 = 0$, or $-x^2 + 3y - 5 = 0$. (Check!)

3. For the circle, the problem is to find the circle passing through three given noncollinear points $\begin{bmatrix} p \\ q \end{bmatrix}, \begin{bmatrix} r \\ s \end{bmatrix}, \begin{bmatrix} t \\ u \end{bmatrix}$. Again, we write the general equation, followed by the equations for the given points:

$$\begin{aligned} a(x^2 + y^2) + ex + fy + g &= 0, \\ a(p^2 + q^2) + ep + fq + g &= 0, \\ a(r^2 + s^2) + er + fs + g &= 0, \\ a(t^2 + u^2) + et + fu + g &= 0. \end{aligned}$$

The corresponding determinant must again be 0, so

$$\begin{vmatrix} x^2+y^2 & x & y & 1 \\ p^2+q^2 & p & q & 1 \\ r^2+s^2 & r & s & 1 \\ t^2+u^2 & t & u & 1 \end{vmatrix} = 0.$$

Expanding along the first row gives us the desired equation. Even before computing it, we again see that replacing x and y by their values for each of the three points results in 0 because of duplicate rows. For instance, when p, q, r, s, t, and u are 1, 0, 0, 1, 1, and 1, the equation is

$$0 = \begin{vmatrix} x^2+y^2 & x & y & 1 \\ p^2+q^2 & 1 & 0 & 1 \\ r^2+s^2 & 0 & 1 & 1 \\ t^2+u^2 & 1 & 1 & 1 \end{vmatrix} = -(x^2 + y^2) + x + y = 0.$$

(Verify!) This is a circle passing through the points $\begin{bmatrix} 1 \\ 0 \end{bmatrix}$, $\begin{bmatrix} 0 \\ 1 \end{bmatrix}$, and $\begin{bmatrix} 1 \\ 1 \end{bmatrix}$. That it also must pass through $\begin{bmatrix} 0 \\ 0 \end{bmatrix}$ should be no surprise! (See Figure 5.14.)

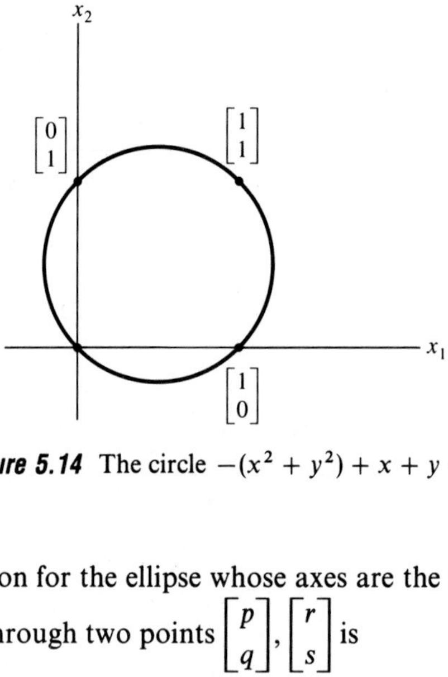

Figure 5.14 The circle $-(x^2 + y^2) + x + y = 0$.

4. The equation for the ellipse whose axes are the coordinate axis and which passes through two points $\begin{bmatrix} p \\ q \end{bmatrix}$, $\begin{bmatrix} r \\ s \end{bmatrix}$ is

$$\begin{vmatrix} x^2 & y^2 & 1 \\ p^2 & q^2 & 1 \\ r^2 & s^2 & 1 \end{vmatrix} = 0.$$

This equation delivers an ellipse if $(q^2 - s^2)(r^2 - p^2) > 0$. (Explain!) For instance, when p, q, r, and s are 1, 1, 2, and 0, the equation is

$$0 = \begin{vmatrix} x^2 & y^2 & 1 \\ 1 & 1 & 1 \\ 4 & 0 & 1 \end{vmatrix} = x^2 + 3y^2 - 4, \quad \text{or} \quad x^2 + 3y^2 = 4$$

(Figure 5.15). (Verify!)

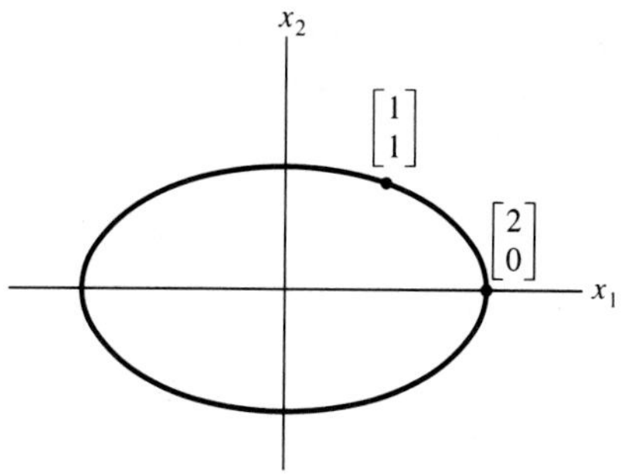

Figure 5.15 The ellipse $x^2 + 3y^2 = 4$ passing through $\begin{bmatrix}1\\1\end{bmatrix}$ and $\begin{bmatrix}2\\0\end{bmatrix}$.

5. The general equation for the plane through **0** is $Ax + By + Cz = 0$. So, the equation for the plane passing through zero and the points

$$\mathbf{v} = \begin{bmatrix}a\\b\\c\end{bmatrix}, \qquad \mathbf{w} = \begin{bmatrix}d\\e\\f\end{bmatrix} \in \mathbb{R}^3$$

is

$$\begin{vmatrix}x & a & d\\ y & b & e\\ z & c & f\end{vmatrix} = 0.$$

Here, we've transposed the coefficient matrix to conform with our column notation. This is justifiable by the rule $|M^T| = |M|$. Expanding along the first column gives the equation $Ax + By + Cz = 0$, where

$$\begin{bmatrix}A\\B\\C\end{bmatrix} = \begin{bmatrix}bf-ce\\dc-af\\ae-bd\end{bmatrix}.$$

This is the *cross product* $\mathbf{v} \times \mathbf{w}$ of $\mathbf{v}$ and $\mathbf{w}$, which we study in the next section. When a, b, c, d, e, and f are 1, -1, 0, -1, 0, and 1, the equation is

$$0 = \begin{vmatrix}x & 1 & -1\\ y & -1 & 0\\ z & 0 & 1\end{vmatrix} = -x - y - z.$$

6. The equation for the plane passing through noncollinear points

$$\begin{bmatrix}a\\b\\c\end{bmatrix}, \quad \begin{bmatrix}d\\e\\f\end{bmatrix}, \quad \begin{bmatrix}g\\h\\i\end{bmatrix} \in \mathbb{R}^3$$

is

$$\begin{vmatrix} x & a & d & g \\ y & b & e & h \\ z & c & f & i \\ 1 & 1 & 1 & 1 \end{vmatrix} = 0,$$

that is,

$$-\begin{vmatrix} x-g & a-g & d-g \\ y-h & b-h & e-h \\ z-i & c-i & f-i \end{vmatrix} = 0.$$

(Explain!) When a, b, c, d, e, f, g, h, and i are 3, 1, 2, 1, 2, 3, 2, 2, and 2, this is the determinant

$$0 = -\begin{vmatrix} x-2 & 1 & -1 \\ y-2 & -1 & 0 \\ z-2 & 0 & 1 \end{vmatrix} = -(x-2)-(y-2)-(z-2).$$

See Figure 5.16. (Compare with Example 4.)

7. With no example for $n = 1$, our list of examples would be incomplete. The general quadratic equation in one variable is $ax^2 + bx + c = 0$ ($a \neq 0$). The corresponding "surface" is a set of at most two points. Stipulating that it passes through p and q ($p \neq q$) results in the specific equation

$$0 = \begin{vmatrix} x^2 & p^2 & q^2 \\ x & p & q \\ 1 & 1 & 1 \end{vmatrix} = ax^2 + bx + c$$

where

$$\begin{bmatrix} a \\ b \\ c \end{bmatrix} = \begin{bmatrix} p^2 \\ p \\ 1 \end{bmatrix} \times \begin{bmatrix} q^2 \\ q \\ 1 \end{bmatrix} = \begin{bmatrix} p-q \\ q^2-p^2 \\ p^2q-pq^2 \end{bmatrix}.$$

(Verify!) Since this equation is a multiple of $(x-p)(x-q)$ (explain) and $a = p - q$, we have computed the **Vandermonde determinant**

$$V(x, p, q) = \begin{vmatrix} x^2 & p^2 & q^2 \\ x & p & q \\ 1 & 1 & 1 \end{vmatrix} = (x-p)(x-q)(p-q).$$

(Explain!)

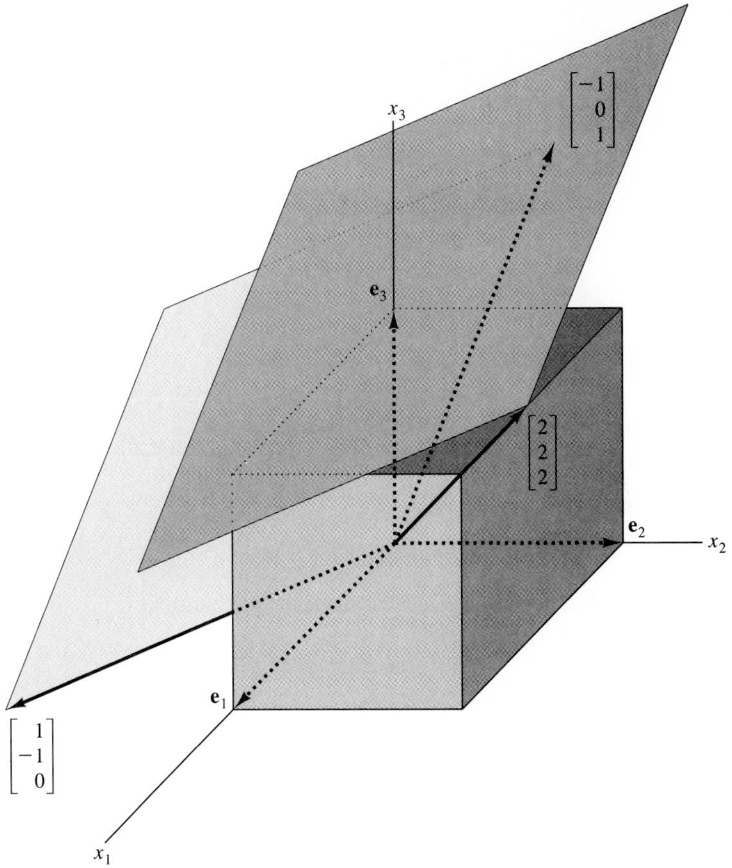

Figure 5.16 The planes through

$$\mathbf{0},\quad \begin{bmatrix}1\\-1\\0\end{bmatrix},\quad \begin{bmatrix}-1\\0\\1\end{bmatrix} \quad\text{and}\quad \mathbf{0}+\begin{bmatrix}2\\2\\2\end{bmatrix},\quad \begin{bmatrix}1\\-1\\0\end{bmatrix}+\begin{bmatrix}2\\2\\2\end{bmatrix},\quad \begin{bmatrix}-1\\0\\1\end{bmatrix}+\begin{bmatrix}2\\2\\2\end{bmatrix}.$$

PROBLEMS

NUMERICAL PROBLEMS

1. Verify that the equation of the circle passing through three points of the rectangle with vertices $\begin{bmatrix}2\\0\end{bmatrix}, \begin{bmatrix}0\\3\end{bmatrix}, \begin{bmatrix}2\\3\end{bmatrix}, \begin{bmatrix}0\\0\end{bmatrix}$ does not depend on which point is left out.

2. Find the equations of the circles through the following sets of points.

(a) $\begin{bmatrix}2\\3\end{bmatrix}, \begin{bmatrix}1\\2\end{bmatrix}, \begin{bmatrix}1\\3\end{bmatrix}$ (b) $\begin{bmatrix}3\\8\end{bmatrix}, \begin{bmatrix}4\\6\end{bmatrix}, \begin{bmatrix}8\\5\end{bmatrix}$ (c) $\begin{bmatrix}1\\5\end{bmatrix}, \begin{bmatrix}4\\3\end{bmatrix}, \begin{bmatrix}2\\6\end{bmatrix}$

3. Find the equations of the ellipses whose axes are the coordinate axes through the following sets of points.

(a) $\begin{bmatrix}2\\3\end{bmatrix}, \begin{bmatrix}1\\3\end{bmatrix}$ (b) $\begin{bmatrix}3\\8\end{bmatrix}, \begin{bmatrix}4\\6\end{bmatrix}$ (c) $\begin{bmatrix}2\\1\end{bmatrix}, \begin{bmatrix}1\\2\end{bmatrix}$

THEORETICAL PROBLEMS

4. Show that the general equation of the circle is

$$a(x^2 + y^2) + ex + fy + g = 0.$$

5. Find the general equation for the line passing through $\begin{bmatrix}p\\q\end{bmatrix}$ and perpendicular to $\begin{bmatrix}r\\s\end{bmatrix}$ in terms of p, q, r, s.

6. Show that the equation for the ellipse whose axes are the coordinate axes and which passes through two points $\begin{bmatrix}p\\q\end{bmatrix}, \begin{bmatrix}r\\s\end{bmatrix}$ is

$$\begin{bmatrix}x^2\\y^2\\1\end{bmatrix} \cdot \mathbf{N} = 0 \quad \text{where} \quad \mathbf{N} = \begin{bmatrix}p^2\\q^2\\1\end{bmatrix} \times \begin{bmatrix}r^2\\s^2\\1\end{bmatrix}.$$

Hard

7. Compute the *Vandermonde determinant*

$$V(x, r, p, q) = \begin{vmatrix} x^3 & r^3 & p^3 & q^3 \\ x^2 & r^2 & p^2 & q^2 \\ x & r & p & q \\ 1 & 1 & 1 & 1 \end{vmatrix}$$

by showing that it is $c(x - r)(x - p)(x - q)$, where $c = V(r, p, q) = (r - p)(r - q)(p - q)$. Here, we assume that r, p, q are all different.

8. Show from the formula

$$V(x, r, p, q) = (x - r)(x - p)(x - q)(r - p)(r - q)(p - q)$$

that the sign of $V(x, r, p, q)$ changes with any interchange of two of the variables x, r, p, and q.

9. Show that if columns 1, 2, 3, and 4 of the 4×4 identity I are rearranged to columns $p(1)$, $p(2)$, $p(3)$, and $p(4)$ to get the permutation matrix P, then $|P| = V(x_1, x_2, x_3, x_4)/V(x_{p(1)}, x_{p(2)}, x_{p(3)}, x_{p(4)})$.

5.6 THE NORMAL TO A HYPERPLANE

The normal and cross product

Consider the determinant of a real matrix A whose first column

$$\mathbf{y} = \begin{bmatrix} y_1 \\ \vdots \\ y_n \end{bmatrix}$$

consists of variable entries and whose other $n - 1$ columns are constant vectors. By first-column expansion, we have

$$|A| = N_1 y_1 + \cdots + N_n y_n,$$

where $N_r = (-1)^{r+1}|A_{r1}|$, A_{r1} being the minor submatrix obtained by deleting the first column of variables and row r. We call

$$\mathbf{N} = \begin{bmatrix} N_1 \\ \vdots \\ N_n \end{bmatrix}$$

the **normal** to the columns $\mathbf{A}_2, \ldots, \mathbf{A}_n$ of A. Writing

$$\mathbf{y} = \begin{bmatrix} y_1 \\ \vdots \\ y_n \end{bmatrix},$$

the determinant $|A|$ is the dot product

$$|A| = \begin{bmatrix} N_1 \\ \vdots \\ N_n \end{bmatrix} \cdot \begin{bmatrix} y_1 \\ \vdots \\ y_n \end{bmatrix}.$$

This gives us the following formula.

Theorem 5.16. *Normal to $n - 1$ Vectors.*
Given vectors $\mathbf{A}_2, \ldots, \mathbf{A}_n$ with normal $\mathbf{N}$, the determinant of the matrix $[\mathbf{y} \quad \mathbf{A}_2 \quad \ldots \quad \mathbf{A}_n]$ is $\mathbf{N} \cdot \mathbf{y}$.

EXAMPLES

1. When $n = 2$, the normal to a vector $\begin{bmatrix} a \\ b \end{bmatrix}$ is the vector $\mathbf{N} = \begin{bmatrix} b \\ -a \end{bmatrix}$, since the determinant of $\begin{bmatrix} x & a \\ y & b \end{bmatrix}$ is $bx - ay = \begin{bmatrix} b \\ -a \end{bmatrix} \cdot \begin{bmatrix} x \\ y \end{bmatrix}$. For instance, the normal to $\begin{bmatrix} 1 \\ 2 \end{bmatrix}$ is the vector $\mathbf{N} = \begin{bmatrix} 2 \\ -1 \end{bmatrix}$. (See Figure 5.17(a).)

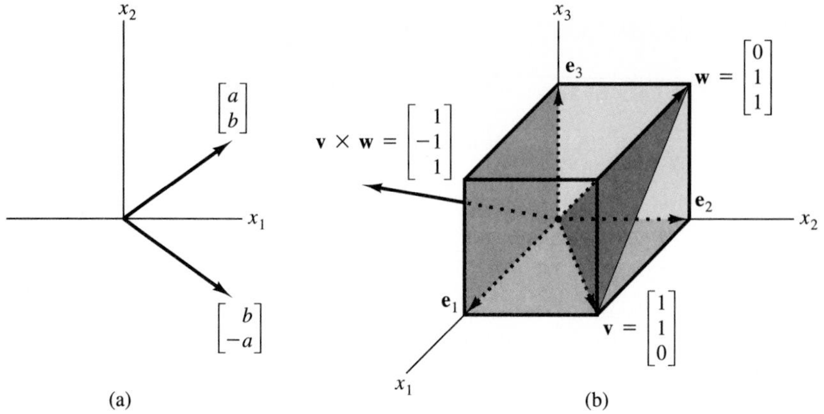

Figure 5.17 (a) The normal to the vector $\begin{bmatrix} a \\ b \end{bmatrix}$ in $\mathbb{R}^2$ is $\begin{bmatrix} b \\ -a \end{bmatrix}$.
(b) The normal $\mathbf{v} \times \mathbf{w}$ to vectors $\mathbf{v}$ and $\mathbf{w}$ in $\mathbb{R}^3$.

2. When $n = 3$, the normal to vectors

$$\mathbf{v} = \begin{bmatrix} a \\ b \\ c \end{bmatrix}, \qquad \mathbf{w} = \begin{bmatrix} d \\ e \\ f \end{bmatrix} \in \mathbb{R}^3$$

is called the **cross product** of $\mathbf{v}$ and $\mathbf{w}$ and is denoted by $\mathbf{v} \times \mathbf{w}$. So,

$$\mathbf{N} = \begin{bmatrix} a \\ b \\ c \end{bmatrix} \times \begin{bmatrix} d \\ e \\ f \end{bmatrix} = \begin{bmatrix} bf - ce \\ dc - af \\ ae - bd \end{bmatrix}$$

since the determinant of

$$\begin{bmatrix} x & a & d \\ y & b & e \\ z & c & f \end{bmatrix} \quad \text{is} \quad \begin{bmatrix} x \\ y \\ z \end{bmatrix} \cdot \begin{bmatrix} bf - ce \\ dc - af \\ ae - bd \end{bmatrix}.$$

(Verify!) So, the equation of a plane through $\mathbf{0}$, $\mathbf{v}$, and $\mathbf{w}$ is

$$\begin{bmatrix} x \\ y \\ z \end{bmatrix} \cdot \begin{bmatrix} bf - ce \\ dc - af \\ ae - bd \end{bmatrix} = 0.$$

Some examples of this are

$$\begin{bmatrix} 1 \\ 0 \\ 0 \end{bmatrix} \times \begin{bmatrix} 0 \\ 1 \\ 0 \end{bmatrix} = \begin{bmatrix} 0 \\ 0 \\ 1 \end{bmatrix}, \qquad \begin{bmatrix} 1 \\ 0 \\ 0 \end{bmatrix} \times \begin{bmatrix} 0 \\ 1 \\ 0 \end{bmatrix} = \begin{bmatrix} 0 \\ 0 \\ -1 \end{bmatrix},$$

$$\begin{bmatrix}1\\2\\0\end{bmatrix} \times \begin{bmatrix}0\\1\\2\end{bmatrix} = \begin{bmatrix}4\\-2\\1\end{bmatrix}, \quad \begin{bmatrix}1\\1\\0\end{bmatrix} \times \begin{bmatrix}0\\1\\1\end{bmatrix} = \begin{bmatrix}1\\-1\\1\end{bmatrix}.$$

(Verify!) See Figure 5.17(b).

3. When $n = 4$, the normal to three vectors **u**, **v**, and **w** can be denoted by $\mathbf{u} \times \mathbf{v} \times \mathbf{w}$. For example,

$$\begin{bmatrix}1\\0\\0\\0\end{bmatrix} \times \begin{bmatrix}0\\1\\0\\0\end{bmatrix} \times \begin{bmatrix}0\\0\\1\\0\end{bmatrix} = \begin{bmatrix}0\\0\\0\\-1\end{bmatrix}, \quad \begin{bmatrix}1\\2\\0\\0\end{bmatrix} \times \begin{bmatrix}0\\1\\2\\0\end{bmatrix} \times \begin{bmatrix}0\\0\\1\\2\end{bmatrix} = \begin{bmatrix}8\\-4\\2\\-1\end{bmatrix}.$$

(Verify!)

If we replace the variable vector $\begin{bmatrix}y_1\\ \vdots \\ y_n\end{bmatrix}$ by any of the $n-1$ columns $\mathbf{A}_2, \ldots, \mathbf{A}_n$ of A, our theorem gives $\mathbf{N} \cdot \mathbf{A}_r = |\mathbf{A}_r, \mathbf{A}_2, \ldots, \mathbf{A}_n|$. Since this is the determinant of a matrix with two identical columns, $\mathbf{N} \cdot \mathbf{A}_r = 0$ and we get the following.

Corollary. Let **N** be the normal to the vectors $\mathbf{A}_2, \ldots, \mathbf{A}_n \in \mathbb{R}^n$. Then $\mathbf{N} \cdot \mathbf{A}_r = 0$ for $2 \leq r \leq n$.

The normal to a hyperplane

If the vectors $\mathbf{A}_2, \ldots, \mathbf{A}_n \in \mathbb{R}^n$ are linearly independent, they do not form a basis; but we can find a vector $\mathbf{A}_1$ such that $\mathbf{A}_1, \mathbf{A}_2, \ldots, \mathbf{A}_n$ do form a basis for $\mathbb{R}^n$. (Explain!) The determinant of the invertible matrix $A = [\mathbf{A}_1 \ \ \mathbf{A}_2 \ \ \ldots \ \ \mathbf{A}_n]$ is nonzero. By Theorem 5.13, this determinant is $\mathbf{N} \cdot \mathbf{A}_1$. It follows that **N** is nonzero. Since the dot products $\mathbf{N} \cdot \mathbf{A}_r$ are all 0, **N** cannot be in the span of $\mathbf{A}_2, \ldots, \mathbf{A}_n$, for otherwise $\mathbf{N} \cdot \mathbf{N}$ would be 0. (Since **N** is nonzero, $\mathbf{N} \cdot \mathbf{N} = 0$ is not possible.) It follows that $\mathbf{A}_2, \ldots, \mathbf{A}_n$, **N** form a basis for $\mathbb{R}^n$ (explain), which gives us the next theorem. (See Figure 5.18.)

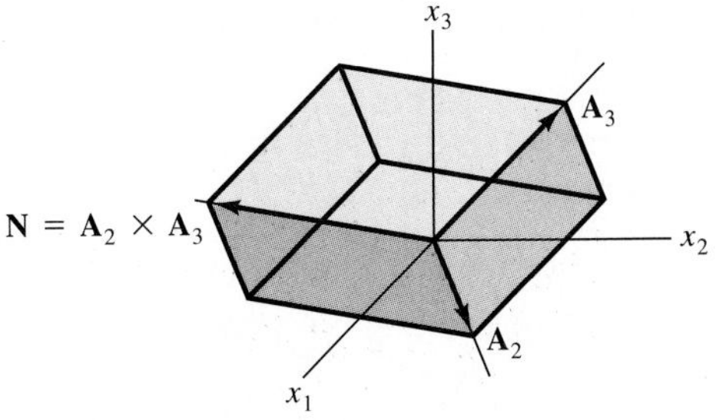

Figure 5.18 The normal **N** as the last member of a basis $\mathbf{A}_2, \mathbf{A}_3, \mathbf{N}$.

Theorem 5.17. *The Normal to an* $(n-1)$*-Dimensional Subspace.*
If $\mathbf{A}_2, \ldots, \mathbf{A}_n \in \mathbb{R}^n$ are linearly independent with normal $\mathbf{N}$, then $\mathbf{A}_2, \ldots, \mathbf{A}_n$, $\mathbf{N}$ form a basis for $\mathbb{R}^n$.

EXAMPLES

1. $\mathbf{e}_1, \mathbf{e}_2 \in \mathbb{R}^3$ are linearly independent, so $\mathbf{e}_1, \mathbf{e}_2, \mathbf{N}$ form a basis for $\mathbb{R}^3$, where $\mathbf{N} = \mathbf{e}_1 \times \mathbf{e}_2$; that is, $\mathbf{N} = \mathbf{e}_3$. (Verify!)

2.
$$\begin{bmatrix}1\\2\\3\end{bmatrix} \times \begin{bmatrix}4\\5\\6\end{bmatrix} = \begin{bmatrix}-3\\6\\-3\end{bmatrix}$$

(verify), so that

$$\begin{bmatrix}1\\2\\3\end{bmatrix}, \quad \begin{bmatrix}4\\5\\6\end{bmatrix}, \quad \begin{bmatrix}-3\\6\\-3\end{bmatrix}$$

form a basis for $\mathbb{R}^3$. Note that the products

$$\begin{bmatrix}1\\2\\3\end{bmatrix} \cdot \begin{bmatrix}-3\\6\\-3\end{bmatrix}, \quad \begin{bmatrix}4\\5\\6\end{bmatrix} \cdot \begin{bmatrix}-3\\6\\-3\end{bmatrix}$$

are 0.

Hyperplanes given parametrically

Theorem 5.17 is the key to expressing an $(n-1)$-dimensional space H given *parametrically* in the form

$$H = \{t_2\mathbf{A}_2 + \cdots + t_n\mathbf{A}_n \mid t_2, \ldots, t_n \in \mathbb{R}^n\}$$

as the hyperplane of solutions of a linear equation $f(\mathbf{x}) = 0$. To do this, simply let $\mathbf{N}$ be the normal to $\mathbf{A}_2, \ldots, \mathbf{A}_n$ and let $f(\mathbf{x}) = \mathbf{N} \cdot \mathbf{x}$. Theorem 5.14 assures that $\mathbf{N}$ is not $\mathbf{0}$, so we recover H as the set of solutions to $f(\mathbf{x}) = 0$. (Explain!)

EXAMPLE

By part 2 of the last example, the hyperplane

$$\left\{ s\begin{bmatrix}1\\2\\3\end{bmatrix} + t\begin{bmatrix}4\\5\\6\end{bmatrix} \,\middle|\, s, t \in \mathbb{R} \right\}$$

is the locus of $f(\mathbf{x}) = 0$, where

$$f(\mathbf{x}) = \begin{bmatrix} -3 \\ 6 \\ -3 \end{bmatrix} \cdot \mathbf{x}.$$

That is, it is the plane $-3x_1 + 6x_2 - 3x_3 = 0$.

Parallel hyperplanes

The simplest surfaces are hyperplanes. To study them, the concept of translation (parallel displacement) is essential.

For any function f from $\mathbb{R}^n$ to $\mathbb{R}$, the locus of $f(\mathbf{x} - \mathbf{u}) = 0$ is $L + \mathbf{u} = \{\mathbf{y} + \mathbf{u} \in \mathbb{R}^n \mid \mathbf{y} \in L\}$, where L is the locus of $f(\mathbf{x}) = 0$. To see this, just check that $f(\mathbf{x} - \mathbf{u}) = 0$ if and only if $\mathbf{x} = \mathbf{y} + \mathbf{u}$, where $f(\mathbf{y}) = 0$. Whereas L passes through $\mathbf{0}$, $L + \mathbf{u}$ passes through $\mathbf{u}$. Note that $L + \mathbf{0} = L$, and $(L + \mathbf{u}) + (\mathbf{v} - \mathbf{u}) = L + \mathbf{v}$. The process of going from $L + \mathbf{u}$ to $L + \mathbf{v}$ is called **translation** by $\mathbf{v} - \mathbf{u}$, since it is achieved by the *translation* $T_{\mathbf{w}}(\mathbf{x}) = \mathbf{x} + \mathbf{w}$ where $\mathbf{w} = \mathbf{v} - \mathbf{u}$.

When f is a *linear* function from $\mathbb{R}^n$ to $\mathbb{R}$ and H is the hyperplane corresponding to $f(\mathbf{x}) = 0$, the hyperplanes $H + \mathbf{u}$ and $H + \mathbf{v}$ are parallel.

Definition. *Parallel Hyperplanes.*
Two hyperplanes are **parallel** if they are either equal or do not intersect.

Theorem 5.18. *The Hyperplane through a Point Parallel to a Given Hyperplane.* Through a given point $v \in \mathbb{R}^n$ and parallel to a given hyperplane in $\mathbb{R}^n$, there is one and only one hyperplane.

Proof. Let the given hyperplane correspond to $f(\mathbf{x}) = p$, f being a nonzero linear function. The given hyperplane is $H + \mathbf{u}$, where $\mathbf{u}$ is any point on it and H is the locus of $f(\mathbf{x}) = 0$. Then $H + \mathbf{v}$ is a hyperplane through $\mathbf{v}$ parallel to $H + \mathbf{u}$. (Prove!)

Conversely, any hyperplane through $\mathbf{v}$ can be expressed as $H' + \mathbf{v}$, where H' is a hyperplane through $\mathbf{0}$. Assuming that $H + \mathbf{v} \neq H' + \mathbf{v}$, we now show that $H' + \mathbf{v}$ is not parallel to $H + \mathbf{u}$. Since the two $(n - 1)$-dimensional subspaces H and H' are not equal, each contains an element not contained in the other, by our results on dimensions of subspaces. (Explain!) Letting $\mathbf{h}' \in H'$, where $\mathbf{h}'$ is not in H, and letting $\mathbf{h}_2, \ldots, \mathbf{h}_n$ be a basis for H, we get a basis $\mathbf{h}', \mathbf{h}_2, \ldots, \mathbf{h}_n$ for $\mathbb{R}^n$. (Explain!) It follows that we can write $\mathbf{u} - \mathbf{v}$ as $\mathbf{u} - \mathbf{v} = c\mathbf{h}' + \mathbf{h}$, where $\mathbf{h}$ is in H. But then $\mathbf{u} - \mathbf{h} = \mathbf{v} + c\mathbf{h}'$, which shows that $H + \mathbf{u}$ and $H' + \mathbf{v}$ have a point in common. (Explain!) This implies that $H + \mathbf{u}$ and $H' + \mathbf{v}$ cannot be parallel, for otherwise $H + \mathbf{u} = H' + \mathbf{v}$, which would imply that $H + \mathbf{v} = H' + \mathbf{v}$ (Problem 8). ■

The line normal to a hyperplane

The span $H = \mathbb{R}A_2 + \cdots + \mathbb{R}A_n$ of $n - 1$ linearly independent vectors A_s is the locus of $\mathbf{N} \cdot \mathbf{y} = 0$, where $\mathbf{N}$ is their normal. (Explain!) So, it is a hyperplane through $\mathbf{0}$. The *normal line* $\mathbb{R}\mathbf{N}$ to the $A_2, \ldots, A_n$ depends only on H because if $B_2, \ldots, B_n$ is also a basis for H, then the normal $\mathbf{M}$ to $B_2, \ldots, B_n$ has dot product 0 with $A_2, \ldots, A_n$. Writing $\mathbf{M} = a\mathbf{N} + a_2A_2 + \cdots + a_nA_n$, it follows that $\mathbf{M} - a\mathbf{N}$ has dot product 0 with $a_2A_2 + \cdots + a_nA_n$ and hence with itself. But then it is 0, so that $\mathbf{M} = a\mathbf{N}$ and $\mathbb{R}\mathbf{M} = \mathbb{R}\mathbf{N}$. This justifies the following definition.

Definition. *The Normal Line to a Hyperplane.*
The **normal line** to a hyperplane parallel to $H = \mathbb{R}A_2 + \cdots + \mathbb{R}A_n$ is the line $\mathbb{R}\mathbf{N}$, where $\mathbf{N}$ is the normal to $A_2, \ldots, A_n$.

The hyperplane normal to a line

There is a *duality* between lines and hyperplanes through $\mathbf{0}$. Given a hyperplane H through $\mathbf{0}$, we get the normal line in the preceding manner. Con-

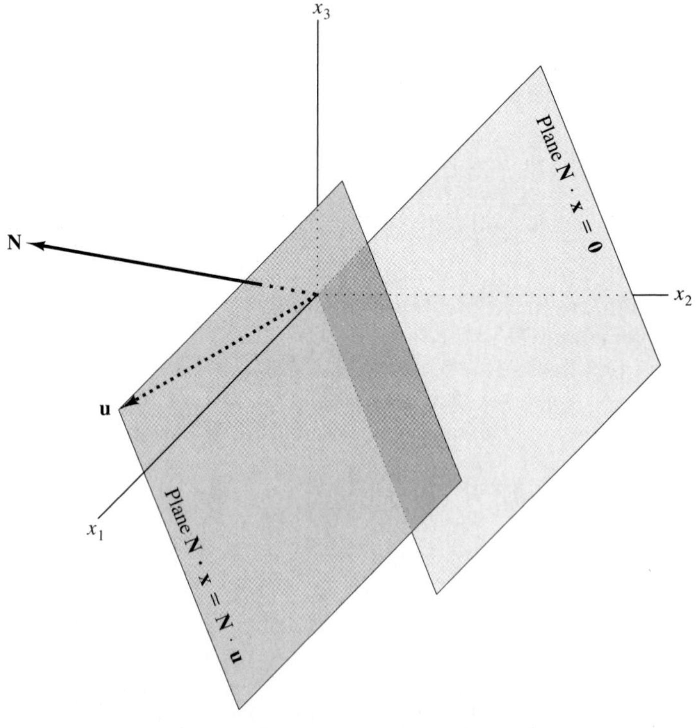

Figure 5.19 The hyperplane $\mathbf{N} \cdot \mathbf{x} = \mathbf{N} \cdot \mathbf{u}$ through $\mathbf{u}$ normal to $\mathbf{N}$.

versely, given a line $\mathbb{R}\mathbf{N}$, there is exactly one hyperplane H through $\mathbf{0}$ for which it is the normal line, namely, $H = \{\mathbf{x} \in \mathbb{R}^n \mid \mathbf{N} \cdot \mathbf{x} = 0\}$ (see Figure 5.19). We now give its equation.

Theorem 5.19. *The Hyperplane through a Point Perpendicular to a Given Line.*
For any $\mathbf{u} \in \mathbb{R}^n$, the hyperplane through $\mathbf{u}$ normal to the line $\mathbb{R}\mathbf{N}$ is $H_{\mathbf{u}} = \{\mathbf{x} \in \mathbb{R}^n \mid \mathbf{N} \cdot \mathbf{x} = \mathbf{N} \cdot \mathbf{u}\}$.

Proof. A vector $\mathbf{x}$ is in $H_{\mathbf{u}}$ if and only if $\mathbf{N} \cdot (\mathbf{x} - \mathbf{u}) = 0$ if and only if $\mathbf{x}$ is the sum of $\mathbf{u}$ and an element $\mathbf{x} - \mathbf{u}$ of $H_{\mathbf{0}} = \{\mathbf{x} \in \mathbb{R}^n \mid \mathbf{N} \cdot \mathbf{x} = 0\}$. So, $H_{\mathbf{u}} = H + \mathbf{u}$ is the hyperplane through $\mathbf{u}$ normal to $\mathbb{R}\mathbf{N}$. ■

EXAMPLE

The plane through $\begin{bmatrix} 1 \\ 1 \\ 2 \end{bmatrix}$ normal to $\begin{bmatrix} 1 \\ 0 \\ 2 \end{bmatrix}$ is the locus of points

$$\begin{bmatrix} x \\ y \\ z \end{bmatrix}$$

of the equation $1x + 0y + 2z = 1 \cdot 1 + 0 \cdot 1 + 2 \cdot 2$.

PROBLEMS

NUMERICAL PROBLEMS

1. Find the cross products of the following pairs of vectors.

(a) $\begin{bmatrix} 1 \\ 3 \\ 2 \end{bmatrix}, \begin{bmatrix} 3 \\ 2 \\ 1 \end{bmatrix}$ **(b)** $\begin{bmatrix} 5 \\ 6 \\ 3 \end{bmatrix}, \begin{bmatrix} 2 \\ 7 \\ 4 \end{bmatrix}$ **(c)** $\begin{bmatrix} 1 \\ 7 \\ 8 \end{bmatrix}, \begin{bmatrix} 3 \\ 2 \\ 6 \end{bmatrix}$

2. Find the equations of the planes:

(a) Through $\begin{bmatrix} 1 \\ 1 \\ 8 \end{bmatrix}$ and normal to $\begin{bmatrix} 3 \\ 1 \\ 6 \end{bmatrix}$;

(b) Through $\begin{bmatrix} 1 \\ 2 \\ 8 \end{bmatrix}$ and normal to $\begin{bmatrix} 3 \\ 3 \\ 6 \end{bmatrix}$;

(c) Through $\begin{bmatrix} 1 \\ 0 \\ 0 \end{bmatrix}$ and normal to $\begin{bmatrix} 0 \\ 1 \\ 1 \end{bmatrix}$.

3. Find the vector normal to

$$\begin{bmatrix}1\\0\\0\\1\end{bmatrix}, \quad \begin{bmatrix}0\\1\\1\\1\end{bmatrix}, \quad \begin{bmatrix}0\\0\\1\\1\end{bmatrix}.$$

4. Find the equation of the hyperplane

$$\mathbb{R}\begin{bmatrix}1\\2\\1\\1\end{bmatrix} + \left\{\begin{bmatrix}x\\z\\w\\y\end{bmatrix} \middle| \; x + y + z = 0\right\}.$$

THEORETICAL PROBLEMS

5. For any hyperplane H, show that $H + \mathbf{u} = H + \mathbf{v}$ if and only if $H + \mathbf{u}$ and $H + \mathbf{v}$ have a point in common.
6. If the vectors $A_2, \ldots, A_n \in \mathbb{R}^n$ are linearly independent, show that they are not a basis and we can find a vector A_1 such that $A_1, A_2, \ldots, A_n$ form a basis for $\mathbb{R}^n$.

Hard

7. Show that if two $(n-1)$-dimensional subspaces H, H' of an n-dimensional vector space V are not equal, then each contains an element not in the other.
8. Let H, H' be two subspaces of a vector space. Show that $H + \mathbf{u} = H' + \mathbf{v}$ if and only if $H = H'$ and $\mathbf{v} - \mathbf{u}$ is in H.

5.7 CHARACTERISTIC ROOTS AND VECTORS

Quadratic forms

To normalize the real quadratic form $\mathbf{x}^T A\mathbf{x} = ax_1^2 + 2bx_1x_2 + dx_2^2$, we let $A = \begin{bmatrix}a & b\\ b & d\end{bmatrix}$ and find orthogonal vectors $\mathbf{v}$, $\mathbf{w}$ of length 1 such that $A\mathbf{v} = a'\mathbf{v}$, $A\mathbf{w} = d'\mathbf{w}$. This is done using the spectral theorem (Section 1.8). The matrix of $R(\mathbf{x}) = A\mathbf{x}$ with respect to the new basis $B = [\mathbf{v} \;\; \mathbf{w}]$ is $\begin{bmatrix}a' & 0\\ 0 & d'\end{bmatrix}$ and we have

$$\begin{aligned} B^{-1}AB &= [\mathbf{v} \;\; \mathbf{w}]^{-1}A[\mathbf{v} \;\; \mathbf{w}] = [\mathbf{v} \;\; \mathbf{w}]^{-1}[A\mathbf{v} \;\; A\mathbf{w}] = [\mathbf{v} \;\; \mathbf{w}]^{-1}[a'\mathbf{v} \;\; d'\mathbf{w}] \\ &= [\mathbf{v} \;\; \mathbf{w}]^{-1}[\mathbf{v} \;\; \mathbf{w}]\begin{bmatrix}a' & 0\\ 0 & d'\end{bmatrix} = \begin{bmatrix}a' & 0\\ 0 & d'\end{bmatrix}. \end{aligned}$$

Since $\mathbf{v}$ and $\mathbf{w}$ are real orthogonal of length 1, $B^{-1} = B^T$. So, the transformation $\mathbf{x} = B\mathbf{x}'$ simplifies $\mathbf{x}^T A\mathbf{x} = ax_1^2 + 2bx_1x_2 + dx_2^2$ to

$$\mathbf{x}^T A\mathbf{x} = \mathbf{x}'^T B^T AB\mathbf{x}' = \mathbf{x}'^T B^{-1} AB\mathbf{x}' = \mathbf{x}'^T \begin{bmatrix} a' & 0 \\ 0 & d' \end{bmatrix} \mathbf{x}' = a'x_1'^2 + d'x_2'^2.$$

So, the normal form of the conic $ax_1^2 + 2bx_1x_2 + dx_2^2 = 1$ is $a'x_1'^2 + d'x_2'^2 = 1$, obtained by the orthogonal transformation $\mathbf{x} = B\mathbf{x}'$ to its principal axes $\mathbf{v}$ and $\mathbf{w}$.

To normalize a quadratic form $\mathbf{x}^T A\mathbf{x} = 1$ for an $n \times n$ real symmetric matrix A, we use the spectral theorem of Section 5.7. Using it, the quadratic form $\mathbf{x}^T A\mathbf{x} = 1$ can be brought to its principal axes in the same manner (Figure 5.20).

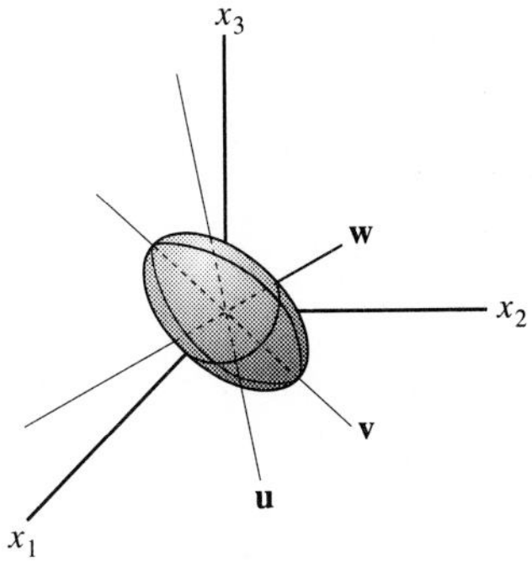

Figure 5.20 The principal axes $\mathbf{u}$, $\mathbf{v}$, $\mathbf{w}$ for an ellipsoid.

Characteristic vectors

A *characteristic vector* of a linear transformation T is a nonzero vector $\mathbf{v}$ stretched by T by a scalar factor c, called a *characteristic root*. Given a basis consisting of characteristic vectors, if one exists, we represent the action of T by looking at its effect on the parallelepiped having these characteristic vectors as edge vectors. Since each edge is stretched (or compressed) by T, the action of T on the span of the edge vectors can be found at once. For instance, if $T(\mathbf{v}) = r\mathbf{v}$ and $T(\mathbf{w}) = s\mathbf{w}$, then $T(a\mathbf{v} + b\mathbf{w}) = ra\mathbf{v} + sb\mathbf{w}$ (Figure 5.21).

Definition. *Characteristic Roots and Vectors of T.*
A **characteristic vector** for a linear transformation T of a vector space V over F is a nonzero vector $\mathbf{v}$ such that $T(\mathbf{v}) = c\mathbf{v}$ for some $c \in F$. A **characteristic root** for T is any value c such that $A\mathbf{v} = c\mathbf{v}$ for some nonzero vector $\mathbf{v}$. Such a c is the characteristic root *corresponding to* $\mathbf{v}$.

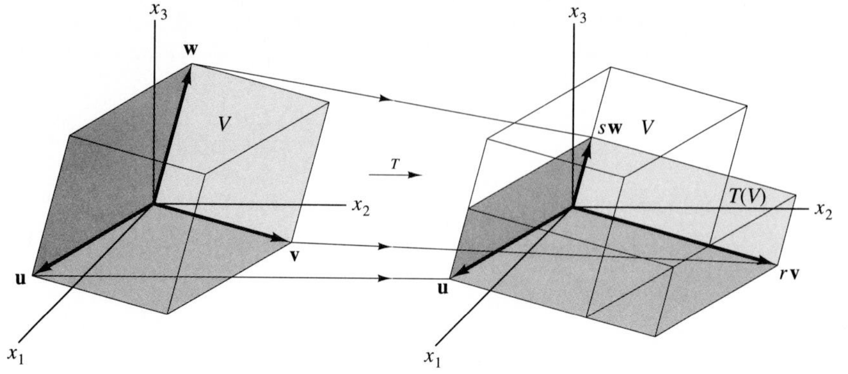

Figure 5.21 The effect $T(\mathbf{u}) = \mathbf{u}$, $T(\mathbf{v}) = r\mathbf{v}$, $T(\mathbf{w}) = s\mathbf{w}$ of T on characteristic vectors $\mathbf{u}$, $\mathbf{v}$, and $\mathbf{w}$. The image of the parallelogram $[\mathbf{u} \quad \mathbf{v} \quad \mathbf{w}]$ represents the action of T on $F\mathbf{u} + F\mathbf{v} + F\mathbf{w}$.

EXAMPLE

Let $T(\mathbf{x}) = \begin{bmatrix} 0 & 1 \\ 1 & 0 \end{bmatrix}\mathbf{x}$. Then there are exactly two characteristic roots, namely, 1 and -1, and the corresponding characteristic vectors are $t\begin{bmatrix} 1 \\ 1 \end{bmatrix}$, $t\begin{bmatrix} -1 \\ 1 \end{bmatrix}$, with t nonzero. To see this, suppose that $\begin{bmatrix} a \\ b \end{bmatrix}$ is a characteristic vector. Then $T\begin{bmatrix} a \\ b \end{bmatrix} = \begin{bmatrix} b \\ a \end{bmatrix} = c\begin{bmatrix} a \\ b \end{bmatrix}$. Since $b = ca$ and $a = cb$, it follows that $b = c^2b$ and $a = c^2a$. Since one of a and b is nonzero, it follows that $c = 1$ or -1 and $\begin{bmatrix} a \\ b \end{bmatrix} = b\begin{bmatrix} 1 \\ 1 \end{bmatrix}$ or $b\begin{bmatrix} -1 \\ 1 \end{bmatrix}$.

For $A \in M_nF$, the *characteristic roots* and *characteristic vectors* are the characteristic roots and vectors for the linear transformation $T(\mathbf{x}) = A\mathbf{x}$. So, a characteristic vector for A is just a nonzero vector $\mathbf{v} \in F^n$ such that $A\mathbf{v} = c\mathbf{v}$ for some $c \in F$. And c is a characteristic root for A if and only if $A\mathbf{v} = c\mathbf{v}$ for some characteristic vector $\mathbf{v}$ for A.

EXAMPLE

By the preceding example, the matrix $\begin{bmatrix} 0 & 1 \\ 1 & 0 \end{bmatrix}$ has exactly two characteristic roots, namely, 1 and -1, and its characteristic vectors are the vectors $t\begin{bmatrix} 1 \\ 1 \end{bmatrix}$ and $t\begin{bmatrix} -1 \\ 1 \end{bmatrix}$, with t nonzero.

The characteristic equation

A few preliminary observations are in order.

1. Let V be a vector space over F. For any $T \in L(V, V)$ and $c \in F$, the set $V_c = \text{Kernel } T = \{\mathbf{v} \in V \mid T(\mathbf{v}) = c\mathbf{v}\}$ is a subspace of V which is nonzero if and only if c is a characteristic root of T. (Verify!) Its nonzero elements are the characteristic vectors *corresponding* to c.
2. By (1), it follows that c is a characteristic root of T if and only if $T - cI$ is not invertible—that is, if and only if $|T - cI| = 0$. So, the characteristic roots of T are the solutions $z = c$ to its *characteristic equation* $|T - zI| = 0$.
3. What we have said for T has counterparts for $A \in M_n F$. The characteristic roots of A are the solutions $z = c$ in F to its *characteristic equation* $|A - zI| = 0$. For each such c, the corresponding characteristic vectors for A are the nonzero elements of the nullspace of $A - cI$.
4. Let V be a vector space over F with basis $\mathbf{v}_1, \ldots, \mathbf{v}_n$, and let

$$R(a_1\mathbf{v}_1 + \cdots + a_n\mathbf{v}_n) = a_1\mathbf{e}_1 + \cdots + a_n\mathbf{e}_n$$

be the corresponding isomorphism from V to F^n. Then a linear transformation T of V and its matrix $m_R(T)$ with respect to the basis $\mathbf{v}_r$ are related by the equation $m_R(T)R(\mathbf{v}) = R(T(\mathbf{v}))$ (Section 4.7). If $\mathbf{v}$ is a characteristic vector for T corresponding to a characteristic root c, then $m_R(T)R(\mathbf{v}) = R(T(\mathbf{v})) = R(c\mathbf{v}) = cR(\mathbf{v})$ for some c. So, $\mathbf{v}' = R(\mathbf{v})$ is a characteristic vector for the matrix $A = m_R(T)$ corresponding to c. Conversely, by the same equations, a characteristic vector $\mathbf{v}' \in F^n$ for A corresponding to c is $\mathbf{v}' = R(\mathbf{v})$, where $\mathbf{v}$ is a characteristic vector for T corresponding to c. Not surprisingly, the characteristic equations $|T - zI| = 0$ for T and $|A - zI|$ for A are the same (Figure 5.22). (Explain!)
5. If A and B are similar, then B is the matrix of the linear transformation $T(\mathbf{x}) = A\mathbf{x}$ with respect to some basis (Section 4.7). By (4), it follows that the characteristic roots of A and B are the same! We can see this another way using determinants. Since A and B are similar, $B = C^{-1}AC$ and $B - cI = C^{-1}AC - cI = C^{-1}(A - cI)C$ for some invertible matrix C. (Prove!) This shows that $A - cI$ and $B - cI$ are similar. But then their determinants are equal, by an application of Theorem 5.13. It follows that the characteristic roots for A and B are the same. Moreover, since $|A - cI| = |B - cI|$, we conclude that the *characteristic equations of similar matrices A and B are the same.*

From this emerges a basic correspondence principle.

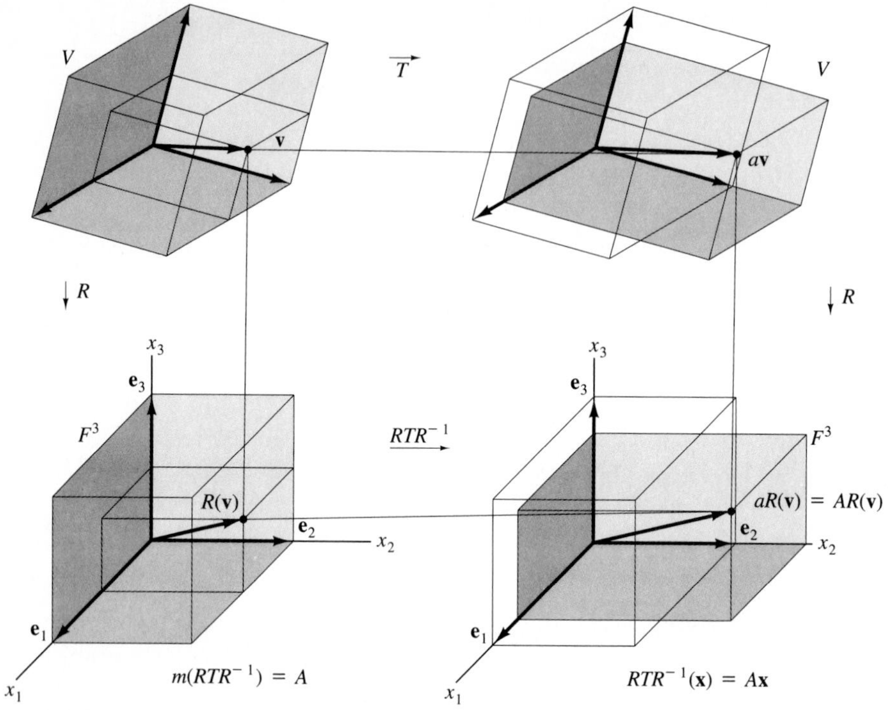

Figure 5.22 Characteristic vectors $\mathbf{v}$ and $R(\mathbf{v})$ for $T \in L(V, V)$ and its matrix A.

Principle of Corresponding Characteristic Vectors.

1. The characteristic roots of a linear transformation T of a finite-dimensional vector space V are the same as those of its matrix with respect to any basis.
2. To find these roots, take any basis $\mathbf{v}_1, \ldots, \mathbf{v}_n$ for V and compute the matrix A of T with respect to this basis. Then a characteristic vector $\mathbf{v} \in V$ for T corresponding to a characteristic root c is $\mathbf{v} = a_1\mathbf{v}_1 + \cdots + a_n\mathbf{v}_n$, where $\mathbf{v}' = a_1\mathbf{e}_1 + \cdots + a_n\mathbf{e}_n$ is a characteristic vector of A corresponding to c.
3. The characteristic roots of a matrix $A \in M_nF$ are the solutions $c \in F$ to the characteristic equation $|A - zI| = 0$. For each such c, the corresponding characteristic vectors are the nonzero vectors in the nullspace of $A - cI$.

EXAMPLES

1. For the matrix $A = \begin{bmatrix} a & b \\ c & d \end{bmatrix}$, the characteristic equation is

$$0 = |A - zI| = \begin{vmatrix} a-z & b \\ c & d-z \end{vmatrix} = z^2 - (a+d)z + ad - bc.$$

(Verify!) Note that Trace $A = a + d$ (the sum of the diagonal elements of A) and $|A| = ad - bc$ give two of the coefficients:

$$|A - zI| = z^2 - (\text{Trace } A)z + |A|$$

For instance, if $A = \begin{bmatrix} 2 & -1 \\ -3 & 2 \end{bmatrix}$, then the characteristic equation is $z^2 - 4z + 1$. Its roots are $2 + \sqrt{3}$ and $2 - \sqrt{3}$. The characteristic vectors are the nonzero elements of the nullspaces of the matrices

$$\begin{bmatrix} 2 & -1 \\ -3 & 2 \end{bmatrix} - (2 + \sqrt{3})I = \begin{bmatrix} -\sqrt{3} & -1 \\ -3 & -\sqrt{3} \end{bmatrix},$$

$$\begin{bmatrix} 2 & -1 \\ -3 & 2 \end{bmatrix} - (2 - \sqrt{3})I = \begin{bmatrix} \sqrt{3} & -1 \\ -3 & \sqrt{3} \end{bmatrix}.$$

These are the vectors $t\begin{bmatrix} -1 \\ \sqrt{3} \end{bmatrix}$ and $t\begin{bmatrix} 1 \\ \sqrt{3} \end{bmatrix}$, where t is nonzero. (Verify!)

2. In particular, the characteristic equation of $A = \begin{bmatrix} a & b \\ b & d \end{bmatrix}$ is

$$z^2 - (a+d)z + ad - b^2 = (z - a')(z - d') = 0,$$

where

$$a' = \frac{a + d + \sqrt{(a-d)^2 + 4b^2}}{2}, \qquad d' = \frac{a + d - \sqrt{(a-d)^2 + 4b^2}}{2}$$

(Section 1.8). So, a' and d' are the characteristic roots of $\begin{bmatrix} a & b \\ b & d \end{bmatrix}$. For instance, if $A = \begin{bmatrix} 2 & -1 \\ -1 & 2 \end{bmatrix}$, then $a' = 3$ and $d' = 1$. So, the corresponding characteristic vectors are the nonzero elements of the nullspaces of

$$\begin{bmatrix} 2 & -1 \\ -1 & 2 \end{bmatrix} - 3I = \begin{bmatrix} -1 & -1 \\ -1 & -1 \end{bmatrix} \quad \text{and} \quad \begin{bmatrix} 2 & -1 \\ -1 & 2 \end{bmatrix} - 1I = \begin{bmatrix} 1 & -1 \\ -1 & 1 \end{bmatrix}.$$

These are $t\begin{bmatrix} -1 \\ 1 \end{bmatrix}$ and $t\begin{bmatrix} 1 \\ 1 \end{bmatrix}$, where t is nonzero. (Verify!)

3. The linear transformations

$$S(\mathbf{x}) = \begin{bmatrix} a & b \\ c & d \end{bmatrix}\mathbf{x} \quad \text{and} \quad T(\mathbf{x}) = \begin{bmatrix} 1 & -1 \\ 0 & 1 \end{bmatrix}\begin{bmatrix} a & b \\ c & d \end{bmatrix}\begin{bmatrix} 1 & 1 \\ 0 & 1 \end{bmatrix}\mathbf{x}$$

have the same characteristic roots. In fact, if $S(\mathbf{v}) = c\mathbf{v}$, then $T(\mathbf{v}') = c\mathbf{v}'$, where $\mathbf{v}' = \begin{bmatrix} 1 & -1 \\ 0 & 1 \end{bmatrix}\mathbf{v}$. (Verify!)

4. A linear transformation T of a vector space V over F with basis $\mathbf{u}$, $\mathbf{v}$, $\mathbf{w}$, where T is described as mapping each of the basis vectors to the sum of the other two. To find its characteristic roots, we compute the matrix A of T with respect to $\mathbf{u}$, $\mathbf{v}$, $\mathbf{w}$. From the description of T,

$$T(\mathbf{u}) = 0\mathbf{u} + 1\mathbf{v} + 1\mathbf{w},$$

$$T(\mathbf{v}) = 1\mathbf{u} + 0\mathbf{v} + 1\mathbf{w},$$

$$T(\mathbf{w}) = 1\mathbf{u} + 1\mathbf{v} + 0\mathbf{w}.$$

So, $A = \begin{bmatrix} 0 & 1 & 1 \\ 1 & 0 & 1 \\ 1 & 1 & 0 \end{bmatrix}$ and the characteristic equation for T is

$$0 = |A - zI| = \begin{vmatrix} 0-z & 1 & 1 \\ 1 & 0-z & 1 \\ 1 & 1 & 0-z \end{vmatrix} = -z^3 + 3z + 2,$$

that is, $0 = -(z-2)(z+1)^2$. (Verify!) The characteristic roots are then $2, -1, -1$, and the corresponding characteristic vectors are

$$r\begin{bmatrix} 1 \\ 1 \\ 1 \end{bmatrix} \quad (r \neq 0) \qquad \text{and} \qquad s\begin{bmatrix} 1 \\ 0 \\ -1 \end{bmatrix} + t\begin{bmatrix} 1 \\ -2 \\ 1 \end{bmatrix} \quad (s \text{ or } t \text{ nonzero}).$$

(Verify!)

The characteristic polynomial

For $A \in M_nF$, the determinant $|A - zI|$ is a polynomial in z. (Explain!)

Definition. *Characteristic Polynomial of A.*
We call $|A - zI|$ the **characteristic polynomial** of A. The set of roots of $|A - zI|$ in $\mathbb{C}$ is called the **spectrum** of A, whereas the set of real roots of $|A - zI|$ is called the **real spectrum** of A.

So, the set of characteristic roots of A is the spectrum of A if F is $\mathbb{C}$, and it is the real spectrum of A if F is $\mathbb{R}$. The following theorem shows that the spectrum of a matrix $A \in M_nF$ has at most n elements.

Theorem 5.20. *Degree of the Characteristic Polynomial.*
The characteristic polynomial of $A \in M_nF$ has degree n.

Proof. The proof is by mathematical induction. If $n = 1$, $|A - zI| = a_{11} - z$, which is of degree 1 in z. Suppose that the theorem is true for matrices $A' \in M_{n-1}F$. Expanding A along the first row, we get

$$|A - zI| = (a_{11} - z)|A_{11} - zI| - a_{12}|B_{12}| + \cdots \pm a_{1n}|B_{1n}|,$$

where $B = A - zI$. The first term is $1 +$ Degree $|A_{11} - zI| = n$, because $A_{11} \in M_{n-1}F$ and Degree $|A_{11} - zI| = n - 1$ by our induction hypothesis. The other terms are of degree at most $n - 1$. (Explain!) So, Degree $|A - zI| = n$. ■

EXAMPLE

For $n = 2$, Theorem 5.20 simply states that $\begin{vmatrix} a-z & b \\ c & d-z \end{vmatrix}$ is of degree 2 in z, which is the number of diagonal entries that appear as factors in exactly one term of the determinant.

●

Similarly, the *characteristic polynomial* of a linear transformation T of a finite-dimensional vector space is the polynomial $|T - zI|$, which is the same as the characteristic polynomial $|m_R(T) - zI|$ of its matrix with respect to any isomorphism R from V to F^n. (Explain!) Its *spectrum* and *real spectrum* are, again, the sets of complex and real roots of the characteristic polynomial.

EXAMPLES

1. If $F = \mathbb{R}$ and $A = \begin{bmatrix} 0 & -1 \\ 1 & 0 \end{bmatrix}$, the characteristic polynomial of A is $z^2 + 1$, which has no real roots. So, A has no characteristic roots. Therefore, it has no characteristic vectors. The same is true for the linear transformation $T(\mathbf{x}) = \begin{bmatrix} 0 & -1 \\ 1 & 0 \end{bmatrix} x$.

2. On the other hand, if $F = \mathbb{C}$, $A = \begin{bmatrix} 0 & -1 \\ 1 & 0 \end{bmatrix}$ has the characteristic roots $\pm i$, the characteristic equation still being $z^2 + 1$. The corresponding characteristic vectors are $\begin{bmatrix} i \\ 1 \end{bmatrix}, \begin{bmatrix} -i \\ 1 \end{bmatrix}$. (Verify!)

3. For any upper or lower triangular matrix $A \in M_nF$, the determinant of $A - zI$ is the product of the diagonal elements $z - d_1, \ldots, z - d_n$. It follows that the characteristic polynomial is the polynomial

$$(z - d_1) \cdots (z - d_n)$$

and the characteristic roots for both are $d_1, \ldots, d_n$. For instance, the characteristic roots of

$$\begin{bmatrix} 2 & 2 & 0 \\ 0 & 3 & 4 \\ 0 & 0 & -1 \end{bmatrix} \text{ and } \begin{bmatrix} 2 & 0 & 0 \\ 1 & 3 & 0 \\ 9 & 9 & -1 \end{bmatrix}$$

are 2, 3, -1, and the characteristic polynomials for both of them are $(z-2)(z-3)(z+1)$. (Verify!)

4. The characteristic vectors $\mathbf{v}$ for

$$A = \begin{bmatrix} 2 & 2 & 0 \\ 0 & 3 & 4 \\ 0 & 0 & -1 \end{bmatrix}$$

can easily be determined, since they are the nonzero elements of the nullspaces for $A - 2I$, $A - 3I$, and $A + I$. These vectors are:

$$t\begin{bmatrix} 1 \\ 0 \\ 0 \end{bmatrix}, \quad t\begin{bmatrix} 2 \\ 1 \\ 0 \end{bmatrix}, \quad t\begin{bmatrix} 2 \\ -3 \\ 3 \end{bmatrix} \quad (t \neq 0).$$

5. The characteristic roots for

$$\begin{bmatrix} 1 & 0 & 0 \\ 1 & 1 & 0 \\ 2 & 3 & 1 \end{bmatrix}$$

are 1, 1, 1. The only characteristic vectors are

$$t\begin{bmatrix} 0 \\ 0 \\ 1 \end{bmatrix} \quad (t \neq 0).$$

(Verify!)

PROBLEMS

NUMERICAL PROBLEMS

1. Find the nullspace of $\begin{bmatrix} 2 & 1 & 0 \\ 0 & 2 & 1 \\ 0 & 0 & 2 \end{bmatrix} - cI$ for all $c \in F$.

2. Find the characteristic equations and roots of the following matrices.

(a) $\begin{bmatrix} 0 & 2 \\ 3 & 0 \end{bmatrix}$ **(b)** $\begin{bmatrix} 2 & 3 \\ 0 & 3 \end{bmatrix}$

(c) $\begin{bmatrix} 0 & -1 \\ 2 & 3 \end{bmatrix}$ **(d)** $\begin{bmatrix} 0 & 1 \\ 3 & -2 \end{bmatrix}$

(e) $\begin{bmatrix} 2 & -1 & 0 \\ -1 & 2 & -1 \\ 0 & -1 & 2 \end{bmatrix}$ **(f)** $\begin{bmatrix} 2 & -4 & 0 & 0 \\ 0 & 4 & 0 & 0 \\ 0 & 0 & 6 & 0 \\ 0 & 0 & -18 & 8 \end{bmatrix}$

3. For each matrix in Problem 1, find the characteristic vectors.

4. Verify that

$$\begin{bmatrix} 2 & 3 \\ 0 & 3 \end{bmatrix} \text{ and } \begin{bmatrix} 0 & 2 \\ 3 & 0 \end{bmatrix}^{-1} \begin{bmatrix} 2 & 3 \\ 0 & 3 \end{bmatrix} \begin{bmatrix} 0 & 2 \\ 3 & 0 \end{bmatrix}$$

have the same trace, determinant, characteristic polynomial, and characteristic roots. Do they have the same characteristic vectors? Explain.

5. Find the characteristic polynomials, characteristic roots, and characteristic vectors of each of the following linear transformations.

(a) $T(a\mathbf{u} + b\mathbf{v}) = 3a\mathbf{u} + 4b\mathbf{v}$

(b) $T(a\mathbf{u} + b\mathbf{v}) = a\mathbf{v} + b\mathbf{u}$

(c) $T(a\mathbf{u} + b\mathbf{v}) = a\mathbf{u} + (2a + b)\mathbf{v}$

Hard

6. Find Kernel $(T - dI)$ for all $d \in F$, where T is the linear transformation $T(a\mathbf{u} + b\mathbf{v} + c\mathbf{w}) = (b + c)\mathbf{u} + (a + c)\mathbf{v} + (a + b)\mathbf{w}$ of a vector space with basis $\mathbf{u}, \mathbf{v}, \mathbf{w}$. What are the characteristic roots and vectors of T?

7. A basis for the vector space V of real polynomials of degree at most 2 is $\mathbf{u} = 1, \mathbf{v} = z, \mathbf{w} = z^2$.

(a) Find the matrix with respect to $\mathbf{u}, \mathbf{v}, \mathbf{w}$ of the linear transformation T of V mapping each element to its derivative with respect to z.

(b) Find the characteristic roots and vectors of T.

(c) Find the matrix with respect to $\mathbf{u}, \mathbf{v}, \mathbf{w}$ of the linear transformation S of V such that $S(\mathbf{f}) = zT(\mathbf{f})$ for each $\mathbf{f} \in V$.

(d) Find the characteristic roots and vectors of S.

THEORETICAL PROBLEMS

8. Show that if the trace $a + d$ of an invertible matrix $A = \begin{bmatrix} a & b \\ c & d \end{bmatrix}$ is 0, then it has two different characteristic roots in $\mathbb{C}$.

9. Show that if the trace $a + d$ of an invertible matrix $A = \begin{bmatrix} a & b \\ c & d \end{bmatrix}$ is 0, then $\mathbb{C}^2$ has a basis $\mathbf{v}, \mathbf{w}$ of characteristic vectors for A.

10. Show that $C^{-1}AC - cI = C^{-1}(A - cI)C$ and $|C^{-1}AC - cI| = |A - cI|$.

11. Show that similar matrices in M_nF have the same trace (sum of diagonal entries).

Hard

12. Explain why the powers $I, A, \ldots, A^{n^2}$ of any $A \in M_nF$ are linearly dependent.

13. For any polynomial $f(z) \in F[z]$, we define $f(A)$ to be the matrix obtained by replacing z^r by A^r for $r > 0$ and z^0 by I in $f(z)$. For example, if $f(z) = 3 - 5z^2 + 2z - 6$, then $f(A) = 3I - 5A^2 + 2A - 6I$.

(a) Show that for any $A \in M_nF$, there is a nonzero polynomial $f(z) \in F[z]$ of degree at most n^2 which *vanishes* at A; that is, $f(A) = 0$.

(b) Show that the set of polynomials in $F[z]$ that vanish at $A \in M_nF$ is a subspace V_A of $F[z]$.

(c) For $f(z) \in V_A$ and $g(z) \in F[z]$, show that $f(z)g(z)$ is in V_A.

(d) Any nonzero $f(z) \in V_A$ whose degree is as small as possible is called a **minimum polynomial** for A. If $f(z)$ is a minimum polynomial for A and $g(z) \in V_A$, show that $f(z)$ *divides* $g(z)$—that is, $g(z)$ is a product $g(z) = m(z)f(z)$ for some $m(z) \in F[z]$. (***Hint:*** Show that there is $m(z)$ such that $g(z) = m(z)f(z) + r(z)$, where $r(z)$ has degree less than $f(z)$. Then show that $r(z) = 0$.)

(e) Use (d) to show that if $f(z)$ and $g(z)$ are minimum polynomials for A, then each is a constant multiple of the other. To eliminate the ambiguity of this constant, we now agree always to take the minimum polynomial whose coefficient of highest degree term is 1. With this convention, *there is only one minimum polynomial for A.*

(f) Show that the minimum polynomial of $A \in M_nF$ has degree at most n^2.

14. Show that the minimal polynomial of a diagonal matrix $A \in M_nF$ has degree at most n.

15. Show that the minimal polynomial of a matrix equals that of any similar matrix.

16. Show that the minimal polynomial of a triangular matrix $A \in M_nF$ with 1s on the diagonal has degree at most n.

17. Show that the minimal polynomial of a triangular matrix $A \in M_4F$ with diagonal entries a, b, c, and d divides $(z - a)(z - b)(z - c)(z - d)$.

5.8 DIAGONALIZABLE MATRICES

Much can be said about a linear transformation $T(\mathbf{x}) = A\mathbf{x}$ of F^n in terms of its characteristic polynomial. The fact that we rarely compute it in practice does not detract at all from its importance in forging the theory upon which our computational strategies are built. From the characteristic polynomial, we get the characteristic roots c, which lead directly to the corresponding characteristic vectors. When either $F = \mathbb{C}$ or all roots of the characteristic polynomial are real, these lead to a basis of F^n, with respect to which the matrix of T is diagonal or, at least, upper triangular. In this section, we show how this goes.

The complex characteristic roots

The characteristic polynomial of $A \in M_nF$ factors as

$$|A - zI| = \pm(z - c_1)\cdots(z - c_n),$$

where the c_i are complex numbers. If $F = \mathbb{C}$, all the c_r are characteristic roots and, for each of them, we get corresponding characteristic vectors $\mathbf{v}_r \in \mathbf{F}^n$.

On the other hand, if $F = \mathbb{R}$, only the real roots c_r of $|A - zI| = \pm(z - c_1)\cdots(z - c_n)$ are characteristic roots for A *over* $\mathbb{R}$. So, only for the real c_r do we get corresponding characteristic vectors $\mathbf{v}_r \in \mathbb{R}^n$. However, $M_n\mathbb{R}$ is a subset of $M_n\mathbb{C}$. So, for the c_s that are not real, we can find corresponding characteristic vectors $\mathbf{v}_s \in \mathbb{C}^n$.

Principle of Complexification.
Even when A has real entries, we may want to view A as an element of $M_n\mathbb{C}$ for the purpose of getting the characteristic vectors corresponding to the characteristic roots that are not real.

Characteristic vectors corresponding to different roots

When an n-tuple $(c_1, \ldots, c_n)$ is chosen *at random* from F^n, the entries are usually all different. The exceptions to this rule, after all, are in the union of $n(n - 1)/2$ hyperplanes, which is relatively small. (Explain in the case of the $3(3 - 1)/2 = 3$ planes $x_1 = x_2, x_1 = x_3, x_2 = x_3$ in $\mathbb{R}^3$!) It is also true, though less obviously, that when A is chosen at random from M_nF, the roots of $|A - zI| = \pm(z - c_1)\cdots(z - c_n)$ are usually all different.

Principle of Different Characteristic Roots.
When A is chosen at random from M_nF, the roots c_i of $|A - zI| = \pm(z - c_1)\cdots(z - c_n)$ and their absolute values $|c_i|$ are usually all different.

Basis of characteristic vectors

Because of this principle, the following two theorems are quite powerful.

Theorem 5.21. *Characteristic Vectors with Distinct Roots Are Independent.* Suppose that V is a vector space over F, and let $T \in L(V, V)$ have n different characteristic roots $c_1, \ldots, c_n \in F$ with corresponding characteristic vectors $\mathbf{v}_1, \ldots, \mathbf{v}_n$. Then the vectors $\mathbf{v}_1, \ldots, \mathbf{v}_n$ are linearly independent.

Proof. Suppose, to the contrary, that $\mathbf{v}_1, \ldots, \mathbf{v}_n$ are linearly dependent. Then there is a nontrivial linear combination $a_1\mathbf{v}_1 + \cdots + a_k\mathbf{v}_k$ which is $\mathbf{0}$. Take such a linear combination with k as small as possible, and note that $k > 1$. (Why?) Applying T, we then get $c_1a_1\mathbf{v}_1 + \cdots + c_ka_k\mathbf{v}_k = \mathbf{0}$. But then a new linear combination comes from multiplying $a_1\mathbf{v}_1 + \cdots + a_k\mathbf{v}_k = \mathbf{0}$ by c_k

and subtracting it from $c_1 a_1 \mathbf{v}_1 + \cdots + c_k a_k \mathbf{v}_k = \mathbf{0}$. Since the last term drops out, we get $(c_1 - c_k)a_1 \mathbf{v}_1 + \cdots + (c_{k-1} - c_k)a_{k-1}\mathbf{v}_{k-1} = \mathbf{0}$. But this is a non-trivial linear combination, which is not possible, since k was taken as small as possible. So, there can be no such nontrivial linear combination in the first place, and the $\mathbf{v}$'s are linearly independent. ∎

We now bring dimension in to further clarify the picture (see Figure 5.23).

$$T(\mathbf{u}) = \mathbf{u}, \quad T(\mathbf{v}) = r\mathbf{v}, \quad T(\mathbf{w}) = s\mathbf{w}$$
$$T(\mathbf{x}) = a\mathbf{u} + rb\mathbf{v} + sc\mathbf{w} \text{ for } \mathbf{x} = a\mathbf{u} + b\mathbf{v} + c\mathbf{w}$$

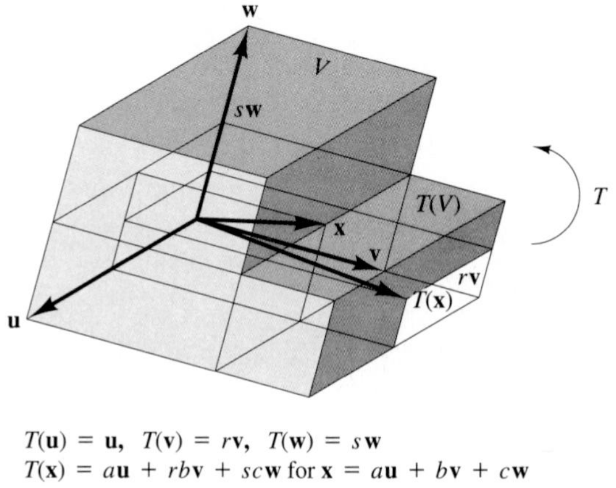

Figure 5.23 A basis $\mathbf{u}$, $\mathbf{v}$, $\mathbf{w}$ of characteristic vectors of T.

Theorem 5.22. *Existence of a Basis of Characteristic Vectors.*

Suppose that V is an n-dimensional vector space over F and $T \in L(V, V)$ has n different characteristic roots $c_1, \ldots, c_n \in F$. Then V has a basis $\mathbf{v}_1, \ldots, \mathbf{v}_n$ consisting of characteristic vectors of A.

Proof. For each characteristic root c_r, there is a corresponding charac-teristic vector $\mathbf{v}_r$ such that $T(\mathbf{v}_r) = c_r \mathbf{v}_r$. By Theorem 5.21, these $\mathbf{v}_1, \ldots, \mathbf{v}_n$ are linearly independent. But then, since V is of dimension n, they form a basis. ∎

The factorization $A = VDV^{-1}$ (D diagonal, V a matrix whose columns are a basis of characteristic vectors for A) of a diagonalizable matrix A corresponds to the factorization of the linear transformation $T(\mathbf{x}) = A\mathbf{x}$ as $T(\mathbf{x}) = V(D(V^{-1}(\mathbf{x})))$ portrayed in Figure 5.24.

EXAMPLES

1. If $A = \begin{bmatrix} a & b \\ c & d \end{bmatrix}$ is invertible of trace $a + d = 0$, then the roots a', d' of $z^2 - (a + d)z + ad - bc$ are different. (Prove!) If a', $d' \in F$, then the corresponding characteristic vectors $\mathbf{v}$, $\mathbf{w}$ form a basis for A.

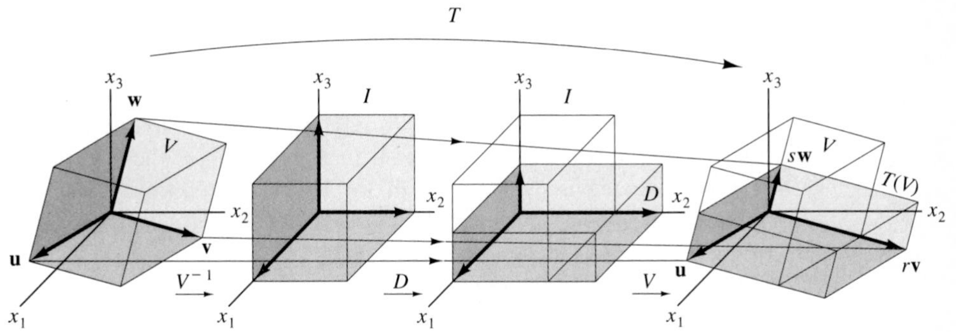

Figure 5.24 Factored action of $T(\mathbf{x}) = VDV^{-1}\mathbf{x}$ on $V = [\mathbf{u} \quad \mathbf{v} \quad \mathbf{w}]$ if $T(\mathbf{u}) = \mathbf{u}$, $T(\mathbf{v}) = r\mathbf{v}$, $T(\mathbf{w}) = s\mathbf{w}$.

2. If $A = \begin{bmatrix} a & b \\ 0 & d \end{bmatrix}$ and $a \neq d$, then the characteristic roots a, d of A are different and the corresponding characteristic vectors $\mathbf{v}$, $\mathbf{w}$ form a basis for A. In fact, they are $\mathbf{v} = \begin{bmatrix} 1 \\ 0 \end{bmatrix}$, $\mathbf{w} = \begin{bmatrix} b \\ d-a \end{bmatrix}$. (Verify!)

3. If $A \in M_nF$ is an upper or lower triangular matrix, all of whose diagonal entries are different, then F^n has a basis $\mathbf{v}_1, \ldots, \mathbf{v}_n$ consisting of characteristic vectors corresponding to the diagonal entries d_r of A.

Diagonalizability

When a matrix A is similar to a diagonal matrix, it and the linear transformation $R(\mathbf{x}) = A\mathbf{x}$ are said to be diagonalizable. As illustrated by Figure 5.21, diagonalizability of a transformation is very useful in describing its action.

Definition. *Diagonalizable Transformations and Matrices.*
A linear transformation T of a vector space V over F is **diagonalizable** over F if V has a basis $\mathbf{v}_1, \ldots, \mathbf{v}_n$ consisting of characteristic vectors of T. We say that $A \in M_nF$ is *diagonalizable over* F if and only if A is similar over F to a diagonal matrix.

The matrix of T with respect to a basis of characteristic vectors is diagonal over F (prove) and, conversely, if the matrix of T with respect to a basis $\mathbf{v}_1, \ldots, \mathbf{v}_n$ is diagonal over F, then the basis consists of characteristic vectors. (Prove!)

Theorem 5.23 *Diagonalizability of T and Its Matrix.*
Let V be a vector space with basis $\mathbf{v}_1, \ldots, \mathbf{v}_n$ over F and let $T \in L(V, V)$. Then T is diagonalizable if and only if its matrix with respect to $\mathbf{v}_1, \ldots, \mathbf{v}_n$ is diagonalizable over F.

Proof. Let A be the matrix of T with respect to $\mathbf{v}_1, \ldots, \mathbf{v}_n$. If T is diagonalizable, V has a basis $\mathbf{w}_1, \ldots, \mathbf{w}_n$ consisting of characteristic vectors, so the matrix B of T with respect to the basis $\mathbf{w}_1, \ldots, \mathbf{w}_n$ is diagonal. Since A and B are similar (Section 4.7), A is diagonalizable. Conversely, if A is diagonalizable, it is similar to a diagonal matrix B. This is the matrix of T with respect to some basis $\mathbf{w}_1, \ldots, \mathbf{w}_n$ of V (Section 4.7). Since B is diagonal, $\mathbf{w}_1, \ldots, \mathbf{w}_n$ consists of characteristic vectors, so T is diagonalizable. ■

Corollary. For $A \in M_n F$, A is diagonalizable over F if and only if the linear transformation $T(\mathbf{x}) = A\mathbf{x}$ is diagonalizable.

Proof. This follows from the theorem, since A is the matrix for T with respect to $\mathbf{e}_1, \ldots, \mathbf{e}_n$. ■

EXAMPLES

1. If $A = \begin{bmatrix} a & b \\ 0 & d \end{bmatrix}$ and $a \neq d$, then $\mathbf{v} = \begin{bmatrix} 1 \\ 0 \end{bmatrix}$, $\mathbf{w} = \begin{bmatrix} b \\ d-a \end{bmatrix}$ is a basis of characteristic vectors for $V = F^2$. (Verify!) So, $T(\mathbf{x}) = A\mathbf{x}$ is diagonalizable. The matrix of $T(\mathbf{x}) = A\mathbf{x}$ with respect to the basis $\mathbf{v}$, $\mathbf{w}$ is $[\mathbf{v} \;\; \mathbf{w}]^{-1} A [\mathbf{v} \;\; \mathbf{w}] = \begin{bmatrix} a & 0 \\ 0 & d \end{bmatrix}$. (Verify!) So, A is similar to a diagonal matrix and A is diagonalizable over F.
2. Any matrix $A \in M_n F$ having n distinct characteristic roots is diagonalizable over F. For instance, if $A \in M_n F$ is an upper or lower triangular matrix with n different diagonal entries, A is diagonalizable over F.

An iterative method

When $A \in M_n\mathbb{R}$ and *the spectrum of A is real*—that is, all the roots of $|A - zI|$ are real—then their absolute values are usually all different, by the principle of different characteristic roots for such A. When this is true, A is diagonalizable over $\mathbb{R}$ and various methods can be used to find roots of the characteristic polynomial for A. Another method, which is iterative in nature, enables us to find a *dominant* characteristic root and corresponding vector for A at the same time. We now describe this method, which is illustrated in Figure 5.25.

A **dominant characteristic root** for a matrix $A \in M_n\mathbb{R}$ is a real characteristic root c whose absolute value is greater than that of any other element of the spectrum of A. Any corresponding characteristic vector is called a **dominant characteristic vector**. For example, as we see in the next section, the spectrum of a real symmetric matrix A is real. So, if its characteristic roots have different absolute values, it is diagonalizable over $\mathbb{R}$ and has a dominant characteristic root. Under such circumstances, the following theorem gives a method for finding the dominant characteristic root and a corresponding characteristic vector, based on the **Rayleigh quotients** $\dfrac{\langle \mathbf{y}, A\mathbf{y}\rangle}{\langle \mathbf{y}, \mathbf{y}\rangle}$. Note that if $\mathbf{y}$ is a characteristic vector with real nonzero characteristic root c, this quotient equals c.

Theorem 5.24. *Finding a Dominant Characteristic Root and Vector.* Let $A \in M_n\mathbb{R}$ be diagonalizable over $\mathbb{R}$ and have a dominant characteristic root c. Then for all $\mathbf{x} \in \mathbb{R}^n$ not in some hyperplane,

1. c can be found as the limit c of the sequence

$$\frac{\langle A^k\mathbf{x}, A^{k+1}\mathbf{x}\rangle}{\langle A^k\mathbf{x}, A^k\mathbf{x}\rangle} \qquad (k = 1, 2, 3, \ldots);$$

2. A corresponding characteristic vector for c is the limit of the sequence $\left(\frac{1}{c}A\right)^k\mathbf{x}$.

Proof. Let $\mathbf{x}_1, \ldots, \mathbf{x}_n$ be a basis for $\mathbb{R}^n$ of characteristic vectors for A corresponding to characteristic roots $c_1, \ldots, c_n$, where $c = c_1 = \cdots = c_r$ and $|c| > |c_s|$ for $s > r$. For $\mathbf{x}$ not in the hyperplane $F\mathbf{x}_2 + \cdots + F\mathbf{x}_n$, we can write $\mathbf{x} = d_1\mathbf{x}_1 + \cdots + d_n\mathbf{x}_n$, where the coefficient d_1 is nonzero. Taking such an $\mathbf{x}$ and letting $\mathbf{y} = (d_1\mathbf{x}_1 + \cdots + d_r\mathbf{x}_r)$, we have

$$\left(\frac{1}{c}A\right)^k\mathbf{x} = \left(\frac{c_1}{c}\right)^k\mathbf{y} + \left(\frac{c_{r+1}}{c}\right)^k d_{r+1}\mathbf{x}_n + \cdots + \left(\frac{c_n}{c}\right)^k d_n\mathbf{x}_n$$

for all k where $c_1/c = 1$ and $c_s/c < 1$ for $r + 1 \le s \le n$. (Explain!) It follows that the limit of the sequence of vectors

$$\mathbf{y}_k = \left(\frac{1}{c}A\right)^k\mathbf{x}$$

is $\mathbf{y}$, which is a characteristic vector corresponding to c. Since

$$\frac{\langle A^k\mathbf{x}, A^{k+1}\mathbf{x}\rangle}{\langle A^k\mathbf{x}, A^k\mathbf{x}\rangle} = \frac{\langle \mathbf{y}_k, A\mathbf{y}_k\rangle}{\langle \mathbf{y}_k, \mathbf{y}_k\rangle}$$

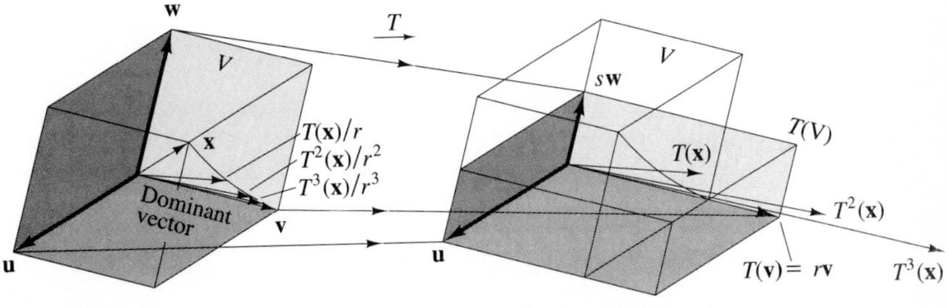

Figure 5.25 A dominant characteristic vector $\mathbf{v}$ for A is mapped by $T(\mathbf{x}) = A\mathbf{x}$ to $r\mathbf{v}$.

(Explain!), the limit of the quotients $\dfrac{\langle A^k\mathbf{x}, A^{k+1}\mathbf{x}\rangle}{\langle A^k\mathbf{x}, A^k\mathbf{x}\rangle}$ is

$$\frac{\langle \mathbf{y}, A\mathbf{y}\rangle}{\langle \mathbf{y}, \mathbf{y}\rangle} = \frac{\langle \mathbf{y}, c\mathbf{y}\rangle}{\langle \mathbf{y}, \mathbf{y}\rangle} = c. \qquad \blacksquare$$

This theorem is very easy to apply, since we really need only compute $\mathbf{y} = A^k\mathbf{x}$ with k large as the approximate characteristic vector and then take $c = \dfrac{\langle \mathbf{y}, A\mathbf{y}\rangle}{\langle \mathbf{y}, \mathbf{y}\rangle}$ as the approximate characteristic value. We illustrate this in the next example.

EXAMPLE

Let $A = \begin{bmatrix} 1 & 2 \\ 2 & 1 \end{bmatrix}$. Taking $\mathbf{x}$ at random, say $\mathbf{x} = \begin{bmatrix} 1 \\ 0 \end{bmatrix}$, we compute $A\mathbf{x} = \begin{bmatrix} 1 \\ 2 \end{bmatrix}$ and $A^2\mathbf{x} = \begin{bmatrix} 5 \\ 4 \end{bmatrix}$. Stopping with

$$\mathbf{y} = A^2\mathbf{x} = \begin{bmatrix} 5 \\ 4 \end{bmatrix} \quad \text{and} \quad c = \frac{\langle \mathbf{y}, A\mathbf{y}\rangle}{\langle \mathbf{y}, \mathbf{y}\rangle} = \frac{121}{41},$$

we are already very close to a true characteristic vector $\begin{bmatrix} 5 \\ 5 \end{bmatrix}$ and corresponding characteristic root 3. (Check!) When using higher powers for greater accuracy, divide or multiply the $A^k\mathbf{x}$ by suitable scalars from time to time along the way to keep the entries from getting too large or small. There is no need to keep track of these scalars. (Explain!)

PROBLEMS

NUMERICAL PROBLEMS

1. For what values of r, s, and t do the following matrices have two different characteristic roots?

 (a) $\begin{bmatrix} s & 3 \\ 0 & t \end{bmatrix}$ **(b)** $\begin{bmatrix} s & 4 \\ 4 & t \end{bmatrix}$ **(c)** $\begin{bmatrix} s & 3 \\ t & 3 \end{bmatrix}$ **(d)** $\begin{bmatrix} r & s \\ t & 1 \end{bmatrix}$

2. Which of the matrices in Problem 2 of Section 5.7 are diagonalizable? For each of them, describe a similar diagonal matrix.

3. Which of the linear transformations in Problem 5 of Section 5.7 are diagonalizable? For each of them, find a basis of characteristic vectors.

4. Find a basis of characteristic vectors for the linear transformation

$$T(\mathbf{x}) = \begin{bmatrix} 0 & 1 & 3 \\ 1 & 0 & 2 \\ 0 & 0 & 2 \end{bmatrix}.$$

5. Find a basis of characteristic vectors for the linear transformation T of the vector space of polynomials of degree at most 2 over the reals which maps 1 to $z + z^2$, z to $1 + z^2$, and z^2 to $1 + z$.

6. In Problem 5, describe all possible bases of characteristic vectors for T.

7. If $A = \begin{bmatrix} a & b \\ 0 & d \end{bmatrix}$ and $a \neq d$, show that a basis of characteristic vectors for A is $\mathbf{v} = \begin{bmatrix} 1 \\ 0 \end{bmatrix}$, $\mathbf{w} = \begin{bmatrix} b \\ d-a \end{bmatrix}$.

8. For $G = \begin{bmatrix} 2 & -1 \\ -3 & 2 \end{bmatrix}$, we found the characteristic roots to be $2 + \sqrt{3}$ and $2 - \sqrt{3}$, with corresponding characteristic vectors $\begin{bmatrix} -1 \\ \sqrt{3} \end{bmatrix}$ and $\begin{bmatrix} 1 \\ \sqrt{3} \end{bmatrix}$. Show that $\mathbf{y} = G^2\begin{bmatrix} 1 \\ 0 \end{bmatrix}$ approximates a multiple of one of these vectors. What is the corresponding approximation of the characteristic root by a Rayleigh quotient?

THEORETICAL PROBLEMS

9. Show that if A is similar to a diagonal matrix D, then the diagonal elements of D are the characteristic roots of A.

10. Show that a matrix A is diagonalizable if and only if A^T is.

11. Show that if a matrix A is diagonalizable, then so is $A + cI$.

12. Show that if $A \in M_n F$ is invertible, then
    - **(a)** The characteristic roots of A are nonzero;
    - **(b)** c^{-1} is a characteristic root for A^{-1} for any characteristic c root for A;
    - **(c)** If A has n distinct characteristic roots, then so does A^{-1};
    - **(d)** $\mathbf{v}$ is a characteristic vector for A if and only if it is a characteristic vector for A^{-1};
    - **(e)** A is diagonalizable if and only if A^{-1} is diagonalizable.

13. Find an example of two invertible diagonalizable matrices A and B such that $A + B$ is not diagonalizable.

Hard

14. Show that if A and B are 2×2 matrices which are diagonalizable and if $AB = BA$, then the matrices $A + B$, AB, and $aA + bB$ are also diagonalizable for any $a, b \in F$.

15. For $A \in M_n F$ and $T(x) = Ax$, show that $F^n = \text{Kernel } T^n + \text{Image } T^n$. (***Hint:*** Show that each $A^n\mathbf{v}$ is $A^{2n}\mathbf{w}$ for some $\mathbf{w}$ by showing that Image $T^n =$ Image T^{2n} by a dimension argument. Let $\mathbf{v} = \mathbf{v} - A^n\mathbf{w} + A^n\mathbf{w}$.)

16. For $A \in M_n F$ and $T(\mathbf{x}) = A\mathbf{x}$, show that $\{\mathbf{0}\} = \text{Kernel } T^n \cap \text{Image } T^n$. (***Hint:*** Use Problem 15 and the dimension formula for sums of subspaces.)

5.9 THE SPECTRAL THEOREM

One of the most valuable classes of matrices are the real symmetric matrices, which we have encountered in two contexts already: in the theory of quadratic forms in two variables (Section 1.8) and the theory of positive definite matrices (Section 3.8). They come up naturally in many applications and are very nice to work with, both theoretically and computationally.

The spectral theorem for real symmetric matrices is the natural conclusion to our discussion of diagonalizable matrices. A stronger geometric version of it, given in Chapter 6, plays the lead role in the theory of quadratic forms in n variables (Chapter 7).

Following the principle of complexification (Section 5.6), we regard the real symmetric matrix A as an element of $M_n\mathbb{C}$. In this section, we then show that:

1. Its characteristic roots are real.
2. It is diagonalizable over $\mathbb{C}$.
3. Regarding it as an element of $M_n\mathbb{R}$, it is diagonalizable over $\mathbb{R}$.

Of course, (3) implies (1) and (2), which were intended as stepping stones to (3).

Hermitian matrices

In $M_n\mathbb{C}$, we need the Hermitian adjoint operation.

Definition. *Hermitian Adjoint and Hermitian Matrix.*
The conjugate transpose $\bar{A}^T$ of A is denoted A^*. It is called the **Hermitian adjoint** of A. If $A = A^*$, we say that A is **Hermitian**.

Some simple properties of the Hermitian adjoint operation are the following. We leave their verification to the reader.

1. $(A + B)^* = A^* + B^*$
2. $(aA)^* = \bar{a}A^*$
3. $A^{**} = A$
4. $(AB)^* = B^*A^*$

Note that $A^* = A^T$ if and only if A is real. So, for real matrices, A is symmetric if and only if A is Hermitian. By complexifying to study real symmetric matrices, we develop the theory of *Hermitian* matrices, which then applies to real symmetric matrices.

EXAMPLE

The matrices $H = \begin{bmatrix} a & c+di \\ c-di & e \end{bmatrix}$ $(a, c, d, e \in \mathbb{R})$ are the Hermitian matrices of $M_2\mathbb{C}$. Among these are the real symmetric matrices $\begin{bmatrix} a & c \\ c & e \end{bmatrix}$ and the pure imaginary Hermitian matrices $\begin{bmatrix} 0 & d \\ -d & 0 \end{bmatrix}i$. Note that

$$\begin{bmatrix} a & c+di \\ c-di & e \end{bmatrix} = \begin{bmatrix} a & c \\ c & e \end{bmatrix} + \begin{bmatrix} 0 & d \\ -d & 0 \end{bmatrix} i.$$

In other words, we can write any Hermitian matrix $H \in M_2\mathbb{C}$ as $H = A + Bi$ where $A, B \in M_2\mathbb{R}$, A is symmetric, and B is **skew-symmetric**—that is, $B = -B^T$.

We need the inner product $\langle \mathbf{v}, \mathbf{w} \rangle = \bar{\mathbf{w}} \cdot \mathbf{v} = \bar{\mathbf{w}}^T\mathbf{v} = \mathbf{w}^*\mathbf{v}$ $(\mathbf{v}, \mathbf{w} \in \mathbb{C}^n)$. Its properties are given in Section 2.3. For $A \in M_n\mathbb{C}$, we have $\langle A\mathbf{v}, \mathbf{w} \rangle = \mathbf{w}^*A\mathbf{v} = (A^*\mathbf{w})^*\mathbf{v} = \langle \mathbf{v}, A^*\mathbf{w} \rangle$, which proves the following theorem.

Theorem 5.25. *The Action of A and Its Hermitian Adjoint A^*.*
$\langle A\mathbf{v}, \mathbf{w} \rangle = \langle \mathbf{v}, A^*\mathbf{w} \rangle$ for $A \in M_n\mathbb{C}$ and $\mathbf{v}, \mathbf{w} \in \mathbb{C}^n$.

This implies the following criteria for when A is Hermitian.

Theorem 5.26. *The Action of a Hermitian Matrix A.*
A is Hermitian if and only if $\langle A\mathbf{v}, \mathbf{w} \rangle = \langle \mathbf{v}, A\mathbf{w} \rangle$ for all $\mathbf{v}, \mathbf{w} \in \mathbb{C}^n$.

Proof. One direction is obvious. For the other, suppose that $\langle A\mathbf{v}, \mathbf{w} \rangle = \langle \mathbf{v}, A\mathbf{w} \rangle$ for all $\mathbf{v}, \mathbf{w} \in \mathbb{C}^n$. Then $\langle \mathbf{v}, A^*\mathbf{w} - A\mathbf{w} \rangle = 0$ for all $\mathbf{v}$. (Explain!) Taking $\mathbf{v} = A^*\mathbf{w} - A\mathbf{w}$, it follows that $A^*\mathbf{w} - A\mathbf{w}$ has squared length 0 and, therefore, that $A^*\mathbf{w} = A\mathbf{w}$. So, $A^* = A$ and A is Hermitian. ■

The spectrum of a Hermitian matrix

We now can show that the characteristic roots of a Hermitian matrix are real.

Corollary. The spectrum of any Hermitian matrix A is real. If $\mathbf{v}$ and $\mathbf{w}$ are characteristic vectors for A corresponding to different characteristic roots, then $\langle \mathbf{v}, \mathbf{w} \rangle = 0$.

Proof. Let $A \in M_n\mathbb{C}$ be Hermitian, and take a characteristic root $c \in \mathbb{C}$ and corresponding characteristic vector $\mathbf{v} \in \mathbb{C}^n$. Then $A\mathbf{v} = c\mathbf{v}$, so that

$$\langle A\mathbf{v}, \mathbf{v} \rangle = \langle c\mathbf{v}, \mathbf{v} \rangle = c\langle \mathbf{v}, \mathbf{v} \rangle,$$

$$\langle \mathbf{v}, A\mathbf{v} \rangle = \langle \mathbf{v}, c\mathbf{v} \rangle = \bar{c}\langle \mathbf{v}, \mathbf{v} \rangle.$$

Since A is Hermitian, we have $\langle A\mathbf{v}, \mathbf{v} \rangle = \langle \mathbf{v}, A\mathbf{v} \rangle$, so that $c\langle \mathbf{v}, \mathbf{v} \rangle = \bar{c}\langle \mathbf{v}, \mathbf{v} \rangle$. Canceling the nonzero $\langle \mathbf{v}, \mathbf{v} \rangle$, we get $c = \bar{c}$, so c is real.

If $d \in \mathbb{R}$ is a different characteristic root of A and if $A\mathbf{w} = d\mathbf{w}$, then we have $c\langle \mathbf{v}, \mathbf{w}\rangle = \langle c\mathbf{v}, \mathbf{w}\rangle = \langle A\mathbf{v}, \mathbf{w}\rangle = \langle \mathbf{v}, A\mathbf{w}\rangle = \langle \mathbf{v}, d\mathbf{w}\rangle = d\langle \mathbf{v}, \mathbf{w}\rangle$. Since $c \neq d$, $\langle \mathbf{v}, \mathbf{w}\rangle$ is 0. ■

The orthogonality of characteristic vectors **v**, **w** corresponding to different characteristic roots has far-reaching consequences, discussed in the next chapter.

EXAMPLE

The characteristic polynomial of $A = \begin{bmatrix} a & c+di \\ c-di & e \end{bmatrix}$ has two real roots r and s. (Verify using the quadratic formula.) When they are different and **v**, **w** are characteristic vectors corresponding to r and s, then $\langle \mathbf{v}, \mathbf{w}\rangle = 0$. This means that once we have found $\mathbf{v} = \begin{bmatrix} g+hi \\ m+ni \end{bmatrix}$, we can take $\mathbf{w} = \begin{bmatrix} -m+ni \\ g-hi \end{bmatrix}$. (Explain!) For instance, consider $A = \begin{bmatrix} 1 & 1+i \\ 1-i & 1 \end{bmatrix}$. Since its characteristic polynomial is $z^2 - 2z - 1$ (verify), its characteristic roots are $1 \pm \sqrt{2}$. Computing one characteristic vector $\mathbf{v} = \begin{bmatrix} \sqrt{2} \\ 1-i \end{bmatrix}$, we get the other as $\mathbf{w} = \begin{bmatrix} -1-i \\ \sqrt{2} \end{bmatrix}$. (Check!) We can divide **v** and **w** by their lengths to get $\mathbf{v}' = \begin{bmatrix} \sqrt{2}/2 \\ (1-i)/2 \end{bmatrix}$ and $\mathbf{w}' = \begin{bmatrix} -(1+i)/2 \\ \sqrt{2}/2 \end{bmatrix}$ of length 1. Letting B be the matrix $[\mathbf{v}' \quad \mathbf{w}'] = \begin{bmatrix} \sqrt{2}/2 & -(1+i)/2 \\ (1-i)/2 & \sqrt{2}/2 \end{bmatrix}$, we have $B^{-1}\begin{bmatrix} 1 & 1+i \\ 1-i & 1 \end{bmatrix}B = \begin{bmatrix} 1+\sqrt{2} & 0 \\ 0 & 1-\sqrt{2} \end{bmatrix}$. Since the columns of B are orthogonal of length 1, we have $B^*B = I$, so that $B^* = B^{-1}$. (Verify!) So, we have the equation $B^*\begin{bmatrix} 1 & 1+i \\ 1-i & 1 \end{bmatrix}B = \begin{bmatrix} 1+\sqrt{2} & 0 \\ 0 & 1-\sqrt{2} \end{bmatrix}$. This equation shows that the *unitary transformation* $x = Bx'$ simplifies the *Hermitian form* $\mathbf{x}^*\begin{bmatrix} 1 & 1+i \\ 1-i & 1 \end{bmatrix}\mathbf{x}$ to

$$\mathbf{x}'^*B^*\begin{bmatrix} 1 & 1+i \\ 1-i & 1 \end{bmatrix}B\mathbf{x} = \mathbf{x}'^*\begin{bmatrix} 1+\sqrt{2} & 0 \\ 0 & 1-\sqrt{2} \end{bmatrix}\mathbf{x}',$$

that is, to

$$\mathbf{x}^*\begin{bmatrix} 1 & 1+i \\ 1-i & 1 \end{bmatrix}\mathbf{x} = (1+\sqrt{2})\mathbf{x}'_1\overline{\mathbf{x}'_1} + (1-\sqrt{2})\mathbf{x}'_2\overline{\mathbf{x}'_2}.$$

Bases of the kernel and image of a linear transformation

The dimension formula Dim V = Dim Kernel T + Dim Image T leads to the following useful tool when the kernel and image of T are disjoint subspaces of V. We use it shortly to prove the spectral theorem.

Theorem 5.27. *Bases for the Kernel and Image of T.*
Let T be a linear transformation of a finite-dimensional vector space V whose kernel and image are disjoint. Suppose that $\mathbf{v}_1, \dots, \mathbf{v}_m$ is a basis for Kernel T and $\mathbf{v}_{m+1}, \dots, \mathbf{v}_n$ is a basis for Image T. Then $\mathbf{v}_1, \dots, \mathbf{v}_n$ is a basis for V.

Proof. To show independence, suppose that $c_1\mathbf{v}_1 + \cdots + c_n\mathbf{v}_n = \mathbf{0}$. Then $c_1\mathbf{v}_1 + \cdots + c_m\mathbf{v}_m = -(c_{m+1}\mathbf{v}_{m+1} + \cdots + c_n\mathbf{v}_n)$ is in both the kernel and the image of T, so it is $\mathbf{0}$. But then all the c's are 0, and the set of vectors $\mathbf{v}_1, \dots, \mathbf{v}_n$ is linearly independent. Since

$$\text{Dim } V = \text{Dim Kernel } T + \text{Dim Image } T = m + (n - m) = n,$$

it is a basis for V. ■

EXAMPLE

If T is a diagonalizable linear transformation of F^n, then the kernel and image of $T - cI$ are disjoint for any $c \in F$. (Prove!)

The spectral theorem for Hermitian matrices

To prove the following spectral theorem (theorem about the spectrum) for Hermitian matrices A amounts to showing that A is diagonalizable, since its spectrum is real. You may skip the proof and that of its counterpart for symmetric matrices, Theorem 5.29, if you like, since stronger versions are proved, independently, in Section 6.7.

Theorem 5.28. *Diagonal Form for Hermitian Matrices.*
Any Hermitian matrix $A \in M_n\mathbb{C}$ is similar over $\mathbb{C}$ to a real diagonal matrix.

Proof. We show, by induction for any subspace V of $\mathbb{C}^n$ such that $A\mathbf{v} \in V$ for all $\mathbf{v} \in V$, that the linear transformation $T(\mathbf{v}) = A\mathbf{v}$ $(\mathbf{v} \in V)$ of V is diagonalizable. If Dim $V = 1$, this is true. (Explain!) Suppose next that Dim $V = m > 1$ and we have proved this for subspaces of lower dimension. Let c be a root of $|T - zI|$, so it is a root of $|A - zI|$. It is then real by the corollary to Theorem 5.26. So, T has a corresponding characteristic vector $\mathbf{v} \in V$. Since $(T - cI)(\mathbf{v}) = \mathbf{0}$, $T - cI$ is not invertible.

We now claim that the kernel and image of $T - cI$ are disjoint. For $\mathbf{w} \in$ Kernel $(T - cI) \cap$ Image $(T - cI)$, we have $\mathbf{w} = (T - cI)(\mathbf{v})$ and $(T - cI)(\mathbf{w}) = \mathbf{0}$, that is, $(T - cI)(T - cI)(\mathbf{v}) = \mathbf{0}$. Since c is real, $A - cI$ is

Hermitian (explain) and we get

$$0 = \langle \mathbf{v}, (A - cI)(A - cI)\mathbf{v} \rangle = \langle (A - cI)\mathbf{v}, (A - cI)\mathbf{v} \rangle.$$

But then $(A - cI)\mathbf{v} = \mathbf{0}$ and $\mathbf{v} = \mathbf{0}$. So, the kernel and image of T are disjoint.

Since the kernel and image of T are disjoint, Theorem 5.27 implies that $\mathbf{v}_1, \ldots, \mathbf{v}_m$ is a basis for V if $\mathbf{v}_1, \ldots, \mathbf{v}_r$ is a basis for Image $(T - cI)$ and $\mathbf{v}_{r+1}, \ldots, \mathbf{v}_m$ is a basis for Kernel $(T - cI)$. For $r + 1 \leq s \leq m$, $T(\mathbf{v}_s) = c\mathbf{v}_s$. Since $T - cI$ is not invertible, the dimension r of Image $(T - cI)$ is less than m. Since $A\mathbf{v} = T(\mathbf{v}) \in$ Image $(T - cI)$ for all $\mathbf{v} \in$ Image $(T - cI)$ (explain), it follows from our induction hypothesis that we can take $\mathbf{v}_1, \ldots, \mathbf{v}_r$ to be characteristic vectors for T. But then $\mathbf{v}_1, \ldots, \mathbf{v}_m$ is a basis for V of characteristic vectors for T, and T is diagonalizable. This completes the induction proof.

Taking $V = \mathbb{C}^n$, we conclude that $T(\mathbf{x}) = A\mathbf{x}$ is diagonalizable, so that A is similar over $\mathbb{C}$ to a diagonal matrix D. Since the spectrum of A is real, D is a real diagonal matrix. ■

EXAMPLE

We've seen examples of this theorem for real symmetric matrices. For the Hermitian matrix $A = \begin{bmatrix} 1 & 1+i \\ 1-i & 1 \end{bmatrix}$ of the preceding example, A was shown to be similar to $\begin{bmatrix} 1+\sqrt{2} & 0 \\ 0 & 1-\sqrt{2} \end{bmatrix}$.

The spectral theorem for real symmetric matrices

The story for real symmetric matrices in the context of $\mathbb{R}^n$ is the same as that for Hermitian matrices in the context of $\mathbb{C}^n$ by the following theorem.

Theorem 5.29. *Diagonal Form for Real Symmetric Matrices.*
Any symmetric matrix $A \in M_n\mathbb{R}$ is similar over $\mathbb{R}$ to a real diagonal matrix.

Proof. We show, by induction for any subspace V of $\mathbb{R}^n$ such that $A\mathbf{v} \in V$ for all $\mathbf{v} \in V$, that the linear transformation $T(\mathbf{x}) = A\mathbf{x}$ $(\mathbf{x} \in V)$ of V is diagonalizable. The argument is, word for word, the same as the corresponding one in the proof of Theorem 5.28 except that $\mathbb{C}$ is replaced by $\mathbb{R}$ and $\mathbb{C}^n$ by $\mathbb{R}^n$.

Taking $V = \mathbb{R}^n$, we conclude that $T(\mathbf{x}) = A\mathbf{x}$ is diagonalizable, so that it is similar over $\mathbb{R}$ to a diagonal matrix D. ■

PROBLEMS

NUMERICAL PROBLEMS

1. Find a real diagonal matrix similar over $\mathbb{R}$ to each of the following matrices.

(a) $\begin{bmatrix} 1 & 2 \\ 2 & 3 \end{bmatrix}$ **(b)** $\begin{bmatrix} 1 & 2 \\ 2 & 4 \end{bmatrix}$ **(c)** $\begin{bmatrix} 4 & 2 \\ 2 & 1 \end{bmatrix}$ **(d)** $\begin{bmatrix} 2 & 4 \\ 0 & 1 \end{bmatrix}$

2. Find a real diagonal matrix D similar over $\mathbb{C}$ to each of the following matrices.

(a) $\begin{bmatrix} 0 & i \\ -i & 3 \end{bmatrix}$ **(b)** $\begin{bmatrix} 2 & i \\ -i & 3 \end{bmatrix}$

(c) $\begin{bmatrix} 3 & bi \\ -bi & 3 \end{bmatrix}$ **(d)** $\begin{bmatrix} 2 & 1+i \\ 0 & 3 \end{bmatrix}$

3. Find a real matrix B whose columns are orthogonal of length 1 such that the transformation $\mathbf{x} = B\mathbf{x}'$ reduces $\mathbf{x}^T A\mathbf{x}$ to $ax_1^2 + bx_2^2$ for each of the first three matrices A listed in Problem 1.

4. Find a matrix B whose columns are both of length 1 and such that the transformation $\mathbf{x} = B\mathbf{x}'$ reduces $\mathbf{x}^* A\mathbf{x}$ to $ax_1^2 + bx_2^2$ for each of the first three matrices A listed in Problem 2.

5. Find a real matrix B whose columns are orthogonal of length 1 such that the transformation $\mathbf{x} = B\mathbf{x}'$ reduces $\mathbf{x}^* A\mathbf{x}$ to $ax_1^2 + bx_2^2 + cx_3^2$ for each of the following matrices.

(a) $A = \begin{bmatrix} 1 & 2 & 0 \\ 2 & 3 & 0 \\ 0 & 0 & 3 \end{bmatrix}$ **(b)** $A = \begin{bmatrix} 2 & 0 & 3 \\ 0 & 2 & 0 \\ 3 & 0 & 2 \end{bmatrix}$ **(c)** $A = \begin{bmatrix} 2 & 0 & 3 \\ 0 & 3 & 0 \\ 3 & 0 & 2 \end{bmatrix}$

Hard

6. Show that if a real matrix A is similar to B over $\mathbb{C}$, then A is similar to B over $\mathbb{R}$ in the following cases.

(a) $B = \begin{bmatrix} 1 & 0 \\ 0 & 2 \end{bmatrix}$ **(b)** $B = \begin{bmatrix} 1 & 0 & 0 \\ 0 & 2 & 0 \\ 0 & 0 & 3 \end{bmatrix}$ **(c)** $B = \begin{bmatrix} 1 & 6 & 5 \\ 0 & 2 & 4 \\ 0 & 0 & 3 \end{bmatrix}$

7. Is it possible to do Problem 3 for the fourth matrix as well?

8. Is it possible to do Problem 4 for the fourth matrix as well?

THEORETICAL PROBLEMS

9. Show that if T is a diagonalizable linear transformation of F^n, then the kernel and image of $T - cI$ are disjoint for any $c \in F$.

10. Show that if T is a diagonalizable linear transformation of F^n, then the kernel and image of $S = (T - c_1 I) \cdots (T - c_r I)$ are disjoint for any $c_1, \ldots, c_r \in F$. (*Hint:* S is also diagonalizable.)

11. Show that any Hermitian matrix $H \in M_n\mathbb{C}$ can be written as $H = A + B\mathbf{i}$ where $A, B \in M_n\mathbb{R}$, A is symmetric, and B is skew-symmetric ($B = -B^T$).

12. Verify the following properties of the Hermitian adjoint operation.

(a) For $A, B \in M_n\mathbb{C}$, $\langle A\mathbf{v}, \mathbf{w}\rangle = \langle \mathbf{v}, B\mathbf{w}\rangle$ for all $\mathbf{v}, \mathbf{w} \in \mathbb{C}^n$ if and only if $B = A^*$.

(*Hint:* For one direction, show that $\langle \mathbf{v}, (A^* - B)\mathbf{w}\rangle$ is 0 for $\mathbf{v} = (A^* - B)\mathbf{w}$.)

(b) The mapping sending A to A^* satisfies

(i) $(A + B)^* = A^* + B^*$;

(ii) $(aA)^* = \bar{a}A^*$;

(iii) $A^{**} = A$;

(iv) $(AB)^* = B^*A^*$.

13. We say that $A \in M_n\mathbb{C}$ is **skew-Hermitian** if $A^* = -A$. Show that $A \in M_n\mathbb{C}$ is skew-Hermitian if and only if $\langle A\mathbf{v}, \mathbf{w}\rangle = -\langle \mathbf{v}, A\mathbf{w}\rangle$ for all $\mathbf{v}, \mathbf{w} \in \mathbb{C}^n$.

14. Show that A is skew-Hermitian if and only if $\mathbf{i}A$ is Hermitian.

15. Show that the characteristic roots of A are pure imaginaries if A is skew-Hermitian.

Hard

16. Show that any $A \in M_n\mathbb{R}$ similar over $\mathbb{C}$ to a diagonal matrix in $M_n\mathbb{R}$ is similar over $\mathbb{R}$ to the same matrix.

5.10 TRIANGULATION OF MATRICES

In Section 5.6, we observed that most matrices $A \in M_n\mathbb{C}$ are similar to a diagonal matrix. When $C^{-1}AC$ is a diagonal matrix D and the columns of C are $\mathbf{v}_1, \ldots, \mathbf{v}_n$, then $\mathbf{v}_1, \ldots, \mathbf{v}_n$ is a basis of F^n of characteristic vectors of A, since $AC = CD$. (Explain!)

However, some matrices, such as $A = \begin{bmatrix} 1 & 1 \\ 0 & 1 \end{bmatrix}$, have no such basis. If $\mathbf{v}, \mathbf{w}$ were a basis of characteristic vectors for $\begin{bmatrix} 1 & 1 \\ 0 & 1 \end{bmatrix}$, then $A\mathbf{v} = 1\mathbf{v}$ and $A\mathbf{w} = 1\mathbf{w}$. After all, the characteristic roots for A are both 1! But this is impossible, for it implies that $A = I$. (Explain!)

Basis of generalized characteristic vectors

Although there may not exist a basis of characteristic vectors for $A \in M_n\mathbb{C}$, we are about to see that there always is a basis of generalized characteristic vectors for $T(\mathbf{x}) = A\mathbf{x}$, which we introduce next. (See Figure 5.26.)

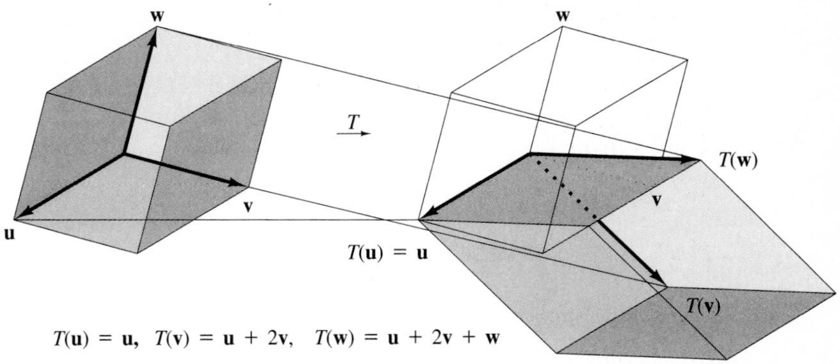

Figure 5.26 Image under T of a basis **u**, **v**, **w** of generalized characteristic vectors for T.

Definition. *Basis of Generalized Characteristic Vectors.*
Let T be a linear transformation of a vector space V. Then any basis $\mathbf{v}_1, \ldots, \mathbf{v}_n$ of V with respect to which the matrix of T is upper triangular is called a **basis of generalized characteristic vectors** for T.

The simplest example is the standard basis $\mathbf{e}_1, \mathbf{e}_2, \mathbf{e}_3$ for

$$T(\mathbf{x}) = \begin{bmatrix} a & b & c \\ 0 & e & f \\ 0 & 0 & g \end{bmatrix} \mathbf{x}.$$

When $\mathbf{v}_1, \ldots, \mathbf{v}_n$ is a basis of generalized characteristic vectors for a linear transformation T of a vector space V and A is the corresponding matrix of T, we have

$$\begin{aligned} T(\mathbf{v}_1) &= a_1\mathbf{v}_1, \\ T(\mathbf{v}_2) &= a_{12}\mathbf{v}_1 + a_{22}\mathbf{v}_2, \\ &\vdots \\ T(\mathbf{v}_n) &= a_{1n}\mathbf{v}_1 + \cdots + a_{nn}\mathbf{v}_n. \end{aligned}$$

We now show how to find such **v**'s and a's.

Theorem 5.30. *Existence of a Generalized Basis of Characteristic Vectors.*
Let V be an n-dimensional vector space over $\mathbb{C}$. Then for any $T \in L(V, V)$, V has a basis of generalized characteristic vectors for T.

Proof. We go by induction on n. If $n = 1$, any basis will do. (Explain!) For $n > 1$, suppose that we've proved this for $(n - 1)$-dimensional vector spaces. Let c be any characteristic root for T and let $U = \text{Image}\,(T - cI)$. Since $T - cI$ is not invertible, U has dimension $m = n - \text{Kernel}\,(T - cI)$ less than n. Define $S \in L(U, U)$ by $S(\mathbf{u}) = T(\mathbf{u})$ for $\mathbf{u} \in U$. Since $\mathbf{u} = (T - cI)\mathbf{v}$ for some $\mathbf{v}$, we have $T(\mathbf{u}) = T((T - cI)\mathbf{v}) = (T^2 - cT)\mathbf{v} = (T - cI)T(\mathbf{v}) \in U$, so S is a linear transformation from U to itself. By induction, U has a basis $\mathbf{v}_1, \ldots, \mathbf{v}_m$ of generalized characteristic vectors for S, and there are scalars a_{rs} such that

$$
\begin{aligned}
S(\mathbf{v}_1) &= a_1\mathbf{v}_1, \\
S(\mathbf{v}_2) &= a_{12}\mathbf{v}_1 + a_{22}\mathbf{v}_2, \\
&\vdots \\
S(\mathbf{v}_m) &= a_{1m}\mathbf{v}_1 + \cdots + a_{mm}\mathbf{v}_m.
\end{aligned}
$$

Extend this basis for U to a basis $\mathbf{v}_1, \ldots, \mathbf{v}_m, \mathbf{v}_{m+1}, \ldots, \mathbf{v}_n$ for V. Since $(T - cI)(\mathbf{v}_{m+i}) = T(\mathbf{v}_{m+i}) - c\mathbf{v}_{m+i}$ is in U for all i, we can find some more scalars a_{rs} such that

$$
\begin{aligned}
T(\mathbf{v}_{m+1}) &= a_{1m+1}\mathbf{v}_1 + \cdots + a_{mm+1}\mathbf{v}_m + c\mathbf{v}_{m+1}, \\
&\vdots \\
T(\mathbf{v}_n) &= a_{1n}\mathbf{v}_1 + \cdots + a_{mn}\mathbf{v}_m + c\mathbf{v}_n.
\end{aligned}
$$

Since $T(\mathbf{v}_s) = S(\mathbf{v}_s)$ for $1 \leq s \leq m$, it follows that the matrix of T is upper triangular. ■

Triangulability of matrices

When we apply the preceding theorem to the linear transformation $T(\mathbf{x}) = A\mathbf{x}$ of $\mathbb{C}^n$, where $A \in M_n\mathbb{C}$, we find the following.

Theorem 5.31. *Triangular Form of a Complex Matrix.*
Every matrix $A \in M_n\mathbb{C}$ is similar to an upper triangular matrix.

The story over $\mathbb{R}$ is the same when the spectrum is real, in the following sense.

Theorem 5.32. *Triangular Form of a Real Matrix.*
Every matrix $A \in M_n\mathbb{R}$ whose spectrum is real is similar over $\mathbb{R}$ to an upper triangular matrix.

Proof. It suffices to prove a variation of Theorem 5.31 for any linear transformation T of any subspace V of $\mathbb{R}^n$. For then, taking $V = \mathbb{R}^n$ and $T(\mathbf{x}) = A\mathbf{x}$, V has a basis $B = [\mathbf{v}_1 \ \ldots \ \mathbf{v}_n]$ of generalized characteristic vectors and its matrix $B^{-1}AB$ with respect to this basis is triangular.
To do this, we essentially use the same proof noting, however, that:

1. Since the spectrum of T is real, T has a real characteristic root c and, as in the earlier proof, Dim $U <$ Dim V for $U =$ Image $(T - cI)$.

2. The spectrum of $S \in L(V, V)$, as defined in the earlier proof, is real. For if $d \in \mathbb{C}$ is a root of $|S - zI|$, there is a complex vector $\mathbf{u} \in \mathbb{C}^n$ such that $T(\mathbf{u}) = S(\mathbf{u}) = d\mathbf{u}$. Since the spectrum of T is real, the roots of $|T - zI|$ are real and d is real.

Given these observations, the earlier proof now goes through without a hitch. ∎

The Cayley-Hamilton Theorem

We now give a simple, but powerful, consequence of the last theorem.

Theorem 5.33. *Cayley-Hamilton Theorem for Matrices.* The characteristic polynomial $|A - zI| = (z - c_1) \cdots (z - c_n)$ of any matrix $A \in M_n F$ vanishes at A. That is, $(A - c_1 I) \cdots (z - c_n I) = 0$, where $c_1, \ldots, c_n$ are the characteristic roots.

Proof. We first apply the principle of complexification. If $F = \mathbb{R}$, the characteristic polynomial $|A - zI|$ is the same whether we view A as an element of $M_n\mathbb{R}$ or as an element of $M_n\mathbb{C}$. So, we may assume that $A \in M_n\mathbb{C}$. The characteristic polynomial for similar matrices is the same. Since A is similar to an upper triangular matrix, by Theorem 5.32, we need only prove this theorem for an upper triangular matrix.

So, we now assume that A is an upper triangular matrix. Let the diagonal entries of A be $c_1, \ldots, c_n$ and let $C_s = (A - c_1 I) \cdots (A - c_s I)$. We propose to show, by induction on s, that the first s columns of C_s are $\mathbf{0}$ for all s. If $s = 1$, this is true for $C_1 = A - c_1 I$, since A and $c_1 I$ are upper triangular with the same (1, 1)-entry. Suppose that the first $s - 1$ columns of C_{s-1} are $\mathbf{0}$. Since the first s columns of $A - c_s I$ have 0s except in the first $s - 1$ rows (explain), and since the first $s - 1$ columns of C_{s-1} are $\mathbf{0}$, c_{s-1} times each of the first s columns of $A - c_s I$ is $\mathbf{0}$. Since these are the first s columns of C_s, the first s columns of C_s are $\mathbf{0}$. This proves the induction hypothesis, so the first s columns of C_s are $\mathbf{0}$ for all s.

Taking $s = n$, we get $0 = C_n = (A - c_1 I) \cdots (A - c_n I) = f(A)$, where $f(z) = (z - c_1) \cdots (z - c_s)$ is the characteristic polynomial of A. ∎

The Cayley-Hamilton Theorem also can be formulated for linear transformations.

Theorem 5.34. *Cayley-Hamilton Theorem for Linear Transformations.* The characteristic polynomial $|T - zI| = (z - c_1) \cdots (z - c_n)$ of a linear transformation of a finite-dimensional vector space V vanishes at T. That is, $(T - c_1 I) \cdots (T - c_n I) = 0$, where $c_1, \ldots, c_n$ are the characteristic roots of T.

Proof. Taking an isomorphism R from V to F^n, the isomorphism m_R

from $L(V, V)$ gives us

$$m_R((T - c_1I) \cdots (T - c_nI)) = m_R(T - c_1I) \cdots m_R(T - c_nI)$$
$$= (m_R(T) - c_1I) \cdots (m_R(T) - c_nI) = 0$$

by the Cayley-Hamilton theorem for matrices, since the characteristic polynomials for T and $m_R(T)$ are the same. ■

PROBLEMS

THEORETICAL PROBLEMS

1. Find an upper triangular matrix similar to A for each of the following matrices A.

(a) $\begin{bmatrix} 1 & 0 \\ 1 & 1 \end{bmatrix}$ **(b)** $\begin{bmatrix} a & 0 \\ c & b \end{bmatrix}$ **(c)** $\begin{bmatrix} 1 & 2 \\ 2 & 0 \end{bmatrix}$ **(d)** $\begin{bmatrix} 0 & 1 \\ 1 & 0 \end{bmatrix}$

2. Find a basis of generalized characteristic vectors for the linear transformation $T(\mathbf{x}) = A\mathbf{x}$ for each of the matrices A in Problem 1.

Hard

3. Determine whether the characteristic roots for the following matrices are all different.

(a) $\begin{bmatrix} 2 & -1 & 0 \\ -1 & 2 & -1 \\ 0 & -1 & 2 \end{bmatrix}$ **(b)** $\begin{bmatrix} 0 & 0 & a \\ 0 & b & 0 \\ a & 0 & 0 \end{bmatrix}$

(c) $\begin{bmatrix} b & 0 & a \\ 0 & b & 0 \\ a & 0 & b \end{bmatrix}$ **(d)** $\begin{bmatrix} b & 0 & a \\ 0 & a & 0 \\ a & 0 & b \end{bmatrix}$

4. Find a basis of generalized characteristic vectors for

(a) $\begin{bmatrix} 1 & 1 & 0 \\ 0 & 1 & 1 \\ 0 & 0 & 1 \end{bmatrix}$; **(b)** $\begin{bmatrix} 1 & 0 & 0 \\ 1 & 1 & 0 \\ 0 & 1 & 1 \end{bmatrix}$;

(c) $\begin{bmatrix} 0 & 1 & 0 \\ 0 & 0 & 1 \\ -1 & 1 & 1 \end{bmatrix}$; **(d)** $\begin{bmatrix} 0 & 1 & 0 \\ 0 & 0 & 1 \\ 0 & 1 & 0 \end{bmatrix}$.

THEORETICAL PROBLEMS

5. Show that the characteristic polynomial of $\begin{bmatrix} 0 & 1 \\ -c & -b \end{bmatrix}$ is $x^2 + bx + c$.

6. Show that $\begin{bmatrix} -1 \\ b+r \end{bmatrix}, \begin{bmatrix} -1 \\ b+s \end{bmatrix}$ is a basis of characteristic vectors for $A = \begin{bmatrix} 0 & 1 \\ -c & -b \end{bmatrix}$ if c and $b^2 - 4c$ are nonzero, where r and s are the characteristic roots of A.

7. Show that $\begin{bmatrix} 0 & 1 \\ -c & -b \end{bmatrix}\begin{bmatrix} -1 & -1 \\ b+r & b+s \end{bmatrix} = \begin{bmatrix} -1 & -1 \\ b+r & b+s \end{bmatrix}\begin{bmatrix} s & 0 \\ 0 & r \end{bmatrix}$, where $(x-r)(x-s) = x^2 + bx + c$.

8. Find the inverse of $\begin{bmatrix} -1 & -1 \\ b+r & b+s \end{bmatrix}$, where $(x-r)(x-s) = x^2 + bx + c$ $(c \neq 0, r \neq s)$.

9. Find a basis of characteristic vectors for $B = \begin{bmatrix} 0 & -c \\ 1 & -b \end{bmatrix}$ if c and $b^2 - 4c$ are nonzero, where r and s are the characteristic roots of B.

Hard

10. Show that the characteristic polynomial of

$$A = \begin{bmatrix} 0 & 1 & 0 \\ 0 & 0 & 1 \\ -d & -c & -b \end{bmatrix}$$

is $-x^3 - bx^2 - cx - d$.

11. Show that

$$\begin{bmatrix} 1 \\ 0 \\ 0 \end{bmatrix}, \quad \begin{bmatrix} -r \\ -c \\ c(b+r) \end{bmatrix}, \quad \begin{bmatrix} -s \\ -c \\ c(b+s) \end{bmatrix}$$

is a basis of characteristic vectors for

$$A = \begin{bmatrix} 0 & 1 & 0 \\ 0 & 0 & 1 \\ 0 & -c & -b \end{bmatrix}$$

if c and $b^2 - 4c$ are nonzero, where r and s are the nonzero characteristic roots of A.

12. If $r \neq s$ and $c \neq 0$, then

$$\begin{bmatrix} 0 & 1 & 0 \\ 0 & 0 & 1 \\ 0 & -c & -b \end{bmatrix}\begin{bmatrix} 1 & -r & -s \\ 0 & -c & -c \\ 0 & c(b+r) & c(b+s) \end{bmatrix} = \begin{bmatrix} 1 & -r & -s \\ 0 & -c & -c \\ 0 & c(b+r) & c(b+s) \end{bmatrix}\begin{bmatrix} 0 & 0 & 0 \\ 0 & s & 0 \\ 0 & 0 & r \end{bmatrix},$$

where $(x-r)(x-s) = x^2 + bx + c$. Explain why.

13. Show that

$$\begin{bmatrix} 1 & -r & -s \\ 0 & -c & -c \\ 0 & c(b+r) & c(b+s) \end{bmatrix}\begin{bmatrix} c(r-s) & s^2 - r^2 & r-s \\ 0 & b+s & 1 \\ 0 & -b-r & -1 \end{bmatrix} = c(r-s)I,$$

where $(x-r)(x-s) = x^2 + bx + c$.

14. Show that

$$\begin{bmatrix} c(r-s) \\ s^2-r^2 \\ r-s \end{bmatrix}, \quad \begin{bmatrix} 0 \\ b+s \\ 1 \end{bmatrix}, \quad \begin{bmatrix} 0 \\ b+r \\ 1 \end{bmatrix}$$

is a basis of characteristic vectors for

$$B = \begin{bmatrix} 0 & 0 & 0 \\ 1 & 0 & -c \\ 0 & 1 & -b \end{bmatrix}$$

if c and $b^2 - 4c$ are nonzero, where r and s are the nonzero characteristic roots of B.

15. Show that

$$\begin{bmatrix} 0 & 0 & 0 \\ 1 & 0 & -c \\ 0 & 1 & -b \end{bmatrix}\begin{bmatrix} c(r-s) & 0 & 0 \\ s^2-r^2 & b+s & b+r \\ r-s & 1 & 1 \end{bmatrix} = \begin{bmatrix} c(r-s) & 0 & 0 \\ s^2-r^2 & b+s & b+r \\ r-s & 1 & 1 \end{bmatrix}\begin{bmatrix} 0 & 0 & 0 \\ 0 & s & 0 \\ 0 & 0 & r \end{bmatrix},$$

where $(x - r)(x - s) = x^2 + bx + c$.

16. Let V be a vector space, $T \in L(V, V)$. For any polynomial $f(z) \in F[z]$, we define $f(T)$ as the matrix obtained by replacing z^r by T^r for $r > 0$ and z^0 by I in $f(z)$. For example, if $f(z) = 3 - 5z^2 + 2z^3$, then $f(T) = 3I - 5T^2 + 2T^3$. If V is n-dimensional, carry over the results of Problem 13 of Section 5.7 from A to T.

17. The **companion matrix** of a polynomial $f(z) = x^n - a_{n-1}x^{n-1} - \cdots - a_0$ is

$$M_f = \begin{bmatrix} a_{n-1} & a_{n-2} & \cdots & a_0 \\ 1 & 0 & & \\ & \ddots & \ddots & \\ & & 1 & 0 \end{bmatrix}.$$

Show that the characteristic polynomial $|M_f - zI|$ of M_f is $(-1)^n f(z)$. (*Hint:* Expand by the last column of $M_f - zI$ and show that you get $(-1)^{n-1}(z^{n-1} - a_{n-1}z^{n-2} - \cdots - a_1)(-z) + (-1)^n a_0$.)

18. Find the companion matrix M_f of $f(z)$ and verify that $|M_f - zI| = (-1)^n f(z)$ for the following polynomials:

(a) $f(z) = 1 + z^2$

(b) $f(z) = 1 + z^2 + 3z^3 + z^4$

(c) $f(z) = 1 + z + z^2$

(d) $f(z) = z^5 - 1$

SUGGESTED READING

F. R. Gantmacher, *Theory of Matrices*, Chelsea, New York, 1959. [Another classic in the subject, which should be kept close at hand.]

T. Muir, *Determinants*, Dover, New York, 1960. [A definitive treatment of determinants from a classical point of view.]

CHAPTER 6

THE GEOMETRY OF n-SPACE

6.1 INTRODUCTION

Whereas Chapter 5 was concerned with the linear algebra of n-space, we now move on to its geometric properties, adding a single new ingredient, the **inner product** $\langle \mathbf{v}, \mathbf{w} \rangle = \mathbf{w}^*\mathbf{v} = \mathbf{v} \cdot \bar{\mathbf{w}}$. The vector space F^n together with its inner product is **Euclidean n-space over F**.

In our development of this geometry, the field F can be either $\mathbb{R}$ or $\mathbb{C}$ unless otherwise stipulated. When $F = \mathbb{C}$, Euclidean n-space is referred to as **unitary n-space** to emphasize that the field F is $\mathbb{C}$. When $F = \mathbb{R}$, it is **real Euclidean n-space**.

The phenomena discussed here are the same for $F = \mathbb{R}$ and $F = \mathbb{C}$ except that conjugation has no effect when $F = \mathbb{R}$. So, for $F = \mathbb{R}$, A^* is just A^T, $\langle \mathbf{v}, \mathbf{w} \rangle$ is just the dot product $\mathbf{w}^T\mathbf{v} = \mathbf{v} \cdot \mathbf{w}$, and $a = \bar{a}$ for $a \in F$. The main emphasis in the examples and figures is when $F = \mathbb{R}$.

The inner product enables us to develop the Euclidean geometry of F^n by introducing and exploiting the concepts of length, distance, angle, and projections. Whereas the linear transformations of F^n were studied in terms of a basis for F^n, we now study them in terms of an **orthonormal basis**—that is, a basis $\mathbf{v}_1, \ldots, \mathbf{v}_n$ of vectors of length 1, where $\mathbf{v}_r$ and $\mathbf{v}_s$ are orthogonal for $r \neq s$. When a linear transformation $T(\mathbf{x}) = A\mathbf{x}$ of F^n maps the orthonormal basis $\mathbf{e}_1, \ldots, \mathbf{e}_n$ of standard unit vectors to an orthonormal basis, it is called a **unitary transformation**, and its matrix A is called a **unitary**

matrix. (When $F = \mathbb{R}$, the word *orthogonal* is often used in place of *unitary* to emphasize that F is $\mathbb{R}$.)

An $n \times n$ matrix A is unitary if and only if its columns are an orthonormal set of vectors. (Prove!) The unitary transformations are the geometric counterparts of the invertible transformations, since a linear transformation is invertible if and only if it maps a basis to a basis. (Explain!)

When $F = \mathbb{R}$, a unitary transformation or matrix is called an *orthogonal* transformation or matrix. When $n = 2$, we know the orthogonal transformations to be the rotations and reflections of the Euclidean plane. When $n = 3$, any orthogonal transformation fixes some axis (line). (See Figure 6.1 and Problem 15.)

Within this framework, our theorems take on a geometric flavor. The spectral theorem of Section 5.9 says any Hermitian matrix A is similar to a real diagonal matrix. In this framework, the more powerful geometric version of it (Section 6.9) states that any Hermitian matrix A is similar by a *unitary matrix* U to real diagonal matrix D. Since $U^{-1} = U^*$ for unitary matrices (prove), this means that U^*AU is the real diagonal matrix D. The *Hermitian form* $\mathbf{x}^*A\mathbf{x}$ ($\mathbf{x} \in F^n$) is then brought to the normal form $\mathbf{x}'^*D\mathbf{x}'$ by the unitary transformation $\mathbf{x} = U\mathbf{x}'$, since $\mathbf{x}^*A\mathbf{x} = \mathbf{x}'^*U^*AU\mathbf{x}' = \mathbf{x}'^*D\mathbf{x}'$.

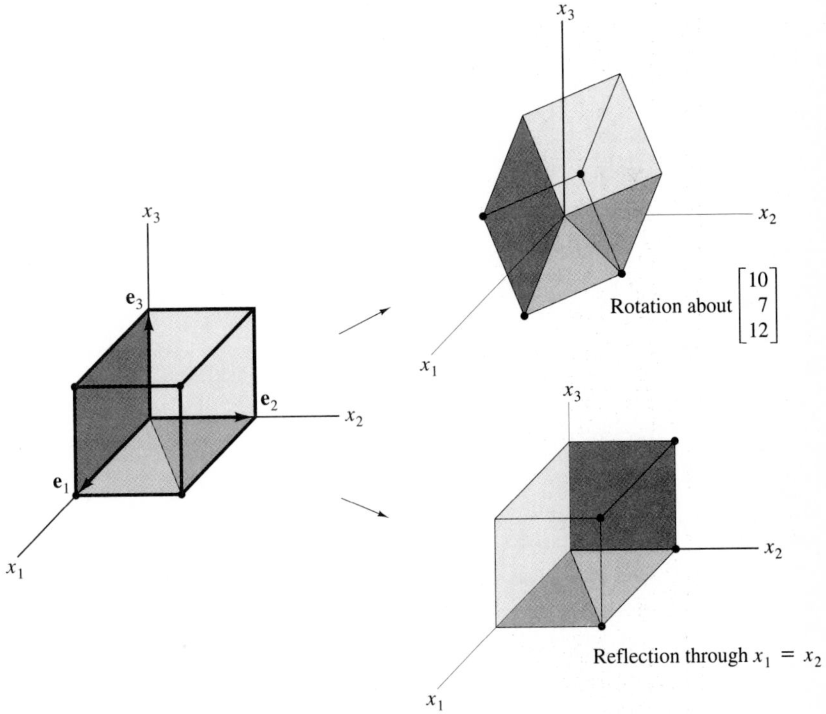

Figure 6.1 Two orthogonal transformations T of $\mathbb{R}^3$.

For a given symmetric bilinear form $\mathbf{x}^T A\mathbf{x}$, we study $\mathbf{x} = U\mathbf{x}'$, the *orthogonal transformation to principal axes*, in the next chapter.

PROBLEMS

NUMERICAL PROBLEMS

1. Which of the following sets $\mathbf{v}$, $\mathbf{w}$ are orthonormal bases of F^2?

(a) $\begin{bmatrix} 1 \\ 2 \end{bmatrix}, \begin{bmatrix} 2 \\ -1 \end{bmatrix}$ **(b)** $\frac{1}{5}\begin{bmatrix} 3 \\ 4 \end{bmatrix}, \frac{1}{5}\begin{bmatrix} -4 \\ 3 \end{bmatrix}$ **(c)** $\frac{1}{5}\begin{bmatrix} 3 \\ 4 \end{bmatrix}, \frac{i}{5}\begin{bmatrix} -4 \\ 3 \end{bmatrix}$

(d) $\frac{1}{2}\begin{bmatrix} 1+i \\ 1-i \end{bmatrix}, \frac{1}{2}\begin{bmatrix} -1+i \\ 1+i \end{bmatrix}$ **(e)** $\frac{1}{2}\begin{bmatrix} 1+i \\ 1-i \end{bmatrix}, \frac{1}{2}\begin{bmatrix} -1-i \\ 1-i \end{bmatrix}$

2. In Problem 1, in which cases is $[\mathbf{v} \quad \mathbf{w}]^{-1} = [\mathbf{v} \quad \mathbf{w}]^T$?

3. In Problem 1, in which cases is $[\mathbf{v} \quad \mathbf{w}]^{-1} = [\mathbf{v} \quad \mathbf{w}]^*$?

4. Show that if the set of rows of A is orthonormal, then so is the set of columns in each of the following cases.

(a) $A = \begin{bmatrix} 1 & a & b \\ 0 & c & d \\ 0 & 0 & 1 \end{bmatrix}$ **(b)** $A = \begin{bmatrix} 1 & 0 & 0 \\ a & c & d \\ a & 0 & f \end{bmatrix}$ **(c)** $A = \begin{bmatrix} 0 & 1 & 0 \\ 1 & c & 0 \\ e & f & 1 \end{bmatrix}$

5. The linear transformation $R(\mathbf{x}) = A\mathbf{x}$ maps a basis to a basis in which of the following cases?

(a) $A = \begin{bmatrix} 1 & 2 \\ 2 & 4 \end{bmatrix}$ **(b)** $A = \begin{bmatrix} 1 & 2 & 4 \\ 0 & 3 & 3 \\ 1 & 4 & 6 \end{bmatrix}$ **(c)** $A = \begin{bmatrix} 1 & 3 & 2 \\ 2 & 3 & 2 \\ 0 & 0 & 1 \end{bmatrix}$

6. The linear transformation $R(\mathbf{x}) = A\mathbf{x}$ maps an orthonormal basis to an orthonormal basis in which of the following cases (see Problem 1)?

(a) $\begin{bmatrix} 1 & 2 \\ 2 & -1 \end{bmatrix}$ **(b)** $\frac{1}{5}\begin{bmatrix} 3 & -4 \\ 4 & 3 \end{bmatrix}$ **(c)** $\frac{1}{5}\begin{bmatrix} 3 & -4i \\ 4 & 3i \end{bmatrix}$

(d) $\frac{1}{2}\begin{bmatrix} 1+i & -1+i \\ 1-i & 1+i \end{bmatrix}$ **(e)** $\frac{1}{2}\begin{bmatrix} 1+i & -1-i \\ 1-i & 1-i \end{bmatrix}$

THEORETICAL PROBLEMS

7. Show that those linear transformations of a finite-dimensional vector space which map a given basis to a basis are the invertible linear transformations.

8. For $A \in M_n F$, show that $T(\mathbf{x}) = A\mathbf{x}$ is unitary if and only if the columns of A form an orthonormal basis of F^n.

9. For $A \in M_n\mathbb{R}$, show that A is orthogonal if and only if A is invertible and $A^{-1} = A^T$.

10. For $A \in M_n\mathbb{C}$, show that A is unitary if and only if A is invertible and $A^{-1} = A^*$.

11. Show that any 2×2 Hermitian matrix A is similar *by a unitary matrix* U to real diagonal matrix D. (Compare with Theorem 1.35.)

Hard

12. Show that products and inverses of unitary transformations are unitary.

13. Show that a unitary linear transformation T of F^n maps any given orthonormal basis to an orthonormal basis.

14. Let

$$A = \begin{bmatrix} a & b & c \\ d & e & f \\ g & h & i \end{bmatrix}$$

have real entries. Show that $|A - rI| = 0$ for some real r.

15. Show that for any real orthogonal 3×3 matrix A, there is a nonzero $\mathbf{v} \in \mathbb{R}^3$ such that $A\mathbf{v} = r\mathbf{v}$ where r is either 1 or -1. (See Figure 6.1.)

6.2 LENGTH, DISTANCE, AND ANGLE

Euclidean space

Without an inner product, we cannot define length and angle. So, we now equip our vector spaces with an inner product.

Definition. *Inner Product.*

An **inner product space** over F is a vector space V over F with an **inner product** $\langle \mathbf{v}, \mathbf{w} \rangle$ satisfying the following properties for all $\mathbf{u}, \mathbf{v}, \mathbf{w} \in F^n$:

1. $\langle \mathbf{v}, \mathbf{w} \rangle$ is in F.
2. $\langle \mathbf{v}, \mathbf{v} \rangle$ is 0 if $\mathbf{v}$ is $\mathbf{0}$ and is a positive real number if $\mathbf{v}$ is nonzero.
3. $\overline{\langle \mathbf{v}, \mathbf{w} \rangle} = \langle \mathbf{w}, \mathbf{v} \rangle$.
4. $\langle \mathbf{u} + \mathbf{v}, \mathbf{w} \rangle = \langle \mathbf{u}, \mathbf{w} \rangle + \langle \mathbf{v}, \mathbf{w} \rangle$ and $\langle \mathbf{u}, \mathbf{v} + \mathbf{w} \rangle = \langle \mathbf{u}, \mathbf{v} \rangle + \langle \mathbf{u}, \mathbf{w} \rangle$
5. $\langle a\mathbf{v}, \mathbf{w} \rangle = a\langle \mathbf{v}, \mathbf{w} \rangle$ and $\langle \mathbf{v}, a\mathbf{w} \rangle = \bar{a}\langle \mathbf{v}, \mathbf{w} \rangle$ for $a \in F$.

Euclidean Space.

A **Euclidean space over F** is a finite-dimensional inner product space.

EXAMPLES

1. $\mathbb{R}^n$ with $\langle \mathbf{v}, \mathbf{w} \rangle = \mathbf{w}^T\mathbf{v}$ is a Euclidean space over $\mathbb{R}$ and $\mathbb{C}^n$ with $\langle \mathbf{v}, \mathbf{w} \rangle = \mathbf{w}^*\mathbf{v}$ is a Euclidean space over $\mathbb{C}$.
2. $\mathbb{R}^n$ with $\langle \mathbf{v}, \mathbf{w} \rangle = \mathbf{w}^T A\mathbf{v}$ is a Euclidean space over $\mathbb{R}$ if A is a positive definite real symmetric matrix. (Prove!)
3. $\mathbb{C}^n$ with $\langle \mathbf{v}, \mathbf{w} \rangle = \mathbf{w}^* A\mathbf{v}$ is a Euclidean space over $\mathbb{C}$ if A is a

Hermitian matrix which is *positive definite*; that is, $\mathbf{v}^*A\mathbf{v}$ is a positive real number for every nonzero vector $\mathbf{v} \in \mathbb{C}^n$. (Prove!)

4. Any finite-dimensional subspace of an inner product space is a Euclidean space, using the same inner product.

5. The vector space Cont($[-1, 1]$, $\mathbb{R}$) of continuous real-valued functions is a subspace of Functions ($[-1, 1]$, $\mathbb{R}$). Together with the inner product $\langle f, g\rangle = \int_{-1}^{1} f(x)g(x)\,dx$, Cont($[-1, 1]$, $\mathbb{R}$) is an inner product space. (Prove!)

6. Any finite-dimensional subspace of Cont($[-1, 1]$, $\mathbb{R}$) is a Euclidean space.

7. The space $\mathbb{R}[x]$ of real polynomials in the real variable x together with the inner product $\langle f, g\rangle = \int_{-1}^{1} f(x)g(x)\,dx$ is an inner product space. (Prove!) Its subspace $\mathbb{R}[x]_n$ of polynomials in x of degree at most n is a Euclidean space (Figure 6.2).

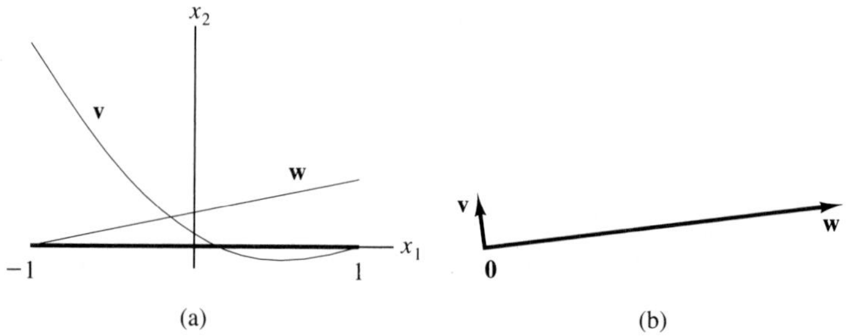

Figure 6.2 The orthogonal functions $\mathbf{v} = 15(x^2 - x)$ and $\mathbf{w} = 9(x + 1)$ (a) as functions and (b) as orthogonal vectors of lengths $\|\mathbf{v}\| = 1$ and $\|\mathbf{w}\| = \sqrt{42}$. (Verify!)

Length, distance, and orthogonality

In any Euclidean space V over F, the concepts of length, distance, and orthogonality can be defined in terms of the inner product just as in F^n.

Definition. *Length, Distance, and Orthogonality.*
Let $\mathbf{v}$, $\mathbf{w}$ be elements of V. Then,

1. The **length** of $\mathbf{v}$ is $\|\mathbf{v}\| = \sqrt{\langle \mathbf{v}, \mathbf{v}\rangle}$.
2. The **distance** from $\mathbf{v}$ to $\mathbf{w}$ is $d(\mathbf{v}, \mathbf{w}) = \|\mathbf{w} - \mathbf{v}\|$.
3. The vectors $\mathbf{v}$ and $\mathbf{w}$ are **orthogonal** if $\langle \mathbf{v}, \mathbf{w}\rangle = 0$. We let $\mathbf{v} \perp \mathbf{w}$ indicate that $\mathbf{v}$ and $\mathbf{w}$ are orthogonal.

EXAMPLES

1. If $\mathbf{v}$ and $\mathbf{w}$ are elements of an inner product space and $\langle \mathbf{v}, \mathbf{w}\rangle = 4$, $\|\mathbf{v}\| = 4$, and $\|\mathbf{w}\| = 5$, then $\|\mathbf{v}+\mathbf{w}\| = \sqrt{\langle \mathbf{v}+\mathbf{w}, \mathbf{v}+\mathbf{w}\rangle}$ and $\|\mathbf{v}+\mathbf{w}\|^2 = \langle \mathbf{v}+\mathbf{w}, \mathbf{v}+\mathbf{w}\rangle = 4^2 + 8 + 5^2 = 49$. So, $\mathbf{v}+\mathbf{w}$ has length 7.
2. For $f(x) = x^2 - x$ and $g(x) = x + 1$, the functions $f(x)$ and $g(x)$ are orthogonal with respect to the inner product $\langle f, g\rangle = \int_{-1}^{1} f(x)g(x)\,dx$, since $\int_{-1}^{1} (x^2 - x)(x+1)\,dx = \int_{-1}^{1} (x^3 - x)\,dx = 0$. (Verify!)

Length in a Euclidean space satisfies the property that $\|a\mathbf{v}\| = |a|\,\|\mathbf{v}\|$, since $\|a\mathbf{v}\| = \sqrt{\langle a\mathbf{v}, a\mathbf{v}\rangle} = \sqrt{a\bar{a}\langle \mathbf{v}, \mathbf{v}\rangle} = |a|\,\|\mathbf{v}\|$. So, for $\mathbf{v}$ nonzero, $\mathbf{v}/\|\mathbf{v}\|$ has length 1. (Explain!) We call $\mathbf{v}/\|\mathbf{v}\|$ the **unit vector** corresponding to $\mathbf{v}$.

EXAMPLE

For $\mathbf{v} = \begin{bmatrix} 3 \\ 4 \end{bmatrix}$, $\|\mathbf{v}\| = 5$ and $\dfrac{\mathbf{v}}{\|\mathbf{v}\|} = \begin{bmatrix} 3/5 \\ 4/5 \end{bmatrix}$ has length 1. (Verify!)

Orthogonality in a Euclidean space V is one of the most important geometric concepts because of the following theorem.

Theorem 6.1. *The Pythagorean Theorem.*
If $\mathbf{v}, \mathbf{w} \in V$ and $\mathbf{v} \perp \mathbf{w}$, then $|\mathbf{v} \pm \mathbf{w}|^2 = |\mathbf{v}|^2 + |\mathbf{w}|^2$ (Figure 6.3).

Proof. $|\mathbf{v} \pm \mathbf{w}|^2 = \langle \mathbf{v} \pm \mathbf{w}, \mathbf{v} \pm \mathbf{w}\rangle = |\mathbf{v}|^2 + 0 + 0 + |\mathbf{w}|^2$. ■

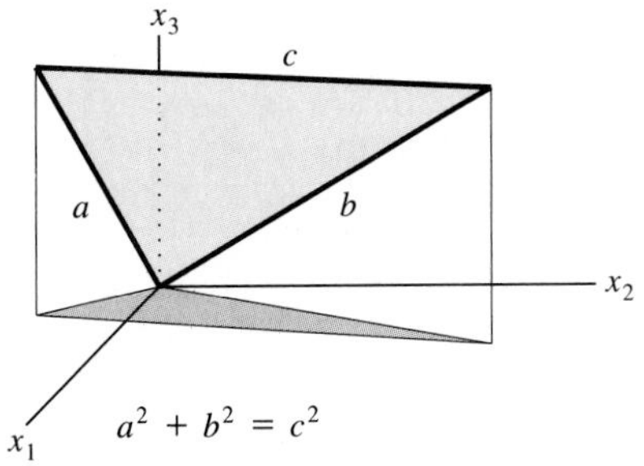

Figure 6.3 The Pythagorean theorem in $\mathbb{R}^3$.

The hyperplane normal to v

For any nonzero vector $\mathbf{v} \in V$, the subspace $\mathbf{v}^\perp = \{\mathbf{u} \in V \mid \langle \mathbf{u}, \mathbf{v}\rangle = 0\}$ is a hyperplane in V. The reason for this is that for any $\mathbf{w} \in V$, $\mathbf{w} - a\mathbf{v}$ is in $\mathbf{v}^\perp$ for $a = \langle \mathbf{w}, \mathbf{v}\rangle / \langle \mathbf{v}, \mathbf{v}\rangle$. (Verify!) So, $\mathbf{w} = a\mathbf{v} + (\mathbf{w} - a\mathbf{v})$ is in $F\mathbf{v} + \mathbf{v}^\perp$. It follows that $V = F\mathbf{v} + \mathbf{v}^\perp$ and $\mathbf{v}^\perp$ is $(n-1)$-dimensional. (Why is $V \neq \mathbf{v}^\perp$?)

Definition. *Hyperplane Normal to* $\mathbf{v}$.
For any nonzero $\mathbf{v} \in V$, $\mathbf{v}^{\perp}$ is called the **hyperplane normal to v** (Figure 6.4).

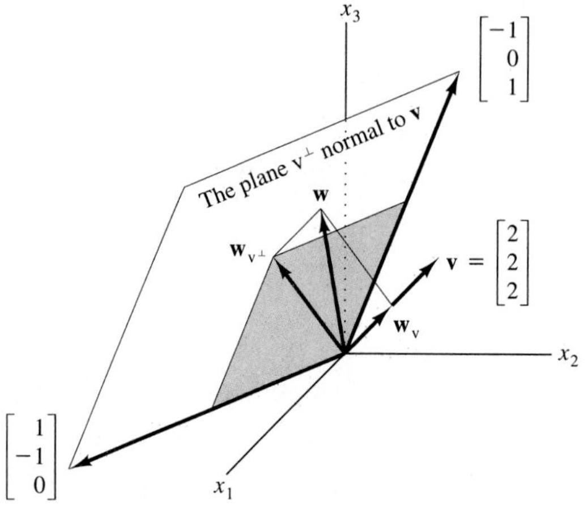

Figure 6.4 The hyperplane $\mathbf{v}^{\perp}$ normal to $\mathbf{v}$. Resolution $\mathbf{w} = \mathbf{w}_{\mathbf{v}} + \mathbf{w}_{\mathbf{v}^{\perp}}$ of $\mathbf{w}$ as the sum of its projections on $\mathbf{v}$ and $\mathbf{v}^{\perp}$.

EXAMPLE

$$\begin{bmatrix} 1 \\ 2 \\ 3 \end{bmatrix}^{\perp} = \left\{ \begin{bmatrix} x \\ y \\ z \end{bmatrix} \middle| \; x + 2y + 3z = 0 \right\}$$

and

$$\begin{bmatrix} 1+i \\ 1-i \\ 1 \end{bmatrix}^{\perp} = \left\{ \begin{bmatrix} x \\ y \\ z \end{bmatrix} \middle| \; x(1 - i) + y(1 + i) + z = 0 \right\}.$$

Projection of one vector on another

For any nonzero vector $\mathbf{v}$ in a Euclidean space V, we have seen that $V = F\mathbf{v} + \mathbf{v}^{\perp}$. Given another vector $\mathbf{w}$, it can be written as $\mathbf{w} = \mathbf{w}_{\mathbf{v}} + \mathbf{w}_{\mathbf{v}^{\perp}}$, where $\mathbf{w}_{\mathbf{v}}$ is a multiple of $\mathbf{v}$ and $\mathbf{w}_{\mathbf{v}^{\perp}}$ is in $\mathbf{v}^{\perp}$. Writing $\mathbf{w}_{\mathbf{v}} = a\mathbf{v}$, we can find a by taking the inner product of $\mathbf{w} = a\mathbf{v} + \mathbf{w}_{\mathbf{v}^{\perp}}$ and $\mathbf{v}$:

$$\langle \mathbf{w}, \mathbf{v} \rangle = \langle a\mathbf{v} + \mathbf{w}_{\mathbf{v}^{\perp}}, \mathbf{v} \rangle = a\langle \mathbf{v}, \mathbf{v} \rangle + \langle \mathbf{w}_{\mathbf{v}^{\perp}}, \mathbf{v} \rangle = a\langle \mathbf{v}, \mathbf{v} \rangle$$

$$a = \frac{\langle \mathbf{w}, \mathbf{v} \rangle}{\langle \mathbf{v}, \mathbf{v} \rangle}$$

We conclude that *there is only one choice* for the $\mathbf{w}_\mathbf{v}$, $\mathbf{w}_{\mathbf{v}^\perp}$. We can now give the rule for resolving $\mathbf{w}$ into its orthogonal parts with respect to $\mathbf{v}$, which leads to the concept of projection.

Resolving $\mathbf{w}$ *into Its Orthogonal Parts.*

$$\mathbf{w} = \mathbf{w}_\mathbf{v} + \mathbf{w}_{\mathbf{v}^\perp}, \text{ where } \mathbf{w}_\mathbf{v} = \frac{\langle \mathbf{w}, \mathbf{v} \rangle}{\langle \mathbf{v}, \mathbf{v} \rangle}\mathbf{v} \text{ and } \mathbf{w}_{\mathbf{v}^\perp} = \mathbf{w} - \frac{\langle \mathbf{w}, \mathbf{v} \rangle}{\langle \mathbf{v}, \mathbf{v} \rangle}\mathbf{v}.$$

Definition. *The Projection of* $\mathbf{w}$ *on* $\mathbf{v}$.

For $\mathbf{v}$, $\mathbf{w}$ in a Euclidean space, the vector $\mathbf{w}_\mathbf{v}$ is the **projection of $\mathbf{w}$ on $\mathbf{v}$** and $\mathbf{w}_{\mathbf{v}^\perp}$ is the **projection of $\mathbf{w}$ on $\mathbf{v}^\perp$**.

EXAMPLES

1. The projections of

$$\begin{bmatrix}1\\2\\3\end{bmatrix}, \quad \begin{bmatrix}1\\3\\3\end{bmatrix}, \quad \begin{bmatrix}1\\4\\3\end{bmatrix} \quad \text{on} \quad \mathbf{v} = \begin{bmatrix}0\\1\\0\end{bmatrix} \quad \text{are} \quad \begin{bmatrix}0\\2\\0\end{bmatrix}, \quad \begin{bmatrix}0\\3\\0\end{bmatrix}, \quad \begin{bmatrix}0\\4\\0\end{bmatrix}$$

and their projections on $\mathbf{v}^\perp$ are

$$\begin{bmatrix}1\\0\\3\end{bmatrix}, \quad \begin{bmatrix}1\\0\\3\end{bmatrix}, \quad \begin{bmatrix}1\\0\\3\end{bmatrix}.$$

(Show!)

2. The projection of $\mathbf{w} = \begin{bmatrix}5\\2\\3\end{bmatrix}$ on $\mathbf{v} = \begin{bmatrix}3\\7\\1\end{bmatrix}$ is

$$\mathbf{w}_\mathbf{v} = \frac{\langle \mathbf{w}, \mathbf{v} \rangle}{\langle \mathbf{v}, \mathbf{v} \rangle}\mathbf{v} = \frac{15 + 14 + 3}{9 + 49 + 1}\begin{bmatrix}3\\7\\1\end{bmatrix}.$$

The triangle inequality. Angles

To complete our discussion of the most basic concepts and principles from Euclidean plane geometry, we use the following theorem.

Theorem 6.2. *The Schwarz Inequality.*

For $\mathbf{v}$, $\mathbf{w}$ in an inner product space V, $|\langle \mathbf{v}, \mathbf{w} \rangle| \leq \|\mathbf{v}\|\|\mathbf{w}\|$, with equality if and only if $\mathbf{v}$ and $\mathbf{w}$ are linearly dependent.

Proof. Resolve $\mathbf{w}$ as sum $\mathbf{w} = \mathbf{w}_{\mathbf{v}} + \mathbf{w}_{\mathbf{v}^\perp}$ of its projections on $\mathbf{v}$ and $\mathbf{v}^\perp$. Then $\|\mathbf{w}\|^2 = \|\mathbf{w}_{\mathbf{v}}\|^2 + \|\mathbf{w}_{\mathbf{v}^\perp}\|^2$, by the Pythagorean theorem, and $\|\mathbf{w}\| \geq \|\mathbf{w}_{\mathbf{v}}\|$. Since $\|\mathbf{w}_{\mathbf{v}}\| = \left\| \dfrac{\langle \mathbf{w}, \mathbf{v} \rangle}{\langle \mathbf{v}, \mathbf{v} \rangle} \mathbf{v} \right\|$, it follows that

$$\|\mathbf{w}\| \geq \left\| \frac{\langle \mathbf{w}, \mathbf{v} \rangle}{\langle \mathbf{v}, \mathbf{v} \rangle} \mathbf{v} \right\| = \left| \frac{\langle \mathbf{w}, \mathbf{v} \rangle}{\langle \mathbf{v}, \mathbf{v} \rangle} \right| \|\mathbf{v}\|,$$

$$\|\mathbf{v}\| \|\mathbf{w}\| \geq \left| \frac{\langle \mathbf{w}, \mathbf{v} \rangle}{\langle \mathbf{v}, \mathbf{v} \rangle} \right| \|\mathbf{v}\|^2 = \left| \frac{\langle \mathbf{w}, \mathbf{v} \rangle}{\langle \mathbf{v}, \mathbf{v} \rangle} \|\mathbf{v}\|^2 \right| = |\langle \mathbf{v}, \mathbf{w} \rangle|.$$

Note that the inequality is equality if and only if $\mathbf{w} = \mathbf{w}_{\mathbf{v}'}$—that is, if and only if $\mathbf{v}$ and $\mathbf{w}$ are linearly dependent. ■

From this, we can generalize the triangle inequality for $\mathbb{R}^2$ as follows.

Theorem 6.3. *The Triangle Inequality.*
For any $\mathbf{v}, \mathbf{w} \in V$, $\|\mathbf{v} \pm \mathbf{w}\| \leq \|\mathbf{v}\| + \|\mathbf{w}\|$ with equality only if $\mathbf{v}$ and $\mathbf{w}$ are linearly dependent.

Proof.
$$\begin{aligned}\|\mathbf{v} \pm \mathbf{w}\|^2 &= \langle \mathbf{v}, \mathbf{v} \rangle + \langle \mathbf{v}, \pm\mathbf{w} \rangle + \langle \overline{\mathbf{v}, \pm\mathbf{w}} \rangle + \langle \pm\mathbf{w}, \pm\mathbf{w} \rangle \\ &\leq \|\mathbf{v}\|^2 + 2\|\mathbf{v}\|\|\mathbf{w}\| + \|\mathbf{w}\|^2,\end{aligned}$$

by applying the Schwarz inequality to the two innermost terms. When this inequality is equality, then $|\langle \mathbf{v}, \pm\mathbf{w} \rangle| = \|\mathbf{v}\|\|\mathbf{w}\|$ and $\mathbf{v}$ and $\mathbf{w}$ are linearly dependent by Theorem 6.2. ■

A more general form of the triangle inequality is

$$d(\mathbf{v}, \mathbf{w}) \leq d(\mathbf{v}, \mathbf{u}) + d(\mathbf{u}, \mathbf{w})$$

(prove), which reduces to $\|\mathbf{v} - \mathbf{w}\| \leq \|\mathbf{v}\| + \|\mathbf{w}\|$ when $\mathbf{u} = 0$ (Figure 6.5).

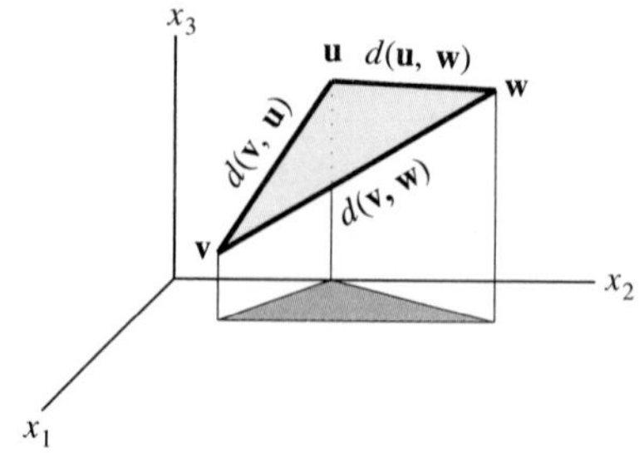

Figure 6.5 The triangle inequality $d(\mathbf{v}, \mathbf{w}) \leq d(\mathbf{v}, \mathbf{u}) + d(\mathbf{u}, \mathbf{w})$ in $\mathbb{R}^3$.

Since $\langle \mathbf{v}, \mathbf{w} \rangle / \|\mathbf{v}\| \|\mathbf{w}\| \leq 1$ for nonzero $\mathbf{v}$ and $\mathbf{w}$, by the Schwarz inequality, we can define angle in $\mathbb{R}^n$ just as in $\mathbb{R}^2$.

Definition. *The Angle Between Two Vectors.*
The **angle** between two nonzero vectors $\mathbf{v}$ and $\mathbf{w}$ in a Euclidean space V over $\mathbb{R}$ is the angle α between 0 and π such that $\cos \alpha = \langle \mathbf{v}, \mathbf{w} \rangle / \|\mathbf{v}\| \|\mathbf{w}\|$.

The angle between $\mathbf{v}$ and $\mathbf{w}$ depends only on the lengths of the vectors $\mathbf{v}$ and $\mathbf{w}$ and the inner product $\langle \mathbf{v}, \mathbf{w} \rangle$. So, it is the same as the angle between $\mathbf{v}$ and $\mathbf{w}$ in the subspace $\mathbb{R}\mathbf{v} + \mathbb{R}\mathbf{w}$. When $\mathbf{u}$ and $\mathbf{v}$ are linearly independent, $\mathbb{R}\mathbf{v} + \mathbb{R}\mathbf{w}$ is isomorphic to $\mathbb{R}^2$ under some linear transformation T which preserves inner products, lengths, and angles. (See Figure 6.6.)

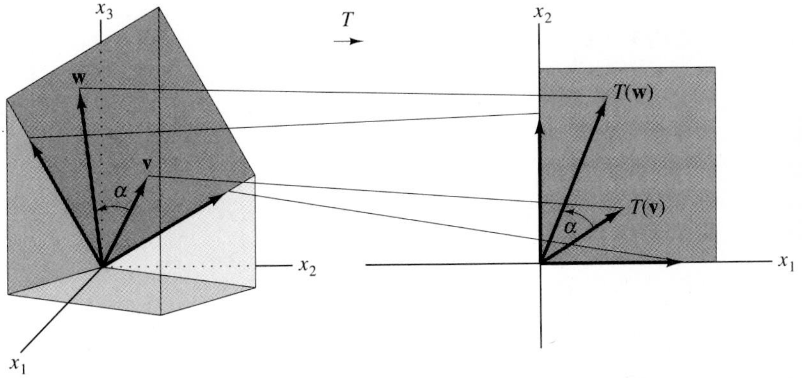

Figure 6.6 The angles between $\mathbf{v}$, $\mathbf{w}$ in $\mathbb{R}\mathbf{v} + \mathbb{R}\mathbf{w}$ and between $T(\mathbf{v})$, $T(\mathbf{w})$ in $\mathbb{R}^2$.

EXAMPLE

If $\mathbf{v}$ and $\mathbf{w}$ are elements of an inner product space and $\langle \mathbf{v}, \mathbf{w} \rangle = 4$, $\|\mathbf{v}\| = 4$, and $\|\mathbf{w}\| = 5$, then the cosine of the angle between $\mathbf{v}$ and $\mathbf{w}$ is $\frac{4}{4 \cdot 5} = \frac{1}{5}$. If $\mathbf{v}', \mathbf{w}' \in \mathbb{R}^2$ are any vectors which satisfy $\langle \mathbf{v}', \mathbf{w}' \rangle = 4$, $\|\mathbf{v}'\| = 4$, and $\|\mathbf{w}'\| = 5$, then the isomorphism $T(r\mathbf{v} + s\mathbf{w}) = r\mathbf{v}' + s\mathbf{w}'$ preserves length and angle. (Prove!)

Length, Distance, and Angle.

$|\mathbf{v} \cdot \mathbf{w}| \leq \|\mathbf{v}\| \|\mathbf{w}\|$ (Schwarz inequality for lengths in F^n)

$d(\mathbf{v}, \mathbf{w}) \leq d(\mathbf{v}, \mathbf{u}) + d(\mathbf{u}, \mathbf{w})$ (Triangle inequality for distances in F^n)

$$\cos \alpha = \frac{\langle \mathbf{v}, \mathbf{w} \rangle}{\|\mathbf{v}\| \|\mathbf{w}\|}$$ (Angle α between vectors $\mathbf{v}$ and $\mathbf{w}$ in $\mathbb{R}^n$)

PROBLEMS

NUMERICAL PROBLEMS

1. Find $\mathbf{v}, \mathbf{w} \in \mathbb{R}^3$ such that $\|\mathbf{v}\| = 4$, $\|\mathbf{w}\| = 5$, and $\langle \mathbf{v}, \mathbf{w} \rangle = 3$.

2. Find $\mathbf{v}, \mathbf{w} \in \mathbb{R}^2$ such that $\|\mathbf{v}\| = 4$, $\|\mathbf{w}\| = 5$, and $\langle \mathbf{v}, \mathbf{w} \rangle = 4$.

3. Letting $\mathbf{v}$ be the first column and $\mathbf{w}$ the second, for the matrices below, resolve $\mathbf{w}$ as sum of its projections on $\mathbf{v}$ and $\mathbf{v}^\perp$.

(a) $\begin{bmatrix} 1 & 2 \\ 1 & 1 \end{bmatrix}$ **(b)** $\begin{bmatrix} 0 & 0 \\ 2 & 5 \\ 1 & 4 \end{bmatrix}$ **(c)** $\begin{bmatrix} 2 & 2 \\ 2 & 3 \\ 2 & 1 \end{bmatrix}$

(d) $\begin{bmatrix} 2 & 2 \\ 2 & 3 \\ -4 & -1 \end{bmatrix}$ **(e)** $\begin{bmatrix} 5 & -1 \\ -3 & 2 \\ 2 & 1 \end{bmatrix}$ **(f)** $\begin{bmatrix} 2 & 2 \\ 2 & 1 \\ 1 & 1 \end{bmatrix}$

4. Show that the projections of

$$\begin{bmatrix} 1 \\ 2 \\ 3 \end{bmatrix}, \quad \begin{bmatrix} 1 \\ 3 \\ 3 \end{bmatrix}, \quad \begin{bmatrix} 1 \\ 4 \\ 3 \end{bmatrix} \quad \text{on} \quad \mathbf{v} = \begin{bmatrix} 0 \\ 1 \\ 0 \end{bmatrix} \quad \text{are} \quad \begin{bmatrix} 0 \\ 2 \\ 0 \end{bmatrix}, \quad \begin{bmatrix} 0 \\ 3 \\ 0 \end{bmatrix}, \quad \begin{bmatrix} 0 \\ 4 \\ 0 \end{bmatrix}$$

and their projections on $\mathbf{v}^\perp$ are

$$\begin{bmatrix} 1 \\ 0 \\ 3 \end{bmatrix}, \quad \begin{bmatrix} 1 \\ 0 \\ 3 \end{bmatrix}, \quad \begin{bmatrix} 1 \\ 0 \\ 3 \end{bmatrix}.$$

5. Verify the Schwarz inequality for the following pairs of vectors.

(a) $\begin{bmatrix} 1 \\ 0 \\ 3 \end{bmatrix}, \begin{bmatrix} 2 \\ 2 \\ 1 \end{bmatrix}$ **(b)** $\begin{bmatrix} 4 \\ 2 \\ 5 \end{bmatrix}, \begin{bmatrix} 2 \\ 3 \\ 4 \end{bmatrix}$ **(c)** $\begin{bmatrix} 3 \\ 7 \\ 2 \end{bmatrix}, \begin{bmatrix} 3 \\ 9 \\ 3 \end{bmatrix}$

6. Verify the triangle inequality for the pairs of vectors in Problem 5.

7. Find the cosine of the angle between the pair of vectors in Problem 5(a).

8. For $V = \mathbb{R}[x]_2 = F1 + Fx + Fx^2$ and $\langle f, g \rangle = \int_{-1}^{1} f(x)g(x)\,dx$

(a) Find the lengths of $x^2 - x$, $x + 1$, 1, x, x^2.

(b) Find $\mathbf{v}^\perp$ for $\mathbf{v} = x^2 - x$.

9. For the inner product of Problem 8 and for $\mathbf{v} = x^2 - x$ and $\mathbf{w} = x - 1$, resolve $\mathbf{w}$ as sum of its projections on $\mathbf{v}$ and $\mathbf{v}^\perp$.

10. For the inner product of Problem 8, verify the triangle inequality $\|1 + x^2\| \leq \|1\| + \|x^2\|$.

11. For the inner product of Problem 8, verify the triangle inequality $d(1, x^2) \leq d(1, x) + d(x, x^2)$.

12. For the inner product of Problem 8, find

(a) The angle between 1 and x;

(b) The angle between x and x^2;

(c) The angle between 1 and x^2.

Hard

13. Let $\mathbf{v}$, $\mathbf{w}$ be linearly independent elements of an inner product space over $\mathbb{R}$ and let $\mathbf{v}'$, $\mathbf{w}'$ be a basis for $\mathbb{R}^2$ such that $\|\mathbf{v}\| = \|\mathbf{v}'\|$, $\|\mathbf{w}\| = \|\mathbf{w}'\|$, $\langle \mathbf{v}, \mathbf{w} \rangle = \langle \mathbf{v}', \mathbf{w}' \rangle$. Show that $T(r\mathbf{v} + s\mathbf{w}) = r\mathbf{v}' + s\mathbf{w}'$ is an isomorphism from $V = F\mathbf{v} + F\mathbf{w}$ to $\mathbb{R}^2$ such that $\langle T(\mathbf{x}), T(\mathbf{y}) \rangle = \langle \mathbf{x}, \mathbf{y} \rangle$ for all $\mathbf{x}, \mathbf{y} \in V$.

THEORETICAL PROBLEMS

14. If b, $c > 0$ and $|a| \leq bc$, find $\mathbf{v}$, $\mathbf{w} \in \mathbb{R}^2$ such that $\langle \mathbf{v}, \mathbf{w} \rangle = a$, $\|\mathbf{v}\| = b$, $\|\mathbf{w}\| = c$.

15. Verify the conditions for an inner product space for:

(a) $\mathbb{R}^n$ with $\langle \mathbf{v}, \mathbf{w} \rangle = \mathbf{w}^T A \mathbf{v}$ if A is a positive definite real symmetric matrix;

(b) $\mathbb{C}^n$ with $\langle \mathbf{v}, \mathbf{w} \rangle = \mathbf{w}^* A \mathbf{v}$ if A is a Hermitian matrix which is positive definite;

(c) Any subspace of an inner product space;

(d) The vector space $\text{Cont}([-1, 1], \mathbb{R})$ of continuous real-valued functions together with the inner product $\langle f, g \rangle = \int_{-1}^{1} f(x)g(x)\,dx$;

(e) $\mathbb{R}[x]$ together with the inner product $\langle f, g \rangle = \int_{-1}^{1} f(x)g(x)\,dx$.

Hard

16. If $\mathbf{v}$, $\mathbf{w}$ are linearly independent elements of $\mathbb{R}^n$, prove that $V = \mathbb{R}\mathbf{v} + \mathbb{R}\mathbf{w}$ is isomorphic to $\mathbb{R}^2$ by an isomorphism T which preserves the inner product—that is, $\langle T(\mathbf{v}), T(\mathbf{w}) \rangle = \langle \mathbf{v}, \mathbf{w} \rangle$. In what sense does this imply that T preserves length and angle?

6.3 ORTHONORMAL SETS AND BASES

The basis of standard unit vectors of F^n is an orthonormal basis, and any subset of it an orthonormal set, according to the following definition.

Definition. *Orthonormal Sets and Bases.*

An **orthonormal set** in a Euclidean space V is a set $\mathbf{v}_1, \ldots, \mathbf{v}_n$ such that $\langle \mathbf{v}_r, \mathbf{v}_s \rangle = 1$ for $r = s$ and $\langle \mathbf{v}_r, \mathbf{v}_s \rangle = 0$ for $r \neq s$. An **orthonormal basis** for V is an orthonormal set which is a basis for V.

Note that

1. If $\mathbf{v}_1, \ldots, \mathbf{v}_n$ is an orthonormal set, then $\langle a_1\mathbf{v}_1 + \cdots + a_n\mathbf{v}_n, \mathbf{v}_r \rangle = a_r$ for all r.
2. By (1), any orthonormal set is linearly independent. (Explain!)

3. If $\mathbf{w}_1, \ldots, \mathbf{w}_n$ is an **orthogonal set**—that is, a set such that $\langle \mathbf{w}_r, \mathbf{w}_s \rangle = 0$ for $r \neq s$ and 1 for $r = s$—an orthonormal set is obtained by replacing each nonzero $\mathbf{w}_r$ by $\mathbf{w}_r/\|\mathbf{w}_r\|$ and discarding those that are $\mathbf{0}$.

EXAMPLES

1. For the Euclidean plane, $\mathbf{u}$, $\mathbf{v}$ is an orthonormal basis if and only if the matrix $[\mathbf{u} \quad \mathbf{v}]$ is orthogonal—that is, if and only if $[\mathbf{u} \quad \mathbf{v}]$ is one of $\begin{bmatrix} \cos\alpha & -\sin\alpha \\ \sin\alpha & \cos\alpha \end{bmatrix}$ (rotation R_α), $\begin{bmatrix} -\cos\alpha & -\sin\alpha \\ -\sin\alpha & \cos\alpha \end{bmatrix}$ (reflection S_α) for some α (Theorem 1.30).

2. An orthonormal basis for $F\begin{bmatrix} 0 \\ 1 \\ 0 \end{bmatrix} + F\begin{bmatrix} 1 \\ 3 \\ 3 \end{bmatrix}$ is $\begin{bmatrix} 0 \\ 1 \\ 0 \end{bmatrix}, \frac{1}{\sqrt{10}}\begin{bmatrix} 1 \\ 0 \\ 3 \end{bmatrix}$. (Verify!)

Orthonormalization

The geometry in a Euclidean space is developed in terms of an orthonormal basis. Fortunately, every basis can be *orthonormalized* in the following sense.

Theorem 6.4. *Orthonormalization of a Basis.*
Let V be a Euclidean space over F with basis $\mathbf{v}_1, \ldots, \mathbf{v}_n$. Then V has an orthonormal basis $\mathbf{u}_1, \ldots, \mathbf{u}_n$ such that

$$F\mathbf{v}_1 + \cdots + F\mathbf{v}_r = F\mathbf{u}_1 + \cdots + F\mathbf{u}_r \qquad \text{for } 1 \leq r \leq n.$$

Proof. Finding the orthonormal basis is done by changing the basis elements to make them orthogonal and then changing them to vectors of length 1.

To make them orthogonal, we perform elementary operations on sets of vectors, going from the original basis $\mathbf{v}_1, \ldots, \mathbf{v}_n$ to a basis $\mathbf{w}_1, \ldots, \mathbf{w}_n$ of vectors, every two of which are orthogonal. Subtract from each of the last $n - 1$ vectors its projection on the first. This makes them orthogonal to the first vector. Then subtract from each of the last $n - 2$ vectors its projection on the second. This makes them orthogonal to the second vector. Continuing in this fashion, we finally get the basis $\mathbf{w}_1, \ldots, \mathbf{w}_n$ as

$$\mathbf{w}_1 = \mathbf{v}_1,$$

$$\mathbf{w}_2 = \mathbf{v}_2 - \frac{\langle \mathbf{v}_2, \mathbf{w}_1 \rangle}{\langle \mathbf{w}_1, \mathbf{w}_1 \rangle}\mathbf{w}_1,$$

$$\mathbf{w}_3 = \mathbf{v}_3 - \frac{\langle \mathbf{v}_3, \mathbf{w}_1 \rangle}{\langle \mathbf{w}_1, \mathbf{w}_1 \rangle}\mathbf{w}_1 - \frac{\langle \mathbf{v}_3, \mathbf{w}_2 \rangle}{\langle \mathbf{w}_2, \mathbf{w}_2 \rangle}\mathbf{w}_2,$$

$$\vdots$$

$$\mathbf{w}_n = \mathbf{v}_n - \frac{\langle \mathbf{v}_n, \mathbf{w}_1 \rangle}{\langle \mathbf{w}_1, \mathbf{w}_1 \rangle}\mathbf{w}_1 - \cdots - \frac{\langle \mathbf{v}_n, \mathbf{w}_{n-1} \rangle}{\langle \mathbf{w}_{n-1}, \mathbf{w}_{n-1} \rangle}\mathbf{w}_{n-1}.$$

The set $\mathbf{w}_1, \ldots, \mathbf{w}_n$ is an **orthogonal basis** (basis in which every two elements are orthogonal).

The process finding the orthogonal basis $\mathbf{w}_1, \ldots, \mathbf{w}_n$ is called **Gram-Schmidt orthogonalization**. Once this process has been completed, to get an orthonormal basis, just replace the $\mathbf{w}_s$ by the corresponding unit vectors $\mathbf{u}_s = \mathbf{w}_s/\|\mathbf{w}_s\|$ to get an orthonormal basis $\mathbf{u}_1, \ldots, \mathbf{u}_n$. The entire process is called **Gram-Schmidt orthonormalization** (Figure 6.7).

For $1 \leq r \leq n$, $F\mathbf{v}_1 + \cdots + F\mathbf{v}_r = F\mathbf{u}_1 + \cdots + F\mathbf{u}_r$, by construction. (Explain!) ■

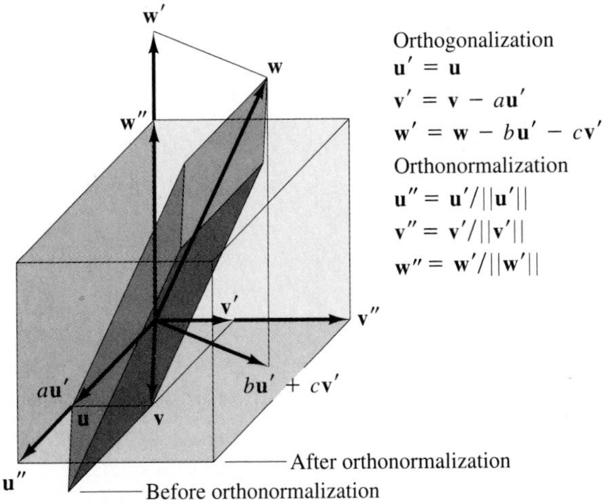

Figure 6.7 Orthogonalization and orthonormalization of the basis **u**, **v**, **w**.

EXAMPLES

1. We get the orthogonal basis

$$\mathbf{u}_1 = \begin{bmatrix} 0 \\ 1 \\ 0 \end{bmatrix}, \qquad \mathbf{u}_2 = \begin{bmatrix} 1 \\ 0 \\ 3 \end{bmatrix}$$

for the span V of

$$\mathbf{v}_1 = \begin{bmatrix} 0 \\ 1 \\ 0 \end{bmatrix}, \qquad \mathbf{v}_2 = \begin{bmatrix} 1 \\ 3 \\ 3 \end{bmatrix}$$

by the Gram-Schmidt orthogonalization

$$\mathbf{w}_1 = \begin{bmatrix} 0 \\ 1 \\ 0 \end{bmatrix}, \qquad \mathbf{w}_2 = \begin{bmatrix} 1 \\ 3 \\ 3 \end{bmatrix} - \begin{bmatrix} 0 \\ 3 \\ 0 \end{bmatrix} = \begin{bmatrix} 1 \\ 0 \\ 3 \end{bmatrix},$$

since

$$\frac{\langle \mathbf{v}_2, \mathbf{w}_1 \rangle}{\langle \mathbf{w}_1, \mathbf{w}_1 \rangle} \mathbf{w}_1 = \frac{3}{1} \begin{bmatrix} 0 \\ 1 \\ 0 \end{bmatrix} = \begin{bmatrix} 0 \\ 3 \\ 0 \end{bmatrix}.$$

2. For

$$V = F \begin{bmatrix} 1 \\ 1 \\ 1 \end{bmatrix} + F \begin{bmatrix} 1 \\ 3 \\ -1 \end{bmatrix} + F \begin{bmatrix} -1 \\ 2 \\ 2 \end{bmatrix} = F^3,$$

we get the two bases

$$\mathbf{w}_1 = \begin{bmatrix} 1 \\ 1 \\ 1 \end{bmatrix}, \quad \mathbf{w}_2 = \begin{bmatrix} 1 \\ 3 \\ -1 \end{bmatrix} - \begin{bmatrix} 1 \\ 1 \\ 1 \end{bmatrix} = \begin{bmatrix} 0 \\ 2 \\ -2 \end{bmatrix}, \quad \mathbf{w}_3 = \begin{bmatrix} -1 \\ 2 \\ 2 \end{bmatrix} - \begin{bmatrix} 1 \\ 1 \\ 1 \end{bmatrix} - \mathbf{0} = \begin{bmatrix} -2 \\ 1 \\ 1 \end{bmatrix},$$

$$\mathbf{u}_1 = \frac{1}{\sqrt{3}} \begin{bmatrix} 1 \\ 1 \\ 1 \end{bmatrix}, \quad \mathbf{u}_2 = \frac{1}{\sqrt{8}} \begin{bmatrix} 0 \\ 2 \\ -2 \end{bmatrix}, \quad \mathbf{u}_3 = \frac{1}{\sqrt{6}} \begin{bmatrix} -2 \\ 1 \\ 1 \end{bmatrix}.$$

Orthonormalization of rows

Orthonormalization of the rows of a matrix, when they are linearly independent, is equivalent to factoring A as a product of two matrices, the second of which holds the orthonormal basis.

Suppose that the rows $\mathbf{v}_1, \ldots, \mathbf{v}_m$ of A are linearly independent, so they form a basis for the row space $V = r(A)$ of A. Then the elementary operations performed on the $\mathbf{v}$'s during their orthonormalization to the $\mathbf{w}$'s come from multiplying by elementary matrices $A_{ij}(-c_{ij})$ to subtract c_{ij} times row j from row i ($i > j$). Then, to get $\mathbf{u}_i$ from $\mathbf{w}_i$ we multiply by the elementary matrix $M_i(d_i)$, where $d_i = 1/\|\mathbf{u}_i\|$.

This process is very like the LDU reduction which resulted in the factorization $A = LDU$, where U is an echelon matrix (Section 3.7). The difference here is that we get, instead, a factorization $A = L'D'U'$, where U' has orthonormal rows.

Factorization of A with Independent Rows.
$A = L'D'U'$, where the rows of U' are orthonormal and

$L' = A_{21}(c_{21}) \cdots A_{m1}(c_{m1}) \cdots A_{mm-1}(c_{mm-1})$ (L' is lower triangular),

$D' = M_1(d_1) \cdots M_m(d_m) = \text{Diag}(d_1, \ldots, d_m)$ (D' is diagonal with positive diagonal entries).

Building L' and D' amounts to writing the c_{ij} ($i > j$) and d_i into the lower triangle diagonal of the matrix. So, *L' and D' are obtained with virtually* *no increase in computation time over what is needed for the orthonormalization itself*. Orthonormalization, however, is *much* slower than the reduction of A to an echelon matrix U. (Explain!)

When the rows of A are not linearly independent, a permutation matrix arranges the rows so that a basis for $r(A)$ comes first in the matrix $P^{-1}A$. Then $P^{-1}A = L'D'U'$ and $A = PL'D'U'$, where P is a permutation matrix, L' and D' are as before, the first r rows of U' are orthonormal, and the remaining $m - r$ rows of U' are $\mathbf{0}$.

Orthonormalization of columns. The *QR* factorization

Factorization of A by orthonormalization of its rows is somewhat similar to the LDU factorization. When transposed, this factorization becomes a factorization of A by orthonormalization of its columns. It is this factorization that is most natural, from our predominantly "column" point of view. It, in turn, gives the QR factorization, which plays a very important role throughout the remainder of the book.

Assume that A has linearly independent columns. Let $B = A^T$ and consider the factorization $B = L'D'U'$ corresponding to orthonormalization of rows. Transposing, we get $A = B^T = U'^T D'^T L'^T$, which, for $Q = U'^T$ and $R = D'^T L'^T$, gives us the ***QR* factorization**

$$A = QR, \qquad R \text{ upper triangular with positive diagonal entries,}$$

where the columns of Q are orthonormal. To get it directly amounts to performing the orthonormalization of columns to get Q using elementary operations on the columns of A.

When A is invertible, it follows that Q is invertible. Since its columns are orthonormal, it is orthogonal if $F = \mathbb{R}$ (unitary if $F = \mathbb{C}$).

Theorem 6.5. *The QR Factorization of an Invertible A.*
Let $A \in M_n F$ be invertible. Then:

1. $A = QR$, where the Q is orthogonal (unitary if $F = \mathbb{C}$) and R is an invertible upper triangular matrix with positive diagonal entries.
2. If $A = PS$, where P is orthogonal (unitary if $F = \mathbb{C}$) and S is upper triangular with positive real diagonal entries, then $Q = P$ and $R = S$.

Proof. We've already seen why (1) is true. For (2), note that $Q^{-1}P = RS^{-1}$, which implies that RS^{-1} is orthogonal (unitary if $F = \mathbb{C}$). So, $RS^{-1} = I$ (the only upper triangular unitary transformation with positive diagonal entries) and $R = S$. ■

When the columns of A are not linearly independent, instead we get $A = B^T = U'^T D'^T L'^T P^T = QR$, where $Q = U'^T$ and $R = D'^T L'^T P^T$. The first r columns of Q are orthonormal and the remaining $n - r$ columns are $\mathbf{0}$. Again, we can leave Q and R in this symbolic form and keep the components U', D', L', P ready to use.

EXAMPLE

Orthonormalization of the columns of $A = \begin{bmatrix} 1 & 1 \\ 2 & 5 \\ 1 & 1 \end{bmatrix}$ leads to

$$Q = \begin{bmatrix} 1/\sqrt{6} & -1/\sqrt{3} \\ 2/\sqrt{6} & 1/\sqrt{3} \\ 1/\sqrt{6} & -1/\sqrt{3} \end{bmatrix}$$

and

$$\begin{bmatrix} 1 & 1 \\ 2 & 5 \\ 1 & 1 \end{bmatrix} = \begin{bmatrix} 1/\sqrt{6} & -1/\sqrt{3} \\ 2/\sqrt{6} & 1/\sqrt{3} \\ 1/\sqrt{6} & -1/\sqrt{3} \end{bmatrix} \begin{bmatrix} \sqrt{6} & 2\sqrt{6} \\ 0 & \sqrt{3} \end{bmatrix}$$

(verify), the corresponding factorization $A = QR$. Here,

$$R = \begin{bmatrix} \sqrt{6} & 2\sqrt{6} \\ 0 & \sqrt{3} \end{bmatrix}.$$

PROBLEMS

NUMERICAL PROBLEMS

1. Find an orthogonal basis for the span of the columns of

(a) $\begin{bmatrix} 1 & 2 \\ 1 & 1 \end{bmatrix}$ **(b)** $\begin{bmatrix} 0 & 0 \\ 2 & 5 \\ 1 & 4 \end{bmatrix}$ **(c)** $\begin{bmatrix} 2 & 2 \\ 2 & 3 \\ 1 & 2 \end{bmatrix}$

(d) $\begin{bmatrix} 1 & 2 & 3 \\ 2 & 3 & 4 \end{bmatrix}$ **(e)** $\begin{bmatrix} 1 & 2 & 1 \\ 1 & 1 & 3 \end{bmatrix}$ **(f)** $\begin{bmatrix} 1 & 1 & 2 \\ 0 & 2 & 3 \\ 0 & 3 & 4 \end{bmatrix}$

2. Find the corresponding orthonormal bases in Problem 1.

3. Find the factorizations $A = QR$ for the matrices A in Problem 1, parts (a) and (e).

4. Find an orthonormal basis for V where $\langle f, g \rangle = \int_{-1}^{1} f(x)g(x)\,dx$ when $V = \mathbb{R}(x^2 - x) + \mathbb{R}(x^2 + 1)$.

THEORETICAL PROBLEMS

5. In the Gram-Schmidt orthogonalization, show that $F\mathbf{u}_1 + \cdots + F\mathbf{u}_r = F\mathbf{v}_1 + \cdots + F\mathbf{v}_r = F\mathbf{w}_1 + \cdots + F\mathbf{w}_r$ for $1 \le r \le n$.

6.4 ISOMETRIES. ORTHOGONAL AND UNITARY TRANSFORMATIONS

Isometries

Linear transformations which preserve the inner product also preserve length, distance, orthogonality, and, when $F = \mathbb{R}$, angle. We now give these important transformations a name.

Definition. *Isometries and Orthogonal and Unitary Transformations.* An **isometry** from a Euclidean space V to a Euclidean space V' is an isomorphism R from V to V' such that $\langle R(\mathbf{v}), R(\mathbf{w})\rangle = \langle \mathbf{v}, \mathbf{w}\rangle$ for all $\mathbf{v}, \mathbf{w} \in V$. If there is an isometry from V to V', we say that V and V' are **isometric**. When $V = V'$, an isometry is called a **unitary** transformation if $F = \mathbb{C}$ and an **orthogonal** transformation if $F = \mathbb{R}$.

Note the following:

1. Products and inverses of isometries are isometries.
2. An isometry R from V to V' preserves length, distance, orthogonality, and, when $F = \mathbb{R}$, angle in the sense that
   a. $\|R(\mathbf{v})\| = \|\mathbf{v}\|$;
   b. $d(R(\mathbf{v}), R(\mathbf{w})) = d(\mathbf{v}, \mathbf{w})$;
   c. $\mathbf{v} \perp \mathbf{w}$ if and only if $R(\mathbf{v}) \perp R(\mathbf{w})$;
   d. The angle between $\mathbf{v}$ and $\mathbf{w}$ equals the angle between $R(\mathbf{v}), R(\mathbf{w})$ for all $\mathbf{v}, \mathbf{w} \in V$. (Prove!)
3. The concept of unitary transformation of V defined here coincides, when $V = F^n$, with the one defined in Section 6.1. The reason for this is that $T \in L(V, V)$ is an isometry if and only if it maps an orthonormal basis to an orthonormal basis (Theorem 6.6).

EXAMPLES

1. The orthogonal transformations from the Euclidean plane $\mathbb{R}^2$ to itself were shown, in Chapter 1, to be the rotations

$$T(\mathbf{x}) = \begin{bmatrix} \cos\alpha & -\sin\alpha \\ \sin\alpha & \cos\alpha \end{bmatrix}\mathbf{x}$$

and reflections

$$T(\mathbf{x}) = \begin{bmatrix} -\cos\alpha & -\sin\alpha \\ -\sin\alpha & \cos\alpha \end{bmatrix}\mathbf{x}.$$

2. $T(\mathbf{x}) = \dfrac{1}{2}\begin{bmatrix} 1+i & -1-i \\ 1-i & 1-i \end{bmatrix}\mathbf{x}$ is unitary. (Verify!)

3. For

$$T\left(r\begin{bmatrix} 2 \\ -1 \\ 2 \end{bmatrix} + s\begin{bmatrix} -1 \\ 2 \\ 2 \end{bmatrix}\right) = 3\begin{bmatrix} s \\ r \end{bmatrix},$$

T is an isometry from $F\begin{bmatrix} 2 \\ -1 \\ 2 \end{bmatrix} + F\begin{bmatrix} -1 \\ 2 \\ 2 \end{bmatrix}$ to F^2.

For vector spaces V and W and basis $\mathbf{v}_1, \ldots, \mathbf{v}_n$ for V, a linear transformation R from V to W is an isomorphism from V to W if and only if $R(\mathbf{v}_1), \ldots, R(\mathbf{v}_n)$ is a basis for W. To formulate the geometric counterpart of this, replace *basis* by *orthonormal basis* and *isomorphism* by *isometry* (see Figure 6.8).

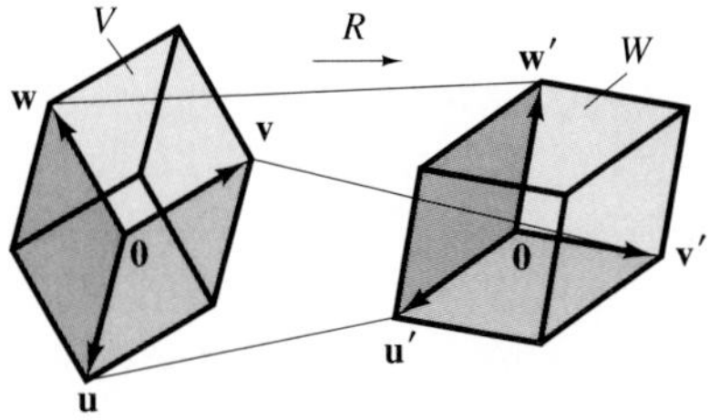

Figure 6.8 An isometry R from V to W, where $\mathbf{u}, \mathbf{v}, \mathbf{w}$ is an orthonormal basis of V.

Theorem 6.6. *Criteria for an Isometry.*
Let V and W be Euclidean spaces and let $\mathbf{v}_1, \ldots, \mathbf{v}_n$ be an orthonormal basis for V. Then a linear transformation R from V to W is an isometry if and only if $R(\mathbf{v}_1), \ldots, R(\mathbf{v}_n)$ is an orthonormal basis for W.

Proof. If R is an isometry, the basis $R(\mathbf{v}_r)$ is orthonormal, since $\langle R(\mathbf{v}_r), R(\mathbf{v}_s)\rangle = \langle \mathbf{v}_r, \mathbf{v}_s\rangle$ is 1 if $r = s$ and 0 otherwise. For the other direction, suppose that $\mathbf{w}_1 = R(\mathbf{v}_1), \ldots, \mathbf{w}_n = R(\mathbf{v}_n)$ is an orthonormal basis for V. Then compute $\langle \mathbf{v}, \mathbf{v}'\rangle$ and $\langle R(\mathbf{v}), R(\mathbf{v}')\rangle$ for $\mathbf{v} = a_1\mathbf{v}_1 + \cdots + a_n\mathbf{v}_n$, and $\mathbf{v}' = a_1'\mathbf{v}_1 + \cdots + a_n'\mathbf{v}_n$ and check that they are equal:

$$\begin{aligned}
\langle \mathbf{v}, \mathbf{v}'\rangle &= \langle a_1\mathbf{v}_1 + \cdots + a_n\mathbf{v}_n, a_1'\mathbf{v}_1 + \cdots + a_n'\mathbf{v}_n\rangle \\
&= \langle a_1\mathbf{v}_1, a_1'\mathbf{v}_1\rangle + \cdots + \langle a_r\mathbf{v}_r, a_s'\mathbf{v}_s\rangle + \cdots + \langle a_n\mathbf{v}_n, a_n'\mathbf{v}_n\rangle \\
&= a_1\overline{a_1'}\langle \mathbf{v}_1, \mathbf{v}_1\rangle + \cdots + a_r\overline{a_s'}\langle \mathbf{v}_r, \mathbf{v}_s\rangle + \cdots + a_n\overline{a_n'}\langle \mathbf{v}_n, \mathbf{v}_n\rangle \\
&= a_1\overline{a_1'} + \cdots + a_n\overline{a_n'} \qquad \text{(Explain!)}
\end{aligned}$$

$$\begin{aligned}
\langle R(\mathbf{v}), R(\mathbf{v}')\rangle &= \langle a_1\mathbf{w}_1 + \cdots + a_n\mathbf{w}_n, a_1'\mathbf{w}_1 + \cdots + a_n'\mathbf{w}_n\rangle \\
&= a_1\overline{a_1'} + \cdots + a_n\overline{a_n'}. \qquad \blacksquare
\end{aligned}$$

The fundamental theorem of Euclidean space

All theorems on the geometry of Euclidean n-space F^n transfer to corresponding theorems for any n-dimensional Euclidean space over F, and conversely. The transfer is by an isometry, whose existence is assured by the following theorem.

Theorem 6.7. *The Fundamental Theorem of Euclidean Spaces.*
Any n-dimensional Euclidean space V over F is isometric to F^n.

Proof. By orthonormalization, we can find an orthonormal basis $\mathbf{v}_1, \ldots, \mathbf{v}_n$ for V, and an orthonormal basis $\mathbf{e}_1, \ldots, \mathbf{e}_n$ for F^n. So, by the preceding theorem, $R(a_1\mathbf{v}_1 + \cdots + a_n\mathbf{v}_n) = a_1\mathbf{e}_1 + \cdots + a_n\mathbf{e}_n$ is an isometry from V to F^n. ■

EXAMPLE

Let

$$V = F\begin{bmatrix} 2 \\ -1 \\ 2 \end{bmatrix} + F\begin{bmatrix} 1 \\ -1 \\ 4 \end{bmatrix}.$$

To find an isometry from V to F^2, we employ the Gram-Schmidt orthonormalization process, which gives the orthonormal basis

$$\frac{1}{3}\begin{bmatrix} 2 \\ -1 \\ 2 \end{bmatrix}, \quad \frac{1}{3}\begin{bmatrix} -1 \\ 2 \\ 2 \end{bmatrix}$$

for V. (Verify!) The linear transformation mapping it to the basis $\mathbf{e}_1, \mathbf{e}_2$ for F^2 is the desired isometry T, so

$$T\left[r\frac{1}{3}\begin{bmatrix} 2 \\ -1 \\ 2 \end{bmatrix} + s\frac{1}{3}\begin{bmatrix} -1 \\ 2 \\ 2 \end{bmatrix}\right] = \begin{bmatrix} s \\ r \end{bmatrix}.$$

(Verify!)

Orthogonal and unitary transformations

Let $\mathbf{v}_1, \ldots, \mathbf{v}_n$ be an orthonormal basis for a Euclidean space V and suppose that $T \in L(V, V)$. Let $R(a_1\mathbf{v}_1 + \cdots + a_n\mathbf{v}_n) = a_1\mathbf{e}_1 + \cdots + a_n\mathbf{e}_n$ be the corresponding isomorphism from V to $\mathbb{R}^n$. Then R is an isometry, by Theorem 6.6. Since products and inverses of isometries are isometries (prove), T is an isometry if and only if RTR^{-1} is an isometry from F^n to F^n. In other words, $T \in L(V, V)$ is unitary if and only if $RTR^{-1} \in L(F^n, F^n)$ is unitary. Since RTR^{-1} is unitary if and only if its matrix $A = m(RTR^{-1})$ is unitary and since A is the matrix $m_R(T)$ of T with respect to the basis $\mathbf{v}_1, \ldots, \mathbf{v}_n$, T is unitary if and only if its matrix $A = m_R(T)$ is unitary. This, in turn, happens if and only if the columns of A form an orthonormal basis for F^n. But that means that $A^*A = I$ and A is invertible with inverse A^*, which proves the following theorem.

Theorem 6.8. *Criteria for a Unitary Transformation.*
Let $\mathbf{v}_1, \ldots, \mathbf{v}_n$ be an orthonormal basis for a Euclidean space V and suppose that $T \in L(V, V)$. Letting the matrix of T with respect to the basis $\mathbf{v}_s$ be A, the following conditions are equivalent:

1. T is unitary (orthogonal if $F = \mathbb{R}$).
2. A is unitary (orthogonal if $F = \mathbb{R}$).
3. A is invertible with inverse A^* (A^T if $F = \mathbb{R}$).

EXAMPLE

Since $A = \frac{1}{\sqrt{2}}\begin{bmatrix} 1 & -1 \\ 1 & 1 \end{bmatrix}$ is unitary, the linear transformation T of a Euclidean space with orthonormal basis $\mathbf{v}, \mathbf{w}$ such that

$$T(\mathbf{v}) = \frac{1}{\sqrt{2}}\mathbf{v} + \frac{1}{\sqrt{2}}\mathbf{w}, \qquad T(\mathbf{w}) = -\frac{1}{\sqrt{2}}\mathbf{v} + \frac{1}{\sqrt{2}}\mathbf{w}$$

is unitary. If $F = \mathbb{R}$, T is orthogonal.

Orthogonal and unitary change of basis

We showed in Section 4.7 that if T is a linear transformation of a vector space V with basis $\mathbf{v}_1, \ldots, \mathbf{v}_n$ and S is an invertible linear transformation of V, then $A^{-1}CA$ is the matrix of T with respect to the basis $S(\mathbf{v}_1), \ldots, S(\mathbf{v}_n)$, where C and A are the matrices of T and S with respect to $\mathbf{v}_1, \ldots, \mathbf{v}_n$. In the version for Euclidean spaces V, the basis $\mathbf{v}_r$ is orthonormal and S is unitary. So, the matrix A of S is unitary with inverse $A^{-1} = A^*$. This proves the following theorem.

Theorem 6.9. *Change of Matrix of T under a Unitary Change of Basis.*
Let T be a linear transformation of a Euclidean space V with orthonormal basis $\mathbf{v}_1, \ldots, \mathbf{v}_n$ and suppose that S is a unitary transformation of V. Letting C and A be the matrices of T and S with respect to $\mathbf{v}_1, \ldots, \mathbf{v}_n$, A is unitary and A^*CA is the matrix of T with respect to the basis $S(\mathbf{v}_1), \ldots, S(\mathbf{v}_n)$.

The geometric counterpart of the relation of similarity is the following.

Definition. *Unitary and Orthogonal Similarity.*
Two $n \times n$ matrices C and D are **unitarily similar** if $D = A^*CA$ for some unitary matrix A. Similarly, two $n \times n$ matrices C and D are **orthogonally similar** if $D = A^TCA$ for some real orthogonal matrix A.

In these terms, we have the next corollary.

Corollary. Given two orthonormal bases for a Euclidean space V, the matrices of $T \in L(V, V)$ with respect to the two bases are unitarily similar (orthogonally similar if $F = \mathbb{R}$).

PROBLEMS

NUMERICAL PROBLEMS

1. Show that the following transformations are unitary.

(a) $T(\mathbf{x}) = \frac{1}{2}\begin{bmatrix} 1+i & -1-i \\ 1-i & 1-i \end{bmatrix}\mathbf{x}$

(b) $T(\mathbf{x}) = c\begin{bmatrix} 1 & 2 \\ -2 & 1 \end{bmatrix}\mathbf{x}$ if $c^2 = 5$

2. Find a diagonal matrix D such that $T(\mathbf{x}) = \begin{bmatrix} 3 & -12 \\ 4 & 9 \end{bmatrix} D\mathbf{x}$ is unitary.

3. Show that

$$T\left(r\begin{bmatrix} 2 \\ -1 \\ 2 \end{bmatrix} + s\begin{bmatrix} -1 \\ 2 \\ 2 \end{bmatrix}\right) = 3\begin{bmatrix} s \\ r \end{bmatrix}$$

is an isometry from

$$V = \mathbb{R}\begin{bmatrix} 2 \\ -1 \\ 2 \end{bmatrix} + \mathbb{R}\begin{bmatrix} -1 \\ 2 \\ 2 \end{bmatrix}$$

to $\mathbb{R}^2$. Then verify directly that if α is the angle between $\mathbf{v}$ and $\mathbf{w}$ in V, then α is the angle between $T(\mathbf{v})$ and $T(\mathbf{w})$ in $\mathbb{R}^2$.

4. Show that the matrices $\begin{bmatrix} 1 & 3 \\ 0 & 2 \end{bmatrix}$ and $\begin{bmatrix} 2 & 0 \\ 0 & 1 \end{bmatrix}$ are similar but that they are not unitarily similar.

5. If $\begin{bmatrix} 1 & 3 \\ 0 & 2 \end{bmatrix}$ is similar to A and to cA, show that $c^2 = 1$.

6. For $A = \begin{bmatrix} 1 & 3 \\ 0 & -1 \end{bmatrix}$, show that A and $-A$ are similar.

7. For $A = \begin{bmatrix} 1 & 3 \\ 0 & 2 \end{bmatrix}$, show that A and $-A$ are not similar.

8. Show that the matrices $\begin{bmatrix} 1 & 3 \\ 3 & 2 \end{bmatrix}$ and $\begin{bmatrix} 2 & 3 \\ 3 & 1 \end{bmatrix}$ are orthogonally similar.

9. Show that the matrices $\begin{bmatrix} 1 & 3 \\ 3 & 2 \end{bmatrix}$ and $\begin{bmatrix} 2 & 3 \\ 4 & 1 \end{bmatrix}$ are not orthogonally similar.

THEORETICAL PROBLEMS

10. Show that any two symmetric 2×2 matrices having the same trace (sum of diagonal elements) and determinant are orthogonally similar.

11. Show that any isometry T preserves length, distance, orthogonality, and, when $F = \mathbb{R}$, angle.

12. Show that inverses and products of isometries are isometries.

13. Show that if a linear transformation T from a Euclidean space V over $\mathbb{R}$ to itself preserves distance, then it is orthogonal. (***Hint:*** Express $\langle \mathbf{v}, \mathbf{w} \rangle$ in terms of $\langle \mathbf{v}, \mathbf{v} \rangle$, $\langle \mathbf{w}, \mathbf{w} \rangle$, $\langle \mathbf{v} + \mathbf{w}, \mathbf{v} + \mathbf{w} \rangle$.)

14. Show that the reflexive, symmetric, and transitive properties given for the relation "C is similar to D" also hold for the relations "C is unitarily similar to D" and to "C is orthogonally similar to D."

15. Show that any real matrix orthogonally similar to a diagonal matrix is symmetric.

16. Show that any real or complex matrix unitarily similar to a diagonal matrix is Hermitian.

Hard

17. Show that if a linear transformation T from a Euclidean space V over $\mathbb{C}$ to itself preserves distance, then it is unitary. (***Hint:*** Express $\langle \mathbf{v}, \mathbf{w} \rangle$ and $\langle \mathbf{w}, \mathbf{v} \rangle$ in terms of $\langle \mathbf{v}, \mathbf{v} \rangle$, $\langle \mathbf{w}, \mathbf{w} \rangle$, $\langle \mathbf{v} + \mathbf{w}, \mathbf{v} + \mathbf{w} \rangle$.)

6.5 RIGID MOTIONS OF $\mathbb{R}^n$

The rigid motions f of the plane $\mathbb{R}^2$ are of the form $f(\mathbf{v}) = T_{f(\mathbf{0})}g(\mathbf{v})$, where $g(\mathbf{v})$ is an orthogonal linear transformation and $T_{f(\mathbf{0})}$ is translation by $f(\mathbf{0})$ (Section 1.7). The purpose of this section is to determine the rigid motions of $\mathbb{R}^n$ for all n.

Throughout the section, V denotes real Euclidean n-space $\mathbb{R}^n$ and the inner product notation $\langle \mathbf{v}, \mathbf{w} \rangle$ represents the dot product $\mathbf{w}^T\mathbf{v}$.

A **rigid motion** of V is a mapping f from V to V which preserves distance; that is, $d(f(\mathbf{v}), f(\mathbf{w})) = d(\mathbf{v}, \mathbf{w})$ for all $\mathbf{v}, \mathbf{w} \in V$. Note the following:

1. Any orthogonal linear transformation of V is a rigid motion of V.
2. Any translation $T_{\mathbf{u}}(\mathbf{v}) = \mathbf{u} + \mathbf{v}$ is a rigid motion of V, since $d(T_{\mathbf{u}}(\mathbf{v}), T_{\mathbf{u}}(\mathbf{w})) = d(\mathbf{u} + \mathbf{v}, \mathbf{u} + \mathbf{w}) = \|\mathbf{u} + \mathbf{w} - \mathbf{u} - \mathbf{v}\| = \|\mathbf{w} - \mathbf{v}\| = d(\mathbf{v}, \mathbf{w})$.
3. Products (composites) of rigid motions of V are rigid motions of V.
4. If f is a rigid motion of V, then $g(\mathbf{v}) = T_{-f(\mathbf{0})}f(\mathbf{v}) = f(\mathbf{v}) - f(\mathbf{0})$ is a rigid motion of V which fixes $\mathbf{0}$ (maps $\mathbf{0}$ to $\mathbf{0}$).

5. If g is a rigid motion of V which fixes $\mathbf{0}$, then it preserves length, since the lengths of $\mathbf{v}$ and $g(\mathbf{v})$ are their distances from $\mathbf{0}$.
6. A rigid motion g of V which fixes $\mathbf{0}$ preserves the inner product $\langle \mathbf{v}, \mathbf{w} \rangle$, since

$$\langle \mathbf{v}, \mathbf{w} \rangle = \frac{\langle \mathbf{v}, \mathbf{v} \rangle + \langle \mathbf{w}, \mathbf{w} \rangle - \langle \mathbf{v} - \mathbf{w}, \mathbf{v} - \mathbf{w} \rangle}{2}$$

$$= \frac{\|\mathbf{v}\|^2 + \|\mathbf{w}\|^2 - d(\mathbf{v}, \mathbf{w})^2}{2}$$

$$= \frac{\|g(\mathbf{v})\|^2 + \|g(\mathbf{w})\|^2 - d(g(\mathbf{v}), g(\mathbf{w}))^2}{2} = \langle g(\mathbf{v}), g(\mathbf{w}) \rangle.$$

So, g must also preserve angle. Therefore, if $\mathbf{v} \perp \mathbf{w}$, then $g(\mathbf{v}) \perp g(\mathbf{w})$.
7. If g is a rigid motion of V which fixes $\mathbf{0}$, it maps any given orthonormal basis of V to an orthonormal basis of V, by (5) and (6).

We pause for a moment to get criteria for when a point $\mathbf{w}$ is on the *segment* $\{\mathbf{u} + t(\mathbf{v} - \mathbf{u}) \mid 0 \le t \le 1\}$ joining $\mathbf{u}$ and $\mathbf{v}$.

Theorem 6.10. *Distance Criteria for Points on a Line Segment.* Let $\mathbf{u}, \mathbf{v}, \mathbf{w} \in V$ and suppose that $d(\mathbf{u}, \mathbf{w}) + d(\mathbf{w}, \mathbf{v}) = d(\mathbf{u}, \mathbf{v})$. Then $\mathbf{w} = \mathbf{u} + t(\mathbf{v} - \mathbf{u})$ for some t, $0 \le t \le 1$.

Proof. Suppose first that $\mathbf{u} = \mathbf{0}$ and $\|\mathbf{w}\| + \|\mathbf{v} - \mathbf{w}\| = \|\mathbf{v}\|$. We then claim that $\mathbf{w} = t\mathbf{v}$ for some t, $0 \le t \le 1$. If $t \in \mathbb{R}$, then $\|t\mathbf{v}\| + \|\mathbf{v} - t\mathbf{v}\| = |t|\|\mathbf{v}\| + |1 - t|\|\mathbf{v}\|$, which equals $\|\mathbf{v}\|$ if $0 \le t \le 1$ and *exceeds* $\|\mathbf{v}\|$ otherwise. So, if $\mathbf{w} = t\mathbf{v}$, $0 \le t \le 1$ as asserted. Otherwise, $\mathbf{w}$ is not in $\mathbb{R}\mathbf{v}$. Resolving $\mathbf{w}$ as the sum $\mathbf{w} = \mathbf{w}_{\mathbf{v}} + \mathbf{w}_{\mathbf{v}^\perp}$ of its projections on $\mathbf{v}$ and $\mathbf{v}^\perp$, $\mathbf{w}_{\mathbf{v}^\perp}$ is nonzero, so $\|\mathbf{w}\| > \|\mathbf{w}_{\mathbf{v}}\|$. Since $\mathbf{v} - \mathbf{w} = (\mathbf{v} - \mathbf{w}_{\mathbf{v}}) - \mathbf{w}_{\mathbf{v}^\perp}$ with $(\mathbf{v} - \mathbf{w}_{\mathbf{v}})$ and $\mathbf{w}_{\mathbf{v}^\perp}$ orthogonal, $\|\mathbf{v} - \mathbf{w}\| > \|\mathbf{v} - \mathbf{w}_{\mathbf{v}}\|$ as well. (Explain!) But then $\|\mathbf{w}\| + \|\mathbf{v} - \mathbf{w}\| > \|\mathbf{w}_{\mathbf{v}}\| + \|\mathbf{v} - \mathbf{w}_{\mathbf{v}}\| = \|t\mathbf{v}\| + \|\mathbf{v} - t\mathbf{v}\| \ge \|\mathbf{v}\|$, so that $\|\mathbf{w}\| + \|\mathbf{v} - \mathbf{w}\| > \|\mathbf{v}\|$. Since this is contrary to our supposition, $\mathbf{w}$ must be in $\mathbb{R}\mathbf{v}$ because $\mathbf{w} = t\mathbf{v}$ with $0 \le t \le 1$.

Suppose next that $d(\mathbf{u}, \mathbf{w}) + d(\mathbf{w}, \mathbf{v}) = d(\mathbf{u}, \mathbf{v})$, and let $\mathbf{v}' = \mathbf{v} - \mathbf{u}$, $\mathbf{w}' = \mathbf{w} - \mathbf{u}$. Then $\|\mathbf{w}'\| + \|\mathbf{v}' - \mathbf{w}'\| = \|\mathbf{v}'\|$. (Explain!) This implies that $\mathbf{w}' = t\mathbf{v}'$; that is, $\mathbf{w} - \mathbf{u} = t(\mathbf{v} - \mathbf{u})$ and $\mathbf{w} = \mathbf{u} + t(\mathbf{v} - \mathbf{u})$ for some t, $0 \le t \le 1$. ■

This theorem says that $d(\mathbf{u}, \mathbf{w}) + d(\mathbf{w}, \mathbf{v}) = d(\mathbf{u}, \mathbf{v})$ if and only if $\mathbf{w} = \mathbf{p}_{\mathbf{w}}$, where $\mathbf{p}_{\mathbf{w}} = \mathbf{u} + \dfrac{\langle \mathbf{w} - \mathbf{u}, \mathbf{v} - \mathbf{u} \rangle}{\langle \mathbf{v} - \mathbf{u}, \mathbf{v} - \mathbf{u} \rangle}(\mathbf{v} - \mathbf{u})$.

Corollary. Let g be a rigid motion of V which fixes $\mathbf{0}$ and the points $\mathbf{u}$ and $\mathbf{v}$. Then it fixes all points on the segment $\{\mathbf{u} + t(\mathbf{v} - \mathbf{u}) \mid 0 \le t \le 1\}$ joining $\mathbf{u}$ and $\mathbf{v}$.

Proof. The proof is the same as in the proof for $n = 2$ of the Corollary to Theorem 1.28. ■

We can now describe the rigid motions of V.

Theorem 6.11. *Rigid Motions, Translations, and Orthogonal Linear Transformations.*
Any rigid motion f of V is $f(v) = T_{f(\mathbf{0})}g(\mathbf{v})$ for some orthogonal linear transformation $g(\mathbf{v})$ of V.

Proof. Letting $g(\mathbf{v}) = T_{-f(\mathbf{0})}f(\mathbf{v})$, g is a rigid motion fixing $\mathbf{0}$. We claim that g is an orthogonal linear transformation of V. Since $g(\mathbf{e}_1), \ldots, g(\mathbf{e}_n)$ is an orthonormal basis for V, the matrix $A = (g(\mathbf{e}_1), \ldots, g(\mathbf{e}_n))$ is an orthogonal matrix and $R(\mathbf{v}) = A\mathbf{v}$ is an orthogonal linear transformation. Letting $h(\mathbf{v}) = R^{-1}g(\mathbf{v})$, h is a rigid motion, by (1) and (3). Moreover, $h(\mathbf{e}_r) = \mathbf{e}_r$ for $1 \le r \le n$.

We claim that $h = I$, that is, $h(\mathbf{v}) = \mathbf{v}$ for all $\mathbf{v} \in V$. Since h preserves angles, whenever $h(\mathbf{v}) = \mathbf{v}$ and $a > 1$, $h(a\mathbf{v})$ is a positive multiple $b\mathbf{v}$ of $\mathbf{v}$. After all, the angle between $\mathbf{v}$ and $a\mathbf{v}$ is 0, so 0 is the angle between $h(\mathbf{v})$ and $h(a\mathbf{v})$, by (6). Since $a\mathbf{v}$ and $h(a\mathbf{v}) = b\mathbf{v}$ have the same length and $a, b > 0$, it follows that $a\mathbf{v} = b\mathbf{v}$; that is, $h(a\mathbf{v}) = a\mathbf{v}$. A similar argument works when $a < 0$, so $h(a\mathbf{v}) = a\mathbf{v}$ for all a and all $\mathbf{v}$ fixed by h.

Since $h(\mathbf{e}_r) = \mathbf{e}_r$ for all r, it follows that $h(a\mathbf{e}_r) = a\mathbf{e}_r$ for all r. So, h fixes all points on all coordinate axes. Using this, we now show by induction on m that h fixes every vector in $F\mathbf{e}_1 + \cdots + F\mathbf{e}_m$ for all $m \le n$. We already know this for $m = 1$. Suppose that $m > 1$ and that we have shown this for $m - 1$. Write $\mathbf{w} = a_1\mathbf{e}_1 + \cdots + a_m\mathbf{e}_m$ as $\mathbf{w} = \frac{1}{2}\mathbf{u} + \frac{1}{2}\mathbf{v}$ where $\frac{1}{2}\mathbf{u} = a_1\mathbf{e}_1 + \cdots + a_{m-1}\mathbf{e}_{m-1}$ and $\frac{1}{2}\mathbf{v} = a_m\mathbf{e}_m$. Then h fixes $\mathbf{u}$ and $\mathbf{v}$ by our induction hypothesis. So, it fixes $\mathbf{w} = \frac{1}{2}\mathbf{u} + \frac{1}{2}\mathbf{v} = \mathbf{u} + \frac{1}{2}(\mathbf{v} - \mathbf{u})$ by the Corollary to Theorem 6.10. Since it is true for $m = 1$ and for m whenever it is true for $m - 1$, it is true for all $m \le n$.

Taking $m = n$, h fixes every element of $\mathbb{R}^n$ and $h = I$. But then $R^{-1}g = h = I$, and g is the orthogonal transformation R. ■

PROBLEMS

NUMERICAL PROBLEMS

1. A box (solid, bounded by orthogonal planes) in $\mathbb{R}^3$ having corner

$$\begin{bmatrix} 7 \\ 7 \\ 7 \end{bmatrix}$$

and three adjacent corners

$$\begin{bmatrix} 9 \\ 6 \\ 9 \end{bmatrix}, \quad \begin{bmatrix} 6 \\ 9 \\ 9 \end{bmatrix}, \quad \begin{bmatrix} 5 \\ 5 \\ 8 \end{bmatrix}$$

must be placed by a rigid motion $f(\mathbf{v})$ so that one point is at the origin and the other three are on the coordinate axes. Describe an $f(\mathbf{v})$ as $T_{f(\mathbf{0})}g(\mathbf{v})$ and give the point $f(\mathbf{0})$ and the matrix $m(g)$ of $g(\mathbf{v})$.

Hard

2. Problem 1 can be solved in six ways. Find the other five rigid motions $f(\mathbf{v})$.

3. Let $A = \begin{bmatrix} \cos\alpha & -\sin\alpha \\ \sin\alpha & \cos\alpha \end{bmatrix}$ and $B = \begin{bmatrix} -\cos\beta & -\sin\beta \\ -\sin\beta & \cos\beta \end{bmatrix}$ (rotation by α and reflection of Theorem 1.30). If $AB = BA$, show that $A = \pm I$. (***Hint:*** If $AB = BA$ and $B\mathbf{v} = \mathbf{v}$, show that $A\mathbf{v} = \mathbf{v}$.)

THEORETICAL PROBLEMS

4. Suppose that S is translation by $\mathbf{v}$ and T is rotation by α.

(a) If $ST = TS$ and $\mathbf{v}$ is nonzero, what can be said about α?

(b) If $ST = TS$ and $\alpha \neq 0, \pi$, what can be said about $\mathbf{v}$?

5. $\left(\mathbf{b} - \dfrac{\langle \mathbf{a}, \mathbf{b} \rangle}{\langle \mathbf{b}, \mathbf{b} \rangle}\mathbf{b}\right) \perp \left(\mathbf{a} - \dfrac{\langle \mathbf{a}, \mathbf{b} \rangle}{\langle \mathbf{b}, \mathbf{b} \rangle}\mathbf{b}\right)$ for any nonzero real $\mathbf{a}, \mathbf{b}$.

6. For $\mathbf{u}, \mathbf{v}, \mathbf{w} \in V$, let $\mathbf{p}_\mathbf{w} = \mathbf{u} + \dfrac{\langle \mathbf{w} - \mathbf{u}, \mathbf{v} - \mathbf{u} \rangle}{\langle \mathbf{v} - \mathbf{u}, \mathbf{v} - \mathbf{u} \rangle}(\mathbf{v} - \mathbf{u})$. Show that $\mathbf{u}, \mathbf{p}_\mathbf{w}, \mathbf{w}$ and $\mathbf{v}, \mathbf{p}_\mathbf{w}, \mathbf{w}$ are right triangles.

6.6 ORTHOGONAL COMPLEMENTS

The Fourier expansion

The condition of orthonormality is quite strong and has many interesting and important consequences. The following theorem, based on ideas from Fourier analysis, is a good illustration.

Theorem 6.12. *Orthogonality and Orthonormal Sets.*
Let $\mathbf{v}_1, \ldots, \mathbf{v}_n$ be an orthonormal set in an inner product space V. Then:

1. $\mathbf{v}_1, \ldots, \mathbf{v}_n$ are linearly independent.
2. For any $\mathbf{v} \in V$, $\mathbf{v} - \langle \mathbf{v}, \mathbf{v}_1 \rangle \mathbf{v}_1 - \cdots - \langle \mathbf{v}, \mathbf{v}_n \rangle \mathbf{v}_n$ is orthogonal to the vectors $\mathbf{v}_r$ for $1 \leq r \leq n$.
3. For any $\mathbf{v} \in V$, $\|\mathbf{v}\|^2 \geq |\langle \mathbf{v}, \mathbf{v}_1 \rangle|^2 + \cdots + |\langle \mathbf{v}, \mathbf{v}_n \rangle|^2$.

4. For any $\mathbf{v}$ in the span of $\mathbf{v}_1, \ldots, \mathbf{v}_n$, $\mathbf{v} = \langle \mathbf{v}, \mathbf{v}_1 \rangle \mathbf{v}_1 + \cdots + \langle \mathbf{v}, \mathbf{v}_n \rangle \mathbf{v}_n$ and $\|\mathbf{v}\|^2 = |\langle \mathbf{v}, \mathbf{v}_1 \rangle|^2 + \cdots + |\langle \mathbf{v}, \mathbf{v}_n \rangle|^2$.

Proof. By the formula $\langle a_1\mathbf{v}_1 + \cdots + a_n\mathbf{v}_n, \mathbf{v}_r \rangle = a_r$ for $1 \le r \le n$, $a_1\mathbf{v}_1 + \cdots + a_n\mathbf{v}_n$ can be $\mathbf{0}$ only if each a_r $(1 \le r \le n)$ is 0. This proves (1). By the same formula, we have

$$\langle \mathbf{v} - \langle \mathbf{v}, \mathbf{v}_1 \rangle \mathbf{v}_1 - \cdots - \langle \mathbf{v}, \mathbf{v}_n \rangle \mathbf{v}_n, \mathbf{v}_r \rangle = \langle \mathbf{v}, \mathbf{v}_r \rangle - \langle \mathbf{v}, \mathbf{v}_r \rangle = 0,$$

which proves (2). For any $\mathbf{v} \in V$, $\mathbf{v} = \mathbf{v}' + (\mathbf{v} - \mathbf{v}')$, where

$$\mathbf{v}' = \langle \mathbf{v}, \mathbf{v}_1 \rangle \mathbf{v}_1 + \cdots + \langle \mathbf{v}, \mathbf{v}_n \rangle \mathbf{v}_n.$$

Applying the Pythagorean theorem to $\mathbf{v} = \mathbf{v}' + (\mathbf{v} - \mathbf{v}')$, we have

$$\|\mathbf{v}\|^2 = |\mathbf{v}' + (\mathbf{v} - \mathbf{v}')|^2 = |\mathbf{v}'|^2 + |(\mathbf{v} - \mathbf{v}')|^2,$$

so

$$|\mathbf{v}| \ge |\mathbf{v}'|.$$

Applying the Pythagorean theorem repeatedly to

$$\mathbf{v}' = \langle \mathbf{v}, \mathbf{v}_1 \rangle \mathbf{v}_1 + \cdots + \langle \mathbf{v}, \mathbf{v}_n \rangle \mathbf{v}_n,$$

we find that

$$\|\mathbf{v}'\|^2 = |\langle \mathbf{v}, \mathbf{v}_1 \rangle|^2 + \cdots + |\langle \mathbf{v}, \mathbf{v}_n \rangle|^2.$$

(Explain!)

Together, we get

$$\|\mathbf{v}\|^2 \ge |\langle \mathbf{v}, \mathbf{v}_1 \rangle|^2 + \cdots + |\langle \mathbf{v}, \mathbf{v}_n \rangle|^2,$$

which proves (3). For $\mathbf{v}$ in the span of $\mathbf{v}_1, \ldots, \mathbf{v}_n$, the vector

$$\mathbf{v} - \langle \mathbf{v}, \mathbf{v}_1 \rangle \mathbf{v}_1 - \cdots - \langle \mathbf{v}, \mathbf{v}_n \rangle \mathbf{v}_n$$

is in the span of $\mathbf{v}_1, \ldots, \mathbf{v}_n$, and it is orthogonal to the $\mathbf{v}_1, \ldots, \mathbf{v}_n$ by (2). So, it is orthogonal to itself and must be $\mathbf{0}$. So, $\mathbf{v} = \mathbf{v}' = \langle \mathbf{v}, \mathbf{v}_1 \rangle \mathbf{v}_1 + \cdots + \langle \mathbf{v}, \mathbf{v}_n \rangle \mathbf{v}_n$. Then we also have $\|\mathbf{v}\|^2 = \|\mathbf{v}'\|^2 = |\langle \mathbf{v}, \mathbf{v}_1 \rangle|^2 + \cdots + |\langle \mathbf{v}, \mathbf{v}_n \rangle|^2$. This proves (4). ∎

Given a vector $\mathbf{v}$ in an inner product space with a set $\mathbf{v}_1, \ldots, \mathbf{v}_n$ of orthonormal vectors, we formalize these key results as follows:

Fourier Expansion of $\mathbf{v}$.

The $\langle \mathbf{v}, \mathbf{v}_r \rangle$ are the **Fourier coefficients** of $\mathbf{v}$. If $\mathbf{v}$ is in the span of the $\mathbf{v}_r$, then $\mathbf{v} = \langle \mathbf{v}, \mathbf{v}_1 \rangle \mathbf{v}_1 + \cdots + \langle \mathbf{v}, \mathbf{v}_n \rangle \mathbf{v}_n$ (Figure 6.9).

Pythagorean Theorem.

For $\mathbf{v}$ in the span of the $\mathbf{v}_r$, $|\mathbf{v}|^2 = |\langle \mathbf{v}, \mathbf{v}_1 \rangle|^2 + \cdots + |\langle \mathbf{v}, \mathbf{v}_n \rangle|^2$.

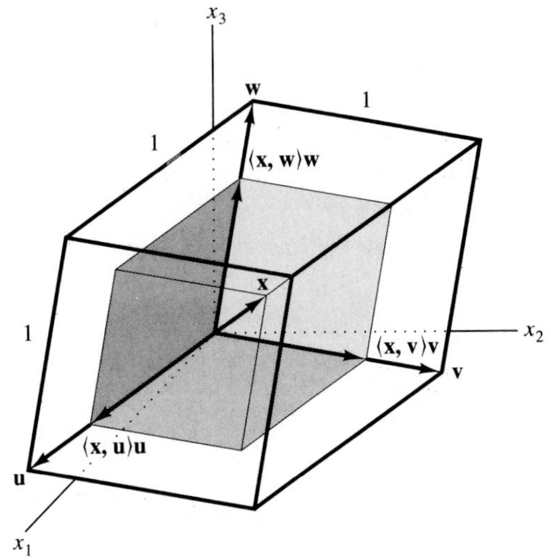

Figure 6.9 The Fourier expansion $\mathbf{x} = \langle \mathbf{x}, \mathbf{u}\rangle\mathbf{u} + \langle \mathbf{x}, \mathbf{v}\rangle\mathbf{v} + \langle \mathbf{x}, \mathbf{w}\rangle\mathbf{w}$ of $\mathbf{x}$.

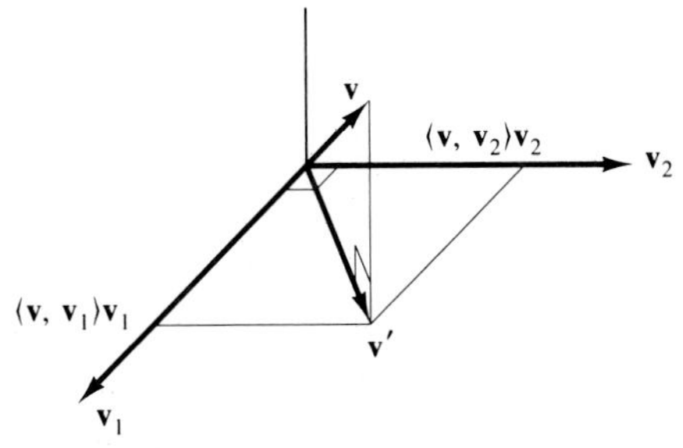

Figure 6.10 Bessel's inequality: $\|\mathbf{v}\|^2 \geq |\langle \mathbf{v}, \mathbf{v}_1\rangle|^2 + |\langle \mathbf{v}, \mathbf{v}_2\rangle|^2 = \|\mathbf{v}'\|^2$.

Bessel's Inequality.

$$\|\mathbf{v}\|^2 \geq |\langle \mathbf{v}, \mathbf{v}_1\rangle|^2 + \cdots + |\langle \mathbf{v}, \mathbf{v}_n\rangle|^2. \qquad \text{(See Figure 6.10.)}$$

EXAMPLES

1. We ask whether $\mathbf{u} = \begin{bmatrix} 1 \\ 1 \\ 1 \end{bmatrix}$ is in the span of

$$\mathbf{v} = \frac{1}{\sqrt{6}}\begin{bmatrix} 1 \\ 2 \\ 1 \end{bmatrix}, \qquad \mathbf{w} = \frac{1}{\sqrt{3}}\begin{bmatrix} -1 \\ 1 \\ -1 \end{bmatrix}.$$

If so, its Fourier expansion would be $\mathbf{u} = \langle \mathbf{u}, \mathbf{v} \rangle \mathbf{v} + \langle \mathbf{u}, \mathbf{w} \rangle \mathbf{w}$—that is,

$$\begin{bmatrix} 1 \\ 1 \\ 1 \end{bmatrix} = \frac{4}{\sqrt{6}} \frac{1}{\sqrt{6}} \begin{bmatrix} 1 \\ 2 \\ 1 \end{bmatrix} - \frac{1}{\sqrt{3}} \frac{1}{\sqrt{3}} \begin{bmatrix} -1 \\ 1 \\ -1 \end{bmatrix}.$$

Checking, we see that it is.

2. For (1), the Pythagorean theorem is $[\sqrt{3}]^2 = [4/\sqrt{6}]^2 + [1/\sqrt{3}]^2$.
3. For the orthonormal set $\mathbf{v}, \mathbf{w}$ in (1) and

$$\mathbf{x} = \begin{bmatrix} 0 \\ 1 \\ 2 \end{bmatrix},$$

Bessel's inequality for $\mathbf{x}$ is $4 \geq [4/\sqrt{6}]^2 + [-1/\sqrt{3}]^2$, since $[4/\sqrt{6}]$ and $[-1/\sqrt{3}]$ are the Fourier coefficients of $\mathbf{x}$. (Verify!)

4. If the columns of A are orthonormal and b is in the column space of A, then the element $\mathbf{x}$ whose coordinates are the Fourier coefficients of b is the unique solution to $A\mathbf{x} = b$. (Verify!)

Orthogonal complement. Orthogonal sums of subspaces

Suppose that $\mathbf{v}_1, \ldots, \mathbf{v}_n$ is an orthonormal basis for a subspace W of an inner product space V. For $\mathbf{v} \in V$, we let

$$\mathbf{v}' = \langle \mathbf{v}, \mathbf{v}_1 \rangle \mathbf{v}_1 + \cdots + \langle \mathbf{v}, \mathbf{v}_n \rangle \mathbf{v}_n.$$

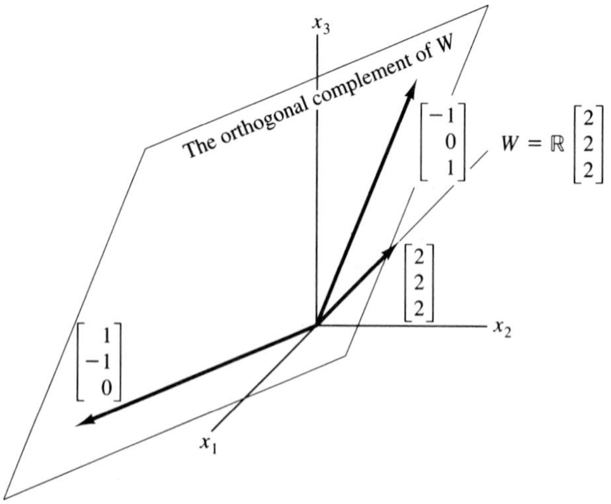

Figure 6.11 The orthogonal complement of W.

By Part (2) of Theorem 6.12, $\mathbf{v} - \mathbf{v}'$ is orthogonal to $\mathbf{v}_1, \ldots, \mathbf{v}_n$. It follows that $\mathbf{v} - \mathbf{v}'$ is in $W^\perp$, as in the next definition.

Definition. *The Orthogonal Complement of W in V.*
The **orthogonal complement** of W in V is the subspace $W^\perp = \{\mathbf{v} \in W \mid \langle \mathbf{v}, \mathbf{w} \rangle = 0$ for all $w \in W\}$ (Figure 6.11).

The orthogonal complement is easy to find. For column spaces, we can use the following rule.

Orthogonal Complement of $c(A)$.
For $V = F^m$ and an $m \times n$ matrix A, the orthogonal complement of the column space of A in V is the nullspace of A^*.

EXAMPLE

Let W be the column space of

$$A = \begin{bmatrix} 1 & 2 \\ 2 & 5 \\ 1 & 2 \end{bmatrix}.$$

The orthogonal complement of W in $\mathbb{R}^3$ is the nullspace of A^T, which is

$$F\begin{bmatrix} 1 \\ 0 \\ -1 \end{bmatrix}.$$

(Verify!)

Since $\mathbf{v} = \mathbf{v}' + (\mathbf{v} - \mathbf{v}')$ is in $W + W^\perp$ for any $\mathbf{v} \in V$, V is the sum $V = W + W^\perp$. So, since each element of W is orthogonal to each element of $W^\perp$, V is the orthogonal sum of W and $W^\perp$ in the sense of the following.

Definition. *The Orthogonal Sum of Subspaces.*
A sum $W = W_1 + \cdots + W_k$ of subspaces W_i of an inner product space V is an **orthogonal sum** if every element of W_i is orthogonal to every element of W_j for $1 \leq i, j \leq k$ and $i \neq j$. To indicate that a sum is an orthogonal sum, we write it as $W = W_1 \oplus \cdots \oplus W_k$.

We state this for future reference.

Theorem 6.13. *The Sum of a Subspace and Its Orthogonal Complement.* For any finite-dimensional subspace W of an inner product space V, $V = W \oplus W^\perp$.

In an orthogonal sum of two spaces $W \oplus W'$ (such as $W \oplus W^\perp$ or $W \oplus W'$, where $W = W_1$ and $W' = W_2 \oplus \cdots \oplus W_k$ from before), any $w \in W \cap W'$ is orthogonal to itself and, as such, must be $\mathbf{0}$. So, $W \cap W' = \{\mathbf{0}\}$. This gives us the following theorem.

Theorem 6.14. *The Intersection of a Subspace and Its Orthogonal Complement.* $W \cap W^\perp = \{\mathbf{0}\}$.

Corollary. $W^{\perp\perp} = W$.

Proof. Since $\langle \mathbf{w}, \mathbf{w}' \rangle = 0$ for all $\mathbf{w} \in W$, we have $W \subseteq W^{\perp\perp}$. For the reverse inclusion, let $\mathbf{v} \in W^{\perp\perp}$ and write it as $\mathbf{v} = \mathbf{w} + \mathbf{w}'$ where $\mathbf{w} \in W$ and $\mathbf{w}' \in W^\perp$. Then $\mathbf{v} - \mathbf{w} = \mathbf{w}'$ is in $W^\perp \cap W^{\perp\perp} = \{\mathbf{0}\}$, which implies that $\mathbf{v} = \mathbf{w} \in W$. Since this is true for all $\mathbf{v} \in W^{\perp\perp}$, $W^{\perp\perp} \subseteq W$. ∎

EXAMPLES

1. The orthogonal complement of

$$F\begin{bmatrix}1\\2\\1\end{bmatrix} + F\begin{bmatrix}2\\5\\2\end{bmatrix} \quad \text{is} \quad F\begin{bmatrix}1\\0\\-1\end{bmatrix}.$$

By the Corollary to Theorem 6.14, the orthogonal complement

$$F\begin{bmatrix}1\\0\\-1\end{bmatrix} \quad \text{is} \quad F\begin{bmatrix}1\\2\\1\end{bmatrix} + F\begin{bmatrix}2\\5\\2\end{bmatrix}.$$

2. Since $n(A^*) = c(A)^\perp$, $n(A^*)^\perp = c(A)^{\perp\perp} = c(A)$ and $F^m = n(A^*) + c(A)$. Similarly, $F^n = n(A) \oplus c(A^*)$.

The formula that rank plus nullity equals the number of columns of a matrix has the following counterpart in a Euclidean space.

Theorem 6.15. *Sum of the Dimensions of W and Its Orthogonal Complement.* Dim W + Dim $W^\perp$ = Dim V for any subspace W of a Euclidean space V.

Proof. Let $\mathbf{v}_1, \ldots, \mathbf{v}_n$ be an orthonormal basis for W. The linear transformation $P(\mathbf{v}) = \langle \mathbf{v}, \mathbf{v}_1 \rangle \mathbf{v}_1 \oplus \cdots \oplus \langle \mathbf{v}, \mathbf{v}_n \rangle \mathbf{v}_n$ has image W and kernel $W^\perp$, where $V = W \oplus W^\perp$ and $W \cap W^\perp = \{\mathbf{0}\}$. So, Theorem 4.15 says that Dim W + Dim $W^\perp$ = Dim V. ∎

EXAMPLES

1. When $V = \mathbb{R}^m$ and Q is an $m \times n$ matrix, the dimension formula just given above comes as no great surprise. The dimension of the column space W of Q is the rank of Q and the dimension of the nullspace $W^\perp$ of Q^T is the nullity of Q^T. But the rank of Q equals that of

Q^T. So, Dim W + Dim $W^\perp$ is just the rank + nullity for Q^T, which is m = Dim V.

2. If Q is a 5×3 matrix of rank 2, then the orthogonal complement of $c(Q)$ in $\mathbb{R}^5$ is of dimension $5 - 2 = 3$.

PROBLEMS

NUMERICAL PROBLEMS

1. For each of the following orthogonal bases, find the corresponding orthonormal basis and compute the Fourier expansion of

$$\begin{bmatrix}1\\1\\1\end{bmatrix}.$$

(a) $\begin{bmatrix}1\\1\\0\end{bmatrix}, \begin{bmatrix}0\\0\\1\end{bmatrix}, \begin{bmatrix}-1\\1\\0\end{bmatrix}$ **(b)** $\begin{bmatrix}1\\-2\\1\end{bmatrix}, \begin{bmatrix}-1\\0\\1\end{bmatrix}, \begin{bmatrix}2\\2\\2\end{bmatrix}$

(c) $\begin{bmatrix}1\\2\\4\end{bmatrix}, \begin{bmatrix}4\\2\\-2\end{bmatrix}, \begin{bmatrix}1\\2\\4\end{bmatrix} \times \begin{bmatrix}4\\2\\-2\end{bmatrix}$

2. Verify Bessel's inequality for

$$\mathbf{v} = \begin{bmatrix}2\\7\\2\end{bmatrix}$$

and the orthonormal set corresponding to the orthogonal vectors $\begin{bmatrix}1\\2\\4\end{bmatrix}, \begin{bmatrix}4\\2\\-2\end{bmatrix}$.

3. Find the orthogonal complement of $\begin{bmatrix}1\\2\\4\end{bmatrix}, \begin{bmatrix}4\\2\\-2\end{bmatrix}$ in F^3.

4. Find the orthogonal complement of $\begin{bmatrix}1\\2\\4\end{bmatrix}$ in $F\begin{bmatrix}1\\2\\4\end{bmatrix} + F\begin{bmatrix}-3\\2\\5\end{bmatrix}$.

5. Find the dimension of the orthogonal complement in $\mathbb{R}^4$ of

$$\begin{bmatrix}1 & 2 & 3\\4 & 5 & 6\\2 & 3 & 4\\5 & 6 & 7\end{bmatrix}.$$

6. Show that the coordinates of the solution y to

$$\begin{bmatrix} 1/\sqrt{6} & -1/\sqrt{3} \\ 2/\sqrt{6} & 1/\sqrt{3} \\ 1/\sqrt{6} & -1/\sqrt{3} \end{bmatrix} y = \begin{bmatrix} 2 \\ 7 \\ 2 \end{bmatrix}$$

are the Fourier coefficients of $\begin{bmatrix} 2 \\ 7 \\ 2 \end{bmatrix}$ in the basis

$$\begin{bmatrix} 1/\sqrt{6} \\ 2/\sqrt{6} \\ 1/\sqrt{6} \end{bmatrix}, \quad \begin{bmatrix} -1/\sqrt{3} \\ 1/\sqrt{3} \\ -1\sqrt{3} \end{bmatrix}.$$

THEORETICAL PROBLEMS

7. If $A^2 = A$, show that each characteristic root of A is 0 or 1.
8. If $A^2 = A$, show that $|A - xI| = x^{n-r}(x-1)^r$, where $r = \text{Rank } A$.
9. In an orthogonal sum $V = W_1 \oplus \cdots \oplus W_k$ of subspaces, show that $W_1^{\perp}$ is the orthogonal sum $W_2 \oplus \cdots \oplus W_k$.
10. If the columns of A are orthonormal and $\mathbf{b}$ is in the column space of A, show that the element $\mathbf{x}$ whose coordinates are the Fourier coefficients of $\mathbf{b}$ is a solution to $A\mathbf{x} = \mathbf{b}$.
11. Prove the *generalized Fourier expansion*

$$\mathbf{v} = \frac{\langle \mathbf{v}, \mathbf{w}_1 \rangle}{\langle \mathbf{w}_1, \mathbf{w}_1 \rangle} \mathbf{w}_1 + \cdots + \frac{\langle \mathbf{v}, \mathbf{w}_n \rangle}{\langle \mathbf{w}_{n-1}, \mathbf{w}_n \rangle} \mathbf{w}_n,$$

for any orthogonal basis $\mathbf{w}_1, \ldots, \mathbf{w}_n$.

12. Prove that $\mathbf{v} = \mathbf{v}_{\mathbf{w}_1} + \cdots + \mathbf{v}_{\mathbf{w}_n}$ for any orthogonal basis $\mathbf{w}_1, \ldots, \mathbf{w}_n$.

6.7 ORTHOGONAL PROJECTIONS

The orthogonal projection of a vector on a subspace

In an orthogonal sum V of subspaces, each element can be written as a sum in only one way, as we now show.

Theorem 6.16. *Unique Representation by Coordinates in an Orthogonal Sum.* Let V be an inner product space which is the orthogonal sum

$$V = W_1 \oplus \cdots \oplus W_k$$

of subspaces W_i. Let $\mathbf{x}_1 + \cdots + \mathbf{x}_k = \mathbf{y}_1 + \cdots + \mathbf{y}_k$, where $\mathbf{x}_i, \mathbf{y}_i \in W_i$ for all i. Then $\mathbf{x}_1 = \mathbf{y}_1, \ldots, \mathbf{x}_k = \mathbf{y}_k$.

Proof. $\mathbf{x}_1 - \mathbf{y}_1 = \mathbf{z}$, where $\mathbf{z}$ is in $W_2 + \cdots + W_k$. (Explain!) Taking the inner product with $\mathbf{x}_1 - \mathbf{y}_1$, we get $\langle \mathbf{x}_1 - \mathbf{y}_1, \mathbf{x}_1 - \mathbf{y}_1 \rangle = \langle \mathbf{x}_1 - \mathbf{y}_1, \mathbf{z} \rangle = 0$. But then $\mathbf{x}_1 - \mathbf{y}_1 = 0$ and $\mathbf{x}_1 = \mathbf{y}_1$. Similarly, $\mathbf{x}_i = \mathbf{y}_i$ for the other i's. ∎

EXAMPLE

When W is the column space of

$$A = \begin{bmatrix} 1 & 2 & 2 \\ 2 & 4 & 5 \\ 1 & 2 & 2 \end{bmatrix}$$

and $W^{\perp} = F\begin{bmatrix} 1 \\ 0 \\ -1 \end{bmatrix}$, the vector $\begin{bmatrix} 2 \\ 7 \\ 4 \end{bmatrix}$ equals

$$\begin{bmatrix} 1a+2b \\ 2a+5b \\ 1a+2b \end{bmatrix} + \begin{bmatrix} 1c \\ 0c \\ -1c \end{bmatrix}$$

only if $a = b = 1$, $c = -1$. (Verify!)

When $\mathbf{x} = \mathbf{x}_1 + \cdots + \mathbf{x}_k$ in an orthogonal sum $W = W_1 \oplus \cdots \oplus W_k$ of subspaces W_i, the $\mathbf{x}_j$ is called the *orthogonal projection* of $\mathbf{x}$ on W_j. Since the orthogonal complement $W_j^{\perp}$ of W_j in W is the sum of the W_i with $i \neq j$ (explain), this is consistent with the general concept of orthogonal projection which we now define.

Definition. *Orthogonal Projection of* $\mathbf{v}$ *on* W.
Let V be an inner product space, W a finite-dimensional subspace of V. For $\mathbf{v} \in V$, write $\mathbf{v}$ as $\mathbf{v} = \mathbf{v}_W + \mathbf{v}_{W^{\perp}}$, where $\mathbf{v}_W \in W$ and $\mathbf{v}_{W^{\perp}} \in W^{\perp}$. Then $\mathbf{v}_W$ is called the **orthogonal projection** of $\mathbf{v}$ on W.

Since $\|\mathbf{v} - \mathbf{w}\|^2 = \|\mathbf{v}_W - \mathbf{w}\|^2 + \|\mathbf{v}_{W^{\perp}}\|^2$ for $\mathbf{w} \in W$ (explain), $d(\mathbf{v}, \mathbf{w}) = \|\mathbf{v} - \mathbf{w}\|$ is minimal for $\mathbf{w} \in W$ if and only if $\mathbf{v}_W = \mathbf{w}$. This proves the following theorem (Figure 6.12).

Theorem 6.17. *The Element of a Subspace Closest to a Given Element of* V.
The orthogonal projection $\mathbf{v}_W$ of $\mathbf{v}$ on W is the element of W closest to $\mathbf{v}$.

Given a vector $\mathbf{v}$ in an inner product space V with a set $\mathbf{v}_1, \ldots, \mathbf{v}_n$ of orthonormal vectors, $\mathbf{v} = \mathbf{v}' + (\mathbf{v} - \mathbf{v}')$, where

$$\mathbf{v}' = \langle \mathbf{v}, \mathbf{v}_1 \rangle \mathbf{v}_1 + \cdots + \langle \mathbf{v}, \mathbf{v}_n \rangle \mathbf{v}_n.$$

Since $\mathbf{v}' \in W = F\mathbf{v}_1 + \cdots + F\mathbf{v}_n$ and $\mathbf{v} - \mathbf{v}' \in W^{\perp}$, by Theorem 6.12, $\mathbf{v}' = \mathbf{v}_W$ and $\mathbf{v}_W = \langle \mathbf{v}, \mathbf{v}_1 \rangle \mathbf{v}_1 + \cdots + \langle \mathbf{v}, \mathbf{v}_n \rangle \mathbf{v}_n$. This is the **Fourier expansion** for the projection $\mathbf{v}_W$ (Figure 6.13).

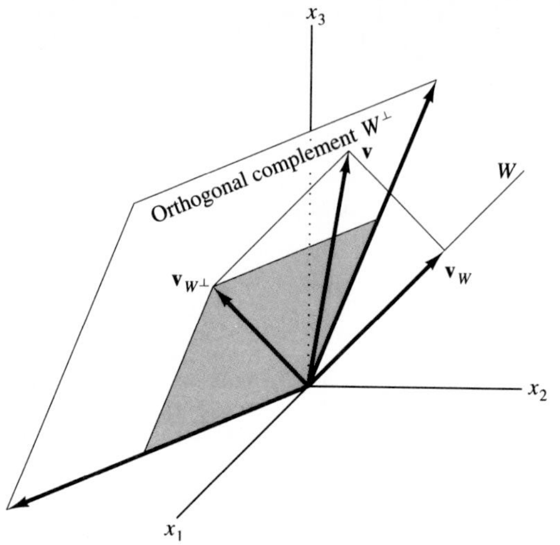

Figure 6.12 The orthogonal projections $\mathbf{v}_W$, $\mathbf{v}_{W^\perp}$ of $\mathbf{v}$ on the subspaces W, $W^\perp$ of $\mathbb{R}^3$.

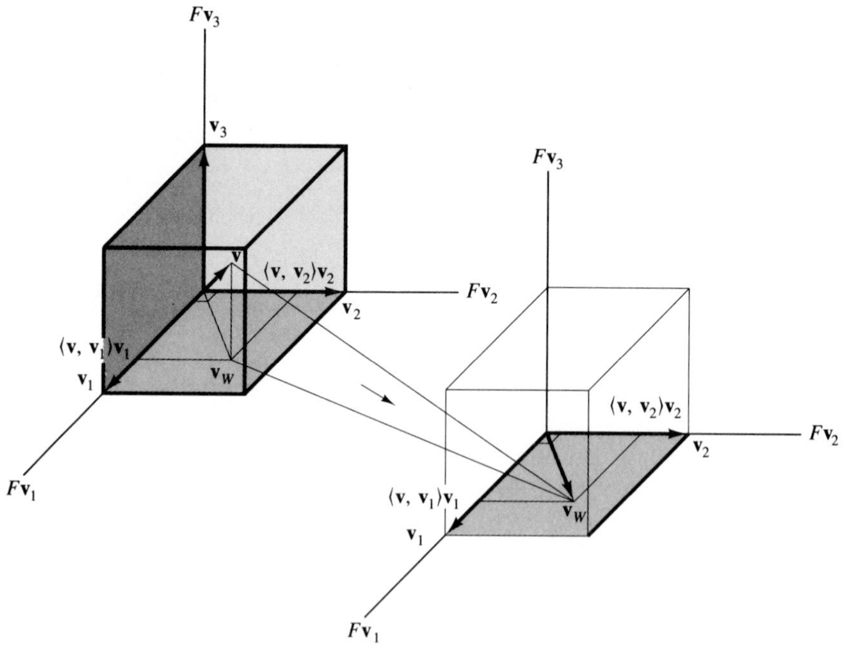

Figure 6.13 The Fourier expansion $\mathbf{v}_W = \langle \mathbf{v}, \mathbf{v}_1 \rangle \mathbf{v}_1 + \langle \mathbf{v}, \mathbf{v}_2 \rangle \mathbf{v}_2$ is the projection of $\mathbf{v}$ onto $W = \mathbb{R}\mathbf{v}_1 + \mathbb{R}\mathbf{v}_2$.

Fourier Expansion of $\mathbf{v}_W$ *as a Projection.*
Let $\mathbf{v}_1, \ldots, \mathbf{v}_n$ be an orthogonal basis for W. Then the orthogonal projection of $\mathbf{v}$ on W is $\mathbf{v}_W = \langle \mathbf{v}, \mathbf{v}_1 \rangle \mathbf{v}_1 + \cdots + \langle \mathbf{v}, \mathbf{v}_n \rangle \mathbf{v}_n$.

EXAMPLE

The orthogonal projection of $\begin{bmatrix} 0 \\ 1 \\ 2 \end{bmatrix}$ on the span W of

$$\mathbf{v} = \frac{1}{\sqrt{6}} \begin{bmatrix} 1 \\ 2 \\ 1 \end{bmatrix}, \qquad \mathbf{w} = \frac{1}{\sqrt{3}} \begin{bmatrix} -1 \\ 1 \\ -1 \end{bmatrix}$$

is

$$\frac{4}{\sqrt{6}} \frac{1}{\sqrt{6}} \begin{bmatrix} 1 \\ 2 \\ 1 \end{bmatrix} - \frac{1}{\sqrt{3}} \frac{1}{\sqrt{3}} \begin{bmatrix} -1 \\ 1 \\ -1 \end{bmatrix} = \begin{bmatrix} 1 \\ 1 \\ 1 \end{bmatrix},$$

since the Fourier coefficients of $\begin{bmatrix} 0 \\ 1 \\ 2 \end{bmatrix}$ are $4/\sqrt{6}$ and $-1/\sqrt{3}$.

When the set of $Q_1, \ldots, Q_n$ is an orthonormal set in F^m, the Fourier expansion for the projection $\mathbf{v}_W$ of $\mathbf{v}$ on $W = c(Q) = FQ_1 + \cdots + FQ_n$ takes on a particularly nice form in terms of the matrix $Q = [Q_1 \quad \ldots \quad Q_n]$:

$$\mathbf{v}_W = \langle \mathbf{v}, Q_1 \rangle Q_1 + \cdots + \langle \mathbf{v}, Q_n \rangle Q_n = Q \begin{bmatrix} \langle v, Q_1 \rangle \\ \vdots \\ \langle v, Q_n \rangle \end{bmatrix} = QQ^*\mathbf{v}.$$

The same is true assuming only that the *nonzero* columns of Q are orthonormal. (Explain!) We formulate this as follows.

Orthogonal Projection of $\mathbf{v}$ *on* $c(Q)$.
$\mathbf{v}_{c(Q)} = QQ^*\mathbf{v}$ if the nonzero columns of $Q \in M_{m \times n}F$ are orthonormal.

EXAMPLE

The orthogonal projection of $\begin{bmatrix} 2 \\ 1 \\ 3 \end{bmatrix}$ on the column space of

$$Q = \frac{1}{\sqrt{2}} \begin{bmatrix} 1 & -1 \\ 0 & 0 \\ 1 & 1 \end{bmatrix}$$

is

$$QQ^* \begin{bmatrix} 2 \\ 1 \\ 3 \end{bmatrix} = \frac{1}{2} \begin{bmatrix} 1 & -1 \\ 0 & 0 \\ 1 & 1 \end{bmatrix} \begin{bmatrix} 1 & 0 & 1 \\ -1 & 0 & 1 \end{bmatrix} \begin{bmatrix} 2 \\ 1 \\ 3 \end{bmatrix} = \begin{bmatrix} 2 \\ 0 \\ 3 \end{bmatrix}.$$

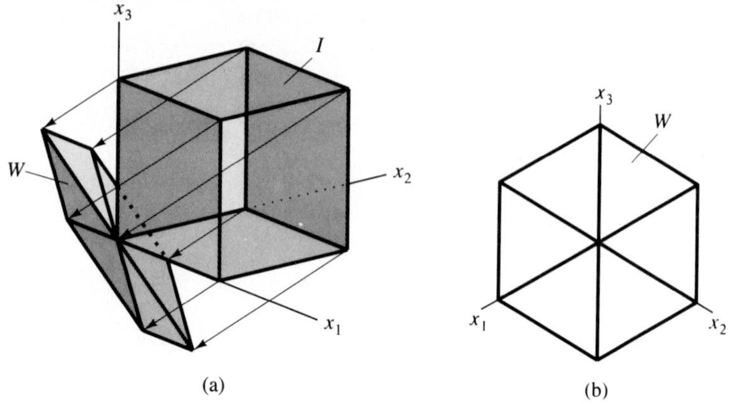

Figure 6.14 Image of the unit cube under the orthogonal projection P_W of $\mathbb{R}^3$ onto the plane $x_1 + x_2 + x_3 = 1$ viewed (a) from $\begin{bmatrix} 4 \\ -5 \\ -2 \end{bmatrix}$ and (b) from $\begin{bmatrix} 5 \\ 5 \\ 5 \end{bmatrix}$.

Orthogonal projection transformations

Let V be a Euclidean space. For any subspace W of V, we define P_W by letting $P_W(\mathbf{v}) = \mathbf{v}_W$, the orthogonal projection of $\mathbf{v}$ onto W. When $\mathbf{v}_1, \ldots, \mathbf{v}_n$ is an orthonormal basis for W, the Fourier expansion for $\mathbf{v}_W$ is

$$P_W(\mathbf{v}) = \langle \mathbf{v}, \mathbf{v}_1 \rangle \mathbf{v}_1 + \cdots + \langle \mathbf{v}, \mathbf{v}_n \rangle \mathbf{v}_n.$$

So, P_W is a linear transformation from V to V such that $P_W(\mathbf{w} + \mathbf{w}') = \mathbf{w}$ for $\mathbf{w} \in W$ and $\mathbf{w}' \in W^\perp$ (Figure 6.14).

Definition. *Orthogonal Projection of V onto W.*
P_W is called the **orthogonal projection** of V onto W.

Note that:

1. $P_W(\mathbf{v}) = \mathbf{v}$ if $\mathbf{v} \in W$.
2. $P(\mathbf{v}) = \mathbf{0}$ if $\mathbf{v} \in W^\perp$.
3. For $\mathbf{v} = \mathbf{v}' + \mathbf{v}''$ $(\mathbf{v}' \in W, \mathbf{v}'' \in W^\perp)$, $\mathbf{v}' = P_W(\mathbf{v})$ and $\mathbf{v}'' = P_{W^\perp}(\mathbf{v})$. So, $\mathbf{v} = P_W(\mathbf{v}) + P_{W^\perp}(\mathbf{v})$.

It follows from this that:

1. $P_W^2 = P_W$, Image $P_W = W$, and Kernel $P_W = W^\perp$.
2. Image $P_W \cap$ Kernel $P_W = \{\mathbf{0}\}$.
3. $I = P_W + P_{W^\perp}$.

EXAMPLE

Let W be the column space of $Q = \frac{1}{\sqrt{2}}\begin{bmatrix} 1 & -1 \\ 0 & 0 \\ 1 & 1 \end{bmatrix}$. Then

$$P_W = QQ^* = \frac{1}{2}\begin{bmatrix} 1 & -1 \\ 0 & 0 \\ 1 & 1 \end{bmatrix}\begin{bmatrix} 1 & 0 & 1 \\ -1 & 0 & 1 \end{bmatrix} = \begin{bmatrix} 1 & 0 & 0 \\ 0 & 0 & 0 \\ 0 & 0 & 1 \end{bmatrix}.$$

(Compare with the preceding example.) By (3),

$$P_{W^\perp} = I - P_W = \begin{bmatrix} 0 & 0 & 0 \\ 0 & 1 & 0 \\ 0 & 0 & 0 \end{bmatrix},$$

and (2) and (3) follow at once. (Verify!)

For $V = F^m$, any subspace W of V is the column space $c(A)$ of any matrix A whose columns span W. For any such A, orthonormalization of its columns always gives us a factorization $A = QR$, where the set of nonzero columns of A is orthonormal and R is invertible (Section 6.3). Since $c(A) = c(Q)$ (explain), we have $P_{c(A)}(\mathbf{v}) = \mathbf{v}_{c(Q)} = QQ^*\mathbf{v}$. So, we get the following rule for computing $P_{c(A)}$.

Orthogonal Projection onto $c(A)$.

1. Orthonormalize the columns of A to get $A = QR$, where the set of nonzero columns of Q is orthonormal and R is invertible.
2. Then $C(A) = C(Q)$ and $P_{c(A)}(\mathbf{v}) = QQ^*\mathbf{v}$ for all $\mathbf{v}$.

EXAMPLE

Let $V = \mathbb{R}^3$ and

$$A = \begin{bmatrix} 2 & 1 \\ -1 & 1 \\ 2 & 4 \end{bmatrix}.$$

Orthonormalization of the columns of A gives us the factorization $A = QR$ where

$$Q = \begin{bmatrix} 2/3 & -1/3 \\ -1/3 & 2/3 \\ 2/3 & 2/3 \end{bmatrix} \quad \text{and} \quad R = \begin{bmatrix} 3 & 3 \\ 0 & 3 \end{bmatrix}.$$

(Verify!) Then

$$P_{c(A)}(\mathbf{x}) = QQ^*\mathbf{x} = \begin{bmatrix} 5/9 & -4/9 & 2/9 \\ -4/9 & 5/9 & 2/9 \\ 2/9 & 2/9 & 8/9 \end{bmatrix}\mathbf{x}.$$

This rule implies that the matrix A of $P_W(\mathbf{x}) = A\mathbf{x}$ is Hermitian for any subspace W of F^m, since $A = QQ^*$, where the columns of Q are an orthonormal basis for W. Since $P_W^2 = P_W$, we have $A^2 = A$ as well. So, A is an orthogonal projection matrix in the following sense.

Definition. *Orthogonal Projection Matrix.*
An **orthogonal projection matrix** is a Hermitian matrix A such that $A^2 = A$.

Conversely, let $P(\mathbf{x}) = A\mathbf{x}$, where A is an orthogonal projection matrix. Let $W = P(F^m)$, $W' = (I - P)(F^m)$. Each $\mathbf{x} \in F^n$ can be written as $\mathbf{x} = I\mathbf{x} = P(\mathbf{x}) + (I - P)(\mathbf{x}) \in W + W'$, so that $F^n = W + W'$. Let $\mathbf{w} = P(\mathbf{u}) \in W$ and $\mathbf{w}' = (P - I)(\mathbf{v}) \in W'$. Then

$$\begin{aligned}\langle \mathbf{w}', \mathbf{w}\rangle &= \langle (I - P)(\mathbf{u}), P(\mathbf{v})\rangle = \langle (I - A)\mathbf{u}, A\mathbf{v}\rangle = (A\mathbf{v}) * (I - A)\mathbf{u} \\ &= \mathbf{v}^*A^*(I - A)\mathbf{u} = \mathbf{v}^*A(I - A)\mathbf{u} = \mathbf{v}^*0\mathbf{u} = \mathbf{0}.\end{aligned}$$

So, $\langle \mathbf{w}, \mathbf{w}'\rangle = 0$ for all $\mathbf{w} \in W$ and $\mathbf{w}' \in W'$, and the sum $F^n = W + W'$ is an orthogonal sum. It follows that $W' = W^\perp$. Since $A^2 = A$, $P^2 = P$ and $P(I - P) = 0$. Then $P(\mathbf{w}) = P^2(\mathbf{u}) = P(\mathbf{u}) = \mathbf{w}$ and $P(\mathbf{w}') = P(P - I)(\mathbf{v}) = 0(\mathbf{v}) = \mathbf{0}$. So, $P(\mathbf{w} + \mathbf{w}') = \mathbf{w}$ for $\mathbf{w} \in W$ and $\mathbf{w}' \in W'$. But then $P = P_W$. This proves the following theorem.

Theorem 6.18. *Criteria for $T \in L(F^m, F^m)$ to Be an Orthogonal Projection.* A linear transformation $P(\mathbf{x}) = A\mathbf{x}$ of F^m is an orthogonal projection P_W for some subspace W of F^m if and only if A is an orthogonal projection matrix.

We transfer this theorem by an isometry to the corresponding theorem for Euclidean spaces.

Theorem 6.19. *Criteria for $T \in L(V, V)$ to Be an Orthogonal Projection.* Let V be a Euclidean space with orthonormal basis $\mathbf{v}_1, \ldots, \mathbf{v}_m$. Then $P \in L(V, V)$ is an orthogonal projection P_W for some subspace W of V if and only if the matrix A of P_W with respect to $\mathbf{v}_1, \ldots, \mathbf{v}_m$ is an orthogonal projection matrix.

Proof. Let R be the isometry $R(a_1\mathbf{v}_1 + \cdots + a_m\mathbf{v}_m) = a_1\mathbf{e}_1 + \cdots + a_m\mathbf{e}_m$. Then A is the matrix $m(RPR^{-1})$. If $P = P_W$ for a subspace W of V, then $RPR^{-1} = P_{R(W)}$, since $F^m = R(W) + R(W^\perp) = R(W) + R(W)^\perp$. (Verify!) So, A is an orthogonal projection matrix by Theorem 6.18. Conversely, suppose that A is an orthogonal projection matrix. Then $RPR^{-1} = P_{R(W)}$ for some subspace W of V. But then $P = P_W$. (Explain!) ■

EXAMPLES

1. The matrix

$$A = \begin{bmatrix} 1/2 & 0 & 1/2 \\ 0 & 1 & 0 \\ 1/2 & 0 & 1/2 \end{bmatrix}$$

is an orthogonal projection matrix. So,

$$P(\mathbf{x}) = \begin{bmatrix} 1/2 & 0 & 1/2 \\ 0 & 1 & 0 \\ 1/2 & 0 & 1/2 \end{bmatrix} \mathbf{x}$$

is P_W, where $W = c(A) = F\begin{bmatrix} 1 \\ 0 \\ 1 \end{bmatrix} + F\begin{bmatrix} 0 \\ 1 \\ 0 \end{bmatrix}$.

2. The matrix

$$\begin{bmatrix} 1 & 0 & 0 \\ 0 & 16/17 & 4/17 \\ 0 & 4/17 & 1/17 \end{bmatrix}$$

is an orthogonal projection matrix. (Verify!) Thus, the transformation

$$P(\mathbf{x}) = \begin{bmatrix} 1 & 0 & 0 \\ 0 & 16/17 & 4/17 \\ 0 & 4/17 & 1/17 \end{bmatrix} \mathbf{x}$$

is $P = P_W$, where W is the image of P—that is, W is the span of

$$\begin{bmatrix} 1 \\ 0 \\ 0 \end{bmatrix}, \quad \begin{bmatrix} 0 \\ 4 \\ 1 \end{bmatrix}.$$

(Explain!).

3. $\frac{1}{3}\begin{bmatrix} 1 & 1+i \\ 1-i & 2 \end{bmatrix}$ is an orthogonal projection matrix, so the transformation $P(\mathbf{x}) = \frac{1}{3}\begin{bmatrix} 1 & 1+i \\ 1-i & 2 \end{bmatrix}\mathbf{x}$ is $P = P_W$, where $W = \mathbb{C}\begin{bmatrix} 1+i \\ 2 \end{bmatrix}$. (Verify!)

PROBLEMS

NUMERICAL PROBLEMS

1. Find the orthogonal projection of $\begin{bmatrix} 1 \\ 2 \\ 3 \end{bmatrix}$ on $F\begin{bmatrix} 4 \\ 5 \\ 6 \end{bmatrix} + F\begin{bmatrix} 7 \\ 8 \\ 9 \end{bmatrix}$.

2. Find the orthogonal projection of $\begin{bmatrix}1\\2\\3\end{bmatrix}$ on $F\begin{bmatrix}1\\1\\1\end{bmatrix}+F\begin{bmatrix}-2\\1\\1\end{bmatrix}$.

3. Find the orthogonal projection of $\begin{bmatrix}1\\2\\3\end{bmatrix}$ on $F\begin{bmatrix}-1\\4\\0\end{bmatrix}+F\begin{bmatrix}1\\2\\2\end{bmatrix}$.

4. Find the vector in the column space of $\begin{bmatrix}-2 & 1\\1 & 1\\1 & 1\end{bmatrix}$ nearest $\begin{bmatrix}2\\2\\1\end{bmatrix}$.

5. Find the vector in the column space of $\begin{bmatrix}-1 & 1\\1 & 3\\0 & 2\end{bmatrix}$ nearest $\begin{bmatrix}1\\2\\3\end{bmatrix}$.

6. Find the vector in the column space of $\begin{bmatrix}-2 & 1\\1 & -1\\1 & -1\end{bmatrix}$ nearest $\begin{bmatrix}2\\4\\9\end{bmatrix}$.

7. Let $P(\mathbf{x})=\begin{bmatrix}1 & a+bi\\0 & 1\end{bmatrix}\mathbf{x}$. For what a and b is $P^2=P$?

8. For what values of a and b is $\begin{bmatrix}1 & a+bi\\0 & 0\end{bmatrix}^2=\begin{bmatrix}1 & a+bi\\0 & 0\end{bmatrix}$?

9. For what values of a and b is $\begin{bmatrix}0 & 0\\1 & a+bi\end{bmatrix}^2=\begin{bmatrix}0 & 0\\1 & a+bi\end{bmatrix}$?

10. Give necessary and sufficient conditions on $a\in\mathbb{C}$ so that $\begin{bmatrix}1/3 & \bar{a}/3\\a/3 & 2/3\end{bmatrix}$ will be an orthogonal projection matrix.

11. Give necessary and sufficient conditions on $a\in\mathbb{C}$ so that $\begin{bmatrix}2/7 & \bar{a}/7\\a/7 & 5/7\end{bmatrix}$ will be an orthogonal projection matrix.

12. For what values of a and b is $\begin{bmatrix}1 & a & b\\0 & 1 & 0\\0 & 0 & 0\end{bmatrix}^2=\begin{bmatrix}1 & a & b\\0 & 1 & 0\\0 & 0 & 0\end{bmatrix}$?

13. For what values of a, b, and c is $\begin{bmatrix}1 & 0 & a\\0 & 1 & b\\0 & 0 & c\end{bmatrix}^2=\begin{bmatrix}1 & 0 & a\\0 & 1 & b\\0 & 0 & c\end{bmatrix}$?

THEORETICAL PROBLEMS

14. If $\mathbf{u}$ and $\mathbf{v}$ are orthogonal, show that the orthogonal projection of $\mathbf{x}$ on $F\mathbf{u}+F\mathbf{v}$ is the sum of its projections $\mathbf{x}_{\mathbf{u}}$, $\mathbf{x}_{\mathbf{v}}$ on $\mathbf{u}$ and $\mathbf{v}$.

15. If $\mathbf{u}$ and $\mathbf{v}$ are not orthogonal, show for $\mathbf{x}=\mathbf{u}$ that the orthogonal projection of $\mathbf{x}$ on $F\mathbf{u}+F\mathbf{v}$ is not the sum of its projections $\mathbf{x}_{\mathbf{u}}$, $\mathbf{x}_{\mathbf{v}}$ on $\mathbf{u}$ and $\mathbf{v}$.

16. Show that if two matrices are unitarily similar and one is Hermitian, then so is the other.

17. If P is a linear transformation from a finite-dimensional vector space V to itself and if $P^2 = P$, show that

(a) $\text{Dim } V = \text{Dim Image } P + \text{Dim Image } (I - P)$;

(b) The matrix of P with respect to any basis for V is similar to a matrix of the form

$$\left[\begin{array}{c|c} J & 0 \\ \hline 0 & 0 \end{array}\right],$$

where J is the identity matrix I_r of degree r;

(c) The ranks of P and $I - P$ are r and $\text{Dim } V - r$.

18. If P is a linear transformation from a finite-dimensional vector space V to itself such that $P = P^2$ and P maps $P(V)^{\perp}$ into $P(V)^{\perp}$, then $\langle P(\mathbf{v}), \mathbf{w} \rangle = \langle \mathbf{v}, P(\mathbf{w}) \rangle$ for all $\mathbf{v}, \mathbf{w} \in V$.

19. Show that a square matrix A such that $A^2 = A$ is diagonalizable.

Hard

20. Show that A is similar to an orthogonal projection matrix if and only if $A^2 = A$.

21. Show that A is unitarily similar to an orthogonal projection matrix if and only if A is an orthogonal projection matrix.

22. If $A = \begin{bmatrix} a & \bar{b} \\ b & d \end{bmatrix}$ has trace $a + d = 1$ and determinant 0, it is an orthogonal projection matrix if and only if a and d are real.

23. If

$$C = \left[\begin{array}{c|c} J & L \\ \hline 0 & K \end{array}\right],$$

where C is of rank r and J is of rank r, show that $K = 0$.

6.8 LEAST SQUARES METHODS

We now address the problem of how best to approximately solve a system of equations $A\mathbf{x} = \mathbf{b}$ if there is no solution $\mathbf{x}$. This is the case where $A\mathbf{x} = \mathbf{b}$ is **inconsistent**. In the discussion, it is assumed that $A \in M_{m \times n}\mathbb{R}$, $\mathbf{x} \in \mathbb{R}^n$, $\mathbf{b} \in \mathbb{R}^m$. Corresponding results can be obtained over $\mathbb{C}$, however, by replacing A^T by A^* in what follows.

The least squares problem

The equation $A\mathbf{x} = \mathbf{b}$ has a solution $\mathbf{x}$ if and only if $\mathbf{b}$ is in the column space $c(A)$ of A. The corresponding *least squares problem* is to find $\mathbf{x}$ such that $A\mathbf{x}$

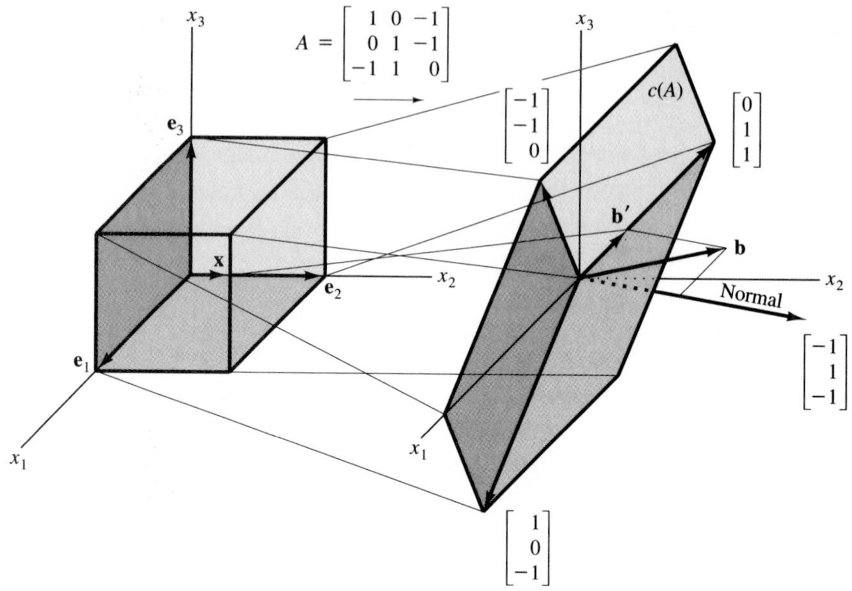

Figure 6.15 A least squares solution $\mathbf{x}$ to $A\mathbf{x} = \mathbf{b}$ is a solution to $A\mathbf{x} = \mathbf{b}'$ for $\mathbf{b}' = \mathbf{b}_{c(A)}$. The condition $A\mathbf{x} = \mathbf{b}'$ is that $\mathbf{b} - A\mathbf{x} \in c(A)^{\perp}$.

is as close to $\mathbf{b}$ as possible. This always has a solution. Since the vector in $c(A)$ closest to $\mathbf{b}$ is the orthogonal projection $\mathbf{b}'$ of $\mathbf{b}$ on $c(A)$, by Theorem 6.16, we can describe the solution as follows.

Definition. *Least Squares Solution to* $A\mathbf{x} = \mathbf{b}$.

A **least squares solution** to $A\mathbf{x} = \mathbf{b}$ is a solution $\mathbf{x}$ to $A\mathbf{x} = \mathbf{b}'$, where $\mathbf{b}'$ is the orthogonal projection of $\mathbf{b}$ on the column space $c(A)$ of A (Figure 6.15).

Note the following:

1. A least squares solution $\mathbf{x}$ to $A\mathbf{x} = \mathbf{b}$ minimizes the sum of squares of the coordinates of the **error vector** $\mathbf{b} - A\mathbf{x}$. This explains the terminology.
2. If $A\mathbf{x} = \mathbf{b}$ has a solution $\mathbf{x}$, then the orthogonal projection $\mathbf{b}'$ of $\mathbf{b}$ on $c(A)$ is $\mathbf{b}$ itself, which proves the following.

   When $A\mathbf{x} = \mathbf{b}$ *is consistent, its least squares solutions are just its solutions.*

The normal equation

In order for $A\mathbf{x} = \mathbf{b}'$ to be the projection of $\mathbf{b}$ on $c(A)$, it is necessary and sufficient that $\mathbf{b} - A\mathbf{x} \in c(A)^{\perp} = n(A^T)$—that is, that $A^T(\mathbf{b} - A\mathbf{x}) = \mathbf{0}$ or

$A^TAx = A^Tb$. This provides a simple method for finding the least squares solutions to $Ax = b$, which we formulate as follows.

Definition. *The Normal Equation.*
The equation $A^TAx = A^Tb$ is called the **normal equation** corresponding to the given equation $Ax = b$.

Theorem 6.20. *Finding the Least Squares Solution to* $Ax = b$.
x is a least squares solution to $Ax = b$ if and only if x is a solution to the normal equation $A^TAx = A^Tb$.

EXAMPLE

Let x be a least squares solution to $Ax = b$, where

$$A = \begin{bmatrix} 1 & 1 \\ 1 & 2 \\ 1 & 1 \end{bmatrix} \quad \text{and} \quad b = \begin{bmatrix} 2 \\ 0 \\ 4 \end{bmatrix}.$$

Then x is a solution to the corresponding normal equation $A^TAx = A^Tb$. Since $A^TA = \begin{bmatrix} 3 & 4 \\ 4 & 6 \end{bmatrix}$ and $A^Tb = \begin{bmatrix} 6 \\ 6 \end{bmatrix}$, we get x by solving $\begin{bmatrix} 3 & 4 \\ 4 & 6 \end{bmatrix} x = \begin{bmatrix} 6 \\ 6 \end{bmatrix}$. The only solution is $x = \begin{bmatrix} 6 \\ -3 \end{bmatrix}$. Having found the least squares solution x, the projection $Ax = b'$ of b on $c(A)$ is

$$\begin{bmatrix} 1 & 1 \\ 1 & 2 \\ 1 & 1 \end{bmatrix} \begin{bmatrix} 6 \\ -3 \end{bmatrix} = \begin{bmatrix} 3 \\ 0 \\ 3 \end{bmatrix}.$$

To check this, simply verify that

$$\begin{bmatrix} 2 \\ 0 \\ 4 \end{bmatrix} - \begin{bmatrix} 3 \\ 0 \\ 3 \end{bmatrix} = \begin{bmatrix} -1 \\ 0 \\ 1 \end{bmatrix}$$

is indeed orthogonal to the columns of A.

When the columns of A are linearly independent, the nullity of A is 0, so $n(A) = 0$. From this, it follows that $n(A^TA) = 0$. For if $A^TAx = 0$, then $0 = x^TA^TAx = (Ax)^TAx = \|Ax\|^2$ and $Ax = 0$, so $x = 0$. But then A^TA is an invertible matrix (why?) and we can solve $Ax = b$ by $x = (A^TA)^{-1}A^Tb$. The matrix $(A^TA)^{-1}A^T$ is called the **pseudoinverse** of A. We denote it by

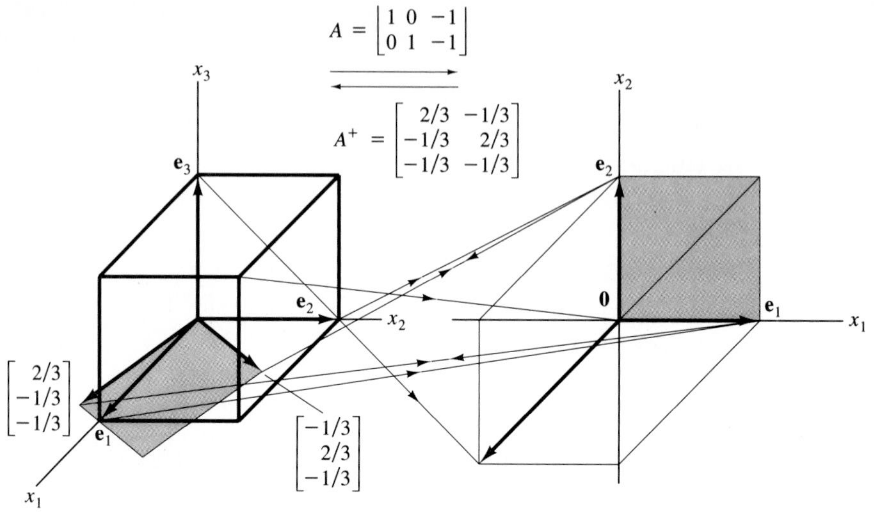

Figure 6.16 $A = \begin{bmatrix} 1 & 0 & -1 \\ 0 & 1 & -1 \end{bmatrix}$ and $A^+ = \begin{bmatrix} 2/3 & -1/3 \\ -1/3 & 2/3 \\ -1/3 & -1/3 \end{bmatrix}$

are mappings from $\mathbb{R}^3$ to $\mathbb{R}^2$ and from $\mathbb{R}^2$ to $\mathbb{R}^3$ that are pseudoinverses of each other.

$A^+ = (A^TA)^{-1}A^T$. This is a special case of the (*Moore-Penrose*) *pseudo-inverse* introduced shortly (Figure 6.16).

Theorem 6.21. *The Pseudoinverse $A^+ = (A^TA)^{-1}A^T$ of A.*
The equation $A\mathbf{x} = \mathbf{b}$ has exactly one least squares solution, namely, $\mathbf{x} = A^+\mathbf{b} = (A^TA)^{-1}A^T\mathbf{b}$.

When the columns of A are linearly independent, $\mathbf{x}$ is the unique solution to $A\mathbf{x} = A\mathbf{x}$ (the equation $A\mathbf{x} = \mathbf{b}$ when $\mathbf{b}$ is $A\mathbf{x}$), so that $\mathbf{x} = A^+A\mathbf{x}$ for all $\mathbf{x}$! This shows that $A^+A = I$. For any $\mathbf{b}$ and any least squares solution $\mathbf{x}$ to $A\mathbf{x} = \mathbf{b}$, we have

$$P_{c(A)}(\mathbf{b}) = A\mathbf{x} = A(A^TA)^{-1}A^T\mathbf{b} = AA^+\mathbf{b}.$$

This proves the following corollary.

Corollary. When the columns of A are linearly independent, then $A^+A = I$ and $P_{c(A)} = AA^+$, where $A^+ = (A^TA)^{-1}A^T$.

EXAMPLE

For $A = \begin{bmatrix} 1 & 1 \\ 1 & 2 \\ 1 & 1 \end{bmatrix}$, $A^TA = \begin{bmatrix} 3 & 4 \\ 4 & 6 \end{bmatrix}$ and $(A^TA)^{-1} = \begin{bmatrix} 3 & -2 \\ -2 & 3/2 \end{bmatrix}$. Then

$$(A^TA)^{-1}A^T = \begin{bmatrix} 1 & -1 & 1 \\ -1/2 & 1 & -1/2 \end{bmatrix} \quad \text{and} \quad A(A^TA)^{-1}A^T = \begin{bmatrix} 1/2 & 0 & 1/2 \\ 0 & 1 & 0 \\ 1/2 & 0 & 1/2 \end{bmatrix}.$$

So,

$$A^+ = \begin{bmatrix} 1 & -1 & 1 \\ -1/2 & 1 & -1/2 \end{bmatrix}$$

and

$$P_{c(A)}(\mathbf{y}) = \begin{bmatrix} 1/2 & 0 & 1/2 \\ 0 & 1 & 0 \\ 1/2 & 0 & 1/2 \end{bmatrix}\mathbf{y}.$$

Checking whether $A^+A = \begin{bmatrix} 1 & 0 \\ 0 & 1 \end{bmatrix}$ quickly shows that it is.

The *QR* decomposition

We can find all least squares solutions $\mathbf{x}$ to $A\mathbf{x} = \mathbf{b}$ by getting the QR decomposition $A = QR$, where the nonzero columns of Q are orthonormal and R is invertible (Section 6.3). Since the least squares solutions to $A\mathbf{x} = \mathbf{b}$ are the solutions to $A\mathbf{x} = \mathbf{b}_{c(A)}$ and $\mathbf{b}_{c(A)} = QQ^T\mathbf{b}$ (Section 6.7), they are the solutions to $QR\mathbf{x} = QQ^T\mathbf{b}$. One such $\mathbf{x}$ is $\mathbf{x} = R^{-1}Q^T\mathbf{b}$, which proves the following theorem.

Theorem 6.22. *Finding the Least Squares Solution to* $QR\mathbf{x} = \mathbf{b}$.
Let $A = QR$, where the nonzero columns of Q are orthonormal and R is invertible. Then $\mathbf{x} = R^{-1}Q^T\mathbf{b}$ is a least squares solution to $A\mathbf{x} = \mathbf{b}$.

When R is also upper triangular (as it is in the QR factorization introduced in Section 6.3), the $\mathbf{x}$ in Theorem 6.22 can be found quickly from $Q^T\mathbf{b}$ by back substitution.

When the columns of A are linearly independent, $A\mathbf{x} = \mathbf{b}$ has a unique least squares solution, namely, $\mathbf{x} = A^+\mathbf{b} = (A^TA)^{-1}A^T\mathbf{b}$. In this case, our theorem gives an alternative description of A^+, which is often superior for its accurate, high-speed computation.

Corollary. Suppose that the columns of A are linearly independent and let $A = QR$, where the columns of Q are orthonormal and R is invertible and upper triangular. Then $A^+ = R^{-1}Q^T$.

EXAMPLE

To find the least squares solution $\mathbf{x}$ to

$$\begin{bmatrix} 1 & 1 \\ 2 & 5 \\ 1 & 1 \end{bmatrix} \mathbf{x} = \begin{bmatrix} 1 \\ 7 \\ 2 \end{bmatrix},$$

orthonormalize the columns of

$$\mathbf{A} = \begin{bmatrix} 1 & 1 \\ 2 & 5 \\ 1 & 1 \end{bmatrix} \quad \text{to} \quad Q = \begin{bmatrix} 1/\sqrt{6} & -1/\sqrt{3} \\ 2/\sqrt{6} & 1/\sqrt{3} \\ 1/\sqrt{6} & -1/\sqrt{3} \end{bmatrix}.$$

The corresponding factorization $A = QR$ of A is then

$$\begin{bmatrix} 1 & 1 \\ 2 & 5 \\ 1 & 1 \end{bmatrix} = \begin{bmatrix} 1/\sqrt{6} & -1/\sqrt{3} \\ 2/\sqrt{6} & 1/\sqrt{3} \\ 1/\sqrt{6} & -1/\sqrt{3} \end{bmatrix} \begin{bmatrix} \sqrt{6} & 2\sqrt{6} \\ 0 & \sqrt{3} \end{bmatrix},$$

so

$$\begin{aligned} A^+ &= \begin{bmatrix} \sqrt{6} & 2\sqrt{6} \\ 0 & \sqrt{3} \end{bmatrix}^{-1} \begin{bmatrix} 1/\sqrt{6} & 2/\sqrt{6} & 1/\sqrt{6} \\ -1/\sqrt{3} & 1/\sqrt{3} & -1/\sqrt{3} \end{bmatrix} \\ &= \begin{bmatrix} 5/6 & -2/6 & 5/6 \\ -2/6 & 2/6 & -2/6 \end{bmatrix} \end{aligned}$$

and

$$P_{c(A)}(\mathbf{y}) = AA^+ = \begin{bmatrix} 1/2 & 0 & 1/2 \\ 0 & 1 & 0 \\ 1/2 & 0 & 1/2 \end{bmatrix}.$$

To check our work, we look to see if $A^+A = I$, which it is.

The pseudoinverse of any A

An equation $A\mathbf{x} = \mathbf{b}$ ($A \in M_{m \times n}F$) may have infinitely many least squares solutions $\mathbf{x}$. Given one such $\mathbf{x}$, it is a solution to $A\mathbf{x} = \mathbf{b}'$, where $\mathbf{b}' = \mathbf{b}_{c(A)}$. The set of all least squares solutions to $A\mathbf{x} = \mathbf{b}$ is then the set $\mathbf{x} + n(A)$ of all solutions to $A\mathbf{x} = \mathbf{b}'$. Since $\mathbb{R}^m = n(A)^\perp + n(A) = c(A^T) + n(A)$ (orthogonal sum), we can write $\mathbf{x} = \mathbf{x}' + \mathbf{x}''$, where $\mathbf{x}' \in c(A^T)$, $\mathbf{x}'' \in n(A)$. Then $A\mathbf{x}' = A\mathbf{x} = \mathbf{b}'$, so that $\mathbf{x}'$ is also a least squares solution to $A\mathbf{x}' = \mathbf{b}$. Note that $\mathbf{x} = \mathbf{x}'$

if and only if $\mathbf{x}$ is orthogonal to $n(A)$. Note also that the squared length of $\mathbf{x}$ is the sum of that of $\mathbf{x}'$ and $\mathbf{x}''$, so that the length of $\mathbf{x}'$ is less than the length of $\mathbf{x}$ if $\mathbf{x}$ and $\mathbf{x}'$ are different. This enables us to give the following definition.

Definition. *The Optimal Least Squares Solution.*
There is exactly one least squares solution $\mathbf{x}$ to $A\mathbf{x} = \mathbf{b}$ which is contained in $c(A^T)$. Its length is less than that of any other least squares solution. We call it the **optimal least squares solution**.

Definition. *The Pseudoinverse of a Real Matrix A.*
Let $T(\mathbf{x}) = A\mathbf{x}$. Then for $\mathbf{b} \in \mathbb{R}^m$, $T^+(\mathbf{b})$ denotes the optimal least squares solution $\mathbf{x}$ to $A\mathbf{x} = \mathbf{b}$. We let A^+ be the $n \times m$ matrix whose columns are $T^+(\mathbf{e}_1), \ldots, T^+(\mathbf{e}_m)$ and call A^+ the (**Moore-Penrose**) **pseudoinverse of** A.

The optimal least squares solution to $A\mathbf{x} = \mathbf{b}$ can always be found as follows:

1. Find one solution $\mathbf{x}$ to the normal equation $A^TA\mathbf{x} = A^T\mathbf{b}$.
2. Then replace $\mathbf{x}$ by $P_{c(A^T)}(\mathbf{x})$.

This sets the stage for the following theorem.

Theorem 6.23. *The Pseudoinverse of $A = QR$.*
Let $T(\mathbf{x}) = A\mathbf{x}$ ($A \in M_{m \times n}\mathbb{R}$) and factor A as $A = QR$, where the nonzero rows of Q are orthonormal and R is invertible. Then $T^+(\mathbf{b}) = P_{c(A^T)}(R^{-1}Q^T\mathbf{b})$.

Proof. $\mathbf{x} = R^{-1}Q^T\mathbf{b}$ is a least squares solution to $A\mathbf{x} = \mathbf{b}$, by Theorem 6.22, so that $T^+(\mathbf{b}) = P_{c(A^T)}(\mathbf{x}) = P_{c(A^T)}(R^{-1}Q^T\mathbf{b})$. ■

Corollary. For $T(\mathbf{x}) = A\mathbf{x}$, $T^+(\mathbf{b})$ is a linear transformation and $T^+(\mathbf{b}) = A^+\mathbf{b}$ for all $\mathbf{b} \in \mathbb{R}^n$.

Computing $B = A^+$ is equivalent to computing its columns by finding the optimal least squares solutions $B_1, \ldots, B_m$ to the equations $AB_1 = \mathbf{e}_1, \ldots, AB_m = \mathbf{e}_m$. These are the optimal least squares solutions $B_1, \ldots, B_m$ to the normal equations $A^TAB_1 = A^T\mathbf{e}_1, \ldots, A^TB_m = A^T\mathbf{e}_m$, which, of course, are actual solutions.

EXAMPLE

Suppose that we are to find a general formula for the optimal least squares solution $\mathbf{x}$ to $\begin{bmatrix} 1 & 1 & 1 \\ 1 & 2 & 1 \end{bmatrix}\mathbf{x} = \mathbf{b}$. Let $A = \begin{bmatrix} 1 & 1 & 1 \\ 1 & 2 & 1 \end{bmatrix}$. Since its columns are linearly dependent, we compute the optimal solutions B_1, B_2 to the normal equations $A^TAB_1 = A^T\mathbf{e}_1$, $A^TAB_2 = A^T\mathbf{e}_2$. The general solution to the first equation is

$$B_1 = \begin{bmatrix} 1 \\ -1 \\ 1 \end{bmatrix} + z \begin{bmatrix} -1 \\ 0 \\ 1 \end{bmatrix},$$

whose projection on $c(A^T) = F\begin{bmatrix} 1 \\ 1 \\ 1 \end{bmatrix} + F\begin{bmatrix} 1 \\ 2 \\ 1 \end{bmatrix}$ is $\begin{bmatrix} 1 \\ -1 \\ 1 \end{bmatrix}$. So,

$$B_1 = \begin{bmatrix} 1 \\ -1 \\ 1 \end{bmatrix}.$$

Similarly, $B_2 = \begin{bmatrix} -1/2 \\ 1 \\ -1/2 \end{bmatrix}$, so that

$$A^+ = \begin{bmatrix} 1 & -1/2 \\ -1 & 1 \\ 1 & -1/2 \end{bmatrix}.$$

(Verify!) We conclude that the optimal least squares solution $\mathbf{x}$ to $\begin{bmatrix} 1 & 1 & 1 \\ 1 & 2 & 1 \end{bmatrix}\mathbf{x} = \mathbf{b}$ is

$$\begin{bmatrix} 1 & -1/2 \\ -1 & 1 \\ 1 & -1/2 \end{bmatrix}\mathbf{b}$$

for all $\mathbf{b} \in \mathbb{R}^2$.

When A is symmetric, A^+ can be computed as follows.

Corollary. Let $A \in M_n\mathbb{R}$ be symmetric and let $A = QR$, where the nonzero columns of Q are orthonormal and R is invertible. Then $A^+ = QQ^TR^{-1}Q^T$.

Proof. Since $P_{c(A^T)}(\mathbf{x}) = P_{c(A)}(\mathbf{x}) = QQ^T\mathbf{x}$, Theorem 6.23 says that $A^+\mathbf{b} = T^+(\mathbf{b}) = P_{c(A^T)}(R^{-1}Q^T\mathbf{b}) = QQ^TR^{-1}Q^T\mathbf{b}$. ■

Now, the pseudoinverse of A can be computed from that of A^TA, as follows.

Theorem 6.24. *Computing the Pseudoinverse of A from That of A^TA.* $A^+ = (A^TA)^+A^T$.

Proof. The optimal least squares solution $\mathbf{x}$ to $A\mathbf{x} = \mathbf{b}$ is the optimal solution to $(A^TA)\mathbf{x} = A^T\mathbf{b}$, which is $\mathbf{x} = (A^TA)^+A^T\mathbf{b}$. ■

Corollary. Let $A \in M_{m \times n}\mathbb{R}$. Then $A^+ = QQ^TR^{-1}Q^TA^T$, where $A^TA = QR$, with the nonzero columns of Q orthonormal and R invertible.

In addition to the methods given previously, there are many other ways to compute A^+. Accurate and efficient computation depends on using the method best suited to the particular matrix. In Section 6.11, we introduce the *singular-value decomposition* of A. We then use it to give yet another method for computing A^+, which is sometimes less susceptible to *roundoff error*.

PROBLEMS

NUMERICAL PROBLEMS

1. Find a least squares solution $\mathbf{x}$ to the following equations $A\mathbf{x} = \mathbf{b}$ by finding a solution to the corresponding normal equation $A^TA\mathbf{x} = A^T\mathbf{b}$.

(a) $\begin{bmatrix} 1 \\ 3 \\ 5 \end{bmatrix} \mathbf{x} = \begin{bmatrix} 1 \\ 2 \\ 4 \end{bmatrix}$ **(b)** $\begin{bmatrix} 1 & 1 \\ 2 & 5 \\ 1 & 1 \end{bmatrix} \mathbf{x} = \begin{bmatrix} 1 \\ 5 \\ 2 \end{bmatrix}$ **(c)** $\begin{bmatrix} 1 & 2 \\ 2 & 4 \\ 1 & 2 \end{bmatrix} \mathbf{x} = \begin{bmatrix} 1 \\ 2 \\ 2 \end{bmatrix}$

2. Compute the nullspaces of the matrices A in Problem 1, and use them to give all least squares solutions in each case.

3. Compute the pseudoinverses A^+ of the matrices A in Problem 1, parts (a) and (b).

4. In Problem 1, compute the projection $\mathbf{b}'$ of $\mathbf{b}$ on $c(A)$ in each case.

5. In Problem 1, compute the length of the error vector $\mathbf{b} - \mathbf{b}' = \mathbf{b} - A\mathbf{x}$ in each case.

6. In Problem 1, compute the QR decomposition for A and verify the formula $A^+ = R^{-1}Q^T$ in parts (a) and (b).

7. In Problem 1, compute A^+ in parts (a) and (b) by computing the least squares solutions B_i to the equations $AB_i = \mathbf{e}_i$.

THEORETICAL PROBLEMS

8. Suppose that an experiment is based on an input variable x and output variable y, whereby input values $x_0, \ldots, x_m$ generate output values $y_0, \ldots, y_m$. The researcher seeks a function $f(x) = y$ which "best fits" the data, where $m = 2$, the x values are 1, 3, 4, and the y values are 2, 2, 3. For these data, answer the following:

(a) To get a first-order polynomial f, the researcher computes the least squares solution $a = \begin{bmatrix} a_0 \\ a_1 \end{bmatrix}$ to

$$\begin{bmatrix} 1 & x_0 \\ \vdots & \vdots \\ 1 & x_m \end{bmatrix} \begin{bmatrix} a_0 \\ a_1 \end{bmatrix} = \begin{bmatrix} y_0 \\ \vdots \\ y_m \end{bmatrix}.$$

What polynomial $f(x) = a_0 + a_1x$ is determined?

(b) To get a second-order polynomial f, the researcher computes the least squares solution $a = \begin{bmatrix} a_0 \\ a_1 \\ a_2 \end{bmatrix}$ to

$$\begin{bmatrix} 1 & x_0 & x_0^2 \\ \vdots & \vdots & \vdots \\ 1 & x_m & x_m^2 \end{bmatrix} \begin{bmatrix} a_0 \\ a_1 \\ a_2 \end{bmatrix} = \begin{bmatrix} y_0 \\ \vdots \\ y_m \end{bmatrix}.$$

What polynomial $f(x) = a_0 + a_1 x + a_2 x^2$ is determined?

(c) Set up the equation the researcher can use in computing a least squares solution to get a third-order polynomial f. (Do not compute the solution.)

9. Prove the formula $(A^T A)^{-1} A^T = R^{-1} Q^T$ by direct substitution when $A = QR$, where Q has nonzero orthonormal columns and R is invertible.

10. If the columns of A are orthonormal, show that the element $\mathbf{x}$ whose coordinates are the Fourier coefficients of $\mathbf{b}$ is the unique least squares solution to $A\mathbf{x} = \mathbf{b}$ for any given $\mathbf{b}$.

Hard

11. Formulate and prove Theorems 6.20, 6.21, 6.22 over $\mathbb{C}$, replacing A^T by A^* in the discussion given previously.

Very Hard

12. For any matrix A, show that there is exactly one matrix B such that $ABA = A$, $BAB = B$, $(AB)^T = AB$, and $(BA)^T = BA$, namely, $B = A^+$.

13. Using Problem 12, show that

(a) $(kA)^+ = k^{-1}A^+$; **(b)** $A^{++} = A$; **(c)** $A^{T+} = A^{+T}$;

(d) $B^+ = B^T$ if $BB^TB = B$;

(e) If $A = LDU$, where A is of rank r, L^T is echelon $r \times m$, D is nonsingular diagonal $r \times r$, and U is echelon $r \times n$, then $A^+ = U^+D^+L^+$.

6.9 THE SPECTRAL THEOREM

Unitary triangulation

Recall that A' is unitarily similar to A if $A' = Q^*AQ$ for some unitary matrix U; and a real matrix A' is orthogonally similar to a real matrix A if $A' = Q^TAQ$ for some real orthogonal matrix Q. To give the spectral theorem in these terms, the following general triangulation theorem is needed.

Theorem 6.25. *Unitary Triangulation of a Square Matrix.*

Any $A \in M_n\mathbb{C}$ is unitarily similar to an upper triangular matrix. If A is real and the spectrum of A is real, then A is similar by an orthogonal matrix Q to a real upper triangular matrix.

Proof. A is similar over F to an upper triangular matrix C, by Theorems 5.31 and 5.32. Take an invertible matrix $B \in M_nF$ such that $B^{-1}AB = C$. Since B is invertible, the QR decomposition of B is $B = QR$, where $Q, R \in M_nF$, Q is unitary, and R is invertible and upper triangular (Section 6.3). Then $C = (QR)^{-1}AQR = R^{-1}Q^*AQR$ and $Q^*AQ = RCR^{-1}$. Since R, C, R^{-1} are upper triangular, so is RCR^{-1}. So, A is unitarily similar to the upper triangular matrix $Q^*AQ = RCR^{-1}$. When $F = \mathbb{R}$, Q is real orthogonal, so A is orthogonally similar to the upper triangular matrix $Q^TAQ = RCR^{-1}$. ■

Corollary. Let T be a linear transformation of a Euclidean space V over F and suppose that $F = \mathbb{C}$ or that $F = \mathbb{R}$ and the spectrum of T is real. Then V has an orthonormal basis of generalized characteristic vectors for T.

Proof. Let $\mathbf{v}_1, \ldots, \mathbf{v}_n$ be an orthonormal basis for V. By Theorem 6.25, the matrix A of T with respect to the basis $\mathbf{v}_s$ is similar to an upper triangular matrix $A' = Q^*AQ$, Q being unitary if $F = \mathbb{C}$ and real orthogonal if $F = \mathbb{R}$. Letting S be the unitary linear transformation of V whose matrix with respect to the basis $\mathbf{v}_s$ is Q, $S(\mathbf{v}_1), \ldots, S(\mathbf{v}_n)$ is an orthonormal basis of generalized characteristic vectors for T, since the matrix of T with respect to this basis is the upper triangular matrix $A' = Q^*AQ$, by Theorem 4.23. ■

The problem of computing the orthonormal basis Q of generalized characteristic vectors for A has been studied in depth from many points of view. One of the best methods is the iterative method discussed in Section 6.12 and, for real symmetric matrices, in Sections 7.6 and 7.7

The spectral theorem

We can now prove spectral theorem in its geometric form.

Theorem 6.26. *Unitary Diagonalization of a Hermitian Matrix.* Any Hermitian matrix $A \in M_n\mathbb{C}$ is unitarily similar to a real diagonal matrix. If A is a real symmetric matrix, it is orthogonally similar to a real diagonal matrix.

Proof. Let Q be a unitary matrix such that $Q^*AQ = C$, where C is an upper triangular matrix, by Theorem 6.25. Since A is Hermitian and Q is unitary, Q^*AQ is Hermitian (verify), so C is Hermitian. Since C is upper triangular, it follows that C is a real diagonal matrix. (Explain!) This proves the first assertion. If A is real, the spectrum of A is real, since C is real. (Explain!) But then we can take the Q in Theorem 6.25 to be a real orthogonal matrix. So, A is orthogonally similar to C. ■

For Hermitian transformations, the counterpart of the corollary to Theorem 6.25 is the following.

Corollary. Let T be a Hermitian linear transformation of a Euclidean space V over F. Then V has an orthonormal basis of characteristic vectors for T.

Proof. Let $\mathbf{v}_1, \ldots, \mathbf{v}_n$ be an orthonormal basis for V. By Theorem 6.26, the matrix A of T with respect to the basis $\mathbf{v}_s$ is similar to a real diagonal matrix $A' = Q^*AQ$, Q being unitary if $F = \mathbb{C}$ and real orthogonal if $F = \mathbb{R}$. Letting S be the unitary linear transformation of V whose matrix with respect to the basis $\mathbf{v}_s$ is Q, $S(\mathbf{v}_1), \ldots, S(\mathbf{v}_n)$ is an orthonormal basis of characteristic vectors for T, since the matrix of T with respect to this basis is the diagonal matrix A', by Theorem 4.23. ∎

The Hermitian adjoint of a linear transformation

For $A \in M_nF$, the **Hermitian adjoint** of $T(\mathbf{x}) = A\mathbf{x}$ is $T^*(\mathbf{x}) = A^*\mathbf{x}$. We now define the Hermitian adjoint in general.

Let V be a Euclidean space with orthonormal basis $\mathbf{v}_1, \ldots, \mathbf{v}_n$ and let $R(a_1\mathbf{v}_1 + \cdots + a_n\mathbf{v}_n) = a_1\mathbf{e}_1 + \cdots + a_n\mathbf{e}_n$ be the corresponding coordinate isometry. For $T \in L(V, V)$, we define T^* as $T^* = R^{-1}(RTR^{-1})^*R$. This cumbersome definition of T^* is quite natural, since it simply transfers the notion of Hermitian adjoint from the linear transformation RTR^{-1} of F^n to T. It is used but once, to give T^* a life of its own, independent of its origins. This is done as follows.

Theorem 6.27. *The Hermitian Adjoint.*
$\langle T(\mathbf{v}), \mathbf{w}\rangle = \langle \mathbf{v}, T^*(\mathbf{w})\rangle$ for all $\mathbf{v}, \mathbf{w} \in V$.

Proof. Since R is an isometry and $T^* = R^{-1}(RTR^{-1})^*R$, we have

$$\begin{aligned}\langle \mathbf{v}, T^*(\mathbf{w})\rangle &= \langle R(\mathbf{v}), RT^*(\mathbf{v})\rangle = \langle R(\mathbf{v}), RR^{-1}(RTR^{-1})^*R(\mathbf{w})\rangle \\ &= \langle R(\mathbf{v}), (RTR^{-1})^*R(\mathbf{w})\rangle = \langle (RTR^{-1})R(\mathbf{v}), R(\mathbf{w})\rangle \\ &= \langle RT(\mathbf{v}), R(\mathbf{w})\rangle = \langle T(\mathbf{v}), \mathbf{w}\rangle. \quad ∎\end{aligned}$$

Corollary. Let $\mathbf{v}_1, \ldots, \mathbf{v}_n$ be any orthonormal basis for a Euclidean space V and let $T \in L(V, V)$ have matrix A with respect to the basis $\mathbf{v}_s$. Then A^* is the matrix of T^* with respect to the basis $\mathbf{v}_s$.

Proof. The condition on the entries of A is $T(\mathbf{v}_s) = a_{1s}\mathbf{v}_1 + \cdots + a_{ns}\mathbf{v}_n$, so that $\langle T(\mathbf{v}_s), \mathbf{v}_r\rangle = a_{rs}$. The condition on the entries of the matrix A' of T^* is $T^*(\mathbf{v}_s) = a'_{1s}\mathbf{v}_1 + \cdots + a'_{ns}\mathbf{v}_n$, so that $\langle \mathbf{v}_s, T^*(\mathbf{v}_r)\rangle = \overline{\langle T^*(\mathbf{v}_r), \mathbf{v}_s\rangle} = \overline{\mathbf{a}'_{sr}}$. But then

$$a_{rs} = \langle T(\mathbf{v}_s), \mathbf{v}_r\rangle = \langle \mathbf{v}_s, T^*(\mathbf{v}_r)\rangle = \overline{a'_{sr}},$$

so that $A' = \bar{A}^T = A^*$. ∎

From this, it follows that *our definition of T^* is independent of the orthonormal basis used in defining it.* (Explain!)

The following theorem gives the properties of T^*, which follow directly from the corresponding properties of the Hermitian adjoint A^* of the matrix A of T with respect to an orthonormal basis.

Theorem 6.28. *Properties of the Hermitian Adjoint of T.*
Let V be a Euclidean space and let $S, T \in L(V, V)$. Then

1. $(S + T)^* = S^* + T^*$ and $(aT)^* = \bar{a}T^*$ for all $a \in F$.
2. $(ST)^* = T^*S^*$.

If $T = T^*$, we say that T is **Hermitian**; and if $T = -T^*$, we say that T is **skew-Hermitian**. As for matrices, in Section 5.7, we get the following equivalent conditions.

Hermitian and Skew-Hermitian Transformations.
Let T be a linear transformation of a Euclidean space. Then

1. T is Hermitian if and only if $\langle T(\mathbf{v}), \mathbf{w}\rangle = \langle \mathbf{v}, T(\mathbf{w})\rangle$ for all $\mathbf{v}, \mathbf{w} \in V$.
2. T is skew-Hermitian if and only if $\langle T(\mathbf{v}), \mathbf{w}\rangle = -\langle \mathbf{v}, T(\mathbf{w})\rangle$ for all $\mathbf{v}, \mathbf{w} \in V$.

The characteristic subspaces of T

The **characteristic subspace** of T corresponding to a characteristic value c of T is $V_c = \text{Kernel}\,(T - cI)$, the nonzero elements of V_c being the characteristic vectors of T corresponding to c. When T is Hermitian, V_c is orthogonal to V_d if $c \neq d$. For if $\mathbf{v} \in V_c$ and $\mathbf{w} \in V_d$, then $c\langle \mathbf{v}, \mathbf{w}\rangle = \langle T(\mathbf{v}), \mathbf{w}\rangle = \langle \mathbf{v}, T(\mathbf{w})\rangle = \langle \mathbf{v}, d(\mathbf{w})\rangle = d\langle \mathbf{v}, \mathbf{w}\rangle$, d being real. So, if $\langle \mathbf{v}, \mathbf{w}\rangle$ is nonzero, then it can be canceled, leaving $c = d$. Since the elements of the basis given in the preceding theorem come from the characteristic subspaces V_c, this proves the following.

Theorem 6.29. *The Sum of the Characteristic Subspaces of a Hermitian Transformation.*
Let T be a Hermitian linear transformation of a Euclidean space V over F. Then $V = V_{c_1} \oplus \cdots \oplus V_{c_k}$ where the V_{c_s} are the characteristic subspaces of T.

EXAMPLE

The characteristic polynomial of $\begin{bmatrix} 6 & -2 \\ -2 & 6 \end{bmatrix}$ is $(z - 2)(z - 4)$. One characteristic vector is $\begin{bmatrix} 1 \\ 1 \end{bmatrix}$, corresponding to 2. By Theorem 6.29, the other is any nonzero vector orthogonal to $\begin{bmatrix} 1 \\ 1 \end{bmatrix}$, such as $\begin{bmatrix} -1 \\ 1 \end{bmatrix}$. It is a characteristic vector corresponding to 4. (Check!)

PROBLEMS

NUMERICAL PROBLEMS

1. For each of the following real symmetric matrices A, find an orthogonal matrix Q such that Q^*AQ is diagonal.

(a) $A = \begin{bmatrix} 1 & 1 \\ 1 & 3 \end{bmatrix}$ **(b)** $A = \begin{bmatrix} 1 & -1 \\ -1 & 2 \end{bmatrix}$ **(c)** $A = \begin{bmatrix} 0 & 1 \\ 1 & 4 \end{bmatrix}$

(d) $A = \begin{bmatrix} 0 & 4 \\ 4 & 1 \end{bmatrix}$ **(e)** $A = \begin{bmatrix} 6 & -2 & 0 \\ -2 & 6 & 0 \\ 0 & 0 & 3 \end{bmatrix}$

(f) $A = \begin{bmatrix} 6 & -2 & 0 & 0 \\ -2 & 6 & 0 & 0 \\ 0 & 0 & 1 & 1 \\ 0 & 0 & 1 & 3 \end{bmatrix}$ **(g)** $A = \begin{bmatrix} 0 & 0 & 0 & 1 \\ 0 & 0 & 1 & 0 \\ 0 & 1 & 0 & 0 \\ 1 & 0 & 0 & 0 \end{bmatrix}$

2. Let V be a Euclidean space over $\mathbb{R}$ with orthonormal basis $\mathbf{v}_1, \mathbf{v}_2, \mathbf{v}_3$. For the linear transformation

$$T(a\mathbf{v}_1 + b\mathbf{v}_2 + c\mathbf{v}_3) = (a + b + c)\mathbf{v}_1 + (b + c)\mathbf{v}_2 + c\mathbf{v}_3,$$

describe T^* and find the matrices of T and T^* with respect to the basis of $\mathbf{v}$'s.

Hard

3. In Problem 2, find an orthonormal basis of characteristic vectors for $T + T^*$.

4. Let V be a Euclidean space over $\mathbb{R}$ with basis $\mathbf{v}_1, \mathbf{v}_2, \mathbf{w}$, where $\mathbf{v}_1$ and $\mathbf{v}_2$ are of length 1 and orthogonal to each other and $\langle \mathbf{v}_1, \mathbf{w} \rangle = \langle \mathbf{v}_2, \mathbf{w} \rangle = 1$.

(a) Find $\mathbf{v}_3$ such that $\mathbf{v}_1, \mathbf{v}_2, \mathbf{v}_3$ is an orthonormal basis for V.

(b) For the linear transformation

$$T(a\mathbf{v}_1 + b\mathbf{v}_2 + c\mathbf{w}) = (a + b + c)\mathbf{v}_1 + (b + c)\mathbf{v}_2 + c\mathbf{w},$$

find the matrix of T and T^* with respect to the basis of $\mathbf{v}$'s.

5. Are the characteristic roots of T the same in Problems 2 and 4? Explain!

6. Are the characteristic roots of $T + T^*$ the same in Problems 2 and 4? Explain!

7. Give an example of a real matrix P which is not symmetric such that $P^2 = P$.

THEORETICAL PROBLEMS

8. If A is Hermitian and invertible, for what integers k is A^k Hermitian?

9. If A is skew-Hermitian and invertible, for what integers k is A^k skew-Hermitian?

10. If A is skew-Hermitian and invertible, for what integers k is A^k Hermitian?

11. Show that A is Hermitian if and only if iA is skew-Hermitian.
12. Show that all characteristic roots of a skew-Hermitian matrix are pure imaginaries.
13. If A is skew-Hermitian and real, show that if a is a characteristic root, then so is $-a$.
14. Show that if A is Hermitian or skew-Hermitian and has only one characteristic root, then A is a scalar matrix.

Hard

15. If A is Hermitian and $A^k = 0$, show that $A = 0$.
16. If $A\mathbf{v} = \mathbf{0}$ and $AA^* = A^*A$, show that $A^*\mathbf{v} = \mathbf{0}$.

6.10 NORMAL TRANSFORMATIONS

Any matrix $A \in M_nF$ can be written as $A = A_+ + A_-$, where $A_+ = (A + A^*)/2$ and $A_- = (A - A^*)/2$. We call A_+ and A_- the *Hermitian* and *skew-Hermitian parts* of A, since $A_+^* = A_+$ and $A_-^* = -A_-$.

EXAMPLE

If $A = \begin{bmatrix} 1 & 1 \\ 3 & 4 \end{bmatrix}$, then $A_+ = \begin{bmatrix} 1 & 2 \\ 2 & 4 \end{bmatrix}$ and $A_- = \begin{bmatrix} 0 & -1 \\ 1 & 0 \end{bmatrix}$.

These parts of A are determined by their properties, in the following sense.

Theorem 6.30. *The Hermitian and Skew-Hermitian Parts of A.* Let $A = B + C$, where B is Hermitian and C is skew-Hermitian. Then $B = A_+$ and $C = A_-$.

Proof. Since $A^* = B^* + C^* = B - C$, $A + A^* = 2B$ and $A - A^* = 2C$. Dividing by 2 gives the stated conclusion. ∎

In the same manner, for a Euclidean space V and $T \in L(V, V)$, T can be written as $T = T_+ + T_-$, where $T_+ = (T + T^*)/2$ and $T_- = (T - T^*)/2$. We call T_+ and T_- the *Hermitian* and *skew-Hermitian parts* of T. As with matrices, if $T = R + S$, where R is Hermitian and S is skew-Hermitian, then $R = T_+$ and $S = T_-$. By the uniqueness given in the preceding theorem, the Hermitian and skew-Hermitian parts of the matrix of a linear transformation T with respect to an orthonormal basis are just the matrices of the Hermitian and skew-Hermitian parts of T with respect to the same basis. (Explain!)

This simple discussion shows that a matrix or linear transformation can be studied in terms of its Hermitian and skew-Hermitian parts. When a linear transformation T comes into being in connection with some mathematical model created to study real-world phenomena, T_+ and T_- often *commute*—that is, $T_+T_- = T_-T_+$. For this reason, we now consider normal matrices and linear transformations in the following sense.

Definition. *Normal Matrix.*
A matrix $A \in M_nF$ or linear transformation T of a Euclidean space V is **normal** if its Hermitian and skew-Hermitian parts commute.

EXAMPLES

1. Let

$$A = \begin{bmatrix} -1 & 1 & 1 \\ -1 & -2 & 1 \\ 1 & -1 & -1 \end{bmatrix}.$$

Then

$$A_+ = \begin{bmatrix} -1 & 0 & 1 \\ 0 & -2 & 0 \\ 1 & 0 & -1 \end{bmatrix}, \quad A_- = \begin{bmatrix} 0 & 1 & 0 \\ -1 & 0 & 1 \\ 0 & -1 & 0 \end{bmatrix},$$

which commute. (Verify!) So, A is normal.

2. If C is real and skew-symmetric, then $A = C^2 + C$ is normal, since its symmetric and skew-symmetric parts C^2 and C commute. (Explain!)

Studying a normal transformation T of a Euclidean space V in terms of T_+ and T_- is quite easy, since we can bring to bear the full power of the spectral theorem. Here is why.

1. Any theorem about a Hermitian transformation R has a counterpart which is a theorem about a skew-Hermitian matrix. The reason for this is that $S^* = S$ if and only if $(iS)^* = \bar{i}S = -iS$; that is, S is skew-Hermitian if and only if iS is Hermitian.

2. Applying this strategy to the spectral theorem, we get a version of it for skew-Hermitian matrices C and skew-Hermitian linear transformations S.

(a) iC is Hermitian and therefore unitarily similar to a real diagonal matrix D. So, C is unitarily similar to the pure imaginary diagonal matrix $-iD$. (Explain!)

(b) $V = V_{c_1} \oplus \cdots \oplus V_{ck}$, where the V_{c_s} are the characteristic subspaces of iS. But $iS(\mathbf{v}) = c\mathbf{v}$ if and only if $S(\mathbf{v}) = -ic\mathbf{v}$. So, the characteristic subspace V_c for iS corresponding to c is the characteristic subspace for S corresponding to $-ic$. It follows that *V is the orthogonal sum of the characteristic subspaces for S.*

3. When $T = T_+ + T_-$ is normal, we can express V as the orthogonal sum $V = V_{c_1} \oplus \cdots \oplus V_{ck}$ of the characteristic subspaces of T_+. Since T_+ and T_- commute, we have $T_-(V_c) \subseteq T_-(V_c)$ for all c, since $T_+(\mathbf{v}) = c\mathbf{v}$ then implies that $T_+(T_-(\mathbf{v})) = T_-(T_+(\mathbf{v})) = T_-(c\mathbf{v}) = cT_-(\mathbf{v})$. Since the linear transformation $S(\mathbf{v}) = T_-(\mathbf{v})$ ($\mathbf{v} \in V_c$) is a skew-Hermitian transformation of V_c, we can then express V_c as the orthogonal sum of the characteristic subspaces $(V_c)_d$ of S. Since $(V_c)_d = V_c \cap W_d$, where W_d is the characteristic subspace of T_- corresponding to d, V is the orthogonal sum of all of the spaces $V_{c_r} \cap W_{d_s}$, where the c_r, d_s are the characteristic roots of T_+, T_-.

4. The matrix A of T with respect to any given orthonormal basis for V is normal if and only if T is normal. (Explain!)

5. If matrices A and B are unitarily similar, A is normal if and only if B is normal. (Explain!).

We can now give the following criteria.

Theorem 6.31. *Criteria for a Normal Linear Transformation.* Let V be a Euclidean space. Then for any $T \in L(V, V)$ and the corresponding matrix A of T with respect to a given orthonormal basis $\mathbf{v}_1, \ldots, \mathbf{v}_n$, the following conditions are equivalent:

1. T is normal.
2. $TT^* = T^*T$.
3. V has an orthonormal basis of characteristic vectors for T.
4. A is unitarily similar to a diagonal matrix.

Proof. If T is normal, T_+ and T_- commute, from which it follows that $T = T_+ + T_-$ commutes with both of T_+ and T_-. (Verify!) Since $T^* = T_+ - T_-$, T must then commute with T^*. Conversely, if $TT^* = T^*T$, then T commutes with T_+ and T_-, since they are linear combinations of T and T^*. (Verify!) This shows that (1) and (2) are equivalent.

If T is normal, we have seen that V is the orthogonal sum of the spaces $V_{c_r} \cap W_{d_s}$, where the c_r and d_s are the characteristic roots of T_+ and T_-. Taking an orthonormal basis $\mathbf{u}_1, \ldots, \mathbf{u}_n$ as the union of orthonormal bases for each of the orthogonal subspaces $V_{c_r} \cap W_{d_s}$, we get an orthonormal basis of vectors which are characteristic vectors for T_+ and T_- *simultaneously*. But then the basis is an orthonormal basis of characteristic vectors for $T = T_+ + T_-$. So, (1) implies (3).

If $\mathbf{u}_1, \ldots, \mathbf{u}_n$ is an orthonormal basis of characteristic vectors for T, then the matrix D of T with respect to $\mathbf{u}_1, \ldots, \mathbf{u}_n$ is a diagonal matrix, which, by the Corollary to Theorem 6.9, is unitarily similar to A. So, (3) implies (4).

Finally, suppose that A is unitarily similar to a diagonal matrix D. Since the Hermitian and skew-Hermitian parts D_+ and D_- of D are also diagonal (explain), D is normal. But then A is unitarily similar to a normal matrix, so A itself is normal. Since the matrix A of T is normal, T is normal. So, (4) implies (1).

It follows that conditions (1)–(4) are equivalent. ■

EXAMPLE

$$A = \begin{bmatrix} 1 & 1 & 1 \\ -1 & 2 & -1 \\ 1 & 1 & 1 \end{bmatrix}$$

is normal with

$$A_+ = \begin{bmatrix} 1 & 0 & 1 \\ 0 & 2 & 0 \\ 1 & 0 & 1 \end{bmatrix}, \qquad A_- = \begin{bmatrix} 0 & 1 & 0 \\ -1 & 0 & -1 \\ 0 & 1 & 0 \end{bmatrix}.$$

(Verify!) The characteristic roots of A_+ are 2, 2, 0, with corresponding characteristic vectors

$$\begin{bmatrix} 1 \\ 0 \\ 1 \end{bmatrix}, \quad \begin{bmatrix} 0 \\ 1 \\ 0 \end{bmatrix}, \quad \begin{bmatrix} 1 \\ 0 \\ -1 \end{bmatrix}.$$

(Verify!) The subspace

$$V = \mathbb{C}\begin{bmatrix} 1 \\ 0 \\ 1 \end{bmatrix} + \mathbb{C}\begin{bmatrix} 0 \\ 1 \\ 0 \end{bmatrix}$$

is mapped into itself by A_- and so has an orthonormal basis $\mathbf{v}_1, \mathbf{v}_2$ of characteristic vectors of A_-. (Find one!) Since $\begin{bmatrix} 1 \\ 0 \\ -1 \end{bmatrix}$ is a characteristic vector for A_- (verify), it follows that there is an orthonormal basis comprising $\mathbf{v}_1, \mathbf{v}_2, \mathbf{v}_3$, which are simultaneously characteristic vectors for A, A_+, A_-. Then A is unitarily similar by $V = [\mathbf{v}_1 \quad \mathbf{v}_2 \quad \mathbf{v}_3]$ to a diagonal matrix.

PROBLEMS

NUMERICAL PROBLEMS

1. Find A_+ and A_- for the following matrices A.

(a) $\begin{bmatrix} 1 & 2 \\ 3 & 5 \end{bmatrix}$ **(b)** $\begin{bmatrix} 2 & 3 \\ 5 & 7 \end{bmatrix}$ **(c)** $\begin{bmatrix} -1 & 2 \\ 4 & 5 \end{bmatrix}$ **(d)** $\begin{bmatrix} 1 & 1 & 3 \\ 1 & 2 & 1 \\ 1 & 1 & 1 \end{bmatrix}$

2. For

$$A = \begin{bmatrix} -1 & 1 & 1 \\ -1 & -2 & 1 \\ 1 & -1 & -1 \end{bmatrix},$$

show that

$$A_+ = \begin{bmatrix} -1 & 0 & 1 \\ 0 & -2 & 0 \\ 1 & 0 & -1 \end{bmatrix}, \quad A_- = \begin{bmatrix} 0 & 1 & 0 \\ -1 & 0 & 1 \\ 0 & -1 & 0 \end{bmatrix},$$

and A is normal.

3. Find an orthonormal basis of characteristic vectors for the matrix A in Problem 2.

4. Find a unitary matrix U such that $U^*AU = D$ is diagonal for the matrix A in Problem 2.

5. For

$$A = \begin{bmatrix} -1 & 1 & 2 \\ -1 & -5 & 2 \\ 2 & -2 & -4 \end{bmatrix},$$

show that

$$A_+ = \begin{bmatrix} -1 & 0 & 2 \\ 0 & -5 & 0 \\ 2 & 0 & -4 \end{bmatrix}, \quad A_- = \begin{bmatrix} 0 & 1 & 0 \\ -1 & 0 & 2 \\ 0 & -2 & 0 \end{bmatrix},$$

and A is normal.

6. Find an orthonormal basis of characteristic vectors for the matrix A in Problem 5.

7. Find a unitary matrix U such that $U^*AU = D$ is diagonal for the matrix A in Problem 5.

8. Show that if A is a real 2×2 matrix, then A is normal if and only if either A is symmetric or $A = \begin{bmatrix} a & b \\ -b & a \end{bmatrix}$ for some a, b.

9. Find all a, b such that

$$\begin{bmatrix} a & b & 0 \\ -b & b & b \\ 0 & -b & a \end{bmatrix}$$

is normal.

10. Describe a normal matrix A such that $A^{10} = I$ and $A^8 \neq I$.

Hard

11. For the matrix A in Problem 2, find two symmetric matrices B such that $B^2 = AA^*$.

THEORETICAL PROBLEMS

12. If A is normal, show that aA is normal.

13. Derive the properties of T^* in Theorem 6.28.

14. If C is real and skew-symmetric, show that $A = C^2 + C$ is normal.

15. If $A \in M_nF$ and $\mathbf{v}$ is a nonzero vector such that $AA^*\mathbf{v} = a\mathbf{v}$, show that $a \geq 0$.

16. If A is Hermitian and $AB = BA$, show that $(AB)_+ = AB_+$ and $(AB)_- = AB_-$.

17. If A is skew-Hermitian and $AB = BA$, show that $(AB)_- = AB_+$, $(AB)_+ = AB_-$.

Hard

18. If $A \in M_nF$ is Hermitian and all its characteristic roots are positive, show that there exists a Hermitian matrix B such that $B^2 = A$.

19. Suppose that A and B are normal and that $AB = BA$ and $AB^* = B^*A$. Show that $rA + sB$ is normal for all scalars r and s.

20. Give an example of normal matrices A and B such that $A + B$ is not normal.

21. Show that if an invertible matrix A is normal, then A^*A^{-1} is unitary.

22. For $A \in M_n\mathbb{R}$, A_+ usually has distinct characteristic roots. Given this, show that a normal matrix A usually is symmetric.

23. If A is normal and $(A - aI)^k\mathbf{v} = \mathbf{0}$ for some positive integer k, show that $A\mathbf{v} = a\mathbf{v}$.

6.11 THE SINGULAR-VALUE DECOMPOSITION

Given $A \in M_{m \times n}F$, the spectral theorem assures us that there is an orthonormal basis $\mathbf{v}_1, \ldots, \mathbf{v}_n$ of F^n of characteristic vectors for the Hermitian matrix A^*A, the corresponding characteristic roots c_i being real. Rearrange the $\mathbf{v}$'s so that $c_1 \geq \cdots \geq c_n$.

Since $A^*A\mathbf{v}_i = c_i\mathbf{v}_i$ and $\langle A^*A\mathbf{v}_i, \mathbf{v}_j\rangle = \langle A\mathbf{v}_i, A\mathbf{v}_j\rangle$, we have $c_i\langle \mathbf{v}_i, \mathbf{v}_j\rangle = \langle A\mathbf{v}_i, A\mathbf{v}_j\rangle$. Since $\langle \mathbf{v}_i, \mathbf{v}_j\rangle$ is 0 if $i \neq j$ and 1 if $i = j$, the set $A\mathbf{v}_1, \ldots, A\mathbf{v}_n$ is an orthogonal set of vectors and, in fact, satisfies

$$\langle A\mathbf{v}_i, A\mathbf{v}_j\rangle = 0 \text{ if } i \neq j;$$

$$\langle A\mathbf{v}_i, A\mathbf{v}_i\rangle = c_i.$$

So, $c_i = \|A\mathbf{v}_i\|^2$ for $1 \leq i \leq n$. Replace the nonzero vectors $A\mathbf{v}_i$ by $\mathbf{w}_i = A\mathbf{v}_i/\|A\mathbf{v}_i\|$ $(1 \leq i \leq r)$ and extend the orthonormal set $\mathbf{w}_1, \ldots, \mathbf{w}_r$ to an orthonormal basis $\mathbf{w}_1, \ldots, \mathbf{w}_m$ for F^m. The matrix of $T(\mathbf{x}) = A\mathbf{x}$ with respect to the orthonormal bases $P = [\mathbf{v}_1 \ \ldots \ \mathbf{v}_n]$ for F^n and $Q = [\mathbf{w}_1 \ \ldots \ \mathbf{w}_m]$ for F^m is the $m \times n$ matrix Q^*AP (Section 4.6, Theorem 4.21). Since $T(\mathbf{v}_i) = A\mathbf{v}_i = d_i\mathbf{w}_i$, where $d_i = \|A\mathbf{v}_i\| = \sqrt{c_i}$ for $1 \leq i \leq r$ and 0 for $r + 1 \leq i \leq n$ (explain), the matrix of $T(\mathbf{x}) = A\mathbf{x}$ with respect to the bases P and $Q = [\mathbf{w}_1 \ \ldots \ \mathbf{w}_m]$ is the $m \times n$ matrix

$$D = \left[\begin{array}{c|c} D_r & 0 \\ \hline 0 & 0 \end{array}\right],$$

where $D_r = \text{Diag}(d_1, \ldots, d_r)$. So, $Q^*AP = D$, which proves the first part of the following theorem.

Theorem 6.32. *Matrix of A with Respect to Bases P and Q.*
Let $A \in M_{m\times n}F$. Then there are unitary matrices $P \in M_nF$, $Q \in M_mF$ such that

$$Q^*AP = \left[\begin{array}{c|c} D_r & 0 \\ \hline 0 & 0 \end{array}\right],$$

where $D_r = \text{Diag}(d_1, \ldots, d_r)$, the d_r are positive real numbers, and $d_1 \geq \cdots \geq d_r$. For any such P and Q, the d_j are unique, and their squares are the nonzero characteristic roots of A^*A.

Proof. We've seen that such P and Q exist. Suppose, conversely, that we are given unitary matrices $P \in M_nF$, $Q \in M_mF$ such that $Q^*AP = D$, where

$$D = \left[\begin{array}{c|c} D_r & 0 \\ \hline 0 & 0 \end{array}\right],$$

$D_r = \text{Diag}(d_1, \ldots, d_r)$, the d_r are positive real numbers, and $d_1 \geq \cdots \geq d_r$. Then $D^2 = D^*D = P^*A^*QQ^*AP = P^*(A^*A)P$, which implies that the characteristic roots d_i^2 of D^2 are the characteristic roots of A^*A. This proves, in particular, that the d_i are unique. ■

The preceding gives the singular-value decomposition.

Singular-Value Decomposition of A.
Any $A \in M_nF$ can be decomposed as $A = QDP^*$, where Q and P are unitary (real orthogonal if A is real) and D is diagonal with real nonnegative entries, which are unique except for order (Figure 6.17).

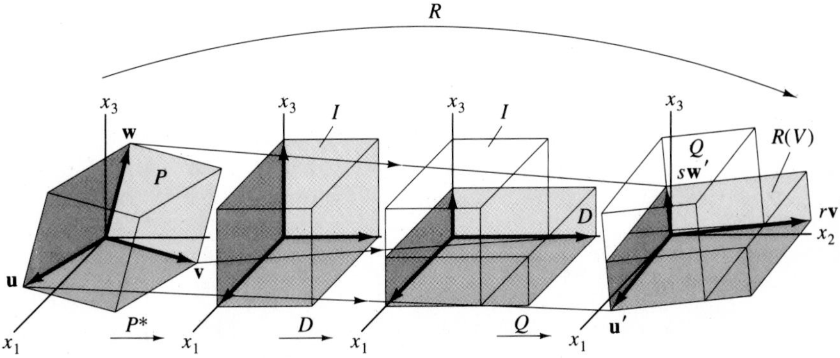

Figure 6.17 The singular-value decomposition $A = QDP^*$ corresponds to the factorization $R(\mathbf{x}) = Q(D(P^*\mathbf{x}))$ of $R(\mathbf{x}) = A\mathbf{x}$. Here, $P = [\mathbf{u} \quad \mathbf{v} \quad \mathbf{w}]$, $D = \text{Diag}(1, r, s)$, and $Q = [\mathbf{u}' \quad \mathbf{v}' \quad \mathbf{w}']$.

EXAMPLE

To get the singular-value decomposition of a matrix such as

$$A = \begin{bmatrix} 2 & 2 \\ 1 & -1 \\ -1 & 1 \\ -2 & -2 \end{bmatrix},$$

we proceed as in the proof of Theorem 6.2. The characteristic roots of $A^TA = \begin{bmatrix} 10 & 6 \\ 6 & 10 \end{bmatrix}$ are 4 and 16, whose square roots are 2 and 4. So, $D = \begin{bmatrix} 4 & 0 \\ 0 & 2 \end{bmatrix}$. The corresponding characteristic vectors are $\begin{bmatrix} 1 \\ 1 \end{bmatrix}$ and $\begin{bmatrix} 1 \\ -1 \end{bmatrix}$, so $P = (1/\sqrt{2}) \begin{bmatrix} 1 & 1 \\ 1 & -1 \end{bmatrix}$. Since

$$A\begin{bmatrix} 1 \\ 1 \end{bmatrix} = \begin{bmatrix} 4 \\ 0 \\ 0 \\ -4 \end{bmatrix} \quad \text{and} \quad A\begin{bmatrix} 1 \\ -1 \end{bmatrix} = \begin{bmatrix} 0 \\ 2 \\ -2 \\ 0 \end{bmatrix},$$

we augment to the orthogonal basis

$$\begin{bmatrix} 4 \\ 0 \\ 0 \\ -4 \end{bmatrix}, \quad \begin{bmatrix} 0 \\ 2 \\ -2 \\ 0 \end{bmatrix}, \quad \begin{bmatrix} 0 \\ 1 \\ 1 \\ 0 \end{bmatrix}, \quad \begin{bmatrix} 1 \\ 0 \\ 0 \\ 1 \end{bmatrix}$$

and let

$$Q = \left(\frac{1}{\sqrt{2}}\right) \begin{bmatrix} 1 & 0 & 0 & 1 \\ 0 & 1 & 1 & 0 \\ 0 & -1 & 1 & 0 \\ -1 & 0 & 0 & 1 \end{bmatrix}.$$

The decomposition $A = QDP^*$ is then

$$A = \left(\frac{1}{\sqrt{2}}\right) \begin{bmatrix} 1 & 0 & 0 & 1 \\ 0 & 1 & 1 & 0 \\ 0 & -1 & 1 & 0 \\ -1 & 0 & 0 & 1 \end{bmatrix} \begin{bmatrix} 4 & 0 \\ 0 & 2 \\ 0 & 0 \\ 0 & 0 \end{bmatrix} \left(\frac{1}{\sqrt{2}}\right) \begin{bmatrix} 1 & 1 \\ 1 & -1 \end{bmatrix}.$$

(Verify!)

Computing the pseudoinverse of *A*

The singular-value decomposition of $A = QDP^T$ provides an excellent method for getting the pseudoinverse A^+ of A. Since D^+, for an $m \times n$ diagonal matrix D, is the $n \times m$ diagonal matrix obtained by replacing each nonzero diagonal entry of D by its inverse and leaving all other entries alone (verify), A^+ can be computed as $A^+ = PD^+Q^T$, as illustrated in Figure 6.18.

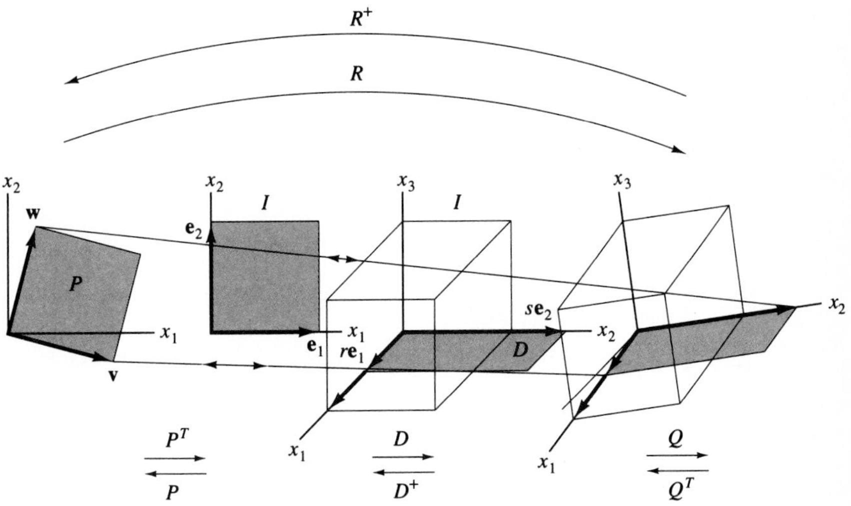

Figure 6.18 The linear transformation $R(\mathbf{x}) = Q\begin{bmatrix} r & 0 \\ 0 & s \\ 0 & 0 \end{bmatrix}P^T$

and its pseudoinverse $R^+(\mathbf{x}) = P\begin{bmatrix} 1/r & 0 & 0 \\ 0 & 1/s & 0 \end{bmatrix}Q^T\mathbf{x}.$

Theorem 6.33. *Pseudoinverse of* $A = QDP^T$.
Let $A \in M_n\mathbb{R}$ and suppose that $A = QDP^T$, where P and Q are real orthogonal matrices. Then $A^+ = PD^+Q^T$.

Proof. To see that $\mathbf{x} = A^+\mathbf{b}$ if and only if $\mathbf{x} = PD^+Q^T\mathbf{b}$, note that $\mathbf{x} = A^+\mathbf{b}$ if and only if $\mathbf{x} = (QDP^T)^+\mathbf{b}$ if and only if $\mathbf{x}$ is the optimal solution to the normal equation $(QDP^T)^TQDP^T\mathbf{x} = (QDP^T)^T\mathbf{b}$, which is equivalent to the equation $PD^TDP^T\mathbf{x} = PD^TQ^T\mathbf{b}$. This, in turn, is equivalent to $D^TDP^T\mathbf{x} = D^TQ^T\mathbf{b}$, whose optimal solution is $P^T\mathbf{x} = D^+Q^T\mathbf{b}$. But then $\mathbf{x} = A^+\mathbf{b}$ if and only if $\mathbf{x} = PD^+Q^T\mathbf{b}$. ■

EXAMPLE

For

$$A = \begin{bmatrix} 2 & 2 \\ 1 & -1 \\ -1 & 1 \\ -2 & -2 \end{bmatrix},$$

the pseudoinverse of A is $A^+ = PD^+Q^T$. By the preceding example, this is

$$A^+ = \left(\frac{1}{\sqrt{2}}\right)\begin{bmatrix} 1 & 1 \\ 1 & -1 \end{bmatrix}\begin{bmatrix} 1/4 & 0 & 0 & 0 \\ 0 & 1/2 & 0 & 0 \end{bmatrix}\left(\frac{1}{\sqrt{2}}\right)\begin{bmatrix} 1 & 0 & 0 & -1 \\ 0 & 1 & -1 & 0 \\ 0 & 1 & 1 & 0 \\ 1 & 0 & 0 & 1 \end{bmatrix}.$$

(Verify!)

PROBLEMS

NUMERICAL PROBLEMS

1. Find the singular-value decomposition of the following matrices.

   (a) $\begin{bmatrix} 5 & 0 \\ 3 & -4 \end{bmatrix}$ (b) $\begin{bmatrix} 5 & 3 \\ 0 & -4 \end{bmatrix}$ (c) $\begin{bmatrix} 1 & 1 \\ 1 & 1 \end{bmatrix}$

2. For the following matrices A, find the pseudoinverse A^+ by way of the singular-value decomposition.

   (a) $A = Q\begin{bmatrix} 1 & 0 & 0 & 0 \\ 0 & 3 & 0 & 0 \end{bmatrix}P^T$ (b) $A = Q\begin{bmatrix} 1 & 0 \\ 0 & 3 \\ 0 & 0 \end{bmatrix}P^T$

THEORETICAL PROBLEMS

3. If D is an $m \times n$ diagonal matrix whose ith diagonal entry is d_i for all i, then D^+ is the $n \times m$ diagonal matrix whose ith diagonal entry is $d_i^+ = 1/d_i$ if d_i is nonzero and $d_i^+ = 0$ if $d_i = 0$.
4. Show that for any characteristic vector $\mathbf{v}$ for A^*A, either $A\mathbf{v} = 0$ or $A\mathbf{v}$ is a characteristic vector for AA^*.

6.12 TRIANGULATION BY ITERATION

One of the long-standing problems in numerical analysis has been that of finding the characteristic roots of a matrix $A \in M_n\mathbb{C}$ quickly and accurately. We refer to this as the **characteristic root problem**. The roots of a polynomial

$$f(x) = x^n - a_{n-1}x^{n-1} - \cdots - a_0$$

are just the characteristic roots of the **companion matrix**

$$A = \begin{bmatrix} a_{n-1} & a_{n-2} & \cdot & \cdot & \cdot & a_0 \\ 1 & 0 & & & & \\ & \cdot & \cdot & & & \\ & & \cdot & \cdot & & \\ & & & \cdot & \cdot & \\ & & & & 1 & 0 \end{bmatrix} \quad \text{(0s in the triangular regions)}$$

(see Section 5.10, Problem 17). So, any complete solution to the characteristic root problem is a solution to another long-standing problem, that of finding the roots of a given complex (or real) polynomial quickly and accurately. For polynomials of degree 4 or less, methods discovered in the sixteenth century by Niccolo Tartaglia and Ludovico Ferrari (1522–1565) show how to find a root from the coefficients using only *rational operations* (addition, subtraction, multiplication, division) and *radicals* (extraction of kth roots for any k). However, with the revolutionary work of Evariste Galois (1811–1832), it became known that *for most polynomials, even of degree as low as* 5, *no method using only rational operations and radicals always produces a root in a finite number of steps.* For such polynomials, methods for finding roots must involve more advanced techniques, or methods such as iteration, requiring an infinite number of steps to get an exact answer.

From this, it follows that methods for finding characteristic roots of most matrices $A \in M_n\mathbb{C}$ must also involve such techniques. The next theorem gives an iterative method to compute, for any invertible matrix A whose characteristic roots are *absolutely different* (their absolute values are different), a unitary matrix Q such that Q^*AQ is upper triangular. In practice, it is implemented by the powerful QR algorithm (see Theorem 6.36 and Section 7.7).

This solves the characteristic root problem for such A, since the *characteristic roots then appear on the diagonal of* Q^*AQ. It also solves the **characteristic vector problem** for A when A is also Hermitian; that is, *it delivers the unitary matrix Q whose columns form an orthonormal basis of characteristic vectors for A.* (Verify!)

Early versions of this theorem were proved in 1962 by Kublanovskaya and in 1964 by Householder. The version presented here is a variation of a theorem taken from Chapter 7 of *The Algebraic Eigenvalue Problem* by J. H. Wilkinson (Oxford University Press, 1965; and Clarendon Press, Oxford, 1972). Wilkinson's beautiful proof is followed fairly closely, except for changes made to bring into full view the role played by the *order P* and *direction E* of the matrix A (defined shortly). This is needed for the purpose of defining a *$Q'R'$ decomposition* (variation of the QR decomposition) of A used in Theorem 6.36, a simple variation of Theorem 6.34 which takes order and direction into account.

We begin with the theorem in its most general form and then state it in the much simpler form it takes on when the characteristic roots are real (Theorem 6.35).

Theorem 6.34. *Unitary Triangulation of A by Iteration.*
Let A be an invertible matrix of degree n whose characteristic roots d_i have absolute values $|d_1| > \cdots > |d_n|$. Let $A^k = Q^{(k)}R^{(k)}$ be the QR decomposition of A^k and set $D = \text{Diag}(d_1, \ldots, d_n)$, $E = \text{Diag}(d_1/|d_1|, \ldots, d_n/|d_n|)$. Then there is a unique permutation matrix P such that $Q^{(k)}P^*E^{k*}P$ converges to a unitary matrix Q such that Q^*AQ is an upper triangular matrix whose diagonal is P^*DP.

Proof. Since the characteristic roots of A are all different, A is diagonalizable, and there exists an invertible matrix X such that $X^{-1}AX = D$ (Section 5.6). Let $X = QR$ be the QR decomposition of X. Then $Q^*AQ = RDR^{-1}$ and $A^k = QRD^kR^{-1}Q^*$ for all k. From the LDU decomposition for $R^{-1}Q^*$ (Section 3.7), we know that $R^{-1}Q^* = PLV$, where P is a permutation matrix, L is lower triangular with 1s on the diagonal, and V is upper triangular.

We pause to adjust V so that its *direction*

$$K = \text{Diag}(v_{11}/|v_{11}|, \ldots, v_{nn}/|v_{nn}|)$$

becomes I, that is, so that the diagonal entries of V become positive. We must then also adjust X, Q, R, and L accordingly and show that our equations $A^k = QRD^kR^{-1}Q^*$, $R^{-1}Q^* = PLV$ are preserved. This being the mandate for the moment, let $J = PKP^*$, $L' = K^*LK$, $V' = K^*V$, $Q' = QJ$, $R' = J^*RJ$, and $X' = Q'R'$ and note that $D^k = J^*D^kJ$. Then $X' = Q'R'$ is the QR decomposition of X' (verify) and

$$Q'R'D^kR'^{-1}Q'^* = QJJ^*RJJ^*D^kJJ^*R^{-1}JJ^*Q^* = QRD^kR^{-1}Q^* = A^k,$$

$$\begin{aligned} R'^{-1}Q'^* &= J^*R^{-1}JJ^*Q^* = J^*R^{-1}Q^* = J^*PLV = PK^*P^*PLV \\ &= PK^*LKK^*V = PL'V'. \end{aligned}$$

Since the direction of V' is I (explain), this adjustment shows that *we can choose X such that the diagonal entries of V are positive.* This having been established, we return to our old notation, but with the diagonal entries of V positive. Since E is diagonal and $EE^* = I$, we have $A^k = QRD^kR^{-1}Q^* = QRD^kPLV$.

Consider first the case $P = I$. Then

$$\begin{aligned} A^k &= QRD^kLV = Q(RD^kL(RD^k)^{-1})E^k(E^{*k}(RD^k)V \\ &= QQ_kE^k(E^{*k}R_kE^k)V_k = QQ_kE^kR^{(k)} = Q^{(k)}R^{(k)} \qquad (QR \text{ decomposition}), \end{aligned}$$

where

$$\begin{aligned} R(D^kLD^{-k})R^{-1} &= Q_kR_k && (QR \text{ decomposition}) \\ E^{*k}(RD^k)V &= V_k && (\text{Upper triangular with positive diagonal entries}) \\ R^{(k)} &= (E^{*k}R_kE^k)V_k && (\text{Upper triangular with positive diagonal entries}) \\ Q^{(k)} &= QQ_kE^k \quad \text{and} \quad Q^{(k)}E^{*k} = QQ_kE^kE^{*k} = QQ_k. \end{aligned}$$

But then $\text{Lim}_k\, D^k L D^{-k} = I$, since the entries of $D^k L D^{-k}$ above the diagonal are 0, those on the diagonal are 1, and the entry of row r and column s $(r > s)$ is $(d_r/d_s)^k$ times then (r, s)-entry of L. It follows that $Q_k R_k$ converges to I, so that Q_k, R_k both converge to I. (Explain!) But then $Q^{(k)}E^{*k} = QQ_k$ converges to Q. Then $Q^*AQ = RDR^{-1}$ is triangular with diagonal D, as asserted.

Consider next the case $P \neq I$, starting over with $X' = XP = QRP$ in place of $X = QR$. Let $X' = Q'R'$ be the QR decomposition of $X' = QRP$, observe that $X'^{-1}AX' = D'$, where $D' = P^*DP$, and let $E'^* = P^*E^*P$. Then $Q'^*AQ' = R'D'R'^{-1}$. Since $QRP = Q'R'$, the equation $R^{-1}Q^* = PLV$ implies that $I = QRPLV = Q'R'LV$ and $R'^{-1}Q'^* = LV$. Substituting in the earlier expression for A^k, we get

$$A^k = QRD^kPLV = QRP(P^*DP)^kLV = Q'R'D'^kLV.$$

Since V is the same as before, its diagonal elements are positive. So, we can continue on as before, but using Q', R', D', and E' in place of Q, R, D, and E. This gives the corresponding equations

$$R'(D'^kLD'^{-k})R'^{-1} = Q_kR_k \qquad (QR \text{ decomposition})$$

$$Q^{(k)}E'^{*k} = Q'Q_k.$$

To show that $Q^{(k)}E'^{*k}$ converges to Q', it now suffices to show that $\text{Lim}_k\, D'^kLD'^{-k} = I$, because then Q_k and R_k converge to I as before.

Letting $D' = \text{Diag}(d_{p_1}, \ldots, d_{p_n})$, the (r, s)-entry of $D'^kLD'^{-k}$ is 0 for $r < s$ and 1 for $r = s$. For $r > s$, it is d_{p_r}/d_{p_s} times the (r, s)-entry of L. Fortunately, in forming the factorization PLV, the (r, s)-entry of L is 0 when $p_r < p_s$ (Problem 21, Section 3.7)—that is, when $d_{p_r} > d_{p_s}$. So, $\text{Lim}_k\, D'^kLD'^{-k} = I$.

We conclude that $Q^{(k)}E'^{*k}$ converges to Q', E'^* being P^*E^*P. And, as asserted, $Q'^*AQ' = R'^{-1}AR'$ is triangular with diagonal $D' = P^*DP$. The uniqueness of P is due to the distinctness of the diagonal entries of D. ■

Theorem 6.35. *Orthogonal Triangulation of A by Iteration.*

Let A be a real invertible matrix of degree n whose characteristic roots d_i are real and absolutely distinct (no two have the same absolute value). Let $A^k = Q^{(k)}R^{(k)}$ be the QR decomposition of A^k. Then $Q^{(2k)}$ converges to an orthogonal matrix Q such that Q^*AQ is an upper triangular matrix.

Proof. By Theorem 6.34, there is a unique permutation matrix P such that $Q^{(k)}P^*E^{k*}P$ converges to a unitary matrix Q, where that Q^*AQ is an upper triangular matrix whose diagonal is P^*DP. Here, D and E are as defined in Theorem 6.34. Since the A and the $Q^{(k)}$ are real, Q is orthogonal, D is real, the diagonal elements of E are ± 1 and $E^2 = I$. The even terms are now just $Q^{(2k)}P^*E^{2k*}P = Q^{(2k)}P^*I^*P = Q^{(2k)}$, and they must converge to Q. Since Q^*AQ is triangular, this completes the proof. ■

In the context of Theorem 6.34, we refer to P and E as the **order** and **direction** of the matrix A. When the characteristic roots of A are real, the direction of E just gives the signs of the characteristic vectors arranged in absolute descending order.

Definition. *The $Q'R'$ Decomposition of an Invertible Matrix.*
Let A be an invertible matrix with absolutely different characteristic roots and let the order and direction of A be P and E. Then the $Q'R'$ **decomposition** of A is $A = Q'R'$, where $A = QR$ is the QR decomposition of A, $Q' = QP^*E^*P$, and $R' = P^*EPR$.

For any invertible matrix A with absolutely different characteristic roots, the order and direction of A^k are P and E^k, where P and E are the order and direction of A. (Prove!) So, the $Q'R'$ decomposition of A^k is given in terms of the QR decomposition $A^k = Q^{(k)}R^{(k)}$ as $A^k = Q'^{(k)}R'^{(k)}$, where $Q'^{(k)} = Q^{(k)}P^*E^{k*}P$ and $R'^{(k)} = P^*E^kPR^{(k)}$. In view of this, Theorem 6.34 is modified as follows.

Theorem 6.36. *Unitary Triangulation of A by $Q'R'$ Iteration.*
Let A be an invertible matrix with absolutely different characteristic roots and let $A^k = Q'^{(k)}R'^{(k)}$ be the $Q'R'$ decomposition of A^k. Then $Q'^{(k)}$ converges to a unitary matrix $Q'^{(\infty)}$ such that $Q'^{(\infty)*}AQ'^{(\infty)}$ is upper triangular.

The order of A is the permutation matrix P that rearranges $D = \text{Diag}(d_1, \ldots, d_n)$ into $D' = P^*DP = \text{Diag}(d_{p_1}, \ldots, d_{p_n})$, as we saw in the proof of Theorem 6.34. It follows that A and $Q'^{(\infty)*}AQ'^{(\infty)}$ have the same order and same direction. (Explain!)

EXAMPLE

Let $A = \begin{bmatrix} 1 & 1 \\ 0 & 2 \end{bmatrix}$. The order of A is $P = \begin{bmatrix} 0 & 1 \\ 1 & 0 \end{bmatrix}$, since this is the permutation needed to rearrange the diagonal of A in absolute descending order. In the proof, it comes from finding the characteristic vectors $\begin{bmatrix} 1 \\ 0 \end{bmatrix}, \begin{bmatrix} 1 \\ 1 \end{bmatrix}$ for A and reversing their order in forming $X = \begin{bmatrix} 1 & 1 \\ 1 & 0 \end{bmatrix}$. Then $X^{-1}AX = \begin{bmatrix} 2 & 0 \\ 0 & 1 \end{bmatrix}$ (verify) and the PLV decomposition of X is

$$X = \begin{bmatrix} 0 & 1 \\ 1 & 0 \end{bmatrix}\begin{bmatrix} 1 & 0 \\ 1 & 1 \end{bmatrix}\begin{bmatrix} 1 & 0 \\ 0 & 1 \end{bmatrix}, \text{ so that } P = \begin{bmatrix} 0 & 1 \\ 1 & 0 \end{bmatrix}.$$

We now pause for some observations.

1. In practice, one usually tries to *preprocess* (simplify) A before running it through the QR algorithm. In the simplest case, where A is real symmetric, this is achieved by the tridiagonalization of Section 7.6.

2. Shifts from A to $A - aI$ can be used to accelerate convergence. For example, when the order is I, the **convergence factor** for the last column of $Q'^{(k)}$ is $|d_n/d_{n-1}|$. Then, once an approximate value a for d_n is known, shifting to $A - aI$ changes the rate of convergence for the last column to $|(d_n - a)/(d_{n-1} - a)|$. This makes a tremendous difference when a is very close to d_n.
3. The $Q^{(k)}$, $R^{(k)}$ should be computed indirectly, using the elegant QR algorithm presented below. (Otherwise, the computations could be disastrously slow and inaccurate.) Since the QR algorithm provides for shifts, convergence is quite fast.
4. The order P and the direction E of A quickly become visible during the iteration, particularly when A and the characteristic roots are real, when the signs of the d's usually become known much sooner than the corresponding d's.
5. Once P and E are known and stored in memory, the $Q'R'$ factorization $A^k = Q'^{(k)}R'^{(k)}$ is known *symbolically* in terms of the $Q^{(k)}$, $R^{(k)}$ produced by the QR algorithm.
6. So, taking k sufficiently large, we eventually get a close approximation $Q'^{(k)}$ to $Q'^{(\infty)}$, the unitary matrix we seek.
7. Even without monitoring P and E, the convergence of $Q^{(k)*}AQ^{(k)}$ to an upper triangular matrix is assured. For $Q'^{(k)*}AQ'^{(k)}$ converges to a triangular matrix T, so $Q^{(k)*}AQ^{(k)}$ converges to $P^*EPTP^*E^*P$, which is also triangular.
8. When A is real symmetric, the columns of $Q'^{(\infty)}$ form an orthonormal basis of characteristic vectors for A.

EXAMPLES

1. For $A = \begin{bmatrix} -1 & 0 \\ 0 & 1 \end{bmatrix}$, $Q^{(k)}R^{(k)} = \begin{bmatrix} -1 & 0 \\ 0 & 1 \end{bmatrix}^k I$ and $Q'^{(k)}R'^{(k)} = I\begin{bmatrix} -1 & 0 \\ 0 & 1 \end{bmatrix}^k$. So, the series $Q^{(k)}$ does not converge, but $Q'^{(k)}$ does.

2. For $A = \begin{bmatrix} 0 & 1 \\ 1 & 0 \end{bmatrix}$, $Q^{(k)}$ does not converge. (Explain!) However, for $a = 0.9$, the $Q'^{(k)}$ for the matrix $A - aI$ do converge.

The *QR* algorithm

To get the $Q^{(k)}$ by computing the QR factorization $A^k = Q^{(k)}R^{(k)}$ directly would be catastrophically slow and inaccurate. Fortunately, however, *we can produce the $Q^{(k)}$ from the Q_k*, which are computed in the following QR algorithm with shifts.

Algorithm. *The QR Algorithm with Shifts.*
Starting from $i = 0$ and $A_i = A$:

1. Choose a shift value a_i by any method.
2. Factor $A_i - a_i I = Q_i R_i$ and define $A_{i+1} = R_i Q_i + a_i I$, so $A_{i+1} = Q_i^* A_i Q_i$.
3. If A_{i+1} is nearly diagonal, stop. If not, let $i = i + 1$ and repeat steps 1, 2, and 3. ■

Virtually no computation time is needed to get $Q'^{(k)}$ from $Q^{(k)}$, once the order and direction of A become known. So, from $Q^{(k)}$ we get $Q'^{(k)}$ as an approximation of the orthonormal basis $Q'^{(\infty)}$ of Theorem 6.36. Any desired degree of accuracy can be achieved by taking k sufficiently large.

When the algorithm continues from i without shifts, in effect it passes to the following subalgorithm until it returns to the main algorithm for the next nonzero shift. In practice, there may be $n + 1$ (or more!) nonzero shifts. The first might be a zero shift to find an approximation a_n for d_n, the next, a shift by $-a_n$ to find d_n and an approximation a_{n-1} for d_{n-1}, etc.

Algorithm. *The QR Algorithm without Shifts.*
Starting from i and A_i:

1. Factor $A_i = Q_i R_i$ and define $A_{i+1} = R_i Q_i$.
2. If called, return to main algorithm. If not, let $i = i + 1$ and repeat steps 1 and 2. ■

The QR algorithm without shifts is easy to analyze in terms of

$$Q^{(i,k)} = Q_i \cdots Q_{i+k-1}, \qquad R^{(i,k)} = R_{i+k-1} \cdots R_i.$$

Then

$$\begin{aligned}
A_i^1 &= Q_i R_i = Q^{(i,1)} R^{(i,1)} \\
A_i^2 &= Q_i R_i Q_i R_i = Q_i Q_{i+1} R_{i+1} R_i = Q^{(i,2)} R^{(i,2)} \\
&\vdots \\
A_i^k &= Q^{(i,k)} R^{(i,k)}
\end{aligned}$$

Since $Q^{(i,k)}$ is orthogonal and $R^{(i,k)}$ is upper triangular with positive diagonal entries, *we have the desired QR decompositions* of A_i^k for any i. Assuming that all shifts preserve the condition of absolutely different characteristic roots, the series $Q'^{(i,k)}$ ($k = 1, 2, 3, \ldots$) converges to a unitary matrix $Q'^{(i,\infty)}$. Of course, for $i = 0$, $Q'^{(k)} = Q'^{(i,k)}$ and $Q'^{(\infty)} = Q'^{(i,\infty)}$.

In practice, once the QR algorithm produces the last column of $Q^{(0,\infty)}$, the last row and column are deleted before the next shift. So, at any stage, we can analyze convergence of the last column in the QR algorithm *if we regard the first i iterations as preprocessing to prepare to find the last column without a further shift.*

Theorem 6.37. *Convergence of the QR Algorithm for Triangulizing A.* Let A be invertible with absolutely different characteristic roots. Suppose that $A_0 = A, \ldots, A_i$ are produced from A by the QR algorithm with shifts, where each shift preserves the condition of absolutely different characteristic roots. Suppose that, thereafter, A_{i+1}, A_{i+2}, etc. are produced without shifts. Then A_{i+1}, A_{i+2} converge to the triangular matrix $Q'^{(i,\infty)*}Q'^{(0,i)*}AQ'^{(0,i)}Q'^{(i,\infty)}$.

Proof. By the formula $A_{j+1} = Q_j^* A_j Q_j$, we have

$$\begin{array}{ll} A_1 = Q_0^* A Q_0 & A_{i+1} = Q_i^* A_i Q_i \\ A_2 = Q_1^* Q_0^* A Q_0 Q_1 & A_{i+2} = Q_{i+1}^* Q_i^* A_i Q_i Q_{i+1} \\ \vdots & \vdots \\ A_i = Q^{(0,i)*} A Q^{(0,i)} & A_{i+k} = Q^{(i,k)*} A_i Q^{(i,k)} \end{array}$$

But then $A_{i+k} = Q^{(i,k)*} A_i Q^{(i,k)}$ converges to the triangular matrix

$$Q^{(i,\infty)*} A_i Q^{(i,\infty)} = Q^{(i,\infty)*} Q^{(0,i)*} A Q^{(0,i)} Q^{(i,\infty)}. \quad \blacksquare$$

PROBLEMS

NUMERICAL PROBLEMS

1. For the following A, compute $P = Q^{(2)}$.

(a) $\begin{bmatrix} 1 & 0 \\ 0 & 2 \end{bmatrix}$ **(b)** $\begin{bmatrix} 1 & 1 \\ 0 & 1 \end{bmatrix}$ **(c)** $\begin{bmatrix} 1 & 1 \\ 0 & 2 \end{bmatrix}$

(d) $\begin{bmatrix} 1 & 1 \\ 1 & 1 \end{bmatrix}$ **(e)** $\begin{bmatrix} 1 & 1 \\ 1 & 2 \end{bmatrix}$ **(f)** $\begin{bmatrix} 0 & 1 \\ -1 & 0 \end{bmatrix}$

2. For each A in Problem 1, compute P^*AP for $P = Q^{(2)}$.

3. Compute P^*DP in the following cases.

(a) $P = \begin{bmatrix} 0 & 1 \\ 1 & 0 \end{bmatrix}, D = \begin{bmatrix} 2 & 0 \\ 0 & 1 \end{bmatrix}$

(b) $P = \begin{bmatrix} 0 & 0 & 1 \\ 0 & 1 & 0 \\ 1 & 0 & 0 \end{bmatrix}, D = \begin{bmatrix} 3 & 0 & 0 \\ 0 & 2 & 0 \\ 0 & 0 & 1 \end{bmatrix}$

(c) $P = \begin{bmatrix} 0 & 1 & 0 \\ 0 & 0 & 1 \\ 1 & 0 & 0 \end{bmatrix}, D = \begin{bmatrix} 3 & 0 & 0 \\ 0 & 2 & 0 \\ 0 & 0 & 1 \end{bmatrix}$

4. In Theorem 6.34, if $Q^{(3)} = \begin{bmatrix} a & b \\ c & d \end{bmatrix}$, $P = \begin{bmatrix} 0 & 1 \\ 1 & 0 \end{bmatrix}$, and $D = \begin{bmatrix} 2 & 0 \\ 0 & -1 \end{bmatrix}$, find $Q^{(3)}P^*E^3P$.

5. In order to compute the roots of $x^4 + x^2 + x + 1$, we could, instead, compute the characteristic roots of what companion matrix?

6. Find the companion matrices for each of the following.
   (a) $x^3 + x^2 + 3x - 7$ (b) $3x^3 + 2x^2 + x + 7$
   (c) $x^5 + 1$ (d) $x^5 - 1$
7. Show that the $Q^{(k)}$ do not converge for $A = \begin{bmatrix} -1 & 0 \\ 0 & 1 \end{bmatrix}$ but that the $Q'^{(k)}$ do converge.
8. Show that the $Q^{(k)}$ do not converge for $A = \begin{bmatrix} 0 & 1 \\ 1 & 0 \end{bmatrix}$.
9. For $A = \begin{bmatrix} 0 & 1 \\ 1 & 0 \end{bmatrix}$ and $a = 0.9$, the $Q'^{(k)}$ for the matrix $A - aI$ do converge.

THEORETICAL PROBLEMS

10. Explain why $P^*\text{Diag}(d_1, \ldots, d_n)P = \text{Diag}(d_{p_1}, \ldots, d_{p_n})$ for any permutation matrix P, the d_{p_i}'s being a rearrangement of the d's.

Hard

11. For an invertible real matrix A, show that if all the *leading principal minors* (determinants of the submatrices located in the first s rows and columns of A for $1 \leq s \leq n$) are nonzero, then A can be factored as $A = LDU$, where L is lower triangular with 1's on the diagonal, D is diagonal, and U is echelon. (That is, the P in a $PLDU$ decomposition of A can be taken to be I.)
12. In Theorem 6.34, show that the order P of A is I if all of the leading principal minors of X^{-1} are nonzero.

SUGGESTED READING

James Hardy Wilkinson, *The Algebraic Eigenvalue Problem*, Clarendon Press, Oxford, 1972. [A definitive and monumental treatment of one of the most important problems of numerical linear algebra. This book is self-contained, easy to read, and very attractively organized.]

CHAPTER 7

QUADRATIC FUNCTIONS

7.1 INTRODUCTION

In Section 1.7, we showed that a real quadratic equation

$$ax_1^2 + cx_1x_2 + dx_2^2 + rx_1 + sx_2 + t = 0 \qquad (a, c, d, r, s, t \in \mathbb{R}, a \text{ or } c \text{ or } d \neq 0)$$

in two variables can be brought to one of the normal forms

$$\frac{x_1''^2}{a'^2} + \frac{x_2''^2}{d'^2} = t' \qquad \text{(ellipse, point, or empty set)}$$

$$\frac{x_1''^2}{a'^2} - \frac{x_2''^2}{d'^2} = t' \qquad \text{(hyperbola if } t' \neq 0\text{, pair of lines if } t' = 0\text{)}$$

$$x_2''^2 = 2px_1'' \qquad \text{(parabola)}$$

by a change of axes $\mathbf{x} = U(\mathbf{x}'' - \mathbf{u})$ of $\mathbb{R}^2$. This change is made in two steps: $\mathbf{x} = U\mathbf{x}'$, $\mathbf{x}' = \mathbf{x}'' - \mathbf{u}$.

To summarize, $f(\mathbf{x}) = ax_1^2 + cx_1x_2 + dx_2^2 + rx_1 + sx_2 + t$ is represented as

$$f(\mathbf{x}) = \mathbf{x}^T\begin{bmatrix} a & c/2 \\ c/2 & d \end{bmatrix}\mathbf{x} + \mathbf{w}^T\mathbf{x} + t \qquad \text{where } \mathbf{w} = \begin{bmatrix} r \\ s \end{bmatrix}.$$

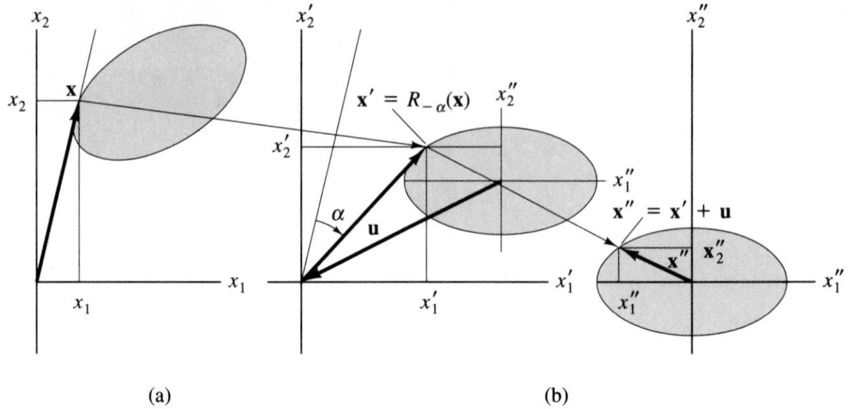

Figure 7.1 Bringing the ellipsoid $\mathbf{x}^T\begin{bmatrix} a & b \\ b & d \end{bmatrix}\mathbf{x} + \mathbf{w}^T\mathbf{x} + t = 1$ to normal form $\mathbf{x}''^T\begin{bmatrix} d_1 & 0 \\ 0 & d_2 \end{bmatrix}\mathbf{x}'' + t' = 1$ by the orthogonal transformation $\mathbf{x} = U\mathbf{x}'$ and translation $\mathbf{x}' = \mathbf{x}'' - \mathbf{u}$: (a) The change of coordinates $\mathbf{x} = U(\mathbf{x}'' - \mathbf{u})$; (b) the mapping $\mathbf{x}'' = U^T\mathbf{x} + \mathbf{u}$ from the ellipse $\mathbf{x}^T\begin{bmatrix} a & b \\ b & d \end{bmatrix}\mathbf{x} + \mathbf{w}^T\mathbf{x} + t = 1$ to the ellipse $\mathbf{x}''^T\begin{bmatrix} d_1 & 0 \\ 0 & d_2 \end{bmatrix}\mathbf{x}'' + t' = 1$.

The quadratic form $\mathbf{x}^T\begin{bmatrix} a & c/2 \\ c/2 & d \end{bmatrix}\mathbf{x}$ is then brought to its normal form

$$\mathbf{x}^T\begin{bmatrix} a & c/2 \\ c/2 & d \end{bmatrix}\mathbf{x} = \mathbf{x}'^T\begin{bmatrix} a' & 0 \\ 0 & d' \end{bmatrix}\mathbf{x}' = a'x_1'^2 + d'x_2'^2$$

by an orthogonal transformation $\mathbf{x} = U\mathbf{x}'$ such that $U^T\begin{bmatrix} a & c/2 \\ c/2 & d \end{bmatrix}U = \begin{bmatrix} a' & 0 \\ 0 & d' \end{bmatrix}$ for some $a', d' \in \mathbb{R}$. As a result, we get

$$f(\mathbf{x}) = a'x_1'^2 + d'x_2'^2 + \mathbf{w}'^T\mathbf{x}' + t \qquad \text{where } \mathbf{w}' = U^T\mathbf{w}.$$

The corresponding equation $f(\mathbf{x}) = 0$ is then brought to normal form by a translation $\mathbf{x}' = \mathbf{x}'' - \mathbf{u}$. The coordinates u_1, u_2 of $\mathbf{u}$ are chosen by completing $a'x_1'^2 + w_1'x_1' + c_1$, $d'x_2'^2 + w_2'x_2' + c_2$ to squares $x_1''^2$, $x_2''^2$, the c's being constants (Figure 7.1).

This chapter is concerned with the general theory of quadratic functions in n variables over $F = \mathbb{R}$:

1. Any quadratic function $f(\mathbf{x})$ can be brought to normal form by some change of axes $\mathbf{x} = U(\mathbf{x}'' - \mathbf{u})$, U being an orthogonal matrix and $\mathbf{u}$ a vector.

2. To bring $f(\mathbf{x})$ to normal form requires first computing U and then finding $\mathbf{u}$ by completing squares. Computing U is done in three steps:
   a. Use Householder reflections (Section 1.7) to tridiagonalize A.
   b. Use Householder reflections to get the QR decomposition $A_i = Q_i R_i$ of a sequence of matrices $A_1 = A, A_2, \ldots, A_i$ orthogonally similar to A and converging to D.
   c. Get the corresponding columns of U at the same time.

This chapter is also concerned with the important subject of minimization of functions built from quadratic forms. For this, the gradient is the perfect tool. Using it, we find that solving $A\mathbf{x} = \mathbf{b}$ amounts, for A positive definite, to minimizing a certain related quadratic form (Theorem 7.7). Equivalently, solving $A\mathbf{x} = \mathbf{b}$ can be interpreted as minimizing the potential energy of a corresponding force field.

Finally, *extrema* (maxima and minima) of $f(\mathbf{x})$ subject to a side condition $g(\mathbf{x}) = c$ are discussed in this chapter. The gradient again plays the lead role. At an extremum, the gradients of $f(\mathbf{x})$ and $g(\mathbf{x})$ are related by a **Lagrange multiplier** λ, which often turns out to be a characteristic root. This leads to diverse results, including Snell's law of optics in $\mathbb{R}^n$.

PROBLEMS

NUMERICAL PROBLEMS

1. Express each of the following functions as $f(\mathbf{x}) = \mathbf{x}^T A\mathbf{x} + \mathbf{w}^T\mathbf{x} + t$, where A is a real symmetric matrix and $\mathbf{w} \in \mathbb{R}^3$.
   (a) $f(\mathbf{x}) = x_1^2 + 2x_1x_3 + x_2^2 + x_3^2 + x_1 + 1$
   (b) $f(\mathbf{x}) = (x_1 + 1)^2 + 2(x_1 + 1)x_3 + x_2^2 + x_3^2 + x_1 + 1$
   (c) $f(\mathbf{x}) = 2x_1x_2 + 3x_3^2 + x_1 + 1$
2. For each of the functions $f(\mathbf{x})$ in Problem 1, find an orthogonal transformation $\mathbf{x} = U\mathbf{x}'$ such that $f(\mathbf{x}) = \mathbf{x}'^T D\mathbf{x}' + \mathbf{w}'^T\mathbf{x}' + t'$ for some real diagonal matrix D.
3. For each of the following functions $f(\mathbf{x})$, either find a translation $\mathbf{x} = \mathbf{x}' - \mathbf{u}$ such that $f(\mathbf{x}) = \mathbf{x}'^T D\mathbf{x}' + \mathbf{t}'$ for some real diagonal matrix D or show that there is none.
   (a) $f(\mathbf{x}) = 2x_1^2 + 3x_2^2 + 4x_3^2 + x_1 + 2x_2 + 1$
   (b) $f(\mathbf{x}) = x_1^2 + 2x_2^2 + x_2 + 4$
   (c) $f(\mathbf{x}) = 3x_3^2 + x_1 + 1$

THEORETICAL PROBLEMS

4. Show that $f(\mathbf{x}) = ax_1^2 + bx_2^2 + cx_3^2 + dx_2x_3 + ex_1x_3 + fx_1x_2 + gx_1 + hx_2 + ix_3 + t$ can be expressed as $f(\mathbf{x}) = \mathbf{x}^T A\mathbf{x} + \mathbf{w}^T\mathbf{x} + t$, where A is a real symmetric matrix and $\mathbf{x}, \mathbf{w} \in \mathbb{R}^3$.

5. If a, b, c are nonzero, show that $f(\mathbf{x}) = ax_1^2 + bx_2^2 + cx_3^2 + gx_1 + hx_2 + ix_3 + t$ can be expressed as $f(\mathbf{x}) = \mathbf{x}''^T D\mathbf{x}'' + t''$, where $D = \text{Diag}(a, b, c)$, $\mathbf{x}'' = \mathbf{x} - \mathbf{u}$ for some $\mathbf{u} \in \mathbb{R}^3$ and $\mathbf{t}'' \in \mathbb{R}$.

7.2 THE NORMAL FORM OF A QUADRATIC FUNCTION

Quadratic functions and quadratic equations

A **quadratic function** $f(\mathbf{x})$ in the variables x_i $(1 \leq i \leq n)$ is a scalar t (the **constant term**) plus a linear combination of the x_i, where $1 \leq i \leq n$ (the **linear term**) plus a linear combination of the $x_i x_j$, where $1 \leq i, j \leq n$ (the **degree 2 term**). We let a_{ij} be the average of the coefficients of $x_i x_j$ and $x_j x_i$. Then, letting the coordinates of $\mathbf{w} \in \mathbb{R}^n$ be the coefficients of the x_i, we can write $f(\mathbf{x})$ in vector form as $f(\mathbf{x}) = \mathbf{x}^T A\mathbf{x} + \mathbf{w}^T\mathbf{x} + t$, where A is a real symmetric matrix.

Definition. *The Language of Quadratic Functions.*
Let $f(\mathbf{x})$ be the quadratic function $\mathbf{x}^T A\mathbf{x} + \mathbf{w}^T\mathbf{x} + t$, A being a real symmetric matrix. Then

1. The function $\mathbf{x}^T A\mathbf{x}$ of $\mathbf{x}$ is called the **quadratic form** of the quadratic function $f(\mathbf{x})$.
2. A is called the **matrix** of the quadratic form $\mathbf{x}^T A\mathbf{x}$.
3. If A is nonsingular, we say that the quadratic form $\mathbf{x}^T A\mathbf{x}$ and the quadratic function $f(\mathbf{x})$ are **nondegenerate**.
4. The equation $f(\mathbf{x}) = 0$ is the corresponding **quadratic equation**.

Orthogonal transformation to principal axes

By the spectral theorem, there is a unitary matrix U such that $U^T AU = D$ is the real matrix $D = \text{Diag}(d_1, \ldots, d_r, 0, \ldots, 0)$, r being the rank of A. The quadratic form is then $\mathbf{x}^T A\mathbf{x} = \mathbf{x}'^T U^T AU\mathbf{x}' = \mathbf{x}'^T D\mathbf{x}' = d_1 x_1'^2 + \cdots + d_r x_r'^2$, where $\mathbf{x} = U\mathbf{x}'$. This proves the following theorem.

Theorem 7.1. *The Normal Form of* $\mathbf{x}^T A\mathbf{x}$.
Every quadratic form $\mathbf{x}^T A\mathbf{x}$ has the **normal form** $d_1 x_1'^2 + \cdots + d_r x_r'^2$ for some unitary transformation $\mathbf{x} = U\mathbf{x}'$, r being the rank of A and the d's being the (real) nonzero characteristic roots of A.

Translation of axes

The cross-product terms of a quadratic function $f(\mathbf{x})$ disappear when the quadratic form is brought to normal form by an orthogonal change of axes $\mathbf{x} = U\mathbf{x}'$. Then we can further simplify $f(\mathbf{x})$ by a translation $\mathbf{x}' = \mathbf{x}'' - \mathbf{u}$ of axes. Here are the details.

Under $\mathbf{x} = U\mathbf{x}'$, our quadratic function $f(\mathbf{x}) = \mathbf{x}^T A\mathbf{x} + \mathbf{w}^T\mathbf{x} + t$ becomes

$$f(\mathbf{x}) = d_1 x_1'^2 + \cdots + d_r x_r'^2 + \mathbf{w}'^T\mathbf{x}' + t \qquad \text{where } \mathbf{w}' = U^T\mathbf{w}.$$

For $1 \le i \le r$, let $x_i'' = x_i' + u_i$, where $u_i = w_i'/2d_i$. This *completes the square* so that $d_i x_i''^2 = d_i(x_i' + w_i'/2d_i)^2 = d_i x_i'^2 + w_i' x_i' + c_i$ for some constant c_i. If $i > r$, we let $x_i'' = x_i'$ and $u_i = 0$. The translation $\mathbf{x}' = \mathbf{x}'' - \mathbf{u}$ then eliminates the linear terms $w_i' x_i'$ $(1 \le i \le r)$. Letting $t' = t - c_1 \cdots - c_r$, $f(x)$ has the following normal form.

Theorem 7.2. *Normal Form for a Quadratic Function.*
$f(\mathbf{x}) = d_1 x_1''^2 + \cdots + d_r x_r''^2 + w_{r+1}' x_{r+1}'' + \cdots + w_n' x_n'' + t'$, where $d_1, \ldots, d_r$ are nonzero real numbers.

EXAMPLES

1. For

$$A = \begin{bmatrix} 1 & 1 & 2 \\ 1 & 2 & 3 \\ 2 & 3 & 5 \end{bmatrix},$$

the normal form of $\mathbf{x}^T A\mathbf{x} + 3x_1 + 1x_2 + 2x_3 + 1$ is $d_1 x_1''^2 + d_2 x_2''^2 + wx_3'' + t$ for some w and t, where d_1 and d_2 are the nonzero characteristic roots of A, since A has rank 2. (Verify!)

2. The normal form of $f(\mathbf{x}) = \mathbf{x}^T \begin{bmatrix} 1 & 2 \\ 2 & 4 \end{bmatrix} \mathbf{x} + 2x_1 + 3x_2 + 4$ is $f(\mathbf{x}) = 5x_1''^2 + bx_2'' + c$ for some b, c where $\mathbf{x} = \frac{1}{\sqrt{5}} \begin{bmatrix} 1 & -2 \\ 2 & 1 \end{bmatrix} \mathbf{x}'$, $\mathbf{x}' = \mathbf{x}'' - \mathbf{u}$. (Verify!) We can find $\mathbf{u}$, b, and c by following the method just discussed. (Do so!)

For nondegenerate quadratic functions in n variables, those where the rank of A is n, we have a more precise description of the normal form.

Normal Form for a Nondegenerate Quadratic Function.
$f(\mathbf{x}) = d_1 x_1''^2 + \cdots + d_n x_n''^2 + t'$, where the $d_1, \ldots, d_n$ are nonzero real numbers.

EXAMPLE

The matrix $A = \begin{bmatrix} 2 & 2 \\ 2 & 5 \end{bmatrix}$ is positive definite, since the pivots in the decomposition $A = LDL^T$ are all positive. From this, one can deduce that the characteristic roots of A must be positive. (Explain!) So, the normal form for $\mathbf{x}^T A\mathbf{x} + 3x_1 + 2$ is $d_1 x_1''^2 + d_2 x_2''^2 + t'$. (Find d_1, d_2, and t'.)

Types of quadratic equations

The normal form can be used to classify the various possibilities for a quadratic equation into different types. To keep things simple, we make no attempt to distinguish cases such as the empty set, point, pairs of lines, or cones. They are included as special cases of the ellipsoids, hyperboloids, and paraboloids we now describe.

For a nondegenerate quadratic function f, the surface $f(\mathbf{x}) = 0$ is of one of two kinds:

1. If the $d_1, \ldots, d_n$ in the normal form are all of the same sign, $f(\mathbf{x}) = 0$ is an **ellipsoid** (Figure 7.2). It is convenient to include the case of a point or empty set. For example, the normal forms for ellipsoids in $\mathbb{R}^3$ are

$$\frac{x^2}{a^2} + \frac{y^2}{b^2} + \frac{z^2}{c^2} = d$$

   where a, b, and c are nonzero. When $d = 0$, this is a point; when $d < 0$, it is the empty set.

2. Otherwise, $f(x) = 0$ is a **hyperboloid**. For example, the normal forms for a hyperboloid in $\mathbb{R}^3$ are

$$\frac{x^2}{a^2} + \frac{y^2}{b^2} - \frac{z^2}{c^2} = d$$

   where a, b, and c are nonzero. There are three kinds of hyperboloids:

   a. When d is negative, $f(\mathbf{x}) = 0$ is a **hyperboloid of two sheets**.

   b. When $d = 0$, it is an **elliptic cone**.

   c. When d is positive, it is a **hyperboloid of one sheet**.

   As d goes from positive to negative, the corresponding surface undergoes a deformation and separates from one sheet into two (Figure 7.2).

The hyperboloid $x^2/a^2 + y^2/b^2 - z^2/c^2 = 1$ of one sheet factors as

$$\left(\frac{x}{a} + \frac{z}{c}\right)\left(\frac{x}{a} - \frac{z}{c}\right) = \left(1 + \frac{y}{b}\right)\left(1 - \frac{y}{b}\right).$$

(Verify!) Multiply by $-s$ and equate the first factor with the first factor and the second with the second. Then it is the union of the lines L_s (s nonzero) of intersection of the two planes

$$\left(\frac{x}{a} + \frac{z}{c}\right) + s\left(1 + \frac{y}{b}\right) = 0, \qquad s\left(\frac{x}{a} - \frac{z}{c}\right) + \left(1 - \frac{y}{b}\right) = 0.$$

(Verify!) Surfaces of this type that are such unions of lines are called **ruled surfaces**, and the lines L_s are called **generators** (Figure 7.3).

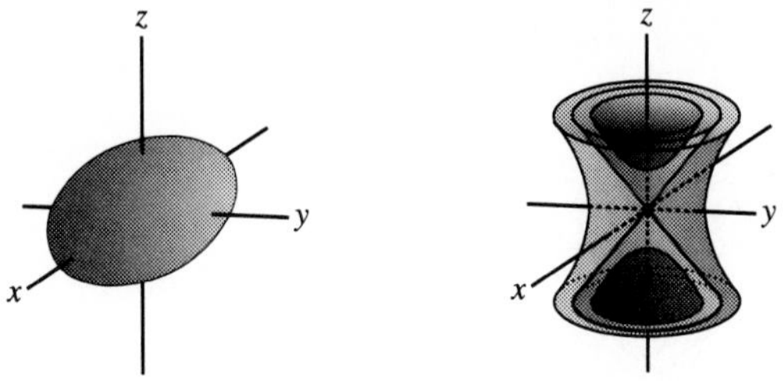

(a) Ellipsoid

$$\frac{x^2}{a^2} + \frac{y^2}{b^2} + \frac{z^2}{c^2} = 1$$

(b) See parts (c), (d), and (e)

$$\frac{x^2}{a^2} + \frac{y^2}{b^2} - \frac{z^2}{c^2} = d, \; -1 \leq d \leq 1$$

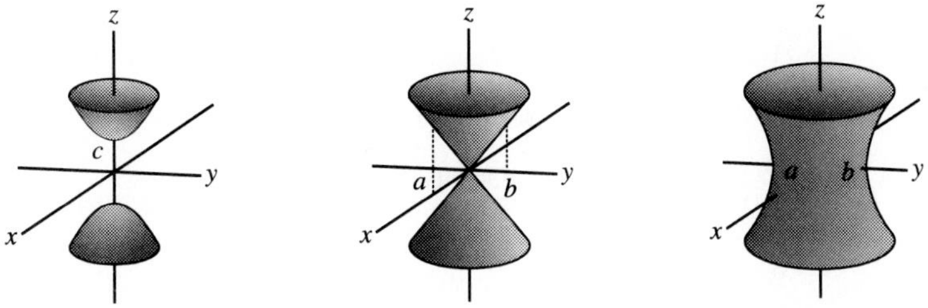

(c) Hyperboloid of two sheets

$$\frac{x^2}{a^2} + \frac{y^2}{b^2} - \frac{z^2}{c^2} = -1$$

(d) Cone

$$\frac{x^2}{a^2} + \frac{y^2}{b^2} - \frac{z^2}{c^2} = 0$$

(e) Hyperboloid of one sheet

$$\frac{x^2}{a^2} + \frac{y^2}{b^2} - \frac{z^2}{c^2} = 1$$

Figure 7.2 The nondegenerate conics $\dfrac{x^2}{a^2} + \dfrac{y^2}{b^2} \pm \dfrac{z^2}{c^2} = d$.

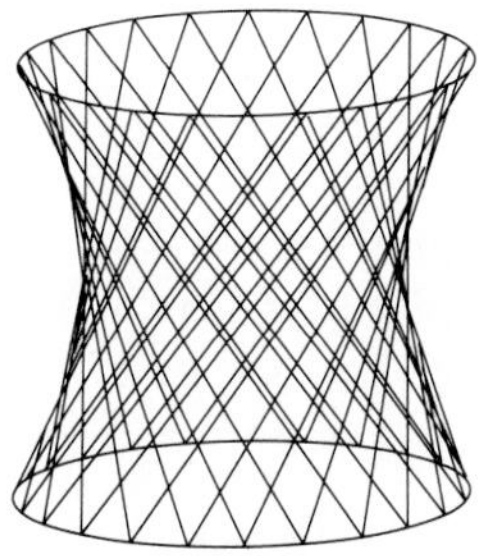

Figure 7.3 The hyperboloid $\dfrac{x^2}{a^2} + \dfrac{y^2}{b^2} - \dfrac{z^2}{c^2} = 1$ of one sheet is a ruled surface.

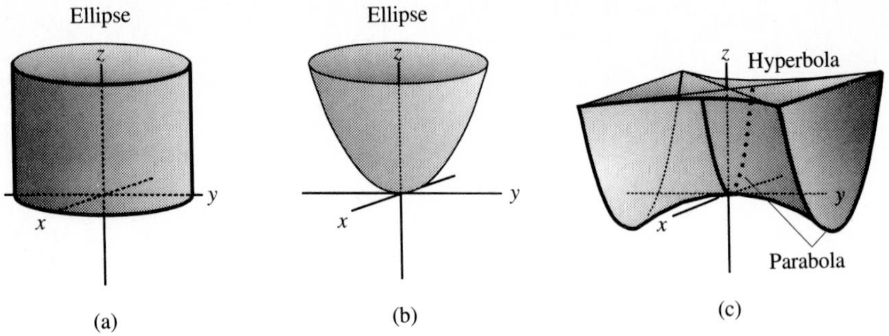

Figure 7.4 (a) The elliptic cylinder $\frac{x^2}{a^2} + \frac{y^2}{b^2} = 1$, whose cross sections $z = c$ are ellipses; (b) the elliptic paraboloid $\frac{x^2}{a^2} + \frac{y^2}{b^2} = z$, whose cross sections $z = c$ are ellipses and whose cross sections $x = d$, $y = e$ are parabolas; (c) The hyperbolic paraboloid $\frac{x^2}{a^2} - \frac{y^2}{d^2} = z$, whose cross sections $z = c$ are hyperbolas and whose cross sections $x = d$, $y = e$ are parabolas.

When a quadratic function $f(\mathbf{x})$ is degenerate, the situation is not so simple, but the pattern is similar:

1. When the $d_1, \ldots, d_r$ ($r = \text{Rank } A$, $r < n$) in the normal form are all of the same sign, any **principal cross section**

$$f(\mathbf{x}) = 0, x''_{r+1} = c_{r+1}, \ldots, x''_n = c_n \qquad (c_{r+1}, \ldots, c_n \text{ constant})$$

of $f(\mathbf{x}) = 0$ is an ellipsoid in $\mathbb{R}^r$. If $w'_j = 0$ for $j > r$, $f(\mathbf{x}) = 0$ is an **elliptic cylinder** of rank r. Otherwise, it is an **elliptic paraboloid** of rank r (Figure 7.4).

2. When the $d_1, \ldots, d_r$ ($r = \text{Rank } A$, $r < n$) in the normal form are not all of the same sign, any principal cross section

$$f(\mathbf{x}) = 0, x''_{r+1} = c_{r+1}, \ldots, x''_n = c_n \qquad (c_{r+1}, \ldots, c_n \text{ constant})$$

of $f(\mathbf{x}) = 0$ is a hyperboloid in $\mathbb{R}^r$. If $w'_j = 0$ for $j > r$, $f(\mathbf{x}) = 0$ is a **hyperbolic cylinder** of rank r. Otherwise, it is a **hyperbolic paraboloid** of rank r (Figure 7.4).

PROBLEMS

NUMERICAL PROBLEMS

1. Find the normal form of $f(\mathbf{x})$ for
   (a) $f(\mathbf{x}) = x_1^2 + 2x_1x_3 + x_2^2 + x_3^2 + x_1 + 1$;
   (b) $f(\mathbf{x}) = 2x_1x_2 + 3x_3^2 + x_1 + 1$.

2. Determine the type (for instance, ellipsoid or hyperbolic paraboloid) for each of the following equations in $\mathbb{R}^3$.

(a) $x_1^2 + 3x_2^2 + x_1 + 1 = 0$

(b) $(x_1 + 1)^2 + 2(x_1 + 1)x_3 + x_3^2 + 1 = 0$

(c) $2x_1x_2 + 3x_3^2 + x_1 + 1 = 0$

(d) $x_1^2 - 3x_2^2 + x_1 + 1 = 0$

(e) $x_1^2 - 3x_2^2 + x_3^2 + 1 = 0$

(f) $x_1^2 + 3x_2^2 - 1 = 0$

(g) $x_1^2 + 3x_2^2 + 6x_1 + 12 = 0$

(h) $x_1^2 - x_2^2 + 2x_1 + 1 = 0$

(i) $x_1^2 + 3x_2^2 + x_3 + x_1 - 100 = 0$

(j) $x_1^2 + 3x_2 + x_1 + 1 = 0.$

3. Which of the equations in Problem 2 is the empty set, a point, two intersecting lines, a cone, or a cylinder?

4. Find the normal form of the quadratic function $f(\mathbf{x}) = \mathbf{x}^T\begin{bmatrix} 1 & 2 \\ 2 & 4 \end{bmatrix}\mathbf{x} + 2x_1 + 3x_2 + 4$ discussed in one of the examples of this section.

5. For $A = \begin{bmatrix} 2 & 2 \\ 2 & 5 \end{bmatrix}$, do the following:

(a) Show that A is positive definite.

(b) Deduce that the characteristic roots of A must be positive.

(c) Determine the type of $\mathbf{x}^T A\mathbf{x} + 3x_1 = 2$ (for instance, ellipse or hyperbola).

THEORETICAL PROBLEMS

6. Let $f(\mathbf{x}) = ax_1^2 + bx_2^2 + cx_3^2 + gx_1 + hx_2 + ix_3 + t$. If a, b, and c are positive, show that $f(\mathbf{x})$ assumes its minimum value at exactly one vector $\mathbf{x}$. (***Hint:*** Use an equation $f(\mathbf{x}) = \mathbf{x}''^T D\mathbf{x}'' + t'$, where $D = \mathrm{Diag}(a, b, c)$.)

7. When one of a, b, or c is negative, show that $f(\mathbf{x}) = ax_1^2 + bx_2^2 + cx_3^2 + gx_1 + hx_2 + ix_3 + t$ never assumes its minimum value.

7.3 POSITIVE AND NEGATIVE DEFINITE MATRICES

Recall from Section 3.8 that $A \in M_n\mathbb{R}$ is *positive definite* if A is symmetric and $\mathbf{v}^T A\mathbf{v} > 0$ for all nonzero $\mathbf{v}$; and for any symmetric matrix $A \in M_n\mathbb{R}$, the quadratic form $f(\mathbf{v}) = \mathbf{v}^T A\mathbf{v}$ ($\mathbf{v} \in \mathbb{R}^n$) is *positive definite* if $f(\mathbf{v}) > 0$ for $\mathbf{v} \neq 0$. Similarly, we say that A and $f(\mathbf{v}) = \mathbf{v}^T A\mathbf{v}$ are *negative definite* if A is symmetric and $f(\mathbf{v}) < 0$ for all $\mathbf{v} \neq 0$. Of course, A is positive definite if and only if $-A$ is negative definite.

Thanks to the spectral theorem, we have the following criteria.

Theorem 7.3. *Characteristic Root Criteria for a Positive Definite Form.*
A symmetric matrix $A \in M_n\mathbb{R}$ is positive definite if and only if its characteristic roots are all positive.

Proof. If A and B are orthogonally similar, then A is positive definite if and only if B is positive definite. By the spectral theorem, A is orthogonally similar to a real diagonal matrix B. Since it is real diagonal, B is positive definite if and only if its diagonal entries are all positive. (Prove!) Since the diagonal entries of B are the characteristic roots of A, it follows that A is positive definite if and only if its characteristic roots are all positive. ■

We now add two conditions to the list of equivalent conditions of Theorem 3.36 for a positive definite matrix, getting the following criteria.

Theorem 7.4. *Criteria for a Real Positive Definite Matrix.*
The following conditions on a real symmetric matrix A are equivalent:

1. A is positive definite.
2. $A = LDL^T$, where D is diagonal with positive diagonal entries.
3. During the symmetric LDU reduction of A, every pivot encountered is positive.
4. $A = B^T B$ for some real matrix B.
5. The characteristic roots of A are all positive.
6. The determinant of the submatrix A_r located in the first r rows and columns of A is positive for $r = 1, \ldots, n$.

Proof. We know that conditions (1) through (4) are equivalent, and we can add (5) as an equivalent condition by the preceding theorem. For (6), the LDU decomposition for A_r is $L_r D_r L_r^T$, where D_r is the diagonal matrix in the first r rows and columns of D. So, if A is positive definite, then the A_r are positive definite by (3), so their determinants are positive by (5). Conversely, suppose that $|A_r|$ is positive for $1 \le r \le n$. The determinant of A_r is the product of the diagonal entries d_i of D_r (Section 5.3). So, $d_1 = |A_1|$ is positive and $d_{r+1} = |A_{r+1}|/|A_r|$ is positive for all $r < n$. But then A is positive definite, by (2). ■

By part (5) of Theorem 7.4, we have the following powerful criteria for recognizing an ellipsoid from its degree 2 coefficients.

Theorem 7.5. *Criteria for Ellipsoids.*
The quadratic equation $\mathbf{x}^T A\mathbf{x} + \mathbf{w}^T\mathbf{x} + t = 0$ is an ellipsoid if and only if A is positive or negative definite.

PROBLEMS

NUMERICAL PROBLEMS

1. Which of the following matrices are positive definite?

(a) $\begin{bmatrix} 1 & 2 \\ 2 & 4 \end{bmatrix}$ (b) $\begin{bmatrix} 1 & 2 \\ 2 & 6 \end{bmatrix}$ (c) $\begin{bmatrix} 6 & 2 \\ 2 & 1 \end{bmatrix}$

(d) $\begin{bmatrix} 0 & 2 \\ 2 & 3 \end{bmatrix}$ (e) $\begin{bmatrix} 3 & 3 \\ 3 & 6 \end{bmatrix}$

2. Which of the following are quadratic equations of ellipses?

(a) $\mathbf{x}^T\begin{bmatrix} 1 & 2 \\ 2 & 4 \end{bmatrix}\mathbf{x} + x_2 = 2$ (b) $\mathbf{x}^T\begin{bmatrix} 1 & 2 \\ 2 & 6 \end{bmatrix}\mathbf{x} + 2x_1 = 4$

(c) $\mathbf{x}^T\begin{bmatrix} 6 & 2 \\ 2 & 1 \end{bmatrix}\mathbf{x} + 3x_2 = 5$ (d) $\mathbf{x}^T\begin{bmatrix} 0 & 2 \\ 2 & 3 \end{bmatrix}\mathbf{x} + x_1 + x_2 = 2$

(e) $\mathbf{x}^T\begin{bmatrix} 3 & 3 \\ 3 & 6 \end{bmatrix}\mathbf{x} + x_2 = 4$

3. For each of the functions

(i) $f(\mathbf{x}) = x_1^2 + 2rx_1x_2 + sx_2^2$,

(ii) $f(\mathbf{x}) = sx_1^2 + 2rx_1x_2 + sx_2^2$,

do the following, r and s being constants:

(a) Express f as $f(\mathbf{x}) = \mathbf{x}^T A\mathbf{x}$, where A is real symmetric.

(b) Find the decomposition $A = LDL^T$ and find $|A| = |D|$.

(c) When is f nondegenerate? (Give conditions on r and s.)

(d) When is f positive definite? (Give conditions on r and s.)

4. For the functions (i) and (ii) of Problem 3 and for the following values of r and s, find the point at which the function assumes its minimum. If no such point exists, explain why.

(a) $r = -1, s = -1$ (b) $r = 1, s = -1$

(c) $r = -1, s = 1$ (d) $r = 1, s = 1$

Hard

5. Show that the stated decomposition $A = LDL^T$ is correct by extracting L and D (Section 3.8) and multiplying it out. In each case, determine the conditions on r and s that make A positive definite, and find $|A|$.

(a) $$\begin{bmatrix} r & r & 0 \\ r & s & s \\ 0 & s & s \end{bmatrix} = \left\|\begin{matrix} \mathbf{r} & 1 & 0 \\ 1 & \mathbf{s-r} & s/(s-r) \\ 0 & s/(s-r) & -\mathbf{rs/(s-r)} \end{matrix}\right\|$$

(b) $$\begin{bmatrix} r & s & 0 \\ s & r & s \\ 0 & s & r \end{bmatrix} = \left\|\begin{matrix} \mathbf{r} & s/r & 0 \\ s/r & (\mathbf{r^2-s^2})/\mathbf{r} & sr/(r^2-s^2) \\ 0 & sr/(r^2-s^2) & (\mathbf{r^3-2rs^2})/(\mathbf{r^2-s^2}) \end{matrix}\right\|$$

6. Find the decomposition $A = LDL^T$ for the following A, and give the conditions on r, s, t, u, and v so that A will be positive definite.

(a) $A = \begin{bmatrix} r & s & 0 \\ s & s & s \\ 0 & s & r \end{bmatrix}$ (b) $A = \begin{bmatrix} r & s & 0 \\ s & s & s \\ 0 & s & s \end{bmatrix}$

7. Show that the hyperbolic paraboloid $x^2/a^2 - y^2/b^2 = z$ is a ruled surface.

8. Show that

$$\begin{bmatrix} 2r^2 & r^2+rs & rs \\ r^2+rs & r^2+2s^2 & 2s^2 \\ rs & 2s^2 & 2s^2 \end{bmatrix}$$

is positive definite if its determinant is nonzero. What is its determinant?

7.4 THE GRADIENT OF A QUADRATIC FUNCTION

Extremum principles

Extremum (maximum and minimum) principles abound in the mathematical sciences. Around the first century A.D., Heron of Alexandria discovered that if the sum $\|\mathbf{x} - \mathbf{p}\| + \|\mathbf{x} - \mathbf{q}\|$ of distances from a point $\mathbf{x}$ on a given line to two given points $\mathbf{p}$ and $\mathbf{q}$ is minimal, then $\overrightarrow{\mathbf{px}}$ and $\overrightarrow{\mathbf{qx}}$ make equal angles with the line. This was an important development for the theory of optics. It had been known that when light from a source $\mathbf{p}$ is reflected at a point $\mathbf{x}$ on a mirror to a point $\mathbf{q}$, $\overrightarrow{\mathbf{px}}$ and $\overrightarrow{\mathbf{qx}}$ make equal angles with the mirror. Since this condition locates the position of $\mathbf{x}$ on the mirror, Heron's theorem establishes the following minimum principle (Figure 7.5).

Minimum Principle for the Path of Light.
Light from $\mathbf{p}$ to a reflection point $\mathbf{x}$ to $\mathbf{q}$ follows the shortest path.

Many physical laws are expressed in a like manner as extremum principles, and, not surprisingly, highly sophisticated mathematics tools have been created to investigate extrema. A *calculus of variations* sprang up from fertile seeds sown in the eighteenth century by Lagrange and Euler. The next section gives a glimpse into Lagrange's fascinating theory of minimization subject to a side condition.

Taylor's theorem and the quadratic part of a function

In the calculus, **Taylor's theorem** states that any function g from $\mathbb{R}^n$ to $\mathbb{R}$ possessing continuous third partial derivatives in a sphere $\|\mathbf{x} - \mathbf{a}\| < d$ at a

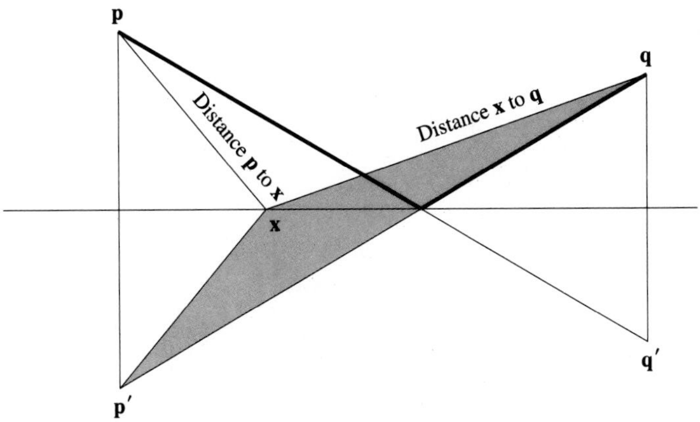

Figure 7.5 The proof of Heron's minimum principle for the path of light. By the triangle inequality, the sum of distances is minimized when the shaded triangle degenerates to a line. (Explain!)

of some positive radius d can be expressed as

$$g(\mathbf{x}) = g(\mathbf{a}) + \mathbf{w}^T(\mathbf{x} - \mathbf{a}) + (\mathbf{x} - \mathbf{a})^T A(\mathbf{x} - \mathbf{a}) + R(\mathbf{x} - \mathbf{a})$$

where $R(\mathbf{x} - \mathbf{a})/\|\mathbf{x} - \mathbf{a}\|^2$ goes to 0 as $\mathbf{x}$ goes to $\mathbf{a}$. The first three terms give the *quadratic part*

$$f(\mathbf{x}) = t + \mathbf{w}^T(\mathbf{x} - \mathbf{a}) + (\mathbf{x} - \mathbf{a})^T A(\mathbf{x} - \mathbf{a}) \qquad (t = g(\mathbf{a}))$$

of $g(\mathbf{x})$ at $\mathbf{a}$, whereas the *remainder* $R(\mathbf{x} - \mathbf{a})$ of $g(\mathbf{x})$ at $\mathbf{a}$ is the sum of the terms in $\mathbf{x} - \mathbf{a}$ of degree greater than 2.

EXAMPLE

Let $g(\mathbf{x}) = 3x_1^2 - 4x_1x_2 + 5x_2^3 + x_1 + x_2 + 1$. Then the quadratic part of $g(\mathbf{x})$ at $\mathbf{x} = \mathbf{0}$ is $f(\mathbf{x}) = 3x_1^2 - 4x_1x_2 + x_1 + x_2 + 1$, which can be written $f(\mathbf{x}) = \mathbf{x}^T A\mathbf{x} + \mathbf{w}^T\mathbf{x} + 1$, where $A = \begin{bmatrix} 3 & -2 \\ -2 & 0 \end{bmatrix}$ and $\mathbf{w} = \begin{bmatrix} 1 \\ 1 \end{bmatrix}$. (Verify!)

For most $g(\mathbf{x})$, only the quadratic part $f(\mathbf{x})$ of $g(\mathbf{x})$ at a critical point $\mathbf{x} = \mathbf{a}$ of $g(\mathbf{x})$ is needed to investigate whether $\mathbf{x} = \mathbf{a}$ is a relative maximum or minimum for $g(\mathbf{x})$, and the remainder $R(\mathbf{x} - \mathbf{a})$ can be ignored. To be specific, let $f(\mathbf{x}) = t + \mathbf{w}^T(\mathbf{x} - \mathbf{a}) + (\mathbf{x} - \mathbf{a})^T A(\mathbf{x} - \mathbf{a})$ be the quadratic part of $g(\mathbf{x}) = g(\mathbf{a}) + \mathbf{w}^T(\mathbf{x} - \mathbf{a}) + (\mathbf{x} - \mathbf{a})^T A(\mathbf{x} - \mathbf{a}) + R(\mathbf{x} - \mathbf{a})$ at $\mathbf{a}$. Then,

1. $\mathbf{w}$ is denoted by $\nabla g(\mathbf{a})$, called the **gradient** of g at $\mathbf{a}$. Its ith coordinate is the ith partial derivative of $g(\mathbf{x})$ evaluated at $\mathbf{x} = \mathbf{a}$.

2. The linear term $w^T(\mathbf{x}-\mathbf{a})$ of $g(\mathbf{x})$ vanishes for all $\mathbf{x}$ if and only if the gradient $\mathbf{w} = \nabla g(\mathbf{a})$ of g at $\mathbf{a}$ is $\mathbf{0}$. If $\nabla g(\mathbf{a}) = \mathbf{0}$, then $g(\mathbf{x}) = g(\mathbf{a}) + (\mathbf{x}-\mathbf{a})^T A(\mathbf{x}-\mathbf{a}) + R(\mathbf{x}-\mathbf{a})$ and $\mathbf{a}$ is called a **critical point** of g.
3. The quadratic form $\mathbf{y}^T A\mathbf{y}$ ($\mathbf{y} = \mathbf{x}-\mathbf{a}$) is called the **Hessian** of g at $\mathbf{a}$. The (i, j)-entry of A is

$$a_{ij} = \frac{1}{2}\frac{\partial^2 f}{\partial x_i \partial x_j}(\mathbf{a}) \qquad \text{for } i \neq j.$$

By the condition that f must have continuous third partial derivatives, *the matrix* $\left[\frac{1}{2}\frac{\partial^2 f}{\partial x_i \partial x_j}(\mathbf{a})\right]$ *is symmetric.*
4. The quadratic part $f(\mathbf{x}) = t + w^T(\mathbf{x}-\mathbf{a}) + (\mathbf{x}-\mathbf{a})^T A(\mathbf{x}-\mathbf{a})$ of $g(\mathbf{x})$ at $\mathbf{x} = \mathbf{a}$ has the following features:
   a. It has the same constant $t = f(\mathbf{a}) = g(\mathbf{a})$, gradient $\nabla f(\mathbf{a}) = \mathbf{w}$, and Hessian $\mathbf{y}^T A\mathbf{y}$ ($\mathbf{y} = \mathbf{x}-\mathbf{a}$) at $\mathbf{a}$ as does $g(\mathbf{x})$. (Explain!)
   b. $\mathbf{x} = \mathbf{a}$ is a critical point for $f(\mathbf{x})$ if and only if it is a critical point for $g(\mathbf{x})$. However, $g(\mathbf{x})$ may have other critical points, whereas $f(\mathbf{x})$ may not. (Explain!)
   c. If $\mathbf{x} = \mathbf{a}$ is a critical point of $g(\mathbf{x})$ and A is positive definite, then $f(\mathbf{x}) = g(\mathbf{a}) + (\mathbf{x}-\mathbf{a})^T A(\mathbf{x}-\mathbf{a})$ and $f(\mathbf{x})$ has a strict absolute minimum at $\mathbf{a}$ by Theorems 7.2 and 7.3. (Explain!) It follows that $g(\mathbf{x})$ has a strict relative minimum at $\mathbf{x}$. To see this, let M be the minimum of $\mathbf{y}^T A\mathbf{y}/\mathbf{y}^T\mathbf{y}$ subject to $\|\mathbf{y}\| = 1$. Then M is positive (by the extremum theorem for continuous functions) and $M\|\mathbf{x}-\mathbf{a}\|^2 \leq \|(\mathbf{x}-\mathbf{a})^T A(\mathbf{x}-\mathbf{a})\|$ for all $\mathbf{x}$. (Prove!) Since

$$g(\mathbf{x}) - g(\mathbf{a}) = (\mathbf{x}-\mathbf{a})^T A(\mathbf{x}-\mathbf{a}) + R(\mathbf{x}-\mathbf{a}) \geq M\|\mathbf{x}-\mathbf{a}\|^2 + R(\mathbf{x}-\mathbf{a})$$

   and $R(\mathbf{x}-\mathbf{a})/\|\mathbf{x}-\mathbf{a}\|^2$ goes to 0 as $\mathbf{x}$ goes to $\mathbf{a}$, it follows that $g(\mathbf{x}) > g(\mathbf{a})$ if $\mathbf{x} \neq \mathbf{a}$ and $\|\mathbf{x}-\mathbf{a}\|$ is sufficiently small.
   d. If $\mathbf{x} = \mathbf{a}$ is a critical point of $g(\mathbf{x})$, where A is invertible and not positive definite, neither $g(\mathbf{x})$ nor $f(\mathbf{x})$ has a relative minimum at $\mathbf{a}$. To see this, take a characteristic vector $\mathbf{v}$ for A of length 1 corresponding to a negative characteristic root d, which exists since A is symmetric, invertible, and not positive definite. (Prove!) Let $\mathbf{x} = s\mathbf{v} + \mathbf{a}$ ($s > 0$). Then $f(\mathbf{x}) - f(\mathbf{a}) = (\mathbf{x}-\mathbf{a})^T A(\mathbf{x}-\mathbf{a}) = s\mathbf{v}^T As\mathbf{v} = s^2 d < 0$, and $\mathbf{a}$ is not a relative minimum for f. Similarly,

$$g(\mathbf{x}) - g(\mathbf{a}) = (\mathbf{x}-\mathbf{a})^T A(\mathbf{x}-\mathbf{a}) + R(\mathbf{x}-\mathbf{a}) = sd + R(\mathbf{x}-\mathbf{a}).$$

   Since $R(\mathbf{x}-\mathbf{a})/\|\mathbf{x}-\mathbf{a}\|^2$ goes to 0 as $\mathbf{x}$ goes to $\mathbf{a}$, this is negative for $\|\mathbf{x}-\mathbf{a}\|$ sufficiently small, and $\mathbf{a}$ is not a relative minimum for g (Figure 7.6).
   e. If $\mathbf{x} = \mathbf{a}$ is a critical point of $g(\mathbf{x})$, where A is invertible, $g(\mathbf{x})$ has a relative minimum at $\mathbf{a}$ if and only if $f(\mathbf{x})$ has a relative minimum at $\mathbf{a}$, by (c) and (d). Replacing $f(\mathbf{x})$ and $g(\mathbf{x})$ by their negatives then

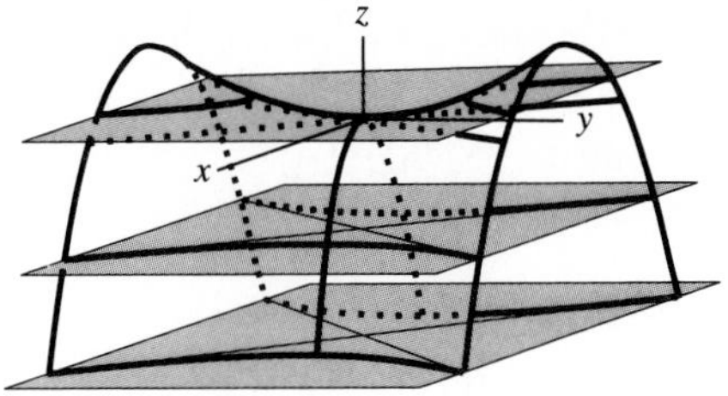

Figure 7.6 The saddle-shaped surface $z = \frac{y^2}{b^2} - \frac{x^2}{a^2}$ has no relative extrema.

shows that $g(\mathbf{x})$ has a relative maximum at $\mathbf{a}$ if and only if $f(\mathbf{x})$ has a relative maximum at $\mathbf{a}$.

f. If $\mathbf{x} = \mathbf{a}$ is not a critical point of $g(\mathbf{x})$, then the critical points of $f(\mathbf{x})$ need not be critical points of $g(\mathbf{x})$. (See (3) in the next example.)

EXAMPLES

1. $f(\mathbf{x}) = s + (\mathbf{x} - \mathbf{a})A(\mathbf{x} - \mathbf{a})$ and $g(\mathbf{x}) = s + (\mathbf{x} - \mathbf{a})A(\mathbf{x} - \mathbf{a}) + 3(\mathbf{x} - \mathbf{a})^3 + 2(\mathbf{x} - \mathbf{a})^5$ both have $\mathbf{x} = \mathbf{a}$ as critical point for any s, A. So, if A is invertible, $g(\mathbf{x})$ has a relative minimum at $\mathbf{a}$ if and only if $f(\mathbf{x})$ has a relative minimum at $\mathbf{x}$.

2. For instance, let $f(\mathbf{x}) = 5 + (\mathbf{x} - \mathbf{a})\begin{bmatrix} 3 & -2 \\ -2 & 0 \end{bmatrix}(\mathbf{x} - \mathbf{a})$ and $g(\mathbf{x}) = 5 + (\mathbf{x} - \mathbf{a})\begin{bmatrix} 3 & -2 \\ -2 & 0 \end{bmatrix}(\mathbf{x} - \mathbf{a}) + 3(\mathbf{x} - \mathbf{a})^3 + 2(\mathbf{x} - \mathbf{a})^5$. Then $f(\mathbf{x})$ and $g(\mathbf{x})$ both have $\mathbf{x} = \mathbf{a}$ as critical point. Since A is invertible with characteristic roots 4 and -1, $f(\mathbf{x})$ does not have a relative minimum at $\mathbf{a}$. (Explain!) So, $\mathbf{a}$ is not a relative minimum for $g(\mathbf{x})$.

3. For $f(\mathbf{x}) = 3x_1^2 - 4x_1x_2 + x_1 + x_2 + 1$, the conditions that the partial derivatives of f with respect to x_1 and x_2 be 0 are that

$$6x_1 - 4x_2 + 1 = 0,$$
$$-4x_1 + 0x_2 + 1 = 0.$$

(Verify!) So, $f(\mathbf{x})$ has exactly one critical point $\frac{1}{8}\begin{bmatrix} 2 \\ 5 \end{bmatrix}$. This is *not* a critical point for $g(\mathbf{x}) = 3x_1^2 - 4x_1x_2 + 5x_2^3 + x_1 + x_2 + 1$.

The gradient of a quadratic function

The constant term of a quadratic function $f(\mathbf{x}) = (\mathbf{x} - \mathbf{a})^T A(\mathbf{x} - \mathbf{a}) + \mathbf{w}^T(\mathbf{x} - \mathbf{a}) + t$ is irrelevant for locating its extrema. The first-degree term, however, is quite relevant. It vanishes if and only if $\mathbf{a}$ is a critical point of $f(\mathbf{x})$. Fortunately, when it does not vanish, we can use an algebraic definition of the *gradient function* of f to describe the critical points.

Definition. *Algebraic Definition of the Gradient Function of $f(\mathbf{x})$.*
For $f(\mathbf{x}) = (\mathbf{x} - \mathbf{a})^T A(\mathbf{x} - \mathbf{a}) + w^T(\mathbf{x} - \mathbf{a}) + t$ (A symmetric), the **gradient function** of f at $\mathbf{a}$ is $\nabla f(\mathbf{x}) = 2A(\mathbf{x} - \mathbf{a}) + \mathbf{w}$. A point $\mathbf{x}$ at which the gradient of f vanishes is called a **critical point** of f.

Note that

1. The gradient function $\nabla f(\mathbf{x})$ delivers the gradient at $\mathbf{a}$ upon setting $\mathbf{x} = \mathbf{a}$: $\nabla f(\mathbf{a}) = 2A(\mathbf{a} - \mathbf{a}) + \mathbf{w} = \mathbf{w}$.
2. Since A is symmetric, the ith coordinate function of $\nabla f(\mathbf{x}) = 2A(\mathbf{x} - \mathbf{a}) + \mathbf{w}$ is the ith partial derivative of $f(\mathbf{x})$ evaluated at $\mathbf{x}$ for any $\mathbf{x}$. (Verify!) So, our algebraic definition of the gradient coincides with the definition used to define the gradient in calculus (Figure 7.7).

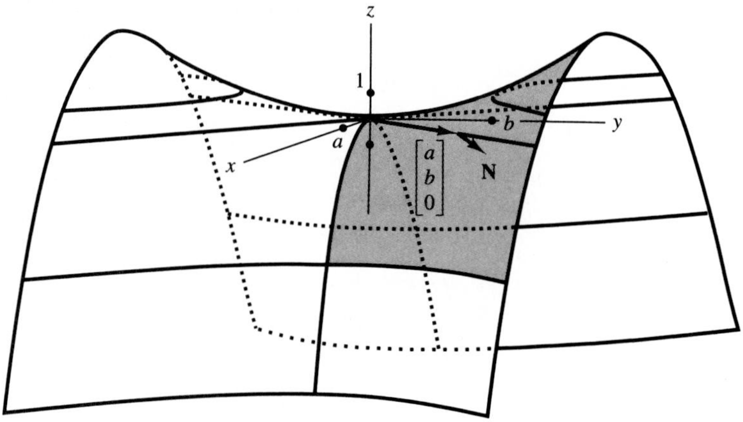

N is translated from the origin to begin at the point $\begin{bmatrix} a \\ b \\ 0 \end{bmatrix}$

Figure 7.7 Let

$$f = (x, y, z)\begin{bmatrix} -1/a^2 & 0 & 0 \\ 0 & 1/b^2 & 0 \\ 0 & 0 & 0 \end{bmatrix}\begin{bmatrix} x \\ y \\ z \end{bmatrix} + [0 \quad 0 \quad -1]\begin{bmatrix} x \\ y \\ z \end{bmatrix}.$$

We know from calculus that the normal $\mathbf{N}$ to the surface $\dfrac{-x^2}{a^2} + \dfrac{y^2}{b^2} - z = 0$ at $\begin{bmatrix} a \\ b \\ c \end{bmatrix}$ is the gradient $\nabla f\begin{bmatrix} a \\ b \\ c \end{bmatrix}$. So,

$$\mathbf{N} = 2A\begin{bmatrix} a \\ b \\ c \end{bmatrix} + \begin{bmatrix} 0 \\ 0 \\ -1 \end{bmatrix} = \begin{bmatrix} -2/a \\ 2/b \\ -1 \end{bmatrix}, \quad \text{where} \quad A = \begin{bmatrix} -1/a^2 & 0 & 0 \\ 0 & 1/b^2 & 0 \\ 0 & 0 & 0 \end{bmatrix}.$$

EXAMPLES

1. For A positive definite of degree $n = 1$, the corresponding quadratic function $f(\mathbf{x}) = \mathbf{x}^T A\mathbf{x} + \mathbf{w}^T\mathbf{x} + t$ is $f(x) = xa_{11}x + xw_1 + t = a_{11}x^2 + w_1x + t$, where $a_{11} > 0$. To investigate it for a minimum using calculus, we set the derivative $f'(x) = 2a_{11}x + w_1$ to 0, getting $x = -w_1/2a_{11}$. Since the second derivative $f''(a) = 2a_{11}$ is positive, the positive definite quadratic function $f(x)$ has its minimum at $x = -w/2a$.

2. For $f(\mathbf{x}) = 3x_1^2 - 4x_1x_2 + x_1 + x_2 + 1$, the gradient function is $\nabla f(\mathbf{x}) = 2\begin{bmatrix} 3 & -2 \\ -2 & 0 \end{bmatrix}(\mathbf{x} - \mathbf{0}) + \begin{bmatrix} 1 \\ 1 \end{bmatrix}$. The conditions under which the partial derivatives of f with respect to x_1 and x_2 are 0 are

$$6x_1 - 4x_2 + 1 = 0,$$
$$-4x_1 + 0x_2 + 1 = 0.$$

These conditions are equivalent to the condition that the gradient $2\begin{bmatrix} 3 & -2 \\ -2 & 0 \end{bmatrix}\mathbf{x} + \begin{bmatrix} 1 \\ 1 \end{bmatrix}$ is $\mathbf{0}$. (Verify!) By Theorem 7.6, the solution $\mathbf{x} = \frac{1}{8}\begin{bmatrix} 2 \\ 5 \end{bmatrix}$ is a minimum for $f(\mathbf{x})$.

3. For $f(\mathbf{x}) = ax_1^2 + 2cx_1x_2 + dx_2^2 + rx_1 + sx_2 + t$,

$$\nabla f(\mathbf{x}) = 2\begin{bmatrix} a & c \\ c & d \end{bmatrix}\mathbf{x} + \begin{bmatrix} r \\ s \end{bmatrix} = \begin{bmatrix} 2ax_1 + 2cx_2 + r \\ 2cx_1 + 2dx_2 + s \end{bmatrix}$$

and the partial derivatives $f_1(\mathbf{x})$ and $f_2(\mathbf{x})$ are $2ax_1 + 2cx_2 + r$, $2cx_1 + 2dx_2 + s$.

4. The gradient of $\frac{1}{2}\mathbf{x}^T B\mathbf{x} + \mathbf{x}^T\mathbf{v} + s$ is $B\mathbf{x} + \mathbf{v}$ if B is symmetric.

Minimum of a positive definite function

Whereas a minimum for $f(\mathbf{x})$ is a point $\mathbf{x}$ such that $f(\mathbf{x} + \mathbf{y}) \geq f(\mathbf{x})$ for all $\mathbf{y}$, a **strict minimum** for $f(\mathbf{x})$ is a point $\mathbf{x}$ such that $f(\mathbf{x} + \mathbf{y}) > f(\mathbf{x})$ for all $\mathbf{y} \neq \mathbf{x}$.

Theorem 7.6. *Minimum Point for a Positive Definite Quadratic Function.* Let $f(\mathbf{x}) = \mathbf{x}^T A\mathbf{x} + \mathbf{w}^T\mathbf{x} + t$ be a positive definite quadratic function. If $\mathbf{x}$ is a minimum for $f(\mathbf{x})$, then $\mathbf{x}$ is a critical point for $f(\mathbf{x})$. Conversely, if $\mathbf{x}$ is a critical point for $f(\mathbf{x})$, $\mathbf{x}$ is a strict minimum for $f(\mathbf{x})$.

Proof. Suppose that $\nabla f(\mathbf{x}) = \mathbf{0}$, that is, that $2A\mathbf{x} + \mathbf{w} = \mathbf{0}$. For any nonzero $\mathbf{y}$, we have

$$\begin{aligned} f(\mathbf{x} + \mathbf{y}) &= (\mathbf{x} + \mathbf{y})^T A(\mathbf{x} + \mathbf{y}) + w^T(\mathbf{x} + \mathbf{y}) + t \\ &= f(\mathbf{x}) + \mathbf{y}^T A\mathbf{y} + \mathbf{w}^T\mathbf{y} + \mathbf{x}^T A\mathbf{y} + \mathbf{y}^T A\mathbf{x}. \end{aligned}$$

Since $\mathbf{x}^T A\mathbf{y} + \mathbf{y}^T A\mathbf{x} = 2\mathbf{y}^T A\mathbf{x}$, and since $\nabla f(\mathbf{x}) = 2A\mathbf{x} + \mathbf{w}$ is $\mathbf{0}$ by hypothesis, we have

$$\begin{aligned} f(\mathbf{x} + \mathbf{y}) &= f(\mathbf{x}) + \mathbf{y}^T A\mathbf{y} + \mathbf{w}^T\mathbf{y} + (-\mathbf{w})^T\mathbf{y} \\ &= f(\mathbf{x}) + \mathbf{y}^T A\mathbf{y} > f(\mathbf{x}). \end{aligned}$$

So, $\mathbf{x}$ is a strict minimum for f.

Suppose, conversely, that $\mathbf{x}'$ is a minimum for f. Since A is positive definite, we can solve $2A\mathbf{x} + \mathbf{w} = \mathbf{0}$ for $\mathbf{x}$, so that $\nabla f(\mathbf{x}) = \mathbf{0}$. Then $\mathbf{x}$ is a strict minimum for f. So, since $\mathbf{x}'$ is a minimum for f and $f(\mathbf{x}') \le f(\mathbf{x})$, $\mathbf{x}' = \mathbf{x}$. But then $\nabla f(\mathbf{x}') = \nabla f(\mathbf{x}) = \mathbf{0}$. ■

Gradient fields and $A\mathbf{x} = \mathbf{b}$

The gradient $\nabla f(\mathbf{x}) = 2A(\mathbf{x} - \mathbf{a}) + \mathbf{w}$ is defined for any quadratic function $f(\mathbf{x}) = (\mathbf{x} - \mathbf{a})^T A(\mathbf{x} - \mathbf{a}) + \mathbf{w}^T(\mathbf{x} - \mathbf{a}) + t$ (A symmetric). More generally, we can define the gradient $\nabla g(\mathbf{x})$ of any scalar-valued function of $\mathbf{x} \in \mathbb{R}^n$ to be the vector-valued function sending $\mathbf{x}$ to the vector $\nabla g(\mathbf{x})$ whose ith coordinate is the partial derivative of g with respect to x_i for all i, assuming that these partial derivatives exist. The result is a special kind of vector field $\nabla g(\mathbf{x})$ called a gradient field (Figure 7.8).

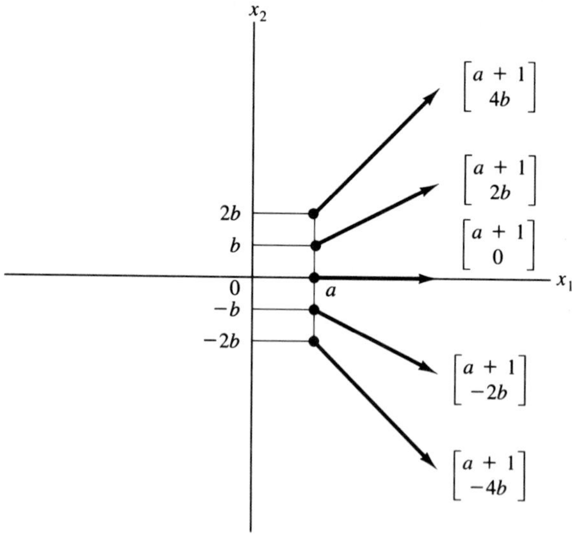

Figure 7.8 The vector field $\begin{bmatrix} 1 & 0 \\ 0 & 2 \end{bmatrix}\begin{bmatrix} x_1 \\ x_2 \end{bmatrix} + \begin{bmatrix} 1 \\ 0 \end{bmatrix} = \begin{bmatrix} x_1 + 1 \\ 2x_2 \end{bmatrix}$ is the gradient of $\frac{1}{2}(x_1, x_2)\begin{bmatrix} 1 & 0 \\ 0 & 2 \end{bmatrix}\begin{bmatrix} x_1 \\ x_2 \end{bmatrix} + (1, 0)\begin{bmatrix} x_1 \\ x_2 \end{bmatrix} + 3 = \frac{1}{2}(x_1^2 + 2x_2^2) + x_1 + 3$. For example, the vector field at $\begin{bmatrix} a \\ b \end{bmatrix}, \begin{bmatrix} a \\ 2b \end{bmatrix}$ is $\begin{bmatrix} a+1 \\ 2b \end{bmatrix}, \begin{bmatrix} a+1 \\ 4b \end{bmatrix}$.

Definition. *Vector Fields and Gradient Fields.*
A **vector field** is a function $F(\mathbf{x})$ from $\mathbb{R}^n$ to itself. A **gradient field** is a vector field $F(\mathbf{x})$ of the form $F(\mathbf{x}) = \nabla g(\mathbf{x})$.

EXAMPLES

1. Any vector field $B(\mathbf{x} - \mathbf{a}) + \mathbf{v}$ (B a real symmetric matrix) is a gradient field. It is the gradient of the quadratic form $\frac{1}{2}(\mathbf{x} - \mathbf{a})^T B(\mathbf{x} - \mathbf{a}) + \mathbf{x}^T\mathbf{v} + s$ (s any constant), called the **antigradient** of $B(\mathbf{x} - \mathbf{a}) + \mathbf{v}$. (Verify!)
2. The antigradient of $A\mathbf{x} - \mathbf{b}$ (A symmetric) is $\frac{1}{2}\mathbf{x}^T A\mathbf{x} - \mathbf{x}^T\mathbf{b} + s$.
3. The antigradient of the force field $F(\mathbf{x}) = -\mathbf{x}/r^3$, $r = \|\mathbf{x}\|$, is the potential energy function $1/r$, as we see below. Although the potential energy function $1/r$ is not a quadratic function, it is the inverse $(\mathbf{x}_1^2 + \mathbf{x}_2^2 + \mathbf{x}_3^2)^{-1/2}$ of the square root of a quadratic function and can be studied as such.

Theorem 7.6 says that a positive definite function $f(\mathbf{x}) = (\mathbf{x} - \mathbf{a})^T A(\mathbf{x} - \mathbf{a}) + \mathbf{w}^T(\mathbf{x} - \mathbf{a}) + t$ (A symmetric) has a minimum at $\mathbf{x}$ if and only if $2A\mathbf{x} + \mathbf{w} = \mathbf{0}$. We now turn this theorem around by viewing $A\mathbf{x} - \mathbf{b}$ (A symmetric) as gradient field. Theorem 7.6 is then recast as a minimum principle for solving $A\mathbf{x} = \mathbf{b}$. In fact, since the antigradient of $A\mathbf{x} - \mathbf{b}$ is $\frac{1}{2}\mathbf{x}^T A\mathbf{x} - \mathbf{x}^T\mathbf{b}$, we have the following.

Theorem 7.7. *Minimum Principle for Solving* $A\mathbf{x} = \mathbf{b}$.
Let A be positive definite. Then $A\mathbf{x} = \mathbf{b}$ if and only if $\frac{1}{2}\mathbf{x}^T A\mathbf{x} - \mathbf{x}^T\mathbf{b}$ takes on its minimum value at x.

Potential energy and work

The gradient field $F(\mathbf{x}) = \nabla f(\mathbf{x})$ of a given real-valued function $f(\mathbf{x})$ can be interpreted as a **force field**, and $f(\mathbf{x})$ can be considered as the **potential energy** of a **unit particle** of some kind located at $\mathbf{x}$. As the unit particle is moved from $\mathbf{x}$ to $\mathbf{y}$, the force field achieves a *change* $W(\mathbf{x}, \mathbf{y}) = f(\mathbf{y}) - f(\mathbf{x})$ in *potential energy*. This change $W(\mathbf{x}, \mathbf{y})$ is called the **work** done by F as the particle moves from $\mathbf{x}$ to $\mathbf{y}$. The path does not matter, since W depends only on $\mathbf{x}$ and $\mathbf{y}$.

EXAMPLE

The minimum principle for solving $A\mathbf{x} = \mathbf{b}$ for A positive definite states, therefore, that $A\mathbf{x} = \mathbf{b}$ *if and only if the potential energy* $\frac{1}{2}\mathbf{x}^T A\mathbf{x} - \mathbf{x}^T\mathbf{b}$ of $\mathbf{x}$ in the *force field* $A\mathbf{y} - \mathbf{b}$ *is minimal.* To get this minimal energy, set $\mathbf{x} = A^{-1}\mathbf{b}$, getting $-\frac{1}{2}\mathbf{b}^T A^{-1}\mathbf{b}$. Then the work done in going from the point $\mathbf{x}$ of minimum potential energy to a point

$\mathbf{x} + \mathbf{y}$ is

$$\begin{aligned} W(\mathbf{x}, \mathbf{x}+\mathbf{y}) &= \tfrac{1}{2}(\mathbf{x}+\mathbf{y})^T A(\mathbf{x}+\mathbf{y}) - (\mathbf{x}+\mathbf{y})^T\mathbf{b} - \tfrac{1}{2}\mathbf{b}^T A^{-1}\mathbf{b} \\ &= \tfrac{1}{2}\mathbf{x}^T A\mathbf{x} - \mathbf{x}^T\mathbf{b} - \tfrac{1}{2}\mathbf{b}^T A^{-1}\mathbf{b} + \tfrac{1}{2}\mathbf{y}^T(A\mathbf{x}) + \tfrac{1}{2}(\mathbf{x}^T A)\mathbf{y} - \mathbf{y}^T\mathbf{b} + \tfrac{1}{2}\mathbf{y}^T A\mathbf{y} \\ &= \qquad 0 \qquad + \tfrac{1}{2}\mathbf{y}^T\mathbf{b} \quad + \tfrac{1}{2}\mathbf{b}^T\mathbf{y} \quad - \mathbf{y}^T\mathbf{b} + \tfrac{1}{2}\mathbf{y}^T A\mathbf{y} \\ &= \qquad 0 \qquad + \qquad 0 \qquad + \tfrac{1}{2}\mathbf{y}^T A\mathbf{y} \end{aligned}$$

and the potential energy at $\mathbf{x} + \mathbf{y}$ is $\tfrac{1}{2}(\mathbf{y}^T A\mathbf{y} - \mathbf{b}^T A^{-1}\mathbf{b})$.

Theorem 7.8. *Potential Energy and Work for the Field $A\mathbf{x} - \mathbf{b}$.* Minimal potential energy in the force field $F(\mathbf{x}) = A\mathbf{x} - \mathbf{b}$ is $-\tfrac{1}{2}\mathbf{b}^T A^{-1}\mathbf{b}$, achieved at $\mathbf{x}$ when $A\mathbf{x} = \mathbf{b}$. The work done by F as the unit particle moves from a solution $\mathbf{x}$ to $A\mathbf{x} = \mathbf{b}$ to $\mathbf{x} + \mathbf{y}$ is $\tfrac{1}{2}\mathbf{y}^T A\mathbf{y}$.

See Figure 7.9.

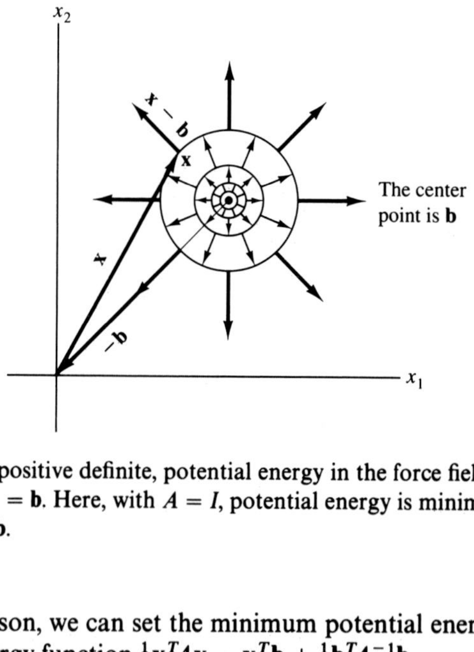

Figure 7.9 For A positive definite, potential energy in the force field $A\mathbf{x} - \mathbf{b}$ at $\mathbf{x}$ is minimal if $A\mathbf{x} = \mathbf{b}$. Here, with $A = I$, potential energy is minimal in the force field $\mathbf{x} - \mathbf{b}$ if $\mathbf{x} = \mathbf{b}$.

For this reason, we can set the minimum potential energy to 0 by using the potential energy function $\tfrac{1}{2}\mathbf{x}^T A\mathbf{x} - \mathbf{x}^T\mathbf{b} + \tfrac{1}{2}\mathbf{b}^T A^{-1}\mathbf{b}$.

Gradients of linear combinations of quadratic functions and their products and powers can be computed quite easily using gradient formulas from calculus:

1. $\nabla(vr(\mathbf{x}) + ws(\mathbf{x})) = v\nabla r(\mathbf{x}) + w\nabla s(\mathbf{x})$ (v, w constants).
2. $\nabla(r(\mathbf{x})s(\mathbf{x})) = r(\mathbf{x})\nabla s(\mathbf{x}) + s(\mathbf{x})\nabla r(\mathbf{x})$.
3. $\nabla(r(\mathbf{x}))^n = nr(\mathbf{x})^{n-1}\nabla r(\mathbf{x})$ (n any integer).

EXAMPLE

Let $f(\mathbf{x})$ be the potential energy function $f(\mathbf{x}) = -1/r$, $r = \|\mathbf{x}\|$, so that 0 is an upper bound for potential energy, and it *decreases* as r gets smaller. Then

$$\nabla f(\mathbf{x}) = -\nabla \frac{1}{r} = -\nabla(\mathbf{x}^T\mathbf{x})^{-1/2} = \frac{1}{2}(\mathbf{x}^T\mathbf{x})^{-3/2}\nabla(\mathbf{x}^T I\mathbf{x})$$

$$= \frac{1}{2}(\mathbf{x}^T\mathbf{x})^{-3/2} 2I\mathbf{x} = \frac{\mathbf{x}}{r^3},$$

and the force field corresponding to the potential energy function $-1/r$ is $F(\mathbf{x}) = \mathbf{x}/r^3$. The work done by $F(\mathbf{x})$ along a path from $\mathbf{x}$ to $\mathbf{y}$ is the change $W(\mathbf{x}, \mathbf{y}) = f(\mathbf{y}) - f(\mathbf{x}) = 1/\|\mathbf{x}\| - 1/\|\mathbf{y}\|$ in potential energy. For example, if $f(\mathbf{x}) = -k/r$ represents *gravitational potential energy* attributed to a certain planet, $F(\mathbf{x}) = k\mathbf{x}/r^3$ represents its *gravitational force field*, and the work done by gravity as a unit mass M moves along a path from $3\mathbf{e}_1$ to $8\mathbf{e}_2$ is $W(3\mathbf{e}_1, 8\mathbf{e}_2) = f(8\mathbf{e}_2) - f(3\mathbf{e}_1) = k/3 - k/8 = 5k/24 > 0$. So, *as positive work $k/3 - k/8$ is done by gravity, the potential energy of the unit mass increases from $-k/3$ to $-k/8$.* The maximum increase for a unit mass at $3\mathbf{e}_1$ is $k/3$, achieved by moving the mass to infinity along any smooth path which does not pass through the point mass representing the planet (Figure 7.10).

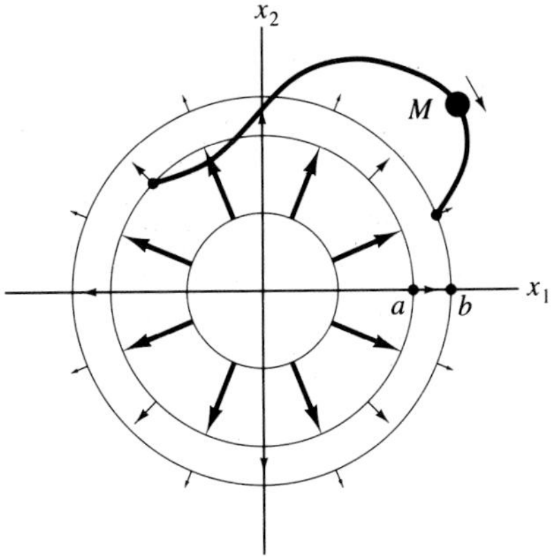

Figure 7.10 The potential energy gained as M moves along any path, not through $\mathbf{0}$, from a units to b units from planet X is $k/a - k/b$.

Using the formula $\nabla\mathbf{x}^T A\mathbf{x} = 2A\mathbf{x}$ in place of the formula $\nabla\mathbf{x}^T I\mathbf{x} = 2I\mathbf{x}$ in the example, a corresponding computation gives the following. (Verify!)

Theorem 7.9. *Force Field for $-1/r$, where $r = \nabla(\mathbf{x}^T A\mathbf{x})^{1/2}$.*
For the potential field $-1/r$, where $r = \nabla(\mathbf{x}^T A\mathbf{x})^{1/2}$, the force field is $\nabla f(\mathbf{x}) = A\mathbf{x}/r^3$.

PROBLEMS

NUMERICAL PROBLEMS

1. Express $f(\mathbf{x})$ as $f(\mathbf{x}) = (\mathbf{x} - \mathbf{u})^T A(\mathbf{x} - \mathbf{u}) + (\mathbf{x} - \mathbf{u})^T \mathbf{w}' + t'$ for some A, $\mathbf{w}'$, and $\mathbf{t}'$ for the following f and $\mathbf{u}$:

   (a) $f(\mathbf{x}) = x_1^2 + x_2^2 + x_1 x_2 + 1, \mathbf{u} = \begin{bmatrix} 1 \\ 1 \end{bmatrix}$

   (b) $f(\mathbf{x}) = x_1^2 - 2x_2^2 + x_1 x_2 + x_1 + x_2 + 1, \mathbf{u} = \begin{bmatrix} 1 \\ 2 \end{bmatrix}$.

2. Give an expansion of the form $f(\mathbf{x}) = \mathbf{x}'^T A \mathbf{x}' + t'$ ($\mathbf{x}' = \mathbf{x} - \mathbf{u}$ for some $\mathbf{u}$) of $f(\mathbf{x}) = \mathbf{x}^T A \mathbf{x} + \mathbf{w}^T \mathbf{x} + t$ for the following f. (Note that the matrix in each expression is A. If no such expansion exists, explain why not.)

   (a) $f(\mathbf{x}) = x_1^2 + x_2^2 + x_1 + x_2 + 1$

   (b) $f(\mathbf{x}) = 2x_2^2 + x_1 x_2 + x_1 + 1$

   (c) $f(\mathbf{x}) = 2x_2^2 + x_1 + x_2 + 1$

3. Find the gradient at $\mathbf{0}$ for each of the functions in Problem 1.

4. For each of the functions $f(\mathbf{x})$ in Problem 2:

   (a) Find the gradient function $\nabla f(\mathbf{x})$.

   (b) Using part (a), find the gradient of $f(\mathbf{x})$ at $\begin{bmatrix} 1 \\ 1 \end{bmatrix}$.

THEORETICAL PROBLEMS

5. Use Heron's minimum principle to explain why, for an ellipse $\{\mathbf{x} \in \mathbb{R}^2 \mid \|\mathbf{x} - \mathbf{p}\| + \|\mathbf{x} - \mathbf{q}\| = 2a\}$ of radius a with foci $\mathbf{p}$ and $\mathbf{q}$, light or sound originating at $\mathbf{p}$ is reflected to $\mathbf{q}$ by any mirror tangent to the ellipse (Figure 7.11).

6. Show that the ith coordinate function of the gradient $\nabla f(\mathbf{x}) = 2A\mathbf{x} + \mathbf{w}$ of $f(\mathbf{x}) = (\mathbf{x} - \mathbf{x})^T A(\mathbf{x} - \mathbf{a}) + \mathbf{w}^T(\mathbf{x} - \mathbf{a}) + t$ is the ith partial derivative of $g(\mathbf{x})$ at $\mathbf{a}$.

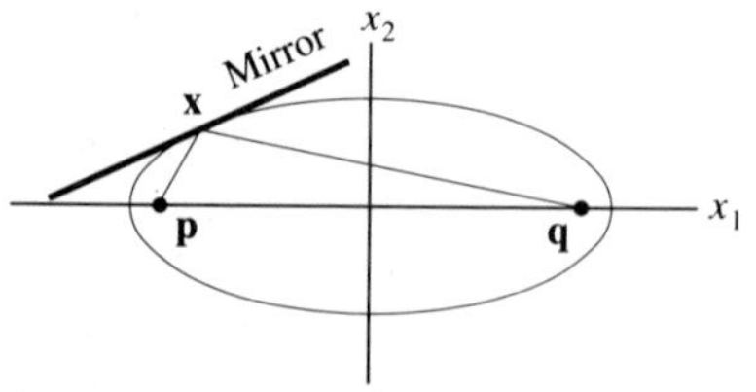

Figure 7.11 The acoustics of an elliptical room in the plane. At each point on the wall, sound is reflected from focal point to focal point as if by a sound mirror tangent at the point on the wall.

7. Give the *Taylor expansion* $f(\mathbf{x}) = \mathbf{x}'^T A\mathbf{x}' + \mathbf{w}'^T\mathbf{x}' + t'$ ($\mathbf{x}' = \mathbf{x} - \mathbf{u}$) at $\mathbf{x} = \mathbf{u}$ of $f(\mathbf{x}) = \mathbf{x}^T A\mathbf{x} + \mathbf{w}^T\mathbf{x} + t$ by expressing $\mathbf{w}'$ and t' in terms of $\mathbf{w}$, t, $\mathbf{u}$, and A.
8. Check your solution to Problem 7 against your solution to Problem 1.
9. For the quadratic part $f(\mathbf{x})$ of $g(\mathbf{x})$ at $\mathbf{a}$, show that:
   - **(a)** $f(\mathbf{x})$ has the same constant $f(\mathbf{a}) = g(\mathbf{a})$, gradient $\nabla f(\mathbf{a}) = \nabla g(\mathbf{a})$, and Hessian $\mathbf{y}^T A\mathbf{y}$ ($\mathbf{y} = \mathbf{x} - \mathbf{a}$) at $\mathbf{a}$, as does $g(\mathbf{x})$.
   - **(b)** $\mathbf{x} = \mathbf{a}$ is a critical point for $f(\mathbf{x})$ if and only if it is a critical point for $g(\mathbf{x})$.
   - **(c)** Even if $\mathbf{a}$ is a critical point for $g(\mathbf{x})$, it is possible that $g(\mathbf{x})$ has other critical points and $f(\mathbf{x})$ does not. (Give an example!)
10. If $f(\mathbf{x}) = (\mathbf{x} - \mathbf{a})^T A(\mathbf{x} - \mathbf{a}) + \mathbf{w}^T(\mathbf{x} - \mathbf{a})$, where $\mathbf{w}$ is real and A is real symmetric, invertible, and has characteristic vectors $\mathbf{v}$ and $\mathbf{w}$ corresponding to positive and negative characteristic roots, show that $f(\mathbf{x})$ has no minimum.
11. Show that any vector field $B(\mathbf{x} - \mathbf{a}) + \mathbf{v}$ (B a real symmetric matrix) is the gradient of the quadratic form $\frac{1}{2}(\mathbf{x} - \mathbf{a})^T B(\mathbf{x} - \mathbf{a}) + \mathbf{x}^T\mathbf{v} + s$ (s any constant).
12. Verify the following gradient formulas:
   - **(a)** $\nabla(vr(\mathbf{x}) + ws(\mathbf{x})) = v\nabla r(\mathbf{x}) + w\nabla s(\mathbf{x})$ (v, w constants)
   - **(b)** $\nabla(r(\mathbf{x})s(\mathbf{x})) = r(\mathbf{x})\nabla s(\mathbf{x}) + s(\mathbf{x})\nabla r(\mathbf{x})$
   - **(c)** $\nabla(r(\mathbf{x}))^n = nr(\mathbf{x})^{n-1}\nabla r(\mathbf{x})$ (n any integer).
13. Let the potential field for a planet be $-k/r$. Show that the maximum increase in potential energy for a unit mass at a distance of 3 units from a planet is $k/3$, achieved by moving the mass to infinity.

Hard

14. Use the formula $\nabla\mathbf{x}^T A\mathbf{x} = 2A\mathbf{x}$ in place of the formula $\nabla\mathbf{x}^T I\mathbf{x} = 2I\mathbf{x}$ to show, for the potential field $-1/r$ with $r = \nabla(\mathbf{x}^T A\mathbf{x})^{1/2}$, that the force field is $\nabla f(\mathbf{x}) = A\mathbf{x}/r^3$.

7.5 EXTREMA SUBJECT TO A SIDE CONDITION

Many extremum principles are expressed *subject to a side condition.* Heron's theorem (Section 7.4), for example, states that when the sum $\|\mathbf{x} - \mathbf{p}\| + \|\mathbf{x} - \mathbf{q}\|$ of distances from $\mathbf{x}$ to two given points is minimized subject to the side condition that $\mathbf{x}$ be on a given line, then $\overrightarrow{\mathbf{xp}}$ and $\overrightarrow{\mathbf{xq}}$ make equal angles to the line. We now discuss extrema subject to a side condition more generally.

Vanishing of the gradient is necessary for a relative extremum without side condition. The counterpart of this principle when there is a side condition is the following theorem from calculus, which we do not re-prove here.

Principle of Lagrange Multipliers.
The condition of a relative extremum for $f(\mathbf{x})$ at $\mathbf{x} = \mathbf{a}$, where $\mathbf{x}$ is subject to a side condition $g(\mathbf{x}) = c$, ∇f and ∇g being continuous in some sphere $\|\mathbf{x} - \mathbf{a}\| < d$, implies that $\nabla f(\mathbf{a}) = \lambda \nabla g(\mathbf{a})$ for some λ, called the **Lagrange multiplier**.

In this section, we illustrate how the principle of Lagrange multipliers can be used to study extrema subject to side conditions for functions built from quadratic forms.

Solving $A\mathbf{x} = \lambda\mathbf{x}$

Let's first apply the principle to $\mathbf{x}^T A\mathbf{x}$ (A symmetric), where the side condition is the condition $\mathbf{x}^T\mathbf{x} = 1$ that $\mathbf{x}$ have length 1. The gradients $\nabla f(\mathbf{x})$ and $\nabla g(\mathbf{x})$ of $f(\mathbf{x}) = \mathbf{x}^T A\mathbf{x}$ and $\mathbf{x}^T\mathbf{x}$ are $2A\mathbf{x}$ and $2I\mathbf{x}$, so the equation $\nabla f(\mathbf{x}) = \lambda\nabla g(\mathbf{x})$ is $2A\mathbf{x} = 2\lambda I\mathbf{x}$. Multiplying by $\mathbf{x}^T/2$ gives $\mathbf{x}^T A\mathbf{x} = \lambda$, since $\mathbf{x}^T\mathbf{x} = 1$. This gives the following principle.

Theorem 7.10. *Extremum Principle for Solving $A\mathbf{x} = \lambda\mathbf{x}$.*
If $\mathbf{x}$ is an extremum of $\mathbf{x}^T A\mathbf{x}$ (A symmetric) subject to $\|\mathbf{x}\| = 1$, then $\mathbf{x}$ is a characteristic vector of A and $\lambda = \mathbf{x}^T A\mathbf{x}$ is the corresponding characteristic root. The absolute maxima and minima $\mathbf{x}$ occur where $|\lambda|$ is maximal and minimal among the characteristic roots of A.

Note the following:

1. By the method discussed in Section 5.6 for finding dominant characteristic vectors, for almost all $\mathbf{y}$ the absolute maximum of $\mathbf{x}^T A\mathbf{x}$ subject to $\|\mathbf{x}\| = 1$ is the limit of $\mathbf{y}_i^T A\mathbf{y}_i$ for $\mathbf{y}_i = A^i\mathbf{y}/\|A^i\mathbf{y}\|$.
2. If A is invertible, then its characteristic roots are the inverses of those of A, since $A\mathbf{v} = d\mathbf{v}$ implies that $d^{-1}\mathbf{v} = A^{-1}\mathbf{v}$. So, by (1), for almost all $\mathbf{y}$ the absolute minimum of $\mathbf{x}^T A\mathbf{x}$ subject to $\|\mathbf{x}\| = 1$ is the limit of $(\mathbf{y}_i^T A^{-1}\mathbf{y}_i)^{-1}$ for $\mathbf{y}_i = A^{-1}\mathbf{y}/\|A^{-i}\mathbf{y}\|$. (Explain!)
3. For a positive definite matrix A of degree n and $\mathbf{b} \in \mathbb{R}^n$, the work done by the force field $A\mathbf{x} - \mathbf{b}$ in moving from a solution $\mathbf{x}$ to $A\mathbf{x} = \mathbf{b}$ to $\mathbf{x} + \mathbf{y}$ is $\frac{1}{2}\mathbf{y}A^T\mathbf{y}$ (Section 7.4).

So, we have the following (see Figure 7.12).

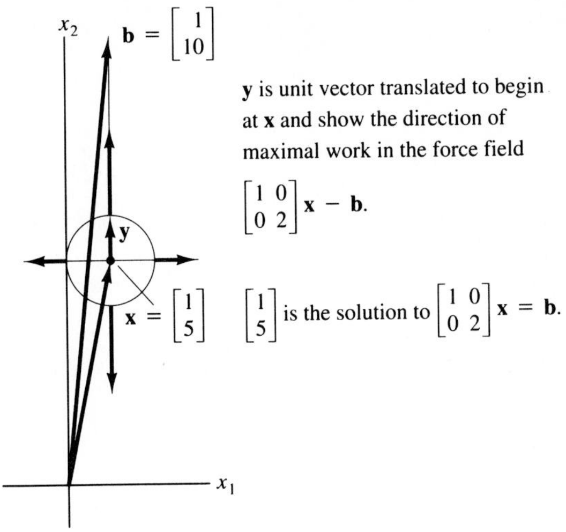

Figure 7.12 Direction of maximum work starting at $\mathbf{x} = \begin{bmatrix} 1 \\ 5 \end{bmatrix}$ in the force field $\begin{bmatrix} 1 & 0 \\ 0 & 2 \end{bmatrix}\mathbf{x} - \begin{bmatrix} 1 \\ 10 \end{bmatrix}$. Maximum work $\frac{1}{2}\mathbf{y}^T A\mathbf{y}$ (A symmetric) for $\mathbf{y}$ of length 1.

Theorem 7.11. *Principal Axis for Work in the Field* $A\mathbf{x} - \mathbf{b}$.
To maximize or minimize work done in going from $\mathbf{x} = A^{-1}\mathbf{b}$ to $\mathbf{x} + \mathbf{y}$ subject to the constraint $\|\mathbf{y}\| = 1$ amounts to choosing $\mathbf{y}$ to be a characteristic vector for A corresponding to an absolute maximal or minimal characteristic root.

The norm of a real matrix

Applying the principle to A^2 (A symmetric) instead of A, an extremum $\mathbf{x}$ for $\mathbf{x}^T A^2 \mathbf{x}$ subject to $\|\mathbf{x}\| = 1$ is a characteristic vector of A^2 with corresponding characteristic root $\lambda = \mathbf{x}^T A^2 \mathbf{x} = \|A\mathbf{x}\|^2$.

Theorem 7.12. *Extrema of* $\|A\mathbf{x}\|$ *Subject to* $\|\mathbf{x}\| = 1$.
If $\mathbf{x}$ is an extremum of $\|A\mathbf{x}\|$ (A symmetric) subject to $\|\mathbf{x}\| = 1$, then $\mathbf{x}$ is a characteristic vector of A^2 and $\|A\mathbf{x}\|^2 = \lambda$, where λ is the corresponding characteristic root.

For a symmetric matrix A, this shows that the norm $\|A\|$ of A is the maximal absolute value $|d|$ achieved by characteristic roots d of A, the norm being defined as follows (see Figure 7.13).

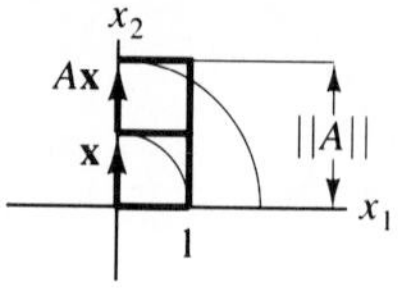

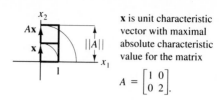

Figure 7.13 If A is symmetric, $A\mathbf{x} = ||A||\mathbf{x}$ or $A\mathbf{x} = -||A||\mathbf{x}$ for some nonzero **x**.

Definition. *The Norm of A.*
For any $A \in M_{m \times n}\mathbb{R}$, the maximum of $||A\mathbf{x}||$ subject to $||\mathbf{x}|| = 1$ is the **norm** $||A||$ of A.

When A is not symmetric, we can study its norm by symmetric methods, since A^TA is symmetric. The norm of A equals $||A\mathbf{x}||$ at a maximum $\mathbf{x}$ for $\mathbf{x}^TA^TA\mathbf{x}$ subject to $\mathbf{x}^T\mathbf{x} = 1$. So, $\mathbf{x}$ is a characteristic vector of A^TA, and the corresponding characteristic root is $\mathbf{x}^TA^TA\mathbf{x} = ||A\mathbf{x}||^2$. This proves the following.

Theorem 7.13. *The Norm of A and Dominant Characteristic Root of A^TA.*
If x is a characteristic vector of A^TA of length 1 whose corresponding characteristic root λ is as large as possible, then $||A|| = ||A\mathbf{x}|| = \sqrt{\lambda}$. Such $\mathbf{x}$ and λ are called **dominant**.

We need the norm and its properties to prove convergence of a sequence of matrices in Section 7.7.

Theorem 7.14. *Properties of the Norm of A.*
The norm satisfies the following conditions:

1. $||A\mathbf{x}|| \leq ||A||\,||\mathbf{x}||$ for all $x \in \mathbb{R}^n$.
2. $||cA|| = |c|\,||A||$ for $c \in \mathbb{R}$.
3. $||A + B|| \leq ||A + B||$.
4. $||AB|| \leq ||A||\,||B||$ when the sizes of A and B are compatible.
5. $||Q|| = 1$, $||QB|| = ||B||$, $||CQ|| = ||C||$ if Q is orthogonal.

Proof. (1) and (2) follow directly from the definition, and (3) follows from the Schwarz inequality. For (4), note that $||AB\mathbf{x}|| \leq ||A||\,||B\mathbf{x}|| \leq ||A||\,||B||\,||\mathbf{x}|| \leq ||A||\,||B||$ for $||\mathbf{x}|| \leq 1$. So, $||AB|| \leq ||A||\,||B||$. For (5), $||Q|| = 1$, since $||Q\mathbf{x}|| = ||\mathbf{x}||$. Then $||QB|| \leq ||B||$, $||B|| = ||Q^{-1}QB|| \leq ||QB||$ (and the corresponding inequalities for C) follow from (4). ∎

Snell's law of optics

Heron's theorem described the minimum point $\mathbf{x}$ for the function $\|\mathbf{x} - \mathbf{p}\| + \|\mathbf{x} - \mathbf{q}\|$ subject to the condition that $\mathbf{x}$ lies on a specified line. We now generalize Heron's theorem by using the principle of Lagrange multipliers to investigate the minima $\mathbf{x}$ of the similar but more general function

$$T(\mathbf{x}) = \frac{1}{v}\sqrt{(\mathbf{x}-\mathbf{p})^T A(\mathbf{x}-\mathbf{p})} + \frac{1}{w}\sqrt{(\mathbf{x}-\mathbf{q})^T B(\mathbf{x}-\mathbf{q})}.$$

Here, v and w represent two constant velocities and $\mathbf{x}$ lies in a given hyperplane $h(\mathbf{x}) = 0$, h being the linear function $h(\mathbf{x}) = \mathbf{x}^T\mathbf{N}$. At a minimum $\mathbf{x}$, the Lagrange multiplier condition $\nabla T(\mathbf{x}) = \lambda \nabla h(\mathbf{x}) = \lambda \mathbf{N}$ holds. As the results unfold in the discussion, two special cases are of particular interest because they correspond to principles of optics:

1. In the case when the velocities are $v = w = 1$, $A = B = I$ and the matrices are 2×2, the results give Heron's theorem.
2. In the case when $A = B = I$ with different velocities and the matrices are 2×2, the results give Snell's law (Theorem 7.16). See Figure 7.14.

To find $\nabla T(\mathbf{x})$, we first find the gradients of the two terms comprising $T(\mathbf{x})$. The gradient of $(\mathbf{x}-\mathbf{p})^T A(\mathbf{x}-\mathbf{p})$ is $2A(\mathbf{x}-\mathbf{p})$. So, the gradient of $\frac{1}{v}\sqrt{(\mathbf{x}-\mathbf{p})^T A(\mathbf{x}-\mathbf{p})}$ is $\frac{1}{v}\cdot\frac{1}{2}((\mathbf{x}-\mathbf{p})^T A(\mathbf{x}-\mathbf{p}))^{-1/2} 2A(\mathbf{x}-\mathbf{p})$. Getting the other term and equating the resulting sum with $\lambda \nabla h(\mathbf{x}) = \lambda N$ yields

$$\lambda N = \frac{1}{v}((\mathbf{x}-\mathbf{p})^T A(\mathbf{x}-\mathbf{p}))^{-1/2} A(\mathbf{x}-\mathbf{p}) + \frac{1}{w}((\mathbf{x}-\mathbf{q})^T B(\mathbf{x}-\mathbf{q}))^{-1/2} B(\mathbf{x}-\mathbf{q}).$$

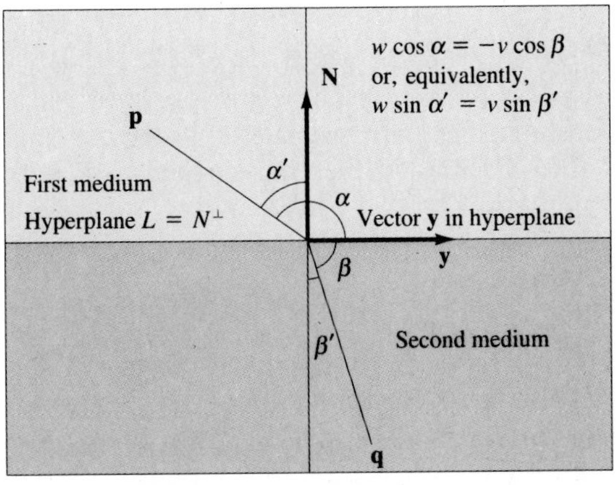

Figure 7.14 Snell's law of optics for light traveling from $\mathbf{p}$ to $\mathbf{q}$. The velocities in the two mediums are v and w.

For any $\mathbf{y}$ in the hyperplane $\mathbf{x}^T\mathbf{N} = 0$, $\mathbf{y}$ is orthogonal to $\mathbf{N}$. Multiply through by $\mathbf{y}^T$ to get

$$0 = \frac{1}{v}((\mathbf{x}-\mathbf{p})^T A(\mathbf{x}-\mathbf{p}))^{-1/2}\mathbf{y}^T A(\mathbf{x}-\mathbf{p}) + \frac{1}{w}((\mathbf{x}-\mathbf{q})^T B(\mathbf{x}-\mathbf{q}))^{-1/2}\mathbf{y}^T B(\mathbf{x}-\mathbf{q}).$$

Move one term to the other side and solve for v/w, which gives

$$\frac{w}{v} = -\frac{((\mathbf{x}-\mathbf{p})^T A(\mathbf{x}-\mathbf{p}))^{1/2}}{\mathbf{y}^T A(\mathbf{x}-\mathbf{p})}\,\frac{\mathbf{y}^T B(\mathbf{x}-\mathbf{q})}{((\mathbf{x}-\mathbf{q})^T B(\mathbf{x}-\mathbf{q}))^{1/2}}.$$

To apply this, consider any invertible matrices C and D and take $A = C^TC$ and $B = D^TD$. Then our expressions simplify to $T(\mathbf{x}) = \frac{1}{v}\|C(\mathbf{x}-\mathbf{p})\| + \frac{1}{w}\|D(\mathbf{x}-\mathbf{q})\|$, and we get

$$\frac{w}{v} = -\frac{((\mathbf{x}-\mathbf{p})^T C^T C(\mathbf{x}-\mathbf{p}))^{1/2}}{\mathbf{y}^T C^T C(\mathbf{x}-\mathbf{p})}\,\frac{\mathbf{y}^T D^T D(\mathbf{x}-\mathbf{q})}{((\mathbf{x}-\mathbf{q})^T D^T D(\mathbf{x}-\mathbf{q}))^{1/2}},$$

$$\frac{w}{v} = -\frac{\|C(\mathbf{x}-\mathbf{p})\|\,\|D\mathbf{y}\|\,\|D(\mathbf{x}-\mathbf{q})\|\cos\beta}{\|C\mathbf{y}\|\,\|C(\mathbf{x}-\mathbf{p})\|\cos\alpha\,\|D(\mathbf{x}-\mathbf{q})\|} = -\frac{\|D\mathbf{y}\|\cos\beta}{\|C\mathbf{y}\|\cos\alpha}.$$

Theorem 7.15. *Minima for* $\frac{1}{v}\|C(\mathbf{x}-\mathbf{p})\| + \frac{1}{w}\|D(\mathbf{x}-\mathbf{q})\|$ *for* $\mathbf{x} \perp N$.

Let v and w be positive constants, C and D be invertible matrices, N be a nonzero vector, and $\mathbf{p}$ and $\mathbf{q}$ be points not in the hyperplane $N^\perp$. Then at a minimum $\mathbf{x}$ for $\frac{1}{v}\|C(\mathbf{x}-\mathbf{p})\| + \frac{1}{w}\|D(\mathbf{x}-\mathbf{q})\|$ subject to $\mathbf{x} \in \mathbf{N}^\perp$, the angle α between $C(\mathbf{x}-\mathbf{p})$ and $C\mathbf{y}$ and the angle β between $D(\mathbf{x}-\mathbf{q})$ and $D\mathbf{y}$ are related by $w\|C\mathbf{y}\|\cos\alpha = -v\|D\mathbf{y}\|\cos\beta$ for every nonzero $\mathbf{y} \in \mathbf{N}^\perp$.

In the case of $\mathbb{R}^n$ when $A = B = C = D = I$, $T(\mathbf{x})$ is the time required to travel in $\mathbb{R}^n$ from a point p in one medium to a point q in the other. The mediums here are assumed to fill the half-spaces $h(\mathbf{x}) > 0$ and $h(\mathbf{x}) < 0$, and the velocities in the two mediums are v and w. At a minimum of $T(\mathbf{x})$, $\overrightarrow{\mathbf{px}}$ and $\overrightarrow{\mathbf{qx}}$ meet the boundary at angles interrelated by v and w. (When C and D are not I, provisions are made for *weighted distances* defined in terms of C and D.)

For $n = 2$, we get the following generalization of Heron's theorem.

Theorem 7.16. *Mathematical Version of Snell's Law.*

In $\mathbb{R}^2$, let L be a line, $\mathbf{p}$ and $\mathbf{q}$ be points, and $\mathbf{x}$ be the point on the line which minimizes $\frac{1}{v}\|\mathbf{x}-\mathbf{p}\| + \frac{1}{w}\|\mathbf{x}-\mathbf{q}\|$, v and w being positive constants. Then $\overrightarrow{\mathbf{px}}$ and $\overrightarrow{\mathbf{qx}}$ meet the normal to L at angles α, β related by $w\sin\alpha' = v\sin\beta'$.

For two (homogeneous) mediums in $\mathbb{R}^3$ separated by the plane $\mathbb{R}\mathbf{e}_1 + \mathbb{R}\mathbf{e}_3$, experiments confirm for $\mathbf{p}, \mathbf{q} \in \mathbb{R}\mathbf{e}_1 + \mathbb{R}\mathbf{e}_2$ that light follows the route $\overrightarrow{\mathbf{px}}, \overrightarrow{\mathbf{xq}}$ described before. So, these experiments support the following.

Optical Version of Snell's Law.
Light traveling from $\mathbf{p}$ to $\mathbf{q}$ in two mediums separated by a plane follows the path that minimizes the time needed to get there.

PROBLEMS

NUMERICAL PROBLEMS

1. Use Theorem 7.10 to find the absolute maximum or minimum of $\mathbf{x}^T A\mathbf{x}$ for the following matrices A. (If no maximum or minimum exists, explain why not.)

   (a) $A = \begin{bmatrix} 1 & 2 \\ 2 & 5 \end{bmatrix}$ (b) $A = \begin{bmatrix} -2 & 4 \\ 4 & -9 \end{bmatrix}$

2. Use Theorem 7.11 to find the axis along which work in the force field $A\mathbf{x} - \mathbf{b}$ is maximized starting from $\mathbf{x} = A^{-1}\mathbf{b}$ when

   (a) $A = \begin{bmatrix} 1 & 0 \\ 0 & 2 \end{bmatrix}, b = \begin{bmatrix} 1 \\ 2 \end{bmatrix}$, (b) $A = \begin{bmatrix} 1 & 1 \\ 1 & 2 \end{bmatrix}, b = \begin{bmatrix} 2 \\ 2 \end{bmatrix}$.

THEORETICAL PROBLEMS

3. Find the extrema of $\mathbf{x}^T A\mathbf{x}$ subject to $\mathbf{x}^T B\mathbf{x} = 1$ for A, B positive definite.

7.6 TRIDIAGONALIZATION OF SYMMETRIC MATRICES

The problem of diagonalizing *A*

Any quadratic form can be brought to normal form. The approximate inverse of a matrix can be computed using the singular-value decomposition. These and many other things involving the spectrum can be done *if* we can find an orthogonal transformation $\mathbf{x} = Q\mathbf{x}'$ which diagonalizes the corresponding symmetric matrix A—that is, such that $Q^T AQ = D$ is diagonal. Accordingly, the problem of computing Q for a given real symmetric matrix in an efficient, numerically stable fashion has been attacked vigorously from many vantage points, depending on the nature of A.

Perhaps the most successful general method for computing Q for a real symmetric matrix A is to do the following:

1. Tridiagonalize A symmetrically (by methods described in this section).
2. Diagonalize the tridiagonalized A by the QR algorithm of Section 6.12 or by the methods described in Section 7.7.

Since A remains symmetric throughout the entire process, this method is quite fast.

Householder reflections

To tridiagonalize A, we use the Householder reflections of $\mathbb{R}^n$, introduced for $n = 2$ in Section 1.6.

Definition. *Householder Reflection from $\mathbb{R}^n$ to Itself.*
For any nonzero $\mathbf{w} \in \mathbb{R}^n$, $r_\mathbf{w}$ is the linear transformation of $\mathbb{R}^n$ defined by $r_\mathbf{w}(\mathbf{v}) = \mathbf{v} - 2\dfrac{\langle \mathbf{v}, \mathbf{w}\rangle}{\langle \mathbf{w}, \mathbf{w}\rangle}\mathbf{w}$ $(\mathbf{v} \in \mathbb{R}^n)$. It is called the **Householder reflection** (or **reflection**) across the hyperplane $w^\perp = \{\mathbf{v} \in \mathbb{R}^n \mid \langle \mathbf{v}, \mathbf{w}\rangle = 0\}$. The matrix $m(r_\mathbf{w})$ of $r_\mathbf{w}$ is called a **reflection matrix** at $\mathbf{w}$ (Figure 7.15).

The reflections $r_\mathbf{w}$ have many interesting features, some of which are as follows:

1. $r_\mathbf{w} = I - 2\dfrac{\mathbf{w}\mathbf{w}^T}{\langle \mathbf{w}, \mathbf{w}\rangle}$, since $r_\mathbf{w}(\mathbf{v}) = \mathbf{v} - 2\dfrac{\mathbf{w}\mathbf{w}^T}{\langle \mathbf{w}, \mathbf{w}\rangle}\mathbf{v}$. (Verify!)

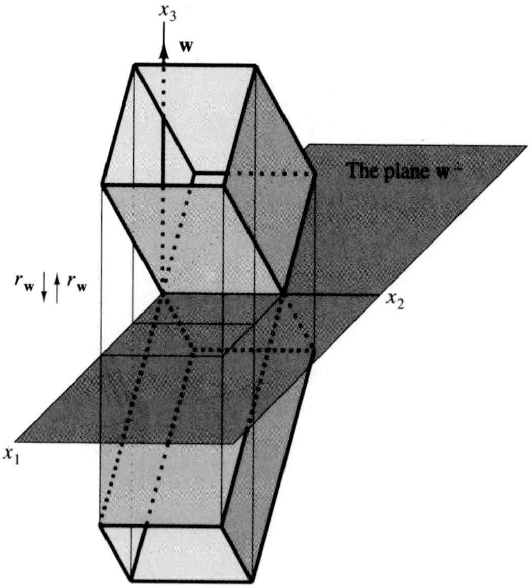

Figure 7.15 The reflection $r_\mathbf{w}$ across $\mathbf{w}^\perp$ for $\mathbf{w} = \begin{bmatrix} 0 \\ 0 \\ 1 \end{bmatrix}$ is

$$\mathbf{r}_\mathbf{w}(\mathbf{v}) = \begin{bmatrix} 1 & 0 & 0 \\ 0 & 1 & 0 \\ 0 & 0 & -1 \end{bmatrix}\mathbf{v}.$$

2. $r_{\mathbf{w}}(\mathbf{w}) = -\mathbf{w}$ and $r_{\mathbf{w}}(\mathbf{v}) = \mathbf{v}$ if $\mathbf{v} \in \mathbf{w}^{\perp}$. (Verify!) It follows that $(r_{\mathbf{w}})^2 = I$ and $r_{\mathbf{w}}^{-1} = r_{\mathbf{w}}$. (Explain!)
3. $r_{\mathbf{w}} = r_{\mathbf{w}'}$ if $\mathbb{R}\mathbf{w} = \mathbb{R}\mathbf{w}'$—that is, if $\mathbf{w}' = a\mathbf{w}$ for some $a \neq 0$. (Verify!)
4. $r_{\mathbf{w}}$ maps some orthonormal basis to an orthonormal basis. (Verify by taking an orthonormal basis for $\mathbf{w}^{\perp}$ and adding $\mathbf{w}/\|\mathbf{w}\|$.)
5. By (4), $r_{\mathbf{w}}$ is an orthogonal linear transformation. Since $r_{\mathbf{w}} = r_{\mathbf{w}}^{-1}$, it follows that $m(r_{\mathbf{w}}) = m(r_{\mathbf{w}})^{-1} = m(r_{\mathbf{w}})^T$. So, *all reflection matrices are symmetric.*
6. For $n = 2$, $r_{\mathbf{w}} = r_{\begin{bmatrix}\cos\alpha\\ \sin\alpha\end{bmatrix}}$ for some α, and we have the formula

$$r_{\begin{bmatrix}\cos\alpha\\ \sin\alpha\end{bmatrix}}(\mathbf{v}) = \begin{bmatrix} -\cos\beta & -\sin\beta \\ -\sin\beta & \cos\beta \end{bmatrix}\mathbf{v} \qquad (\mathbf{v} \in \mathbb{R}^2) \text{ where } \beta = 2\alpha$$

(Section 1.6). See Figure 7.16.

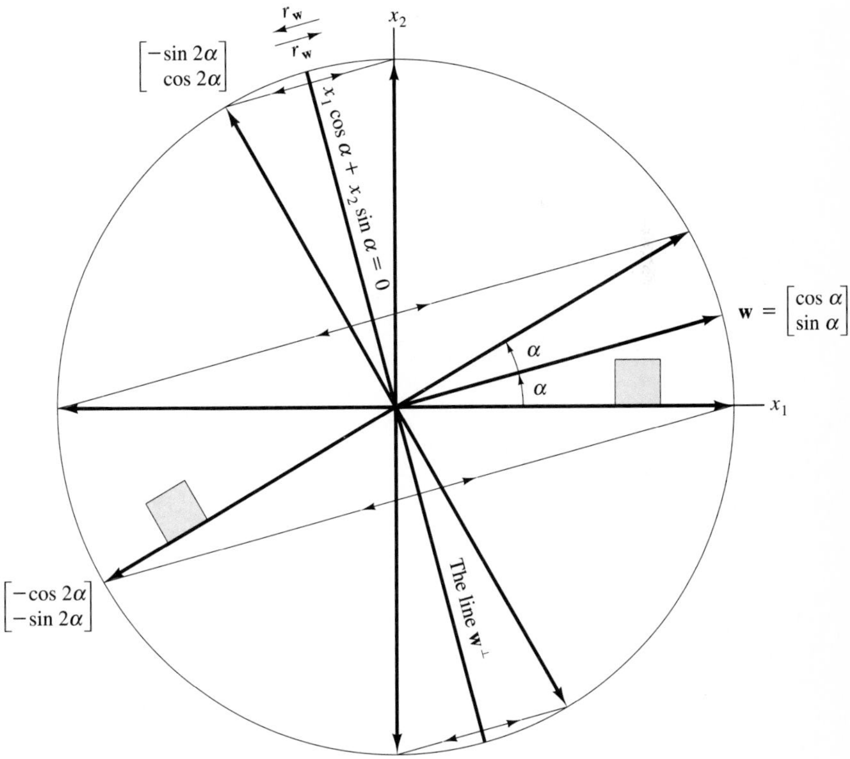

Figure 7.16 The reflection $r_{\begin{bmatrix}\cos\alpha\\ \sin\alpha\end{bmatrix}}(\mathbf{v}) = \begin{bmatrix} -\cos 2\alpha & -\sin 2\alpha \\ -\sin 2\alpha & \cos 2\alpha \end{bmatrix}\mathbf{v}.$

The reflection theorem

The following theorem is the key to a very powerful **symmetric reduction** of any symmetric A by orthogonal transformations.

Theorem 7.17. *The Reflection Theorem.*
Let $\mathbf{x}$, $\mathbf{y}$, and $\mathbf{x}+\mathbf{y}$ be nonzero and suppose that $\|\mathbf{x}\| = \|\mathbf{y}\|$. Then $r_{\mathbf{x}+\mathbf{y}}(\mathbf{x}) = -\mathbf{y}$.

Proof.

$$r_{\mathbf{x}+\mathbf{y}}(\mathbf{x}) = \mathbf{x} - 2\frac{\langle \mathbf{x}, \mathbf{x}+\mathbf{y}\rangle}{\langle \mathbf{x}+\mathbf{y}, \mathbf{x}+\mathbf{y}\rangle}(\mathbf{x}+\mathbf{y})$$

$$= \mathbf{x} - 2\frac{\langle \mathbf{x}, \mathbf{x}\rangle + \langle \mathbf{x}, \mathbf{x}\rangle}{\langle \mathbf{x}, \mathbf{x}\rangle + \langle \mathbf{y}, \mathbf{y}\rangle + 2\langle \mathbf{x}, \mathbf{y}\rangle}(\mathbf{x}+\mathbf{y}) = \mathbf{x} - 1(\mathbf{x}+\mathbf{y}) = -\mathbf{y}.$$

See Figure 7.17. ■

Symmetric tridiagonalization of *A* by reflections

Let $A \in M_n\mathbb{R}$ be symmetric. We want to find an orthogonal matrix U, a product of reflection matrices $m(r_{\mathbf{w}})$, such that U^TAU is *tridiagonal*, that is,

$$U^TAU = \begin{bmatrix} a_1 & b_1 & & & \\ b_1 & a_2 & b_2 & & \\ & b_2 & \ddots & \ddots & \\ & & \ddots & a_{n-1} & b_{n-1} \\ & & & b_{n-1} & a_n \end{bmatrix} \qquad \text{(0s in triangular regions)}$$

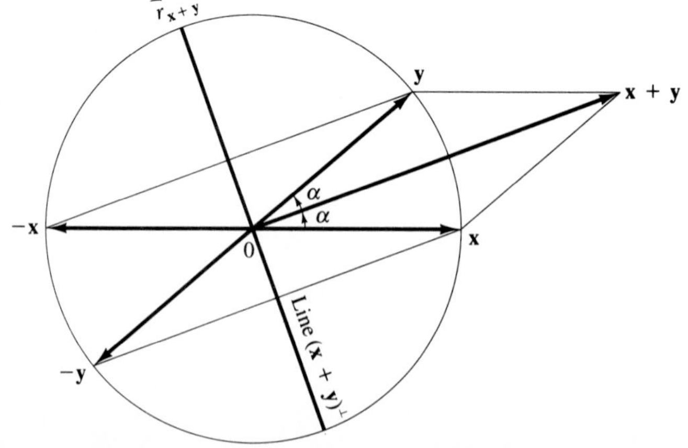

Figure 7.17 Geometric proof of the reflection theorem $r_{\mathbf{x}+\mathbf{y}}(\mathbf{x}) = -\mathbf{y}$, which takes place in the plane $\mathbb{R}\mathbf{x} + \mathbb{R}\mathbf{y}$ containing $\mathbf{x}$ and $\mathbf{y}$. The perpendicular bisector of the segment $\overline{-\mathbf{y}\,\mathbf{x}}$ is on the line through $\mathbf{0}$ perpendicular to $\mathbf{x}+\mathbf{y}$.

The condition that A be tridiagonal is that its nonzero entries are on the *main diagonal*, *subdiagonal*, and *super diagonal*; that is, its nonzero entries are a_{ii} $(1 \leq i \leq n)$, $a_{i+1,i}$ $(1 \leq i \leq n-1)$, and $a_{i,i+1}$ $(1 \leq i \leq n-1)$. We transform a symmetric matrix A to such a tridiagonal matrix in stages, A being r-fold tridiagonal at the beginning of stage r in the following sense.

Definition. *r-Fold Tridiagonal Matrix A.*
If A is symmetric and all the nonzero entries in the first r columns are on the main, sub- and super diagonals, we say that A is **r-fold tridiagonal.**

EXAMPLE

$$A = \begin{bmatrix} 1 & 2 & 0 & 0 & 0 \\ 2 & 1 & 3 & 0 & 0 \\ 0 & 3 & 2 & 5 & 1 \\ 0 & 0 & 5 & 6 & 1 \\ 0 & 0 & 1 & 1 & 1 \end{bmatrix}$$

is two-fold tridiagonal but is not three-fold tridiagonal.

Of course, any symmetric matrix A is symmetric and 0-fold tridiagonal, which gives us a place to start. And, if A is symmetric and n-fold tridiagonal, then A is symmetric and tridiagonal, which is where we want to end.

Suppose that A is symmetric and r-fold tridiagonal but not $(r+1)$-fold tridiagonal, where $0 \leq r < n$. We seek a reflection matrix $m(r_{\mathbf{w}})$ such that $m(r_{\mathbf{w}})A$ has the same first $r+1$ columns as A and the symmetric matrix $m(r_{\mathbf{w}})Am(r_{\mathbf{w}})$ is $(r+1)$-fold tridiagonal. The strategy is to find $\mathbf{w}$ such that the first r columns of A are in $\mathbf{w}^{\perp}$ and so are not disturbed by $r_{\mathbf{w}}$, and such that $r_{\mathbf{w}}$ maps column A_{r+1} of A to a column vector having 0's in rows $r+3$ through n. Letting $\mathbf{x}$ be the vector $\mathbf{x} = A_{r+1} - a_{r+1}\mathbf{e}_{r+1} - b_r\mathbf{e}_r$ whose first $r+1$ entries are 0 and whose sth entry is the sth entry of column A_{r+1} of A, $\mathbf{x}$ and $\mathbf{w} = \mathbf{x} - \|\mathbf{x}\|\mathbf{e}_{r+2}$ are nonzero, for otherwise A would be $(r+1)$-fold tridiagonal. (Verify!) Since $\mathbf{x}$ and $-\|\mathbf{x}\|\mathbf{e}_{r+2}$ are nonzero of the same length, the reflection theorem implies that $r_{\mathbf{w}}$ maps $\mathbf{x}$ to $\|\mathbf{x}\|\mathbf{e}_{r+2}$. Since the first r columns of A are in $\mathbf{w}^{\perp}$, $r_{\mathbf{w}}$ does not change the first r columns of A. For the same reason, $r_{\mathbf{w}}$ does not change $\mathbf{e}_r$, $\mathbf{e}_{r+1}$ and we have:

$$r_{\mathbf{w}}(A_{r+1}) = r_{\mathbf{w}}(\mathbf{x} + a_{r+1}\mathbf{e}_{r+1} + b_r\mathbf{e}_r) = \|\mathbf{x}\|\mathbf{e}_{r+2} + a_{r+1}\mathbf{e}_{r+1} + b_r\mathbf{e}_r.$$

Having successfully carried out our strategy, we get a reflection matrix $m(r_{\mathbf{w}})$ such that $m(r_{\mathbf{w}})A$ has the same first r columns as A and the symmetric matrix $m(r_{\mathbf{w}})Am(r_{\mathbf{w}})$ is $(r+1)$-fold tridiagonal. This proves the following.

Theorem 7.18. *Principle of Symmetric Reduction by Reflections.*
Let A be a symmetric matrix which is r-fold tridiagonal, where $0 \leq r < n$. Then $m(r_{\mathbf{w}})A$ has the same first $r+1$ columns as A and $m(r_{\mathbf{w}})Am(r_{\mathbf{w}})$ is symmetric and $(r+1)$-fold tridiagonal, where $\mathbf{w} = \mathbf{x} - \|\mathbf{x}\|\mathbf{e}_{r+2}$, $\mathbf{x} = A_{r+1} - a_{r+1}\mathbf{e}_{r+1} - b_r\mathbf{e}_r$.

EXAMPLE

The matrix

$$A = \begin{bmatrix} a & b & 0 & 0 \\ b & c & d & e \\ 0 & d & f & g \\ 0 & e & g & h \end{bmatrix}$$

is one-fold tridiagonal but not necessarily two-fold tridiagonal. So, we let

$$\mathbf{x} = A_2 - c\mathbf{e}_2 - b\mathbf{e}_1 = \begin{bmatrix} 0 \\ 0 \\ d \\ e \end{bmatrix} \quad \text{and} \quad \mathbf{w} = \mathbf{x} - \|\mathbf{x}\|\mathbf{e}_3 = \begin{bmatrix} 0 \\ 0 \\ d - \|\mathbf{x}\| \\ e \end{bmatrix}.$$

Then

$$\begin{aligned} r_{\mathbf{w}}(A_2) &= r_{\mathbf{w}}(\mathbf{x} + c\mathbf{e}_2 + b\mathbf{e}_1) \\ &= \|\mathbf{x}\|\mathbf{e}_3 + c\mathbf{e}_2 + b\mathbf{e}_1 = \begin{bmatrix} b \\ c \\ \|\mathbf{x}\| \\ 0 \end{bmatrix} \end{aligned}$$

and

$$m(r_{\mathbf{w}})Am(r_{\mathbf{w}}) = \begin{bmatrix} a & b & 0 & 0 \\ b & c & \|\mathbf{x}\| & 0 \\ 0 & \|\mathbf{x}\| & f' & g' \\ 0 & 0 & g' & h' \end{bmatrix}.$$

PROBLEMS

NUMERICAL PROBLEMS

1. Tridiagonalize the following matrices.

(a) $\begin{bmatrix} 1 & 2 & 0 & 0 \\ 2 & 1 & 3 & 0 \\ 0 & 3 & 2 & 5 \\ 0 & 2 & 5 & 6 \end{bmatrix}$ **(b)** $\begin{bmatrix} 1 & 2 & 0 & 0 & 0 \\ 2 & 1 & 3 & 0 & 0 \\ 0 & 3 & 2 & 5 & 1 \\ 0 & 0 & 5 & 6 & 1 \\ 0 & 0 & 1 & 1 & 1 \end{bmatrix}$

7.7 DIAGONALIZATION OF SYMMETRIC MATRICES

In Section 5.6, we showed how to find a dominant characteristic vector for a real symmetric matrix A. This produces the first column of an orthogonal matrix Q such that Q^TAQ is diagonal. Finding all the columns of such a Q

is much harder and is one of the important long-standing problems of numerical analysis. As such, solutions exist to fit many occasions. Among these, one solution stands alone for its elegance, simplicity, efficiency, generality, and numerical stability. Although other methods are sometimes more suitable—e.g., for *sparse* matrices (those having relatively few nonzero entries)—this solution is one of the best for *dense* (nonsparse) matrices and tridiagonal matrices. It is based on

1. The symmetric version of the QR algorithm, presented in Section 6.11;
2. Symmetric tridiagonalization, as presented in Section 7.6;
3. Symmetric tridiagonal QR factorization, as presented in this section.

Preservation of symmetry by shifts

In Section 6.11, shifts played the role in the QR algorithm of ensuring rapid convergence. Before we apply the QR algorithm to a real symmetric matrix, it is important to note that if a matrix A is symmetric before shifting by aI where a is real, then the resulting matrix $A - aI$ is also symmetric. (Explain!)

The *QR* algorithm for symmetric tridiagonal matrices

Since we can symmetrically tridiagonalize a given real symmetric matrix A quickly and accurately in a finite number of steps, we should start the QR algorithm from a tridiagonal matrix A. After all, we then start with a matrix with at least $n(n-3)$ 0s and the (theoretically infinite) iteration converges to accurate values much sooner. What makes this truly significant is the fact that, *throughout the QR algorithm with shifts, all A_i produced from A by the algorithm are also symmetric and tridiagonal.*

Theorem 7.19. *Preservation of Symmetry and Tridiagonality.*
Let A be a tridiagonal real symmetric matrix and suppose that A_i is produced from A by the QR algorithm with shifts. Then A is a tridiagonal real symmetric matrix.

Proof. Suppose then that A is symmetric and tridiagonal with QR decomposition $A = QR$. Then $A' = RQ$ can be written as $A' = R(AR^{-1})$, R and R^{-1} being upper triangular and A having 0s below the subdiagonal. It follows that A' has 0s below the subdiagonal, as in the 4×4 case:

$$\begin{bmatrix} A & B & C & D \\ 0 & E & F & G \\ 0 & 0 & H & I \\ 0 & 0 & 0 & J \end{bmatrix} \begin{bmatrix} a & b & 0 & 0 \\ b & c & d & 0 \\ 0 & d & e & f \\ 0 & 0 & f & g \end{bmatrix} \begin{bmatrix} K & L & M & N \\ 0 & P & Q & R \\ 0 & 0 & S & T \\ 0 & 0 & 0 & U \end{bmatrix} = \begin{bmatrix} h & i & j & k \\ l & m & n & o \\ 0 & p & q & r \\ 0 & 0 & s & t \end{bmatrix}$$

But A' is also symmetric, since $Q^TAQ = A'$. So, A' is symmetric and tridiagonal. Shifts preserve symmetry and tridiagonality, so any A_i produced from A by the algorithm is tridiagonal. ■

The *QR* decomposition of a tridiagonal real symmetric matrix

Once the problem has been reduced to diagonalizing a tridiagonal real symmetric matrix A, the QR algorithm of Section 6.11 produces the sequence $A_1, A_2, \ldots$ of symmetric matrices converging to the diagonal matrix similar to A. However, it must be instructed as to how to perform the QR factorizations along the way. So, we now describe how to get the QR factorization of a tridiagonal matrix A. In fact, we need only assume that A is *nearly upper triangular*, meaning that the only nonzero entries below the diagonal are on the lower subdiagonal.

Assume then, that A is nearly upper triangular. To finish reducing A to upper triangular form, it suffices to multiply on the left by certain orthogonal matrices $H_1, H_2, \ldots, H_m$, as shown next. Then when $R = H_m \cdots H_1 A$ is upper triangular, we set $Q = (H_m \cdots H_1)^T$, getting the QR decomposition $A = QR$ for A.

We first show how to get H_1, thereby upper triangularizing the first column of A. If

$$A = \begin{bmatrix} a & b & c & d \\ e & f & g & h \\ 0 & i & j & k \\ 0 & 0 & l & m \end{bmatrix},$$

we take $H_1 = m(r_w)$, where $\mathbf{w} = \mathbf{x} - \|\mathbf{x}\|\mathbf{e}_1$, $\mathbf{x}$ being the first column

$$\mathbf{x} = \begin{bmatrix} a \\ e \\ 0 \\ 0 \end{bmatrix}$$

of A. Since $r_{\mathbf{w}}(\mathbf{x}) = \|\mathbf{x}\|\mathbf{e}_1$ by the reflection theorem (Theorem 7.17), the first column of $H_1 A = m(r_{\mathbf{w}})A$ is $\|\mathbf{x}\|\mathbf{e}_1$. Since $\mathbf{w}$ is in the span of $\mathbf{e}_1$ and $\mathbf{e}_2$, multiplying A on the left by $H_1 = m(r_{\mathbf{w}})$ affects only the entries of the first two rows of A, and we get

$$H_1 A = A = \begin{bmatrix} \|\mathbf{x}\| & b' & c' & d' \\ 0 & f' & g' & h' \\ 0 & i & j & k \\ 0 & 0 & l & m \end{bmatrix}.$$

We next show how to find H_2, assuming that we start with

$$H_1 A = \begin{bmatrix} a & b & c & d \\ 0 & f & g & h \\ 0 & i & j & k \\ 0 & 0 & l & m \end{bmatrix}.$$

Let

$$\mathbf{x} = \begin{bmatrix} 0 \\ f \\ i \\ 0 \end{bmatrix},$$

the part of the second column to be altered, and let $\mathbf{w} = \mathbf{x} - \|\mathbf{x}\|\mathbf{e}_2$. Again, we use the reflection theorem, this time to show that

$$r_{\mathbf{w}} \begin{bmatrix} b \\ f \\ i \\ 0 \end{bmatrix} = r_{\mathbf{w}} \begin{bmatrix} b \\ 0 \\ 0 \\ 0 \end{bmatrix} + r_{\mathbf{w}}(\mathbf{x}) = \begin{bmatrix} b \\ 0 \\ 0 \\ 0 \end{bmatrix} + \|\mathbf{x}\| e_2 = \begin{bmatrix} b \\ \|\mathbf{x}\| \\ 0 \\ 0 \end{bmatrix}.$$

Letting $H_2 = m(r_{\mathbf{w}})$, it follows that

$$H_2 H_1 A = m(r_{\mathbf{w}}) \begin{bmatrix} a & b & c & d \\ 0 & f & g & h \\ 0 & i & j & k \\ 0 & 0 & l & m \end{bmatrix} = \begin{bmatrix} a & b & c & d \\ 0 & \|\mathbf{x}\| & g' & h' \\ 0 & 0 & j' & k' \\ 0 & 0 & l & m \end{bmatrix}.$$

Note here that since $\mathbf{w}$ is of the form $\mathbf{w} = u\mathbf{e}_2 + v\mathbf{e}_3$, $r_{\mathbf{w}}$ alters only entries in rows 2 and 3.

The remaining matrices $H_3, H_4, \ldots$ are found in the same manner as was H_2. Each of these matrices has only four entries of which we must keep track to know how to perform products, the other nonzero entries being 1s on the diagonal. We saw in Section 1.6 that

$$r_{\begin{bmatrix} \cos\alpha \\ \sin\alpha \end{bmatrix}}(\mathbf{v}) = \begin{bmatrix} -\cos 2\alpha & -\sin 2\alpha \\ -\sin 2\alpha & \cos 2\alpha \end{bmatrix} \mathbf{v} \qquad (\mathbf{v} \in \mathbb{R}^2).$$

Here, this rule is

$$r_{\mathbf{w}}(\mathbf{e}_i) = -\cos 2\alpha \mathbf{e}_i - \sin 2\alpha \mathbf{e}_{i+1}, \qquad r_{\mathbf{w}}(\mathbf{e}_{i+1}) = -\sin 2\alpha \mathbf{e}_i + \cos 2\alpha \mathbf{e}_{i+1}$$

where α is the angle between $\mathbf{w}$ and $\mathbf{e}_i$. (Verify!) So, we have

$$H_i = m(r_{\mathbf{w}}) = \left[\begin{array}{c|cc|c} I & 0 & & 0 \\ \hline 0 & -\cos 2\alpha & -\sin 2\alpha & 0 \\ & -\sin 2\alpha & \cos 2\alpha & \\ \hline 0 & 0 & & I \end{array}\right]$$

where the I's and 0s are identity and 0 matrices of the appropriate sizes.

PROBLEMS

NUMERICAL PROBLEMS

1. Find $H = m(r_{\mathbf{w}})$ for the following $\mathbf{w}$ in $\mathbb{R}^4$.

(a) $\mathbf{w} = 2\mathbf{e}_1 + 3\mathbf{e}_2$ **(b)** $\mathbf{w} = 2\mathbf{e}_2 + 3\mathbf{e}_3$ **(c)** $\mathbf{w} = 2\mathbf{e}_3 + 3\mathbf{e}_4$

THEORETICAL PROBLEMS

2. Show that if A is a real symmetric matrix, then

(a) a can be found such that $A - aI$ is positive definite;

(b) a can be found such that $A - aI$ is negative definite;

(c) If the characteristic roots of A are different, then a can be found such that the absolute values of the characteristic roots of $A - aI$ are nonzero and different.

SUGGESTED READING

B. N. Parlett, *The Symmetric Eigenvalue Problem*, Prentice Hall, Englewood Cliffs, N. J., 1981.

G. W. Stewart, *Introduction to Matrix Computations*, Academic Press, New York, 1973.

APPENDIX A

SETS, ELEMENTS, AND FUNCTIONS

A.1 SETS AND ELEMENTS

Sets, elements, and natural numbers

Underlying every mathematical idea is the concept of a **set**, or *collection*, consisting of **elements**, or objects. Most sets are specified by giving their elements. For example, $A = \{a, d, e\}$ is the set whose elements are a, d, and e. The set $\mathbb{N} = \{0, 1, 2, \ldots\}$ of **natural numbers** plays an important role. So does the **empty set**, which is denoted by $\{\ \}$ since it has no elements.

The set of elements satisfying a condition

Given any set T and condition $C(t)$ on its elements,

$$S = \{t \in T \mid C(t)\}$$

denotes the *set S of all elements t of T satisfying the condition $C(t)$*. When T is the set $\mathbb{N}$, such sets are just sets of natural numbers satisfying the specified conditions. For example, $S = \{t \in \mathbb{N} \mid t \text{ is even and } t > 2\}$ is the set $S = \{4, 6, 8, \ldots\}$.

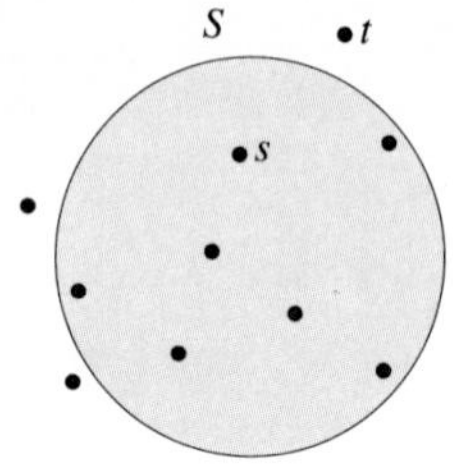

Figure A.1 Venn diagram illustrating $s \in S$, $t \notin S$. The point t is outside.

Venn diagrams

Let $s \in S$ indicate that s *is an element of* S and let $s \notin S$ indicate that it is not. Venn diagrams, such as those given in Figure A.1, express these conditions visually.

Equal sets

Two sets S and T are **equal** if they have the same elements, in any order. So, the condition that $S = T$ is that $x \in S$ if and only if $x \in T$ for all x. For example,

$$\{2, 3, 5\} = \{3, 2, 5\}, \qquad \{2, 3, 5, 3\} = \{3, 2, 5\} \qquad \{3, 3, 3\} = \{3\}.$$

Note that the multiple presence of 3 has no effect once we know that 3 is present in the set. If an element occurs, it occurs only with multiplicity one! On the other hand, $\{2, 5\} \neq \{3, 2, 5\}$, since $3 \notin \{2, 5\}$, and $\{\ \} \neq \{2\}$, since $2 \notin \{\ \}$.

The number of elements of a set

The empty set $\{\ \}$ has no elements, and the **singleton set** $\{a\}$, consisting solely of a, has one element.

A set S is **finite** if its elements can be exhausted by counting them from 1 to n for some natural number n, in which case we can write $S = \{s_1, \ldots, s_n\}$ and use $\#S$ to denote n. When S is empty, n is 0. For example,

$$\#S = 0 \text{ for } S = \{\ \},$$

$$\#S = 1 \text{ for } S = \{a\},$$

$$\#S = 5 \text{ for } S = \{2, 3, 3, 6, 8, 3, 6, 23\} = \{2, 3, 6, 8, 23\}.$$

Subsets of a set

A set S is a **subset** of a set T, denoted $S \subseteq T$, if every element of S is an element of T. Of course, the set $S = \{t \in T \mid C(t)\}$ of elements of T satisfying $C(t)$ is a subset of T.

If $S \subseteq T$, we say that S **is contained** (*as a subset*) **in** T. So, another condition that $S = T$ is that $S \subseteq T$ and $T \subseteq S$. (Prove!)

Unions and intersections of sets

Given two sets S and T, their **union** $S \cup T$ is the set consisting of the elements in S or T (or both). And their **intersection** $S \cap T$ is the set consisting of the elements in both S and T. For example,

$$\{2, 1, 5\} \cup \{3, 2, 1\} = \{2, 1, 5, 3\},$$
$$\{\ \} \cup \{2, 1\} = \{2, 1\},$$
$$\{1, 3, 2, 5, 56\} \cap \{3, 8, 9, 2, 5\} = \{3, 2, 5\},$$
$$\{\ \} \cap \{2, 1\} = \{\ \}.$$

If the intersection of A and B is empty, that is, $A \cap B = \{\ \}$, we say that A and B are **disjoint**. For example, the sets $\{2, 5\}$ and $\{3, 2, 5\}$ are not disjoint, but the sets $A = \{1, 3, 5, \ldots\}$ and $B = \{2, 4, 6, \ldots\}$ are. (See Figure A.2.)

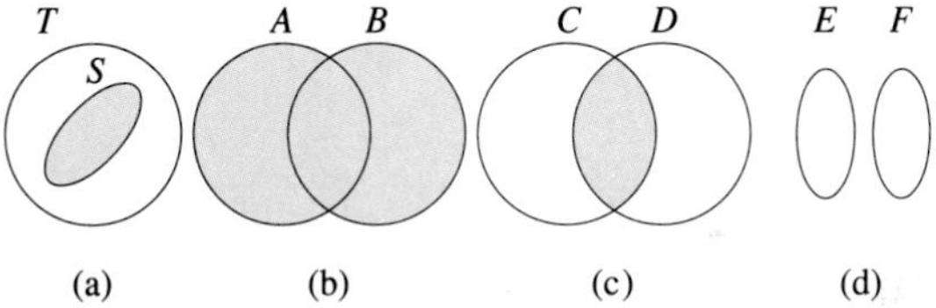

Figure A.2 Venn diagrams illustrating (a) $S \subseteq T$, (b) $A \cup B$, (c) $C \cap D$, (d) $E \cap F = \{\ \}$. The shaded sets represent S, $A \cup B$, $C \cap D$, and $E \cap F$ (vacuous), respectively.

PROBLEMS

NUMERICAL PROBLEMS

1. Find the union $A \cup B$ and intersection $A \cap B$ of each of the following pairs A, B of sets. Verify that $\#(A \cup B) = \#A + \#B - \#(A \cap B)$ in each case.

(a) $A = \{1, 2, 3, 4, 2, 5\}$, $B = \{2, 3, 4, 5, 3, 1\}$

(b) $A = \{1, 2, 3, 4, 3, 4, 3\}$, $B = \{3, 2, 3, 4, 3, 4, 5\}$

(c) $A = \{2, 3, 4\}$, $B = \{1, 2, 3, 4, 5\}$

(d) $A = \{2, 3, 4\}$, $B = \{10, 20, 30, 40, 50\}$

2. In each case of Problem 1, determine whether $A \subseteq B$, whether $B \subseteq A$, whether $A = B$, or whether A and B are disjoint. Support your answers using Venn diagrams.

THEORETICAL PROBLEMS

3. Verify the following set properties, using Venn diagrams when appropriate.

(a) $A \cup (B \cup C) = (A \cup B) \cup C$, $A \cap (B \cap C) = (A \cap B) \cap C$

(b) $A \cup \{\ \} = A$; $A \cap \{\ \} = \{\ \}$

(c) $A \cup B = B \cup A$, $A \cap B = B \cap A$

(d) $A \cup B = B$ if $A \subseteq B$; $A \cap B = A$ if $A \subseteq B$

(e) $A \cap (B \cup C) = (A \cap B) \cup (A \cap C)$

(f) If $A \subseteq B$ and $B \subseteq C$, then $A \subseteq C$.

(g) Subsets of finite sets are finite.

(h) A union or intersection of two finite sets is finite.

(i) For finite sets A and B, $\#(A \cup B) = \#A + \#B - \#(A \cap B)$.

Hard

4. Verify the properties of $\cup$ and $\cap$ listed in Problem 3 using the condition that $S = T$ if and only if $S \subseteq T$ and $T \subseteq S$.

5. The **symmetric difference** of two sets A, B is the set $A + B = \{x \mid x \in A \cup B, x \notin A \cap B\}$. Illustrate $A + B$ by a Venn diagram and show that

(a) $\#(A \cup B) = \#(A + B) + \#(A \cap B)$;

(b) $A + A = \{\ \}$ and $A + \{\ \} = A$;

(c) $A \cap (B + C) = A \cap B + A \cap C$.

A.2 FUNCTIONS

Sets, by themselves, are passive, and their elements are as lifeless as props in a movie. The action starts when functions enter into the picture. When mathematics is used as a language for creating models of real-world phenomena, functions usually carry the show.

Definition. By a **function** from a set P to a set Q we mean a recipe f for assigning to each element p of P a corresponding element $q = f(p)$ of Q called the **image** of p under f. The set P is called the **domain** of f and Q, its **range**.

Ordered pairs, Cartesian products, and graphs

In order to emphasize the *outcome* of the recipe, we say that two functions f and g with the same domain P are **equal** if $f(x) = g(x)$ for all $x \in P$. So, a function f from P to Q is completely determined by its **graph**, which is the set of **ordered pairs** $(x, f(x))$ $(x \in P)$ which lists, along with each x, the corresponding image $f(x)$ of x under f. Here, we assume the following.

Fundamental Property of Ordered Pairs.
$(x, y) = (x', y')$ if and only if $x = x'$ and $y = y'$.

Cartesian Product Axiom.
Given any two sets P and Q, there exists a set $P \times Q$ consisting of the ordered pairs (x, y) for which $x \in P$ and $y \in Q$.

Then $\{(x, y) \in P \times Q \mid y = f(x) \text{ for some } x \in P\}$ is the graph of a function f from P to Q.
See Figure A.3.

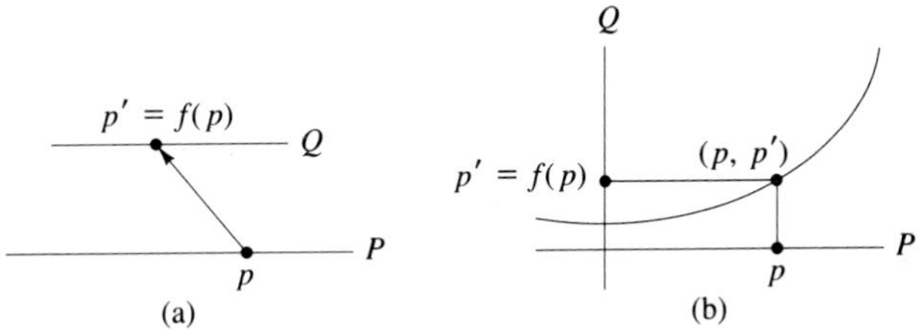

Figure A.3 (a) A function $f(p) = p'$ from P to Q and (b) the graph of f. Ordered pairs (p, q) are represented by points in the plane.

n-fold Cartesian products

Taking the Cartesian product P^n of P with itself n times, an element

$$x = (x_1, \ldots, x_n)$$

of P^n is called an n-tuple, and the x_i's are called the **coordinates** of x. For a function f from P^n to Q, a point (x, y) in the graph of f holds the coordinates of x as well as the image y of x under f.

EXAMPLES

1. The graph of the function $f(x) = x^2 + 1$ from $\mathbb{N}$ to itself is the set

$$\{(x, y) \in \mathbb{N} \times \mathbb{N} \mid y = x^2 + 1\}.$$

2. The polynomial $f(x_1, x_2) = x_1^2 + 2x_2^2 + 1$ is a function from $\mathbb{N}^2$ to $\mathbb{N}$. Its graph is

$$\begin{aligned}\{(x_1, x_2, y) \mid x_1, x_2 \in \mathbb{N}, y = x_1^2 + 2x_2^2 + 1\} \\ = \{(x_1, x_2, x_1 + 2x_2^2 + 1) \mid x_1, x_2 \in \mathbb{N}\}.\end{aligned}$$

Images and preimages

Let f be a function from P to Q. If S is a subset of P, then the set $\{y \in Q \mid y = f(p) \text{ for some } p \in S\}$ is called the **image** of S under f, denoted

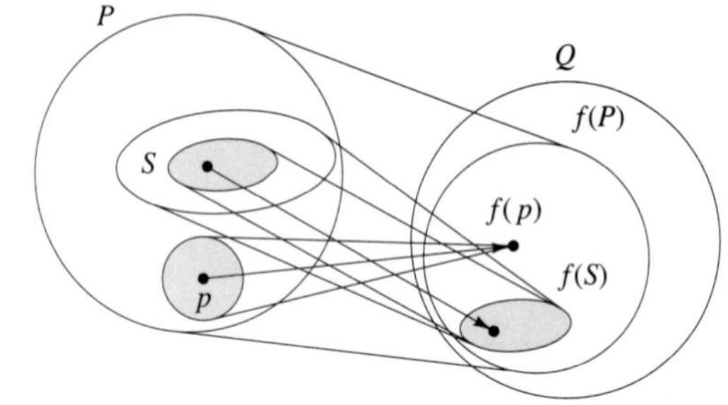

Figure A.4 A function f from P to Q. Images and preimages of elements and subsets. Note that the preimage of $f(S)$ contains S, and the image of the preimage of $f(p)$ is $\{f(p)\}$.

by $\{f(p) \mid p \in S\}$ or by $f(S)$. If T is a subset of Q, the set $\{p \in P \mid f(p) = q$ for some $q \in T\}$ is called the **preimage** of T under f. The *preimage* of a point q of Q is $\{p \in P \mid f(p) = q\}$, which is the preimage of the singleton set $\{q\}$ (Figure A.4).

EXAMPLE

The image of $\mathbb{N}$ under $f(x) = x^2 + 1$ is $f(\mathbb{N}) = \{x^2 + 1 \mid x \in \mathbb{N}\}$. The only preimage of 5 is $x = 2$, and 4 has no preimage. The graph of f is the image $\{(x, x^2+1) \in \mathbb{N} \times \mathbb{N} \mid x \in \mathbb{N}\}$ of $\mathbb{N}$ under $g(x) = (x, x^2+1)$.

Composite of two functions

Definition. Given a function h from a set A to a set B and g from B to a set C, the **product**, or **composite**, of g and h is the function gh from A to C whose image $(gh)(a)$ of any $a \in A$ is just the image $g(h(a))$ under g of the image $h(a)$ of a under h; that is, $(gh)(a) = g(h(a))$ for all $a \in A$. (See Figure A.5.)

EXAMPLE

The composite of $g(x) = x + 1$ and $h(x) = 2x$ is $(gh)(x) = 2x + 1$, since $g(2x) = (2x) + 1$.

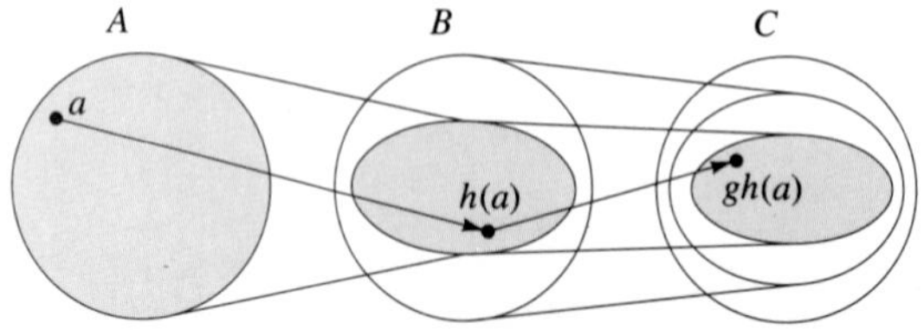

Figure A.5 The composite of g and h maps a to $(gh)(a)$ in two steps.

Powers of a function

The simplest function is the **identity function** i_B from a set B to itself, defined by $i_B(x) = x$ for all $x \in B$. For any functions h from A to B and g from B to C, we have $i_B h = h$ and $g i_B = g$. (Verify!)

If f is a function from A to A, the nth **power** of f is $f^n = ff \cdots f$ (product of f with itself n times) for $n \in \mathbb{N}$, f^0 being the identity function i_A. Then $f^m f^n = f^{m+n}$ for all natural numbers m and n. (Verify!)

EXAMPLE

Let $f(x) = \dfrac{1}{1-x}$ (x a real number, $x \neq 0, 1$). Then

$$f^2(x) = \frac{1}{1 - \dfrac{1}{1-x}} = \frac{1-x}{1-x-1} = \frac{x-1}{x} = 1 - \frac{1}{x}$$

and

$$f^3(x) = 1 - \frac{1}{\dfrac{1}{1-x}} = 1 - (1-x) = x.$$

So, f^3 is the identity function! The powers are just $f^{3k+r} = f^r$, where r is 0, 1, or 2.

Associative law for functions

Some phenomena in the world we live in are **associative** in nature. This section is concerned with associative phenomena for functions.

Theorem A.1. *The Associative Law for Composition of Functions.*
Let h be a function from A to B, g be a function from B to C, and f be a function from C to D. Then $(fg)h = f(gh)$.

Proof. For any $x \in A$, we have $((fg)h)(x) = (fg)(h(x)) = f(g(h(x)))$ and $(f(gh))(x) = f((gh)(x)) = f(g(h(x)))$. So, $((fg)h)(x) = (f(gh))(x)$ hold for all x. But then $(fg)h = f(gh)$. ■

It assures that parentheses can be arranged in any manner in composites of functions without affecting the result. For this reason, *we can drop all parentheses in such products.* For example, we can write $(fg)(h((rs)(tu))) = fghrstu$ (Figure A.6).

One-to-one, onto, and invertible functions

Among all functions, the invertible ones are of special significance.

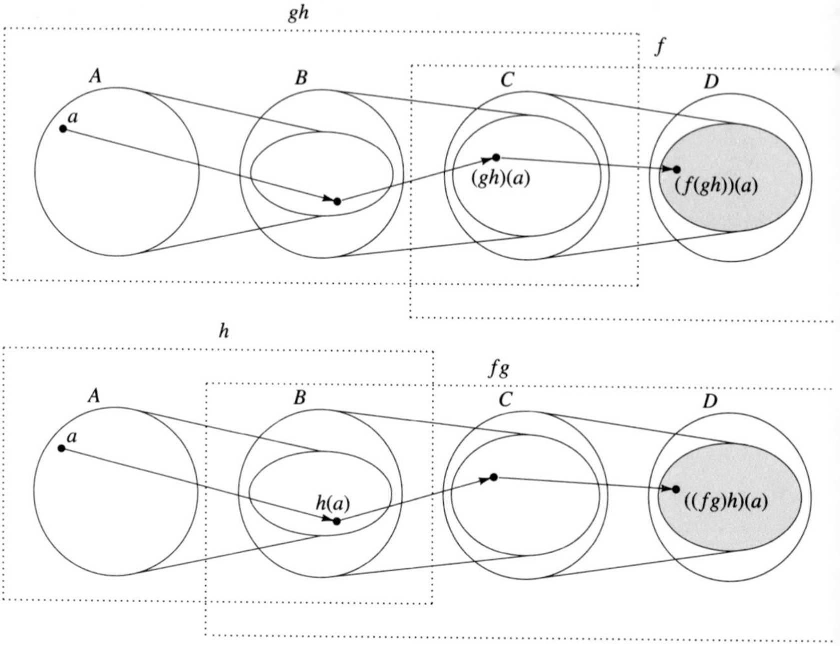

Figure A.6 The associative law for functions: Composing to get gh and then to get $f(gh)$ is the same as composing to get fg and then to get $(fg)h$.

Definition. A function f from a set P to a set Q is said to be **invertible** if there is a function g from Q to P such that for all $p \in P$, $q \in Q$, if $f(p) = q$, then $g(q) = p$, and if $g(q) = p$, then $f(p) = q$. When this is true the function g is called the **inverse** of f and is denoted $g = f^{-1}$.

Since there is only one such g, invertible functions can be characterized as follows.

Corollary. A function f from a set P to a set Q is invertible if and only if there is a function g from Q to P such that $fg = i_P$ and $gf = i_Q$. When f is invertible, there is exactly one such g, namely, $g = f^{-1}$.

EXAMPLE

Let f be the function $f(x) = 1/(1 - x)$ (x a real number, $x \neq 0, 1$) discussed in the preceding example. Since f^3 is the identity, f is invertible with inverse $g = f^2$. (Verify!) See Figure A.7.

A necessary and sufficient condition that a function from P to Q be invertible is that each element q of Q have one and only one preimage. It breaks into two parts.

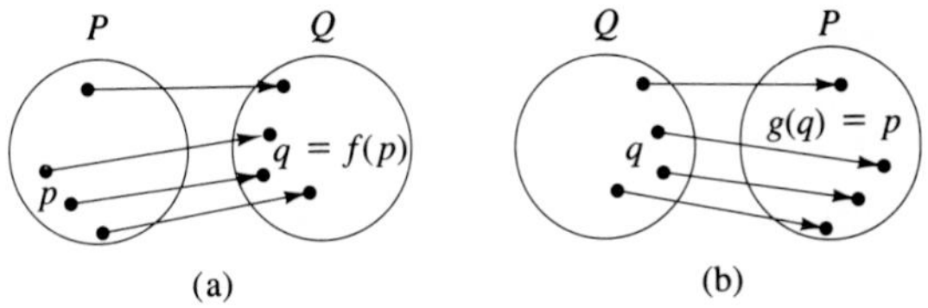

Figure A.7 (a) An invertible function f from P to Q and (b) its inverse g.

Definition. A function f from P to Q is **one-one** (or, simply, 1-1) if for any $p, p' \in P$, $f(p) = f(p')$ only if $p = p'$. See Figures A.8 and A.9.

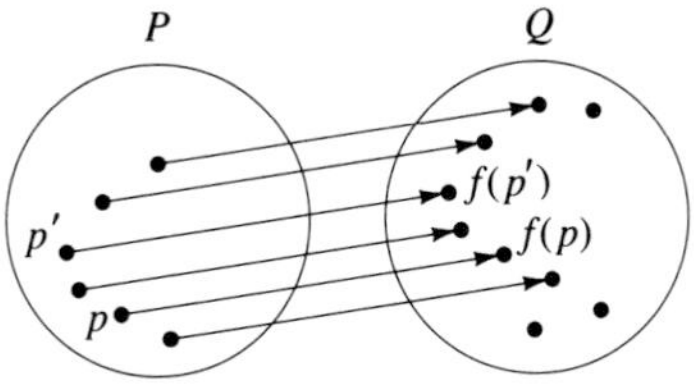

Figure A.8 A one-one function. Note that P does not have more elements than Q.

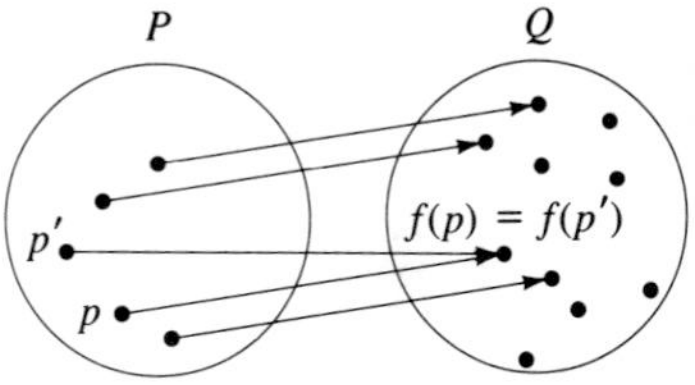

Figure A.9 A function that is not one-one.

Definition. A function f from P to Q is **onto** if Q is the image of P under f—that is, for each $q \in Q$, there exists $p \in P$ such that $f(p) = q$ (Figures A.10 and A.11).

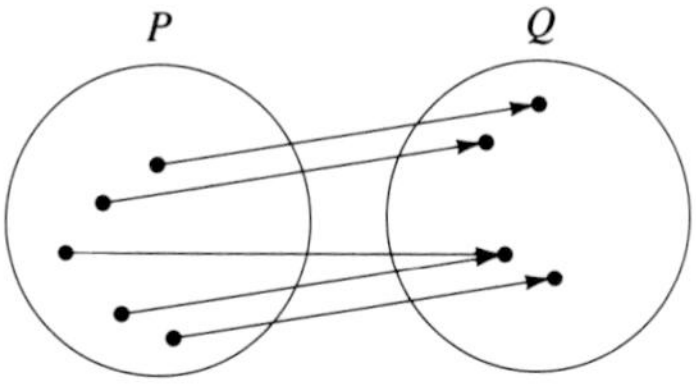

Figure A.10 An onto function. Note that Q has no more elements than does P.

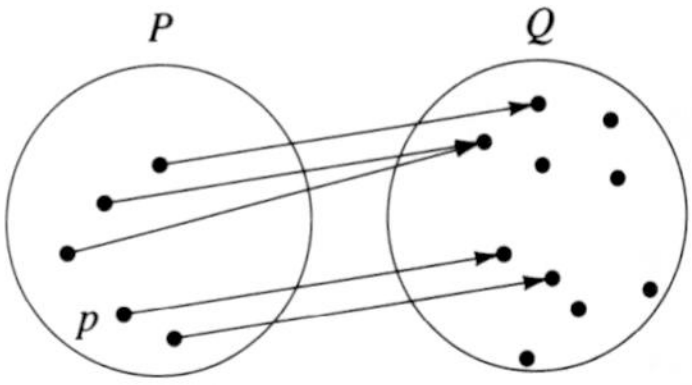

Figure A.11 A function that is not onto.

EXAMPLE

The function $f(x) = x^2 + 1$ from $\mathbb{N}$ to itself is 1-1, but it is not onto, since $f(\mathbb{N})$ does not contain 4. (Explain!).

Theorem A.2. *Criteria for Invertibility.*
A function f from a set P to a set Q is invertible if and only if f is 1-1 and onto.

Proof. Suppose first that f is invertible with inverse f^{-1}. For $q \in Q$, f maps $f^{-1}(q)$ to q. So, f is onto. For $p, p' \in P$ and $f(p) = f(p')$, f^{-1} can be applied to get $f^{-1}(f(p)) = f^{-1}(f(p'))$, that is, $p = p'$. So, f is 1-1.

Suppose, conversely, that f is 1-1 and onto. For each q in Q, there exists $p \in P$ such that $f(p) = q$. Since f is 1-1, there is only one such p. (Prove!) But then we can define $g(q) = p$. Doing this for each $q \in Q$, we get a function g from Q to P such that if $q \in Q$ and $g(q) = p$, then $f(p) = q$. And if $p \in P$, then letting $f(p) = q$, we know that $g(q) = p$ by the definition of g. So, f is invertible with inverse g. ■

We often use the next two theorems, which you should verify.

Theorem A.3. *The Inverse of gh.*
If h is an invertible function from A to B and g is an invertible function from B to C, then gh is an invertible function from A to C and its inverse is given by $(gh)^{-1} = h^{-1}g^{-1}$.

Theorem A.4. *The Negative Powers of f.*
When f is an invertible function from a set A to itself, we define $f^{-n} = (f^{-1})^n$ (the nth **negative power** of f) for all natural numbers n. The functions f^{-n} and f^n are then inverses of each other for all natural numbers n.

Mathematical induction

Let $C(n)$ be a condition on the natural numbers

$$n \in \mathbb{N} = \{0, 1, 2, \ldots\}.$$

If we can show that

$$\begin{aligned} &C(0) \text{ is true,} \\ &C(0) \text{ implies } C(1), \\ &C(1) \text{ implies } C(2), \\ &\quad\vdots \\ &C(n) \text{ implies } C(n+1) \end{aligned}$$

for all $n = 0, 1, 2, 3, \ldots$, then $C(n)$ is true for all n by the following.

Principle of Mathematical Induction.
Let $C(n)$ be a condition which is true if $n = 0$ and suppose that $C(n)$ implies $C(n + 1)$ for all $n \in \mathbb{N}$. Then $C(n)$ is true for all $n \in \mathbb{N}$.

Since we use this principle occasionally in this book, a simple example is in order.

EXAMPLE

Let $C(n)$ be the condition $0 + 1 + \cdots + n = \frac{n(n+1)}{2}$. Then $C(0)$ is true. Suppose that $C(n)$ is true. Adding $n + 1$ to both sides gives $0 + 1 + \cdots + (n+1) = \frac{n(n+1)}{2} + (n+1) = \frac{(n+1)(n+2)}{2}$. (Verify!) So, $C(n)$ implies $C(n+1)$. Since this is true for all $n \in \mathbb{N}$, $C(n)$ is true for all $n \in \mathbb{N}$, by mathematical induction.

PROBLEMS

NUMERICAL PROBLEMS

1. How many functions are there from A to B if $\#A = 4$ and $\#B = 6$?

2. For the given function f, determine whether each of the following statements is true:

(i) f is properly defined. **(ii)** f is 1-1.
(iii) f is onto. **(iv)** f is invertible.

(a) $f(x) = (x+3)^2 - (x-3)^2$ from $\mathbb{N}$ to $\mathbb{N}$
(b) $f(x) = 2x + 5$ from $\mathbb{N}$ to $\{5, 7, 9, \ldots\}$
(c) $f(x) = 5x^2 - x^3$ from $\mathbb{N}$ to $\mathbb{N}$
(d) $f(x) = x^3 - 5x^2 + 1$ from $\mathbb{N}$ to $\mathbb{N}$.

3. Let f be the function $f(n) = n + 1$ from $\mathbb{N}$ to itself. Describe the image $f^{101}(\mathbb{N})$ of $\mathbb{N}$ under the function f^{101}.

4. Describe a function from a circle to a circle which is not onto but is 1-1.

5. Describe a function from a circle to a circle which is onto but is not 1-1.

6. Find functions f and g such that $fg \neq gf$ but $f^{101}g = gf^{101}$.

7. Show that f^2 is the inverse of $f(x) = 1/(1-x)$ (x a real number, $x \neq 0, 1$).

Hard

8. Using mathematical induction, show that

$$1^2 + 2^2 + \cdots + n^2 = \frac{n(n+1)(2n+1)}{6}.$$

9. If f, g are invertible functions from S to S such that $f^5 = f^2$, $g^3 = g^8$, and $f^4g^4 = g^4f^4$, show that $fg = gf$.

10. Let f be the successor function $f(n) = n + 1$ from $\mathbb{N}$ to itself. What elements of $\mathbb{N}$ are contained in the image of $\mathbb{N}$ under f^k for every positive integer k?

11. Compute $f^{206}(x)$ for $f(x) = 1/(1-x)$.

THEORETICAL PROBLEMS

12. How many functions are there from A to A if $\#A = n$? Of these, how many are invertible? How many onto? How many 1-1?

13. For what (if any) values of $n \geq 1$ are most functions from a set of n elements to itself invertible?

14. For A finite and f a function from A to A, show that $f^m = f^n$ for some $m \neq n$.

15. For A finite and f an invertible function from A to A, show that f^m is the identity function for some $m \neq 0$.

16. Show that products and inverses of invertible functions from a set S to itself are invertible by verifying that they are 1-1 and onto.

17. Show that if f and g are invertible functions from a set S to itself, then $(fg)^{-1} = g^{-1}f^{-1}$ and $(f^{-1})^{-1} = f$.

18. Show that if f is an invertible function from P to Q and if functions g and h both qualify as an inverse of f, then $g = h$.

19. Show that if S is a finite set and f and g are functions from S to itself such that $fg = i_S$, then f and g are invertible.

20. Let h be a function from A to B and g be a function from B to C. Show that

(a) If gh is 1-1, so is g;

(b) If gh is onto, so is h;

(c) For some A, B, C, g, and h, gh is invertible and g and h are not.

21. If g and h are invertible functions from a set A to itself and $(gh)^2 = g^2h^2$, show that $gh = hg$.

22. The function $f(x_1, \ldots, x_n) = x_i$ from P^n to P is the ith **coordinate function** on P. Show that

(a) f is onto;

(b) f is 1-1 if and only if $n = 1$ or P has at most one element;

(c) There is an invertible function from the preimage of any $y \in P$ under f to P^{n-1}.

23. The function $f(x_1, \ldots, x_n) = (x_1, \ldots, x_m)$ from P^n to P^m $(m \leq n)$ is called the **projection** of P^n onto P^m. Show that

(a) f is onto;

(b) f is 1-1 if and only if $m = n$ or P has at most one element;

(c) There is an invertible function from the preimage of any $y \in P^m$ to P^{n-m}.

Hard

24. For A finite and f an invertible function from A to A, show that $f^m f = ff^m = f$ for some $m \neq 0$.

25. Give an example of functions f and g from a set S to itself where $fg = i_S$ but f and g are not invertible.

26. Give an example of functions f and g from a set S to itself where $(gh)^2 = g^2h^2$, but $gh \neq hg$.

SUGGESTED READING

Richard Courant and Herbert Robbins, *What is Mathematics*, Oxford University Press, London, 1978. [A beautiful book on what mathematics is about, including topics discussed in this appendix.]

APPENDIX B

REAL NUMBERS

B.1 REAL NUMBERS AND THEIR PROPERTIES

No attempt is made here to describe *how* to add, subtract, and multiply real numbers. Rather, their most fundamental properties are summarized.

Real numbers (or *reals*) are zero, positive, or negative decimal expressions and their equivalents, such as $0 = 0.0000\ldots$, $+1 = 1$, $-3.565\ldots = -(3 + \frac{5}{10} + \frac{6}{100} + \frac{5}{1000} + \cdots)$, 540, $+12.4531313\ldots$, $-24 = -23.999\ldots$, $11 + \frac{1}{3} = 11.333\ldots$, $\pi = 3.14159\ldots$, and so on. The positive sign usually is omitted. The decimal expression can be finite or it can be infinite, as in several of the examples just given. This gives us great liberty to form numbers with desired properties. For example, we can get a positive real number $\sqrt{2}$ whose square is 2 as an infinite decimal expression $a = 1.4142\ldots$ by the method of successive *extraction*. (After finding a to r places as a_r, find a_{r+1} by taking the next decimal term to maximize $a_{r+1}^2 \leq 2$.)

Special kinds of real numbers

The most elementary real numbers are the **integers**, those real numbers such as -50, -34, 0, 34, 50 with nothing to the right of the decimal. Nonnegative integers such as 0, 34, and 50 are called **natural numbers**. Real numbers that can be expressed as ratios of integers, such as $\frac{25}{53}$, $0 = \frac{0}{2}$, $-\frac{35}{189}$, $-5 = \frac{40}{-8}$, and $2 = \frac{2}{1}$ are called **rational numbers** (or *rationals*).

So, *natural numbers are integers, integers are rationals, and rationals are reals.* The set of natural numbers is denoted by $\mathbb{N} = \{0, 1, \ldots\}$, the set of integers by $\mathbb{Z} = \{\ldots, -1, 0, 1, \ldots\}$ and the set of rational numbers by $\mathbb{Q}$, so $\mathbb{N} \subseteq \mathbb{Z} \subseteq \mathbb{Q} \subseteq \mathbb{R}$ by what we have said.

The set $\mathbb{Q}$ of rational numbers is actually just a small part of $\mathbb{R}$, which, nevertheless, is widely and densely distributed.

Theorem B.1. *Criteria for Rational Numbers.*
A real number is rational if and only if its decimal expression has a repetitive pattern.

(See Problem 10.)

Algebraic properties of the real numbers

From an algebraic viewpoint, the set $\mathbb{R}$ of real numbers has operations of *addition, subtraction,* and *multiplication* and two special numbers 0 (*zero*) and 1 (*one*) satisfying the following properties.

Field Properties.

1. $(z + z') + z'' = z + (z' + z'')$.
2. $z + 0 = 0 + z = z$.
3. $z + z'' = z'$ has a *unique* (only one) solution z'' for any z and z', namely, $z'' = z' - z$.
4. $1z = z1 = z$, $0z = z0 = 0$, and $0 \neq 1$.
5. $(zz')z'' = z(z'z'')$.
6. $(z + z')z'' = zz'' + z'z''$ and $z''(z + z') = z''z + z''z'$.
7. $zz'' = 1$ has a unique solution z'', denoted by $1/z$ and called the **inverse** of z, for every nonzero z.
8. $z + z' = z' + z$ and $zz' = z'z$.

By field property 3, we can define the **negative** $-z$ of z as $-z = 0 - z$. So, $-z$ is the unique real number such that $z + (-z) = 0$. But then z is the unique real number such that $(-z) + z = 0$, which implies that $z = -(-z)$.

By field property 7, we can define the quotient $z'/z = z'(1/z)$ for any nonzero z. Reasoning along much the same lines as we did in the preceding paragraph, we see that $z'/(1/z) = zz'$. (Explain!)

Associative laws

The first and fifth field properties are called **associative laws**. As for composition of functions, the significance of the associative law for addition is that you need not be concerned with how the parentheses are arranged in sums.

So, you can leave them out entirely or arrange them in any manner that simplifies computation or makes it more meaningful. For example, if we perform the sum $(5 - 4) + ((4 - 3) + ((3 - 2) + ((2 - 1) + (1 - 0))))$ following the given arrangement of parentheses, we get $1 + (1 + (1 + (1 + 1))) = 1 + (1 + (1 + 2)) = 1 + (1 + 3) = 1 + 4 = 5$, whereas if we drop the parentheses and cancel terms of opposite sign, the computation simplifies to $5 - 4 + 4 - 3 + 3 - 2 + 2 - 1 + 1 - 0 = 5 + 0 + 0 + 0 + 0 = 5$. The same goes for multiplication.

Fields and subfields

The system of real numbers is only one of many systems satisfying the field properties. *Any* system F with addition, subtraction, and multiplication and two special numbers 0 and 1 satisfying the field properties is called a **field**. Given a field F, any subset F' of F containing 0 and 1 such that sums, products, and quotients of nonzero elements of F' are still in F' is also a field, called a **subfield** of F. (Prove!) So, the set $\mathbb{Q}$ of rational numbers is also a field, since it is a subfield of the field $\mathbb{R}$ of reals. On the other hand, the set $\mathbb{Z}$ of integers is not a field. Although it is a system with addition, multiplication, and special numbers 0 and 1 that satisfies all these properties except the seventh, the solution a' to an equation such as $5a' = 1$ is not in the system, since $\frac{1}{5}$ is not an integer. So, the seventh field property is not true for the system $\mathbb{Z}$.

PROBLEMS

NUMERICAL PROBLEMS

1. Extract a decimal a such that $a^2 = 2$ is accurate to two decimal places, without using a computer.
2. Find a repeating decimal expression for each of the following fractions.
   (a) $\frac{3}{11}$ **(b)** $\frac{32}{25}$ **(c)** $\frac{81}{32}$
3. Express $r = 203.101322532253225\ldots$ as a ratio $r = m/n$ of integers.
4. Show that the **successor function** $f(x) = x + 1$ $(x \in \mathbb{Z})$ is an invertible function whose inverse is the **predecessor function** $g(x) = x - 1$ $(x \in \mathbb{Z})$. Describe f^m and g^m.

THEORETICAL PROBLEMS

5. Show that the set $\mathbb{Q}$ of rationals is a subfield of the field $\mathbb{R}$.
6. Show that the subfield $\mathbb{Q}$ of $\mathbb{R}$ satisfies the properties for a field, since they are satisfied by $\mathbb{R}$.
7. Show that any subfield F' of a field F is a field.
8. For an *invertible* function f from a set A to itself, show that $f^m f^n = f^{m+n}$ for all integers m and n.

Hard

9. Let U be a set, $\mathscr{R}_U = \{S \mid S \subseteq U\}$. Define $S + T$ and ST by

$$S + T = \{x \in S \cup T \mid x \notin S \cap T\} \qquad \text{(symmetric difference)}$$

$$ST = S \cap T \qquad \text{(intersection)}$$

and special elements $0 = \{\ \}$ (empty set) and $1 = U$ (whole set U). Furthermore, let $S - T = S + T$ by definition.

(a) Show that $\mathscr{R}_U$ with these operations and special elements satisfies all field properties except the seventh.

(b) Show that $S + S = 0$ and $S = 0 - S$ for all S.

10. Show that a real number r is rational if and only if its decimal pattern is eventually a repetitive pattern $r_1 \cdots r_k$ for some k, that is, if $r = ab \cdots c.de \cdots fr_1 \cdots r_k r_1 \cdots r_k r_1 \cdots r_k r_1 \cdots r_k \cdots$. (***Hint:*** Do this first for $0.r_1 \cdots r_k r_1 \cdots r_k r_1 \cdots r_k r_1 \cdots r_k \cdots$.)

B.2 ORDER AND THE REAL LINE

Signs

Let $\mathbb{R}_+$ be the set of *positive* reals (the nonzero real numbers not preceded by a negative sign) and $\mathbb{R}_- = \{-r \mid r \in \mathbb{R}_+\}$ be the set of *negative* reals. Then every real number is positive, negative, or 0. Moreover, sums and products of positive numbers are positive, and we have the following.

Theorem B.2. *The Sign Properties of Real Numbers.*
Every element of $\mathbb{R}$ is in exactly one of the sets $\mathbb{R}_-$, $\{0\}$, $\mathbb{R}_+$. If $a, b \in \mathbb{R}_+$, then $a + b \in \mathbb{R}_+$ and $ab \in \mathbb{R}_+$.

Order

The concept of "positive" translates at once to the concept of "less than."

Definition. We say that $a < b$ (a **is less than** b) if $b - a$ is positive.

The sign properties imply the following.

Theorem B.3. *Laws of Trichotomy and Transitivity for Real Numbers.*
For real numbers a, b, c,

1. Exactly one of the conditions $a < b$, $a = b$, $b < a$ holds.
2. If $a < b$ and $b < c$, then $a < c$.

Proof. To establish (1), simply use the property that the real number $b - a$ is in exactly one of the sets $\mathbb{R}_-$, $\{0\}$, $\mathbb{R}_+$. If it is in $\mathbb{R}_-$, then $a - b$

is in $\mathbb{R}_+$ and $b < a$. If it is in $\{0\}$, then $a = b$. And if it is in $\mathbb{R}_+$, then $a < b$. For (2), suppose that $a < b$ and $b < c$. Then $b - a$ and $c - b$ are positive, so their sum $(b - a) + (c - b) = c - a$ is positive. But this implies that $a < c$. ■

The order relation $a < b$ arranges real numbers in linear order to form the real line, whereby a lies to the left of b if $a < b$. To visualize this, start with the integers equally spaced and then add the rationals and the other reals. The positive numbers lie to the right of 0, and the negative numbers lie to the left (Figure B.1).

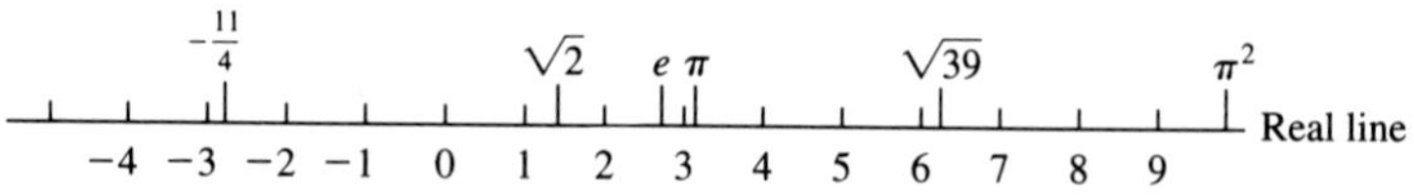

Figure B.1 Arrangement of real numbers to form the real line.

Preservation of order

If the only properties of order on the real line came from the laws of trichotomy and transitivity, life on the real line would be boring indeed! Fortunately, however, this order is *preserved* under addition and multiplication by positive numbers. From this preservation of order come many important things.

Theorem B.4. *Order Properties of Real Numbers.*
For any real numbers a, b, c, d, we have

1. If $a < b$ and $c < d$, then $a + c < b + d$.
2. If $a < b$ and c is positive, then $ac < bc$ and $a/c < b/c$.
3. If $a < b$ and c is negative, then $bc < ac$ and $b/c < a/c$.

Proof. For (1), suppose that $a < b$ and $c < d$. Then $b - a$ and $d - c$ are positive, so their sum $(b - a) + (d - c) = (b + d) - (a + c)$ is positive. But then $a + c < b + d$.

For (2), suppose that $a < b$ and c is positive. Since $b - a$ and c are positive, their product $(b - a)c = bc - ac$ is positive, so that $ac < bc$. Similarly, since $1/c$ is positive, $a(1/c) < b(1/c)$, that is, $a/c < b/c$.

For (3), suppose that $a < b$ and c is negative. Then $-c$ is positive, so that $-ac < -bc$ by (2). But then $bc < ac$. (Explain!) ■

Taking $c = -1$ in Part (3) of our theorem, we see that $a < b$ if and only if $-b < -a$; that is, *negation reverses the order of the real line.*

Absolute value. Distance

To get from any real number a to a nonnegative real number, we need only take its *absolute value* $|a|$, which is a if a is positive and $-a$ otherwise. Our theorem on order then implies the following.

Theorem B.5. *Properties of Absolute Values of Real Numbers.*
For real numbers a, b,

1. $|a + b| \leq |a| + |b|$ and $||a| - |b|| \leq |a - b|$.
2. $|ab| = |a||b|$.

(Prove!)

EXAMPLES

1. The absolute value of 3 is $|3| = 3$ and that of -3 is $|-3| = 3$. The absolute values $|3| = 3$ and $|-3| = 3$ can be regarded as the unsigned distances of 3 and -3 from 0.
2. The absolute value of $|a - b|$ equals the absolute value of $|b - a|$.

The **distance** from a to b along the real line is the absolute value $|b - a|$, so that our second example just says that *the distance from a to b equals the distance from b to a.* From our properties for absolute values, we get the distance property:

Theorem B.6. *Distance Property for Real Numbers.*
The distance from a to c is at most the sum of the distances from a to b and from b to c; that is, $|c - a| \leq |b - a| + |c - b|$.

(Prove!)

Completeness

By including infinite decimal expressions in the set $\mathbb{R}$ of real numbers, we are assured that whenever we have a **Cauchy sequence**

$$r_1, r_2, r_3, \ldots, r_j, \ldots$$

of real numbers (one such that for any small positive number s, $|r_j - r_k| < s$ for j and k sufficiently large), it actually *converges* to some real number r, called its **limit**. This limit r is easy to describe. We simply find all the numbers in its infinite decimal expression using those in the decimal expressions for the r_j, taking larger and larger j as needed to get the succession of numbers. (See Problem 10.) The geometric interpretation of this is that there are no "gaps," or "missing numbers," on the real line, even though there can be on the rational line $\mathbb{Q}$. For example, the real number $\sqrt{2} = 1.41\ldots$ is not rational, so there is a gap in $\mathbb{Q}$ between the sets $\{r \mid r^2 < 2, r \text{ rational}\}$ and $\{r \mid r^2 > 2, r \text{ rational}\}$, but there is no gap between the same sets in $\mathbb{R}$. Since $\mathbb{R}$ contains the limits of its Cauchy sequences, we say that $\mathbb{R}$ is **complete**. The completeness of $\mathbb{R}$ plays a central role in the rich theory of real functions. It is by the completeness of $\mathbb{R}^2$ that important functions such as the square root, sine, cosine, exponential, and logarithm are introduced using power series. As Cauchy sequences, their convergence is assured (see Problems 1 and 2).

Square roots. The quadratic formula

Thanks to completeness, the field $\mathbb{R}$ has a great advantage over the field $\mathbb{Q}$, since any nonnegative real number r has a **square root** $\sqrt{r} \geq 0$, which is real. The existence of such square roots is extremely important. Using them, we can find real solutions to any quadratic equation $ax^2 + bx + c = 0$ $(a \neq 0)$ with real coefficients a, b, c for which the **discriminant** $b^2 - 4ac$ of the polynomial $ax^2 + bx + c$ is nonnegative. These solutions are given by the **quadratic formula**

$$x = \frac{-b + \sqrt{b^2 - 4ac}}{2a} \quad \text{or} \quad x = \frac{-b - \sqrt{b^2 - 4ac}}{2a},$$

where $\sqrt{b^2 - 4ac}$ is a square root of $b^2 - 4ac$. (Verify!)

The solutions to the equation $ax^2 + bx + c = 0$ are called the **roots** of $ax^2 + bx + c$. For example, the roots of $2x^2 + 5x + 2$ are

$$x = \frac{-5 + \sqrt{5^2 - 4 \cdot 4}}{2 \cdot 2} = \frac{-1}{2} \quad \text{and} \quad x = \frac{-5 - \sqrt{5^2 - 4 \cdot 4}}{2 \cdot 2} = -2,$$

and the roots of $x^2 = 3$ are the positive and negative square roots $x = \sqrt{3}$ and $x = -\sqrt{3}$.

When the discriminant of $ax^2 + bx + c$ is negative, the polynomial $ax^2 + bx + c$ has no real roots. (Prove!) For example, the discriminant of the polynomial $x^2 + x + 1$ is $1 - 4 \cdot 1 = -3$, so $x^2 + x + 1$ has no real roots.

PROBLEMS

NUMERICAL PROBLEMS

1. Find approximate decimal expressions for e^0, e^1, and e^2 using the first three terms of the series

$$e^x = 1 + x + \frac{x^2}{2!} + \frac{x^3}{3!} + \frac{x^4}{4!} + \cdots.$$

2. Find approximate decimal expressions for sin 0 and sin 1 using the first three terms of the series

$$\sin x = x - \frac{x^3}{3!} + \frac{x^5}{5!} - \frac{x^7}{7!} + \cdots.$$

3. Find the real solutions to the equations listed or show that they have none.

   (a) $a^2 + a = 1$ **(b)** $2a^2 + 5a + 4 = 0$

4. Show that $\sqrt{2}$ is irrational. (***Hint:*** Show that if the square of m/n is 2, where m and n are positive integers, then $m^2 = 2n^2$. Show that this is impossible by comparing the number of times 2 is a factor of m^2 to the number of times it is a factor of $2n^2$.)

5. Find the real roots of the following polynomials or show that they have none.

   (a) $a^4 - 1$ **(b)** $a^3 + a^2 + a + 1$

THEORETICAL PROBLEMS

6. Explain why $bc < ac$ if $a < b$ and c is negative.
7. Represent all the roots of $a^n = 1$ on the real line for any natural number n.
8. Show that the subset $\{a + b\sqrt{3} \mid a, b \text{ rational}\}$ is a subfield of $\mathbb{R}$.
9. Show that if a_n is the decimal expansion of a positive real number a to n decimal places, then $|a - a_n| \leq 10^{-n}$.
10. Show that if r_j is a sequence and $|r_k - r_j| < 10^{-n-1}$, then r_j and r_k have the same numbers in their decimal expansions to n decimal places.
11. Show that the polynomial $x^2 + bx + c$ can be written in the form $x^2 + bx + c = (x - r)^2 + s$ (*completion of the square*), where r and s are real constants.
12. Show that quadratic equation $ax^2 + bx + c = 0$ has no solution if the discriminant is negative. (***Hint:*** Use the result of Problem 11.)

Hard

13. If T is a nonempty subset of $\mathbb{N}$, then T has a least element. (***Hint:*** Show by mathematical induction that if T has no least element, then $S = \{x \in \mathbb{N} \mid x < t \text{ for all } t \in T\}$ is $\mathbb{N}$.)
14. Prove that any polynomial of odd degree with real coefficients has at least one real root (Figure B.2). (***Hint:*** Prove that its graph in the Cartesian plane has points above and below the x-axis. Use the intermediate value theorem, which states that if a continuous function on a closed interval takes on the values r and s at the endpoints of the interval, then it takes on every value between r and s as well.)

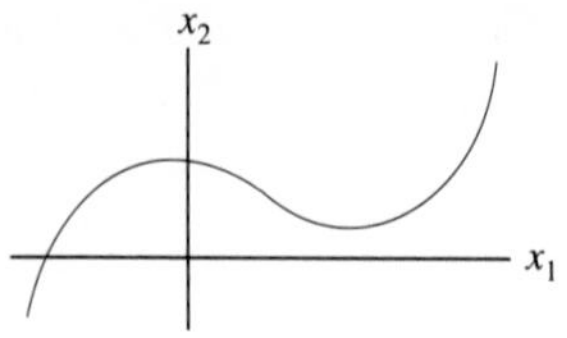

Figure B.2 Graph of a real polynomial of odd degree always has points both above and below—and hence on—the x_1-axis.

SUGGESTED READING

Richard Courant and Herbert Robbins, *What is Mathematics*, Oxford University Press, London, 1978. [This book, mentioned in Appendix A, also includes topics discussed in this appendix.]

APPENDIX C

COMPLEX NUMBERS

C.1 COMPLEX NUMBERS AND THEIR PROPERTIES

Some complex computations

The field $\mathbb{R}$ of real numbers is inadequate when we need roots of polynomials such as $x^2 - 2x + 5$ whose discriminant $(-2)^2 - 4 \cdot 5 = 4 - 20$ is *negative*. When this happens, the roots

$$\frac{2 + \sqrt{4 - 4 \cdot 5}}{2} = 1 + \frac{\sqrt{4 - 20}}{2} = 1 + 2\sqrt{-1}$$

$$\frac{2 - \sqrt{4 - 4 \cdot 5}}{2} = 1 - \frac{\sqrt{4 - 20}}{2} = 1 - 2\sqrt{-1}$$

of $x^2 - 2x + 5$ given by the quadratic formula do not make sense as *real numbers*. Still, we can try to compute with them as though they do make sense. Letting $x = 1 + 2\sqrt{-1}$, we get

$$\begin{aligned} x^2 &= (1 + 2\sqrt{-1})(1 + 2\sqrt{-1}) \\ &= 1 + 4\sqrt{-1} + 4(\sqrt{-1})^2 \\ &= 1 + 4\sqrt{-1} - 4 = -3 + 4\sqrt{-1} \end{aligned}$$

and

$$x^2 - 2x + 5 = -3 + 4\sqrt{-1} - 2(1 + 2\sqrt{-1}) + 5 = 0.$$

In other words, even without knowing what $\sqrt{-1}$ is, we seem to be able to calculate coherently using it.

Calculations such as these go as far back as A.D. 1545, when the Italian mathematician Girolamo Cardano (1501–1576) wrote, upon observing that 40 could be expressed as the product of $5+\sqrt{-15}$ and $5-\sqrt{-15}$, that he experienced "mental torture" in using them.

Complex numbers and the complex plane

Fortunately for us, complex numbers now have explicit geometric representations and their existence is secured by the following definition.

Definition. *A* **complex number** is a formal expression $z = a + bi$, where a and b are real and i plays the role of $\sqrt{-1}$. Two complex numbers $a + bi$ and $a' + b'i$ are said to be **equal** if and only if $a = a'$ and $b = b'$. A complex number $a + bi$ is *represented* by the vector $\begin{bmatrix} a \\ b \end{bmatrix}$ in the Cartesian plane $\mathbb{R}^2$. The set of complex numbers is denoted by $\mathbb{C}$ (Figure C.1).

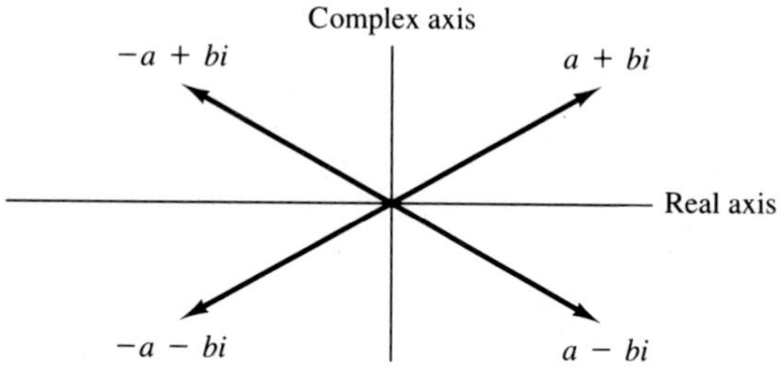

Figure C.1 Representations of various complex numbers $a + bi$, $a - bi$, $-a - bi$, $-a + bi$.

But, unfortunately for Cardano, Descartes (1595–1650) did not introduce the Cartesian plane until more than half a century after his death, so he was unable to represent $5+\sqrt{-15}$ as the point

$$5+\sqrt{-15} = 5+\sqrt{15}\,i = \begin{bmatrix} 5 \\ \sqrt{15} \end{bmatrix}$$

in the Cartesian plane (Figure C.2). This, however, did not deter Cardano from using complex numbers in publishing, without permission, a secret solution by Niccolo Tartaglia (ca.1500–1557) to the cubic equation.

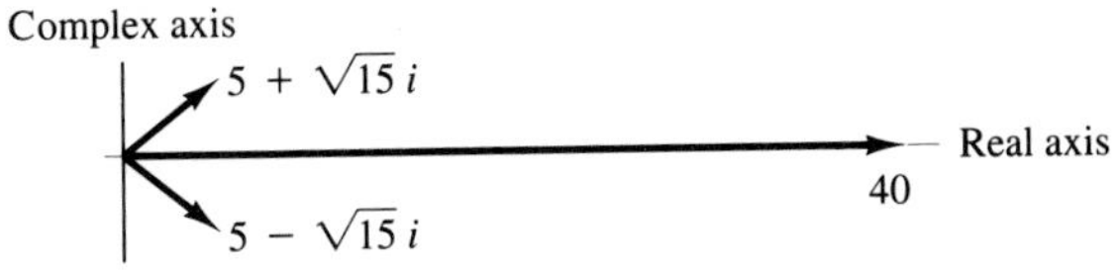

Figure C.2 Cardano's product $(5 - \sqrt{-15})(5 + \sqrt{-15}) = 25 + 15 = 40$.

Definition. **Addition**, **subtraction**, and **muliplication** of complex numbers $z = a + bi$, $z' = a' + b'i$ are defined as follows:

$$z + z' = (a + a') + (b + b')i$$

$$z' - z = (a' - a) + (b' - b)i$$

$$zz' = (ab - a'b') + (ab' + ba')i$$

EXAMPLES

1. Regarding i as $(0 + 1i)$, the square of i is $(0 + 1i)(0 + 1i) = (0 - 1) + (0 + 0)i = -1 + 0i$, which is regarded as -1. So, $i^2 = -1$.
2. By our definition of zz', we can recalculate $\sqrt{-15}$ Cardano's product as $(5 - \sqrt{15}\, i)(5 + \sqrt{15}\, i) = (25 + 15) + (5\sqrt{15} - 5\sqrt{15})i = 40$.

Here, sums, differences, and products are as they must be defined to legitimize the calculations in the preceding example. We then see that:

Addition and subtraction of complex numbers is the same as addition and subtraction of vectors in $\mathbb{R}^2$.

Real parts and pure imaginaries

We say that the complex number $a + 0i$ is **real** and denote it simply by a. Similarly, we say that the complex number $0 + bi$ is a **pure imaginary** for any real number b, and we denote it simply by bi. If $b = 1$, we denote $0 + 1i$ by i or, since $i^2 = -1$, by $i = \sqrt{-1}$. This enables us to regard real numbers as special complex numbers, those located on the x_1-axis, with the pure imaginaries on the x_2-axis perpendicular to the line of reals. The only number that is both real and pure imaginary is 0. Any complex number $z = a + bi$ is the sum of its **real part** a and its **pure imaginary part** bi.

In this way, we enlarge our number system from $\mathbb{R}$ to $\mathbb{C}$. Then $\mathbb{Z} \subseteq \mathbb{Q} \subseteq \mathbb{R} \subseteq \mathbb{C}$ and we have the following.

Theorem C.1. *Rules for Multiplying z by a Real or Pure Imaginary Number.* For a, a', and b real and $z = a + bi$, $a'z = a'a + a'bi$ and $a'iz = -a'b + a'ai$.

In particular, for $z = \begin{bmatrix} a \\ b \end{bmatrix}$, $a'z = \begin{bmatrix} a'a \\ a'b \end{bmatrix}$ and *multiplication of a complex number z by a real number a' is just the scalar product of a' and z in the plane.*

Algebraic properties of complex numbers

Already, we have enlarged our system of numbers from $\mathbb{R}$ to the set $\mathbb{C}$ of complex numbers z, z', etc. containing the solution $i = \sqrt{-1}$ to the equation $z^2 = -1$. And, we have extended the operations $z + z'$, $z' - z$, zz' from $\mathbb{R}$ to $\mathbb{C}$. With these operations, we have the following.

Theorem C.2. *Algebraic Properties of Complex Numbers.*
$\mathbb{C}$ satisfies the field properties.

As for the reals, the negative $-z$ of z is defined as $0 - z$, which satisfies the property $-(-z) = z$. And, as for the reals, we define $z'/z = z'(1/z)$ for any nonzero z, which satisfies the property that $z'/(1/z) = zz'$.

Proof of the field properties for $\mathbb{C}$. The distributive law

Field properties 1, 2, 3, 4, 5, 6, and 8 (see Section B.1) can be verified easily for $\mathbb{C}$ by calculating each side of the equation. For instance, to verify the *distributive law* $(z + z')z'' = zz'' + z'z''$, just calculate

$$\begin{aligned}(z + z')z'' &= (a + a' + (b + b')i)(a'' + b''i) \\ &= (a + a')a'' - (b + b')b'' + ((a + a')b'' + (b + b')a'')i, \\ zz'' + z'z'' &= (a + bi)(a'' + b''i) + (a' + b'i)(a'' + b''i) \\ &= (aa'' - bb'' + (ab'' + ba'')i + a'a'' - b'b'' + (a'b'' + b'a'')i.\end{aligned}$$

The results are the same (check), so we've verified that $(z + z')z'' = zz'' + z'z''$. For example,

$$\begin{aligned}((1 + i) + (3 + i))(1 - i) &= (1 + i)(1 - i) + (3 + i)(1 - i) \\ &= (1 + 1) + (3 + 1) - 2i = 6 - 2i.\end{aligned}$$

The inverse of z

A field property that needs more discussion is Property 7, which asserts that if $z = a + bi$ is nonzero, then $zz'' = 1$ has a solution $z'' = a'' + b''i$, denoted $1/z$. If you try to get $1/z$ by finding the conditions on a'' and b'' such that $(a + bi)(a'' + b''i) = 1$, you find that

$$a'' = \frac{a}{a^2 + b^2} \quad \text{and} \quad b'' = -\frac{b}{a^2 + b^2}.$$

This leads to the formula

$$\frac{1}{z} = \frac{a}{a^2 + b^2} - \frac{b}{a^2 + b^2} i.$$

For example, if $z = 3 - 4i$, then

$$\frac{1}{z} = \frac{3}{3^2 + 4^2} - \frac{-4}{3^2 + 4^2} i = \frac{3}{25} + \left(\frac{4}{25}\right)i,$$

which we check by calculating: $(3 - 4i)(\frac{3}{25} + \frac{4}{25}i) = \frac{9+16}{25} + 0i = 1$.

A better way to get this formula is by way of the equation

$$(a + bi)(a - bi) = a^2 + b^2,$$

which is a special case of a formula from algebra, namely, $(r + s)(r - s) = r^2 - s^2$. Here, the sign changes to plus since $(bi)^2 = -b^2$. Since $a^2 + b^2$ is nonzero (explain), we can multiply both sides by $\frac{1}{a^2 + b^2}$, which gives $(a + bi)(a - bi)\frac{1}{a^2 + b^2} = 1$, showing that

$$(a + bi)\left(\frac{a}{a^2 + b^2} - \frac{b}{a^2 + b^2} i\right) = 1$$

and determines the following.

Theorem C.3. *Inverse of a Complex Number.*

The inverse of $z = a + bi$ is $z^{-1} = \dfrac{a}{a^2 + b^2} - \dfrac{b}{a^2 + b^2} i.$

Complex conjugation

The formula $(a - bi)(a + bi) = a^2 + b^2$ is so useful that we give a name to $a - bi$.

Definition. If $z = a + bi$, then $a - bi$ is called the **conjugate** of z and it is denoted by $\bar{z}$.

The formula then becomes $\bar{z}z = a^2 + b^2$. It follows that $z\bar{z}$ is always nonnegative and we have the following properties.

Theorem C.4. *Properties of Conjugation.*

The conjugation operation, which takes $z = a + bi$ to $\bar{z} = a - bi$, satisfies the following properties.

1. $\overline{z + z'} = \bar{z} + \bar{z}'$, $\overline{zz'} = \bar{z}\bar{z}'$ and $\bar{\bar{z}} = z$.
2. $z = \bar{z}$ if and only if z is real.

3. $z = -\bar{z}$ if and only if z is a pure imaginary.
4. The real part of z is $(z + \bar{z})/2$.
5. The pure imaginary part of z is $(z - \bar{z})/2$.
6. $z\bar{z}$ is always a nonnegative real number and is 0 only if z is 0.
7. If z is invertible, $1/z = \bar{z}/z\bar{z}$.

(Prove!)

Absolute value of a complex number

Representing the complex number $z = a + bi$ as the point $a + bi = \begin{bmatrix} a \\ b \end{bmatrix}$ in the Cartesian plane $\mathbb{R}^2$, the length of $z = a + bi = \begin{bmatrix} a \\ b \end{bmatrix}$ as a vector in the plane is $\sqrt{a^2 + b^2}$. Just as the absolute value $|a|$ of a real number a is its unsigned distance from 0 on the real line, the absolute value of $z = a + bi$ is the unsigned distance of $\begin{bmatrix} a \\ b \end{bmatrix}$ to the origin, which we state for the record as follows.

Definition. The **absolute value** $|z|$ of the complex number $z = a + bi$ is just the length $\|z\| = \sqrt{a^2 + b^2}$ of the vector $z = \begin{bmatrix} a \\ b \end{bmatrix}$.

If $z = a + bi$, then $|z|^2 = a^2 + b^2 = z\bar{z}$. So, even if we do not know the values of a and b, we can express the absolute value of z by the formula

$$|z| = \sqrt{z\bar{z}}.$$

By the triangle inequality $|z + z'| \leq |z| + |z'|$ for lengths of vectors in the plane (Chapter 1), we get the same inequality for the absolute values of complex numbers. This proves two properties of absolute value, and we leave a third for the reader to verify by a simple and direct computation.

Theorem C.5. *Properties of Absolute Value.*
Let z and z' be complex numbers. Then

1. $|z| = \sqrt{z\bar{z}}$.
2. $|z + z'| \leq |z| + |z'|$.
3. $|zz'| = |z||z'|$.

Completeness of the complex plane

In representing complex numbers in the Cartesian plane, the set $\mathbb{C}$ of complex numbers becomes the Cartesian plane itself. So, we refer to the Cartesian plane as the *complex plane* when we use it to represent $\mathbb{C}$.

Since $\mathbb{R}$ is complete, it follows that if $z_r = a_r + b_r i$ is a sequence of complex numbers such that the sequences a_r and b_r are Cauchy sequences of real numbers, then the sequences a_r and b_r both converge to real numbers a and b. In this event, we say the sequence z_r of complex numbers *converges* to $z = a + bi$. Geometrically, this means that there are no "missing numbers" in the complex plane. As for the reals, we represent this property by saying that $\mathbb{C}$ is *complete*.

Addition, subtraction, multiplication, scalar multiplication, conjugation, and inversion

For $z, z' \in \mathbb{C}$ and a real, the numbers $z + z'$, $z - z'$, zz', az, $\bar{z}$, z^{-1} appear in interrelated positions on the plane, as shown in Figure C.3.

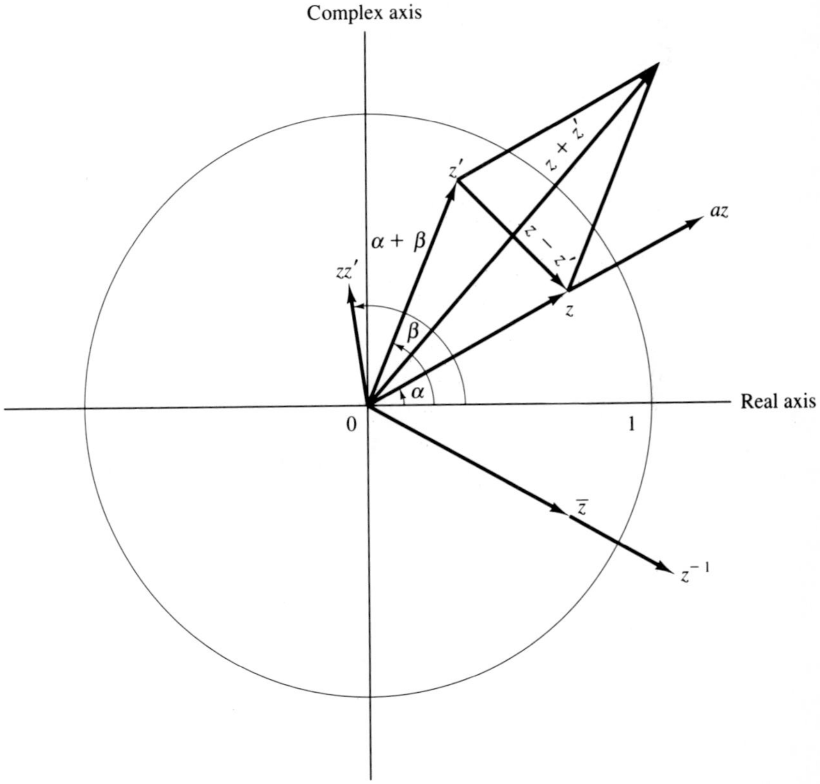

Figure C.3 The complex numbers $z + z'$, $z - z'$, zz', az, $\bar{z}$, and z^{-1} for a real.

Theorem C.6. *Multiplication of Complex Numbers.*

Let z and z' be complex numbers. Then the product zz' is the vector whose length is the product of the lengths of z and z' and whose angle to the real axis is the sum of those of z and z'.

Polar representation $z = r(\cos\alpha + \sin\alpha)$

To see *why* complex numbers z and z' multiply this way, let's go to the **polar representation**

$$z = r(\cos\alpha + i\sin\alpha) = a + bi$$

where $a = r\cos\alpha$ and $b = r\sin\alpha$, r being the absolute value $r = |z|$ (Figure C.4). Our rule for multiplication is then as follows.

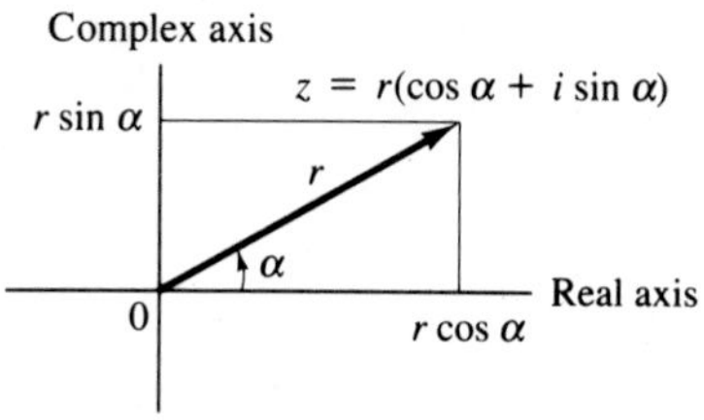

Figure C.4 Polar representation $r(\cos\alpha + i\sin\alpha)$ of a complex number.

Theorem C.7. *Multiplication of Complex Numbers in Polar Form.*
If $z = r(\cos\alpha + i\sin\alpha)$ and $z' = r'(\cos\alpha' + i\sin\alpha')$, then

$$zz' = rr'(\cos(\alpha + \alpha') + i\sin(\alpha + \alpha')).$$

Proof. It is enough to verify that the product of $z = \cos\alpha + i\sin\alpha$ and $z' = \cos\alpha' + i\sin\alpha'$ is $zz' = \cos(\alpha + \alpha') + i\sin(\alpha + \alpha')$. (Explain!) So we calculate

$$\begin{aligned} zz' &= (\cos\alpha + i\sin\alpha)(\cos\alpha' + i\sin\alpha') \\ &= \cos\alpha\cos\alpha' - \sin\alpha\sin\alpha' + i(\cos\alpha\sin\alpha' + \sin\alpha\cos\alpha'). \end{aligned}$$

Then $zz' = \cos(\alpha + \alpha') + i\sin(\alpha + \alpha')$ by the double-angle formulas for sine and cosine:

$$\cos(\alpha + \alpha') = \cos\alpha\cos\alpha' - \sin\alpha\sin\alpha',$$

$$\sin(\alpha + \alpha') = \cos\alpha\sin\alpha' + \sin\alpha\cos\alpha'. \quad \blacksquare$$

Square roots and the quadratic formula for complex numbers

Our rules for multiplication of complex numbers can easily be used to get square roots.

Theorem C.8. *Square Roots of a Complex Number.*
If $z = r(\cos\alpha + i\sin\alpha)$, where r is positive, then the square of

$$y = \sqrt{r}(\cos(\alpha/2) + i\sin(\alpha/2))$$

is z and the numbers $\pm y$ are **square roots** of z, denoted $\pm\sqrt{z}$.

EXAMPLE

For $z = 5(\cos(\pi/3) + i\sin(\pi/3))$, $y = \sqrt{5}(\cos(\pi/6) + i\sin(\pi/6))$ is a square root of z (Figure C.5).

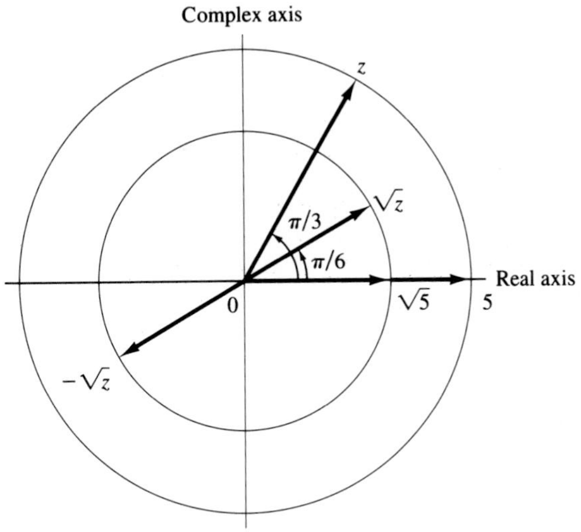

Figure C.5 The two square roots of $z = 5(\cos(\pi/3) + i\sin(\pi/3))$.

Since every complex number has square roots, we have the following:

Theorem C.9. *The Quadratic Formula for Complex Polynomials.*
For any complex (or real) coefficients a, b, c with a nonzero, the quadratic equation $az^2 + bz + c = 0$ has exactly one solution if discriminant $b^2 - 4ac$ is 0 and exactly two solutions otherwise. The solutions are

$$z = \frac{-b + \sqrt{b^2 - 4ac}}{2a}, \qquad \frac{-b - \sqrt{b^2 - 4ac}}{2a}.$$

(Prove!)

Polynomials

Just as a function $f(z) = a_0 + a_1 z^1 + \cdots + a_n z^n$ $(a_0, \ldots, a_n \in \mathbb{R})$ is called a polynomial over $\mathbb{R}$ in the real variable $z \in \mathbb{R}$, a function $f(z) = a_0 + a_1 z^1 + \cdots + a_n z^n$ $(a_0, \ldots, a_n \in \mathbb{C})$ is called a *polynomial over* $\mathbb{C}$ in the complex variable $z \in \mathbb{C}$. If a_n is nonzero, its *degree* is n. Any value of z for which $f(z) = 0$ is called a *root* of the polynomial f. Letting F be either $\mathbb{R}$ or $\mathbb{C}$, we have the following basic theorem from elementary algebra. (A sketch of its proof is requested in Problems 27 and 28.)

Theorem C.10. *Number of Roots of a Polynomial.*
A polynomial $f(z)$ of degree n has at most n roots.

We will make use, later on, of the following corollary.

Corollary. Suppose that the polynomials $f(z) = a_0 + a_1 z^1 + \cdots + a_n z^n$ and $g(z) = b_0 + b_1 z^1 + \cdots + b_n z^n$ are equal for $n + 1$ different values of z. Then $a_j = b_j$ for all j.

Proof. The difference $g(z) - f(z) = (b_0 - a_0) + (b_1 - a_1)z^1 + \cdots + (b_n - a_n)z^n$ is 0 for $n + 1$ values of z, so it has $n + 1$ roots. Therefore, it cannot have a nonzero coefficient $b_j - a_j$, and $a_j = b_j$ for all j. ■

That every quadratic polynomial $az^2 + bz + c$ has a complex root is a special case of the following theorem, proved by Carl Friedrich Gauss (1777–1855), one of the greatest pioneers in mathematics and related sciences. This theorem plays a vitally important role in mathematics and in applications as well. Gauss gave several proofs, the first as his doctoral thesis in 1798 and the last about 52 years later.

Theorem C.11. *Fundamental Theorem of Algebra.*
Any nonconstant polynomial $f(z)$ with complex coefficients has a complex root z.

Since to prove this theorem would divert us from our goal, we omit the proof. Instead, in Section 6.12 we give numerical methods for finding the roots of a polynomial by finding the characteristic roots of its companion matrix.

PROBLEMS

NUMERICAL PROBLEMS

1. Perform the following operations on real and complex numbers.
 (a) $(3 + 4i) + (6 - 4i)$ **(b)** $(5 + 3i) - (3 - 5i)$
 (c) $(2 + 6i)(6 - 4i)$ **(d)** $(3 + 2i)^{-1}(3 - 4i)$

2. Find the square roots of the following complex numbers.
 (a) i **(b)** $-3 - 4i$
 (c) $4(\cos\alpha + i\sin\alpha)$, where $\alpha = \pi/8$.

3. Find $|4(\cos\alpha + i\sin\alpha)|$ where $\alpha = \pi/8$.

4. Find all complex roots of the following polynomials, and represent them as vectors in the complex plane.

(a) $z^2 = 1$ **(b)** $2z^2 + 2z + 3 = 0$ **(c)** $z^3 = 1$

(d) $z^2 + z + 1 = 0$ **(e)** $z^4 = 1$

THEORETICAL PROBLEMS

5. For $z = a + bi = \begin{bmatrix} a \\ b \end{bmatrix}$ and $z' = c + di = \begin{bmatrix} c \\ d \end{bmatrix}$, show that zz' is the first column of $\begin{bmatrix} a & -b \\ b & a \end{bmatrix}\begin{bmatrix} c & -d \\ d & c \end{bmatrix}$ (product of matrices). Use this to prove the associative law $(zz')z'' = z(z'z'')$ for complex multiplication.

6. Show that the subset $\{a + bi \mid a, b \text{ rational}\}$ is a subfield of $\mathbb{C}$.

7. Using the field properties for $\mathbb{C}$, prove that $(r + s)(r - s) = r^2 + s^2$ for any complex numbers r and s.

8. Let $f(x)$ be a polynomial in the real variable x with complex coefficients. Using the assumption that x is real—that is, that $x = \bar{x}$—show that the conjugate of $f(x)$ is a polynomial in x too. What are the coefficients of the conjugate of $f(x)$?

9. Verify the quadratic formula over the complex numbers.

10. Prove the following properties.

(a) $\overline{z + z'} = \bar{z} + \bar{z}'$ **(b)** $\overline{zz'} = \bar{z}\bar{z}'$ **(c)** $\bar{\bar{z}} = z$

(d) $z = \bar{z}$ if and only if z is real.

(e) $z = -\bar{z}$ if and only if z is a pure imaginary.

(f) The real part of z is $(z + \bar{z})/2$.

(g) The pure imaginary part of z is $(z - \bar{z})/2$.

(h) $||z'| - |z|| \leq |z' - z|$ for complex numbers z and z'.

Definition. The **conjugate** of a polynomial $f(z)$ with complex coefficients is the polynomial $\bar{f}(z)$ whose coefficients are the complex conjugates of those of $f(z)$.

11. Show that $\overline{f(z)} = \bar{f}(\bar{z})$.

12. Show that the roots of $\bar{f}(z)$ are the conjugates $\bar{r}$ of the roots r of $f(z)$.

13. Show that if $z^n = 1$, then $|z| = 1$.

Hard

14. Define $\beta(a + bi) = \begin{bmatrix} a & -b \\ b & a \end{bmatrix}$. Show that $\beta(z + z') = \beta(z) + \beta(z')$, $\beta(zz') = \beta(z)\beta(z')$ (product of matrices), and $\beta(\bar{z}) = \beta(z)^T$ for all complex numbers z and z'. Use this to deduce the field properties of complex numbers from corresponding properties of matrices.

15. Show that $\beta(z)$ is a rotation matrix if and only if $z = e^{\alpha i}$ for some real number α.

16. Show that $\beta(a + bi)\begin{bmatrix} c \\ d \end{bmatrix} = (a + bi)(c + di)$ for all real numbers a, b, c, and d.

17. Use Problem 16 to show that rotating a vector $(c + di) = \begin{bmatrix} c \\ d \end{bmatrix}$ through an angle of α is the same as multiplying it by $\cos \alpha + i \sin \alpha$.

18. Show that $\{a + bi \mid a, b \text{ rational}\}$ contains no element whose square is 2. (See Problem 4 of Section B.2.)

19. Show that the conjugate of the product $h(z) = g(z)h(z)$ of two polynomials is $\bar{h}(z) = \bar{g}(z)\bar{h}(z)$.

20. Show that the conjugate of the sum $g(z) + h(z)$ of two polynomials is $\bar{h}(z) = \bar{g}(z) + \bar{h}(z)$.

21. Show that the conjugate of the product $h(z) = uf(z)$ of a complex number and a polynomial is $\bar{h}(z) = \bar{u}\bar{f}(z)$.

22. Show that the coefficients of $f(z)$ are real if and only if $f(r)$ is real for all real numbers r.

23. Show that the coefficients of $f(z)\bar{f}(z)$ are real.

24. Show that if u is a root of the polynomial $f(z)\bar{f}(z)$, then either u or $\bar{u}$ is a root of $f(z)$.

25. Show that $z^n - 1$ is divisible by $z - z_1, \ldots, z - z_n$, where $z_1, \ldots, z_n$ are its n roots from the preceding problem.

26. Show that for any complex polynomial $f(z)$ of degree $n > 1$ and any $a \in \mathbb{C}$, there is a complex polynomial $g(z)$ of degree $n - 1$ such that $f(z) = (z - a)g(z) + f(a)$. (***Hint:*** This is a variation of Taylor's theorem for complex polynomials, which can be proved by dividing by $z - a$.)

27. Show that for any complex polynomial $f(z)$ of degree $n > 1$ and any root $a \in \mathbb{C}$ of $f(z)$, there is a complex polynomial $g(z)$ of degree $n - 1$ such that $f(z) = (z - a)g(z)$. Show that any other root of $f(z)$ is also a root of $g(z)$.

28. Using Problem 27, show by mathematical induction that a complex polynomial $f(z)$ of degree n has at most n different roots.

C.2 EXPONENTIAL NOTATION FOR COMPLEX NUMBERS

Our rule for multiplication of complex numbers can be restated in a very nice form if we write the positive number r in the form $r = e^t$, where $t = \ln r$, and *define*

$$e^{\alpha i} = \cos \alpha + i \sin \alpha,$$

$$e^{t + \alpha i} = e^t e^{\alpha i} = e^t(\cos \alpha + i \sin \alpha).$$

This **exponential notation** $z = e^{t+\alpha i} = e^t(\cos\alpha + i\sin\alpha)$ simplifies the polar notation $z = r(\cos\alpha + i\sin\alpha)$. By the multiplication property $e^t e^u = e^{t+u}$ for real exponentials and our rule for multiplying complex numbers, we get

$$\begin{aligned} e^{t+\alpha i}e^{u+\beta i} &= e^t(\cos\alpha + i\sin\alpha)e^u(\cos\beta + i\sin\beta) \\ &= e^t e^u(\cos\alpha + i\sin\alpha)(\cos\beta + i\sin\beta) \\ &= e^{t+u}(\cos(\alpha+\beta) + i\sin(\alpha+\beta)) \\ &= e^{t+u}e^{(\alpha+\beta)i} = e^{t+u+(\alpha+\beta)i} = e^{(t+\alpha i)+(u+\beta i)}, \end{aligned}$$

which gives the following two theorems.

Theorem C.12. *Multiplication of Complex Numbers in Exponential Form.* Let $z = e^{t+\alpha i}$ and $z' = e^{t'+\alpha' i}$. Then $zz' = e^{(t+t')+(\alpha+\alpha')i}$.

Theorem C.13. *Law of Exponents for Complex Numbers.* For $y = t + \alpha i$ and $y' = t' + \alpha' i$, $e^y e^{y'} = e^{y+y'}$.

Note that if $z = a + 0i$, the preceding definition simply equates the complex exponential $e^z = e^{a+0i}$ with the real exponential e^a. And if $z = 0 + bi$, it equates $e^z = e^{0+bi}$ with the complex number $e^{bi} = \cos b + i\sin b$ on the **unit circle**, the circle in the plane with radius 1 and center at the origin. So, the exponentials e^{a+bi}, e^a, and e^{bi} are represented in the complex plane as shown in Figure C.6.

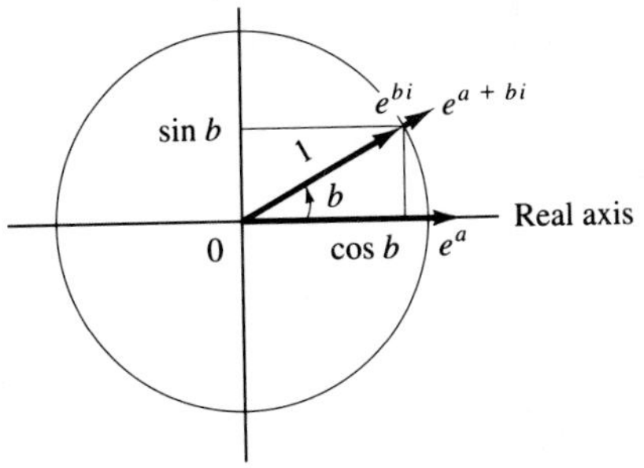

Figure C.6 The complex numbers e^{a+bi}, e^a, and e^{bi}.

The complex numbers on the unit circle are multiplied by adding their angles, as illustrated in Figure C.7.

As a special case, we have **De Moivre's formula**:

Theorem C.14. *Powers of Complex Numbers on the Unit Circle.* For any positive integer n, the nth power of $z = \cos\alpha + i\sin\alpha$ is $z^n = \cos n\alpha + i\sin n\alpha$. (Prove!)

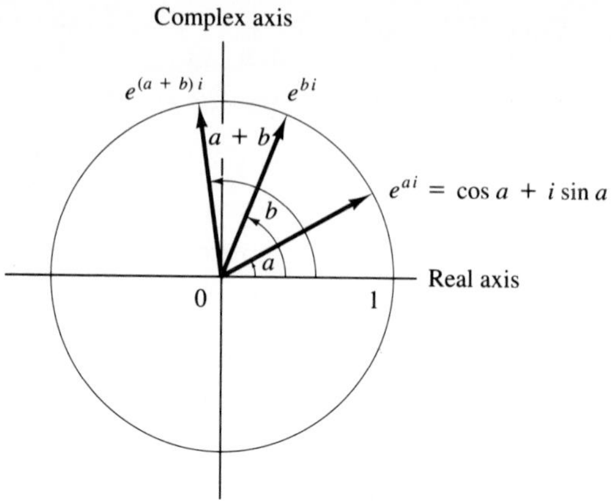

Figure C.7 The product $e^{ai}e^{bi} = e^{(a+b)i}$.

EXAMPLE

1. Trying out this formula for $z = (\cos(\pi/3) + i\sin(\pi/3))$, we find that $z^n = (\cos(\pi/3) + i\sin(\pi/3))^n = (\cos(n\pi/3) + i\sin(n\pi/3))$. Taking $n = 6$, we therefore get $z^6 = 1$.

2. The *n*th *roots of unity* are the roots $z_1, \ldots, z_n$ of the polynomial $z^n = 1$. They are given by $z_j = e^{(2\pi j/n)i}$ and so are located on the unit circle, as shown in Figure C.8.

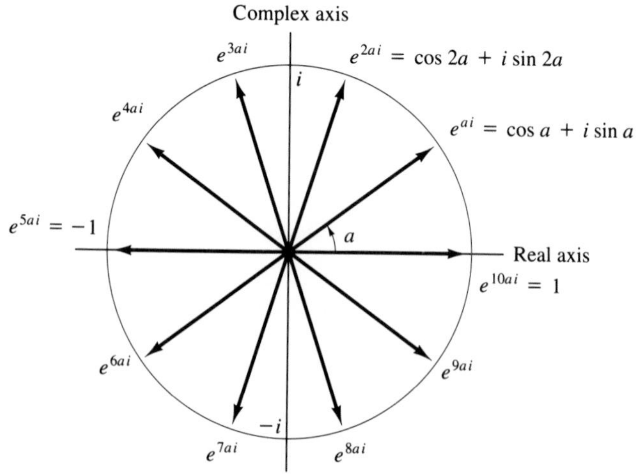

Figure C.8 The ten 10th roots of unity.

PROBLEMS

NUMERICAL PROBLEMS

1. Represent the following complex numbers as points in the complex plane by finding their coordinates.
   (a) $e^{(\ln 2)+(\pi/4)i}$. (b) $3e^{(\pi/6)i} + 4 + 5i$.
2. Find the product $e^{(\ln 2)+(\pi/3)i}3e^{(\pi/6)i}$
3. Represent the following complex numbers in exponential notation, using the formula $e^{\ln x} = x$, which relates exponentials and natural logarithms of real numbers x.
   (a) $3 + 4i$ (b) $-4 + 3i$

THEORETICAL PROBLEMS

4. The power series

$$e^z = 1 + z + \frac{z^2}{2!} + \frac{z^3}{3!} + \frac{z^4}{4!} + \cdots$$

$$\sin z = z - \frac{z^3}{3!} + \frac{z^5}{5!} - \frac{z^7}{7!} + \cdots$$

$$\cos z = 1 - \frac{z^2}{2!} + \frac{z^4}{4!} - \frac{z^6}{6!} + \cdots$$

   converge for all complex numbers z. Disregarding all terms involving z^6 and higher powers of z, compute e^{iz} and compare it with $\cos z + i \sin z$.
5. Prove the formula of De Moivre for nth powers of complex numbers on the unit circle.

Hard

6. Use De Moivre's formula to show that if $z = \cos\alpha + i\sin\alpha$, where $\alpha = 2\pi k/n$, then $z^n = 1$. Then show that $z^n - 1$ has exactly n different roots $z_1, \ldots, z_n$ and illustrate how they are distributed on the unit circle.

SUGGESTED READING

Richard Courant and Herbert Robbins, *What is Mathematics*, Oxford University Press, London, 1978. [Complex numbers are discussed in Section 2.5.]

I. N. Bronshtein and K. A. Semendyayev, *Handbook of Mathematics*, Van Nostrand Reinhold Co., New York, 1985. [Complex numbers are discussed in Sections 3.4.2.1–3.4.2.5.]

INDEX